BIOLOGY
THE BEHAVIORAL VIEW

Roderick A. Suthers   INDIANA UNIVERSITY
Advisory Editor

Roy A. Gallant   THE AMERICAN MUSEUM – HAYDEN PLANETARIUM

BIOLOGY
THE BEHAVIORAL VIEW

XEROX

XEROX COLLEGE PUBLISHING   Lexington, Massachusetts • Toronto

ISB Number: 0-536-00695-4 (Domestic)
ISB Number: 0-536-00901-5 (International)
Library of Congress Catalog Card Number: 72-93154
Printed in the United States of America.

PROGRAM DIRECTOR	Ralph S. Protsik
DESIGN	Science Photo/Graphics, Ltd., Harriet S. Gallant
DIAGRAMS	Joseph M. Sedacca, Juan Barberis, Simon Siflinger
PICTURE RESEARCH	Gabriele Wunderlich
EDITOR	Connie Day Protsik

ILLUSTRATION CREDITS

Cover: Laurence Pringle

Chapter opening sketches: Lorna Waldron

AERO SERVICE: Page 539
THE AMERICAN MUSEUM OF NATURAL HISTORY: Pages 82, 96 (A), 186, 240
THE BETTMAN ARCHIVE: Page 221 (bottom)
DR. PAUL BROWN: Page 336 (right)
DR. JOHN B. CALHOUN: Page 158
THE CELL RESEARCH INSTITUTE: Page 426
STEPHEN DALTON: Page 207 (G)
JACK DERMID: Pages 207 (C), 276
DR. IRENÄUS EIBL-EIBESFELDT: Pages 522 (right), 523 (left), 524, 526, 528, 533, 534
THOMAS EISNER: Page 326 (top and bottom)
ROY A. GALLANT, Courtesy The American Museum of Natural History: Pages 5, 10 (top), 29 (right), 72, 107, 109, 152, 168, 203, 234, 460, 484, 502, 548
ERIC V. GRAVÉ: Pages 305, 308, 313, 397
DR. P. P. C. GRAZIADEI: Page 331
RONALD HAEBERLE: Page 545
GRANT HAIST: Pages 154, 207 (D), 208 (I), 209 (M), 225 (bottom)
H. HASS: Page 525
ECKHARD H. HESS: Page 489 (bottom)
PHILIPPE HALSMAN: Page 209 (P)
KEN HEYMAN: Page xvi
DR. ROSS E. HUTCHINS: Page 97 (E), 103, 116 (left)
JAPAN CONSULATE GENERAL: Page 179
JEOL: Page 431
JANE C. KALTENBACH: Page 362 (top)
LEONARD LEE RUE III: Pages 96 (B), 97 (F), 110 (left), 167, 202, 206 (B), 208 (I), 209 (N), 242, 249, 252, 354, 489

ROBERT MEYERRIECKS: Pages 110 (right), 111 (left and right)
NASA: Page 217
NATIONAL AUDUBON SOCIETY: Hugh M. Halliday: Page 166; A. W. Ambler: 206 (A); Robert C. Hermes: 207 (E); Ray Hunold: 207 (F); Eric Hosking: 225 (top); Bucky Reeves: 265; Jerome Wexler: ii
OMIKRON: Pages 55, 94, 204, 228, 231, 478; D. W. McNeil: 22; Leonard Ross: 55, 67, 291, 310 (bottom); W. Suschitsky: 209 (O); Richard Trump: 96 (C), 97 (D), 235
KEITH PORTER: Pages 390, 430
KIMBERLY CLARK: Page 535
DR. ALEXANDER RICH: Page 440
DR. KENNETH ROEDER: Pages 296 (right), 321 (top), 351
ROTKIN, P. F. I.: Page 188
SCIENCE PHOTO/GRAPHICS, LTD.: Pages 2, 3 (bottom), 4, 100, 114, 122, 126, 127, 128, 129, 148, 149 (top), 163, 171 (top), 173 (top), 175, 195 (right), 196, 198, 213, 304, 341 (left), 374, 408, 430 (left), 518, 527
B. F. SKINNER: Page 499
DR. RODERICK A. SUTHERS: Page 349
SUZANNE SZASZ: Page 221
N. TINBERGEN: Page 101
U. P. I.: Page 197
UNITED STATES DEPARTMENT OF AGRICULTURE: Pages 98, 138, 179, 195 (left)
FREDERIC WEBSTER: Page 351 (bottom)
WIDE WORLD PHOTOS: Pages 11, 523
WISCONSIN PRIMATE RESEARCH CENTER: Page 488
Page 492: *Science*, Vol. 146, pp. 610–619, "Chemical and Anatomical Plasticity of Brain" by E. L. Bennett, M. C. Diamond, D. Kretch, and M. R. Rosensweig.

THE WRITING OF THIS BOOK was a team effort involving specialists from many biological disciplines. All manuscript contributed underwent extensive reviews, subsequent revision, and final editing in order that each chapter might function as a smoothly integrated part of the whole. The authors, under the advisory editorship of Roderick A. Suthers, are as follows:

MAJOR CONTRIBUTORS

Jack W. Bradbury, ROCKEFELLER UNIVERSITY [SOCIAL BEHAVIOR]
Peter F. Brussard, CORNELL UNIVERSITY   [ECOLOGY]
Gloria V. Callard, TUFTS UNIVERSITY   [ENDOCRINOLOGY]
Irenäus Eibl-Eibesfeldt, MAX PLANCK INSTITUTE FOR BEHAVIORAL PHYSIOLOGY
                                          [HUMAN ETHOLOGY]
Roy A. Gallant, THE AMERICAN MUSEUM–HAYDEN PLANETARIUM
                                          [GENERAL BIOLOGY]
Richard W. Glade, UNIVERSITY OF VERMONT [EMBRYOLOGY]
Terrell H. Hamilton, UNIVERSITY OF TEXAS   [EVOLUTION]
Lewis F. Petrinovich, UNIVERSITY OF CALIFORNIA, RIVERSIDE
                                          [LEARNING AND DEVELOPMENT]
Rollin C. Richmond, INDIANA UNIVERSITY   [ETHOLOGY]
Kenneth D. Roeder, TUFTS UNIVERSITY   [ETHOLOGY, NEUROPHYSIOLOGY]
Howard Rothstein, UNIVERSITY OF VERMONT [CELL AND ORGAN PHYSIOLOGY]
Roderick A. Suthers, INDIANA UNIVERSITY   [NEUROPHYSIOLOGY]

SPECIAL CONTRIBUTIONS

Barry R. Komisaruk, RUTGERS UNIVERSITY
William D. McElroy, CHANCELLOR, UNIVERSITY OF CALIFORNIA AT SAN DIEGO
Roger P. Maickel, INDIANA UNIVERSITY
Nancy A. Muckenhirn, NATIONAL ZOOLOGICAL PARK
Richard A. White, DUKE UNIVERSITY

THE GENESIS OF THIS BOOK cannot be attributed to any one individual. The outline went through many extensive revisions based on detailed comments by more than 20 biologists, and the final order of topics reflects the contributions of all of them. Those individuals are listed here, and to them we express our most sincere thanks.

ACKNOWLEDGMENTS　Special acknowledgment to Walter Konetzka, Indiana University, who first suggested the idea and helped develop the first outline; Andrew J. Meyerriecks, University of South Florida, who helped so generously in the area of adaptive diversity; Karl F. Guthe, The University of Michigan, who read and critiqued a good part of the manuscript; James L. McGaugh, University of California, Irvine, who gave major assistance in developing the outline and critiqued the chapters on learning and instinct; Paul Ehrlich, Stanford University, who provided a detailed review of Chapters 6, 7, and 8; Joan Wilentz, who contributed the introductory section to Chapter 24; and John C. McGrath, who was responsible for organizing the nucleus of the team.

We also wish to acknowledge the assistance of the following individuals, in some cases for advising us in the development of the final outline, and in others for critiquing sections of the manuscript: J. P. Scott, Bowling Green State University; Allen W. Stokes, Utah State University; Jack P. Hailman, The University of Wisconsin; Charles F. Lytle, North Carolina State University; Edward J. Kormondy, The Evergreen State College; Donald Kennedy, Stanford University; Stefan O. Schiff, The George Washington University; Robert L. Singletary, University of Bridgeport; Bruce H. Carpenter, California State College, Long Beach; Charles R. Botticelli, Newton College of the Sacred Heart; Michael D. Ward, William Rainey Harper College; Craig L. Himes, Bloomsburg State College; Robert H. Catlett, San Diego State College; R. D. Guthrie, University of Alaska; Michael W. Fox, Washington University, St. Louis; J. Merritt Emlen, Indiana University; Douglass H. Morse, University of Maryland; Donald I. Patt, Boston University; Alan D. Grinnell, UCLA; W. H. Murdy, Emory University; and William M. Hexter, Amherst College.

"I feel very strongly that an intense effort

ought to be made to understand the *effects* of behavior;

of the ways in which it influences the survival

of the species; and that we should try much harder

to understand the state of adaptedness and the process

of evolutionary adaptation, if for no other reason than

that this has led to the structuring of our own behavior."

NIKO TINBERGEN

This textbook is based on three premises: First, that behavior—what an organism does—provides a logical and forceful means to introduce biology; second, that using behavior as a unifying framework for an introductory course in biology is long overdue; and third, that such an approach can be presented at a level and within a scope appropriate to science and non-science majors alike. From our earliest years we are observers of what organisms do, and consciously and unconsciously we try to comprehend the significance of their behavior. The knowledge such observations afford may be useful to us in questioning our own behavior, but, perhaps just as important, it gives us our first glimpse of the mystery and complexity of the biological world. Here we continue our search.

In choosing to emphasize behavior, we choose to emphasize the evolutionary process as a central theme in biology, for the adaptiveness, or survival value, of behavior is the ultimate cause for its existence. Textbooks in biology have traditionally described in detail what an organism looks like, how it functions, and where it fits into the taxonomic scheme. Evolution is dutifully covered at the text's end; behavior appears as a single chapter, or not at all. Yet it is evolution that unifies all of biology, and it is behavior that often determines whether or not morphological and physiological characteristics of an organism have selective advantage. Throughout this text, the theme of evolution and adaptation is used to place behavior within the larger perspective of selection, survival, and the conquest of the physical environment by living organisms. It is within this framework that we examine the proximate causes or mechanisms of behavior. We begin with communities and populations and progress through social behavior and organ systems to the cellular and subcellular level. The reader thus proceeds from the familiar to the less familiar, and at each step questions arise that can only be answered by continuing to the next stage.

Biology: The Behavioral View covers all the topics normally appearing in an introductory biology text. Chapter 2 presents an overview of the origins of life and its levels of organization. Chapters 3 and 4 take up reproduction, Mendelian and non-Mendelian inheritance, and the mechanisms of evolution. Chapter 5 presents a comprehensive discussion of adaptations that have evolved and given rise to morphological, physiological, and behavioral diversity. Concepts of the ecosystem and population ecology are covered in Chapters 6, 7, and 8, while social behavior in a wide spectrum of organisms is the subject of Chapters 9 and 10. Organismic and cellular biology, including molecular genetics, embryology, organ physiology, and neurophysiology are covered thoroughly in Parts 3, 4, and 5.

The strength of this book, however, does not lie only in what is covered, but in the way the material is integrated by the behavioral theme. Behavior is defined as a response to a change in the internal or external environment of an organism—plant or animal, unicellular or multicellular. To understand how and why a given organism behaves as it does, we must know something of its evolutionary history, its genetic make-up, its physiological state, and its relationship to the environment, which includes other organisms as well. Behavior, then, is a natural vehicle for discussion of evolution, ecology, and genetics within a framework of *Adaptation* and *Interaction*; of nerve, sensory, hormone, and muscle physiology within a framework of *Integration*; of cellular energetics, protein synthesis, and organ physiology within a framework of *Maintenance*; and of embryology, growth, the development of behavior, and the role of learning within a framework of *Maturation*.

In our concluding section we focus on human behavior and ask a number of searching questions in an attempt to discover roots of why we behave as we do—from being able to express love and a sense of humanity, on the one hand, to unbridled violence and mass destruction of our fellow human beings on the other. We have only begun the vast investigation of human behavior in the brief 100 years since Darwin made ethology a branch of biology, yet important new insights are emerging each year through the combined efforts of ethologists, anthropologists, and psychologists. At this stage, some of the questions we ask about human behavior—for example, whether man is innately aggressive and, if so, whether he can learn to control his aggressive nature—are as intriguing as the emerging answers. It may be decades before clear answers are found; in the meantime a great deal of speculation—some of it erroneous or misleading—will be offered up in popular and scientific literature alike. Our goal in this text is to provide the student with a solid introduction to biology and to behavior, in short to help him understand and appreciate two fascinating arenas: that of the human mind and that of the biological world.

CONTENTS

Special Photographic Essays

Figure 1–1 As infants, our interpretations of the world are based entirely on nonverbal cues; only later do we come to use words to sharpen our perceptions. Chances are that most observers of this photograph would identify the emotion expressed as "grief," but to be certain we would need to know the cultural cues involved. Nonverbal communication constitutes a far greater part of our behavioral repertoire than most of us realize.

1

BIOLOGY, BEHAVIOR, AND MAN

Why study behavior?

As you pick up this book you may be asking yourself, "Why study behavior?" The fact is you have been studying behavior, and probably with some interest, in man and other organisms from the day you were born (Fig. 1–1). In this book we attempt to present biology within a behavioral framework. Perhaps unconsciously you have already learned a great deal about the signals animals use when they communicate with one another. Perhaps you have also questioned the meaning or usefulness of this or that action in yourself and in the other living things around you. Questioning why a certain action takes place usually leads to questions about the circumstances and how the action was accomplished.

Perhaps in early childhood you were awakened at daybreak by a chorus of bird song. The singers seemed to be trying to draw attention to themselves and attempting to outdo each other. Later, you may have found cunningly concealed nests with birds silently sitting on their eggs. Why do birds draw attention to themselves under one circumstance and not under another? Perhaps you were able to answer this question for yourself or by asking your parents. You probably found that an answer only led to more questions. In any case, you had already begun the study of behavior.

Perhaps your mother kept house plants on the windowsill and turned them frequently to prevent them from growing toward the window and becoming lopsided. Why didn't they seek the warmth of the room rather than the light outside? Perhaps in an early encounter with a hostile world you unknowingly touched a hot radiator or pan on the stove. Your hand pulled back quickly almost as if it were not a part of you, and only later did you feel the pain and begin to howl. How could this be? You may have tried to swat a pesky fly as it zigzagged over the table top and then became motionless over a grain of sugar. How did it find the food? How did it manage to avoid your efforts to kill it?

Most people are likely at some time to have established a friendship with an animal, usually a cat or a dog. This friendship was not instantaneous but took time to develop, just as a human friendship does. If you and your pet were no longer infants there was probably a little mistrust on both sides at the first encounter. This problem is usually solved by food or some other form of comfort. Eventually you came to know your pet as a character distinct from other members of its species, and you learned to read its needs and its moods, both amiable and aggressive. Your pet probably performed a parallel assessment of you as distinct from other people. The two of you established a relationship and gained knowledge about each other through a very complex exchange of signals that did not require the use of words. The signals passed between you in the form of nonverbal behavior.

Nonverbal communication

Verbal communication is unique to man and has been responsible for his social evolution and civilization. Words are so overwhelmingly important to us that we are apt to discount our heritage of being able to communicate nonverbally, that is to convey information about our feelings and intentions through behavior without using words. Nonverbal communication has a profound, often unconscious, and sometimes uncontrollable influence on the impressions we give and receive.

Some obvious examples of nonverbal communication in humans are laughing, weeping, the clenched fist, the open extended hand, a raised eyebrow, and the scratched head. It is interesting to note how many students scratch their heads or chew their pencils when taking an examination. Each of these behaviors conveys a mood or feeling, and the receiver of a given signal is conscious that it generates in him a complementary feeling or sensation. Something has been communicated; information has been exchanged.

Nonverbal communication is not limited to visible actions. A curse or the tone of a familiar voice over the telephone often contains more information than the words actually spoken. Even if the speaker is a stranger, his tone conveys a definite impression, though it may be false. Nor is our nonverbal communication confined to sounds and gestures. Odors play a lesser role in communication among men than among most other animals, yet an odor, particularly if it was first encountered at an early age, can have a strong effect on our feelings and mood. The cosmetics and deodorant industry knows this well. For some reason civilized man often chooses to disguise his feelings with words, his skin with cosmetics, and his personal odor with deodorants and perfumes.

Charles Darwin, who will be mentioned many times in this book, understood the importance of nonverbal communication in man and realized that it comes from a very ancient heritage. Recently there has been a revival of interest in human communication through nonverbal behavior. The impetus has come largely from the assembly by **ethologists**, scientists who study the behavior of animals in their natural environment, of "glossaries" of the behavioral signals used by members of various animal species.

One interesting question is whether the nonverbal behaviors of man are common to all human races and cultures, and to what extent they may be shared with other species (Fig.1–2). Some nonverbal behaviors such as laughing, smiling, and weeping are common to all humans and universally understood; others such as hand-shaking are culturally determined. I. Eibl-Eibesfeldt recently has drawn attention to a small and very rapid up-and-down movement of the eyebrows—the eyebrow flash—that he has observed in many human cultures as well as in monkeys. (Chapter 24). The eyebrow flashes seem to occur at the moment of friendly greeting and say "yes" to the social contact or "I recognize and attend to you," or may be a sign of flirtatious interest. If, as Eibl-Eibesfeldt says, the eyebrow flash is so universally used and

Figure 1–2 To what extent nonverbal expressions of closely related species can be communicated is of major interest to biologists. When chimps smile, they never bare the upper teeth, although sometimes the lower ones are visible. Baring the teeth denotes aggression or fear. When humans smile we invariably bare our upper teeth. Chimps often respond to our "friendly" or amused gesture in kind, but they are displaying an emotion rather different from the one we might infer.

"understood" in primate species, it is a most curious and significant fact that has escaped our *conscious* notice, even though we must make and receive the signal several times each day and are most disconcerted if we are greeted by a deadpan stare or steadily raised eyebrows.

Biological unity and diversity

Living things show both unity and diversity. Plants and animals evolved from an unknown ancestral organism some three billion years ago, and as we shall see, they have similar basic mechanisms of reproduction, cell replication, and growth regulation, and a host of biochemical processes whereby energy is gathered from the environment, stored in chemical bonds, and used. At the biochemical level of organization many similar processes take place in animals and plants. Among organisms living today the **motile** (capable of actively moving about) single-celled green algae suggest what the common ancestral form may have been like. *Chlamydomonas* (Fig. 1–3) swims actively. In the light it develops a chloroplast containing chlorophyll and can synthesize complex compounds from simple chemicals, using sunlight as its energy source. If *Chlamydomonas* is kept in darkness its chlorophyll is lost and it then requires more complex compounds for its growth and metabolism.

It is most likely that plants and animals diverged when they became multicellular. Motility posed mechanical problems for a cell aggregate or colony. Most plants followed the sedentary or **sessile** (permanently attached) way of existence, and stored chemical energy from sunlight; animals became mobile and obtained their energy from plants, either directly as vegetarian feeders or indirectly by eating other animals. Motility required a "motor" and a means of steering it. The origins of this "motor" are discussed in Chapter 11 and the details of behavioral mechanisms are covered in following chapters.

From this dividing point in their evolutionary histories, animals and plants each blossomed into a great diversity of forms and habits, some of which overlap here and there in the two great groups. Many animals are just as sessile as plants when they are adults—for example, the coral organism and many other coelenterates, and some mollusks. Certain plants have evolved surprisingly animal-like behavior that includes fairly rapid movements (Fig. 1–4) and in

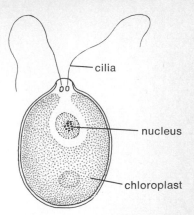

Figure 1–3 *Chlamydomonas* is a single-celled organism that propels itself by means of two flagella (whip-like organs). In the presence of light it functions as a green plant by producing its own food.

Figure 1–4 Plants can be said to "behave" in several ways. Shown here is mimosa; at left the leaves appear in their normal (open) attitude. When the stem is tapped with a pencil or when the leaves are gently brushed, the plant folds its leaves closed within two seconds and the stem droops.

some cases a semi-carnivorous habit. Examples include species of mimosa, the Venus's-flytrap, and the pitcher plants. However, none of the higher plants can move as a whole except by growing, horror films to the contrary!

Lacking a nervous system, plants cannot be said to behave in the same way that animals do. Yet plants show a variety of self-protective reactions of the sort that are accomplished by movement in animals. In addition to orienting themselves with respect to light and gravity, many plants show movements—daily opening and closing of leaves and flowers—in response to changes in light intensity, temperature, or humidity. Plants have also evolved in their diversity under the same general principles of natural selection that have brought about species formation in animals.

The term "animal" is used throughout this book to include mammals, birds, reptiles, amphibians, and fish among the vertebrate organisms as well as crustaceans, insects, mollusks, worms, and a number of smaller invertebrate groups. Multicellular animals, except for simplest forms such as sponges, are equipped with a nervous system, sense organs, and muscles, and are capable of motility at some stage of life. These are some of the important respects in which they differ from plants. Animal is still not a rigidly defined term, and may or may not be used to include all or some of those single-celled organisms called **protozoans**. **Organism** is much broader still, and applies to all living things.

THE NATURE OF BEHAVIOR STUDY

Origins of behavior study

The study of behavior is probably the most ancient of sciences. In his early history when man was a hunter and food gatherer (Fig. 1–5) his survival depended on being able to read the trails left by game animals as well as potential predators, on knowing where game was most likely to be found, and on learning how best to stalk it. He also had to know when certain fruits were likely to be ripe and how to compete for them with birds and monkeys. It seems likely that primitive man watched animals out of pure curiosity as well as for practical reasons. He probably felt a greater affinity or even kinship with some animals than with others, and he certainly feared the larger predators. In most early cultures certain animals were looked on as being superhuman.

By early historical times, a great many facts must have been gathered about the behavior of lower forms, but they became largely obscured and distorted by myth and folklore. In those times there was no broad concept or theory to provide a framework for arranging and relating observations of various animal species made by different people, so the observations were passed on to others in the form of anecdotes. During the 18th century, biologists such as Buffon, Cuvier, and Linnaeus began ordering and classifying organisms in a scientific fashion and determining affinities on the basis of anatomy. These studies provided a foundation for the monumental work of Darwin and Alfred Russell Wallace, which came to be known as evolution through natural selection. These ideas were widely broadcast with the 1859 publication of Darwin's *The Origin of Species*.

Today Darwin's idea that natural selection through survival of the fittest in-

Figure 1–5 Many cave paintings reveal early man's knowledge of nature's ways and his dependence on plants and animals. The paintng here, made during the Middle Stone Age and discovered in Valltorta, Spain, shows a person robbing a hive of honey.

dividuals of a species is the basic mechanism of evolution constitutes the central core of most hypotheses about animal behavior. Two other developments during the 19th century were also important. One, a direct consequence of Darwin's ideas, was rapid growth of comparative studies of animals, known today as comparative anatomy and comparative physiology. Also, with the framework of evolution as a guide, the classification of species became more than merely a means of ordering the kinds of organisms; clues to their ancestry were now available. The second development took place quite independently of evolutionary theory, at least in the beginning. This was Mendelian genetics, the principles of which were worked out by Gregor Mendel, an Augustinian monk in Austria, and published in 1865. Mendelian genetics accounted for the natural variations in an interbreeding population of organisms. Darwin's theory presupposed that no two individuals of a species are exactly alike (except for identical twins) and, therefore, have inherited different chances for survival, but he could not explain the mechanism that caused them to vary. Mendel's discoveries suggested a mechanism for natural variation, though it was nearly 40 years before the importance of his discovery was recognized by biologists.

At the present time, studying the behavior of organisms is one of the most challenging branches of biology. This is because what an organism does—how it behaves under given circumstances—may determine whether it has offspring to continue its genetic line. For example, "what the animal does" may be a slight variation in some elemental action such as remaining motionless and hidden upon the approach of a predator. Or it may be springing from ambush at just the right moment when prey is within reach, or perhaps being able to follow the faint and fading scent train left by a potential mate. All animals have evolved mechanisms enabling them to avoid being eaten, to gather food, and to reproduce. So have predatory animals evolved mechanisms enabling them to outwit or otherwise overpower prey on a regular basis, which is what any successful predator must do (Fig. 1–6). *A central concern of the student of*

Figure 1–6 Predator species, such as this leopard guarding its peacock prey, have evolved physiological and behavioral mechanisms enabling them to be successful enough at hunting to ensure survival.

behavior is to discover the adaptive significance, or species survival value, of the manifold action patterns directed to these ends in different species.

Beyond its scientific value, watching what animals do is rewarding for its own sake. Man has been doing this for thousands of years, but it was not until Darwin's discoveries provided impetus for so many branches of biology that behavior study became a powerful discipline in the mainstream of biology. In a way, behavior study is the final objective of all these other branches. For instance, if we look closely at any one of the elemental actions mentioned above, we find that it depends on an extraordinarily complex and beautifully synchronized mechanism of nerve cells, glands, and muscles, plus a supporting skeleton. The conduction velocity in a nerve fiber saves an earthworm from a robin; the speed of a muscle contraction determines whether a predator shall feed or go hungry; a single molecule falling on an olfactory receptor cell determines whether two moths will mate. These structures are only parts of complex mechanisms that must mesh properly through the inherited constitution of each individual. If they did not, the animals would not be here to behave. Therefore, the student of behavior must be familiar with the structure and function of this elegant mechanism—the special concerns of **organismic anatomy** and **physiology**.

If we look more closely at the components that interact to generate behavior —sense organs, nerve cells, glands, muscles, and supporting tissues—we find that they in their turn depend for their operation (and the organism for its survival) on an equally elegant set of intercellular and intracellular mechanisms. The study of structure and function at this cellular level is the concern of **histology**, **cytology**, and **cellular physiology**. Probing still deeper to a finer level of organization, we find that these cellular transactions depend on an armament of chemicals and enzymes that promote growth and repair, intercellular communication, and food utilization. We are now in the province of **molecular biology** and **biochemistry**.

Obviously, each of these branches of biology is concerned with separate links in a chain forged by evolution. Even though we take it apart in order to study it, the chain must be complete in a surviving organism. The particular challenge and responsibility of behavior study lie in the fact that it deals with the end result—the total organism, and the population to which it belongs, in its natural environment. But if the student of behavior is to deal as a professional with the actions of organisms, then he must be familiar with the principles of what goes on inside organisms, with their development, and with their evolutionary history and mechanisms of inheritance.

Ethology and behavior

Near the beginning of the 20th century, students of bird behavior, particularly O. Heinroth and C. O. Whitman, found that certain patterns of action are just as *fixed* and characteristic of different species as their plumage and form. Konrad Lorenz, a tireless Austrian observer of the behavior of many species, greatly expanded these early observations and ideas and developed a number of important concepts based largely on these **fixed action patterns**. Lorenz's methods assume that one can draw valid conclusions about the significance of an animal's behavior only if its actions are observed while it is undisturbed and in its natural surroundings. For it is under these conditions that the behavior evolved and presently has adaptive value in survival.

This viewpoint suggested a "new" way of studying the relationships and evolution of different species. Actually it is the oldest way used by prehistoric observers of animals. Lorenz's students became known as ethologists. One of their methods was to assemble **ethograms**, catalogs of the various behavior patterns of the species belonging to certain **taxa**, or groups of organisms. (The singular is **taxon**.) These ethograms were built up through field observations and then compared with each other in a manner similar to that employed by museum workers and comparative anatomists in comparing the structure and form of different groups. Thus, an organism's behavior became just as valuable in establishing its species relationships as the shape of its body or its color patterns. For example, the bird species grouped and classified as pigeons vary so greatly in form and other respects that no one common structural characteristic could be found to label a bird a pigeon. Lorenz showed that the group can be distinguished from other birds by the way they drink water. Pigeons all make sucking movements while other birds lift their heads and swallow.

In addition to providing a new way of studying the relationships of organisms, the work of Lorenz and his students brought to light a number of exciting and often subtle ways in which the actions of a species promote its survival. New avenues for studying animals were opened up and a great and still growing number of biologists were attracted to the field of ethology. One of the earliest and most notable of these students is Niko Tinbergen. The major questions asked by ethologists have recently been stated by Tinbergen as follows:

1   In what ways does this phenomenon (behavior) influence the survival, the success of the animal?
2   What makes behavior happen at any given moment? How does its machinery work?
3   How does the behavior machinery develop as the individual grows up?
4   How have the behavior systems of each species evolved until they became what they are now?

Tinbergen goes on to point out that "The first question, that of survival value, has to do with the effects of behavior; the other three are, each on a different time scale, concerned with its causes."

Let us see how these questions apply to a simple case, available to anyone with sharp eyes, patience, and access to a number of tree trunks and foliage in a wood or park. How far will these questions lead us?

Many moths rest by day on the bark of tree trunks or among leaves. The pattern of their folded wings blends so closely with the pattern and texture of these backgrounds that they are almost invisible. When one finds such a moth and gently pokes it with a stick it may do one of three things. It may fly rapidly away or it may fall to the ground. In these cases its hind wings, concealed in the resting position, are usually plain brown or grey. The third possibility is that the moth will raise the camouflaged forewings and flap them slowly, revealing hindwings that are bright red or yellow or perhaps ornamented with a

Figure 1–7 In a hypothetical moth species, the moth is seen at rest and camouflaged (top). If disturbed, it responds by raising its forewings and revealing on its hindwings "eye" spots that startle its predator for that second or less necessary for escape.

pair of startlingly realistic "eyes" (Fig. 1–7). (See also the color section facing page 112.) Let us consider these behavior patterns in the light of Tinbergen's questions.

The first question concerns survival value. The answer is quite complex. The main predators of moths are small insectivorous birds that search the tree trunks and foliage either in flight or on foot. The "eyed" moth species has two forms of defense, both of which work through a combination of structure and function. The first is to remain quite motionless while the camouflage of its forewings may cause an inquisitive bird to pass it by. The second defense is to startle the bird if it should poke the moth with its beak. The sudden presentation of bright color or, better still, a pair of cat-like or owl-like eyes causes the little predator to pause or to retreat and investigate no further.

The second question concerns the mechanism. That of the first line of defense is simple—do nothing. That of the second is quite specific and not shown by the moth at other times—draw the front wings forward and perhaps move them slowly on being poked. Stimulation of certain sense organs causes this reflex (automatic) movement. The details of the nerve connections concerned have not been worked out, but they are clearly different from those in the moth species with dull-colored hindwings.

The third question concerns development. Again, the details are unknown in this particular case. The point is that the development of the protective and of the startle coloration must proceed hand-in-hand with the development of the appropriate behavior patterns. One would be useless without the other. The moth does not "know" that it has camouflaged forewings and startling hind-wings, and he probably never sees them. The behavior and the patterns have both been programmed into its development.

The fourth question concerns evolution. Here we can do little but speculate since the moth's ancestors have left no trace. We can only suppose that flying away or dropping groundward were the original reactions to a predator's attack. A slight advantage to the moth species in being better able to leave offspring was on the side of those genetic variants having some color contrast on the hindwings, thus causing the predator to "look twice." What appeared to be tree bark suddenly turned out to be something else. In each of an untold number of moth generations some variants gained percentage points in survival as these spots came more and more to resemble eyes. An experiment that demonstrates this is described in Chapter 11.

This example is only one of many in which an inquiry into the relation between structure and behavior leads to interesting trains of thought. A vast number of similar cases remain to be explored.

Psychology and behavior

The interest of psychology in behavior had origins entirely different from those of ethology. Classical psychologists of the last century focused their attention on the workings of the human mind. They did this mainly through introspection about their own feelings, motives, sensations, and urges. However, their findings could not be checked and repeated by others and were considered to be outside the purview of science. Early in the present century the attitudes of psychologists underwent a complete change, leading to what is now known as **behavioristic psychology**. This was mainly due to the experiments of the Russian physiologist Ivan Pavlov, supported by those of the American physiologist Jacques Loeb and the ideas and experiments of the American psychologists John B. Watson and E. L. Thorndike.

Pavlov demonstrated the **conditioned reflex** (Fig. 1–8). A hungry dog salivates on seeing or smelling meat. Pavlov rang a bell each time the dog was fed. After a few repetitions, the ringing of the bell alone would cause the dog to salivate. The dog had learned that the sound of the bell usually meant food. Any stimulus perceivable by the dog could be used in place of the bell.

The principle of the conditioned reflex was and has remained a powerful psychological tool. It made possible an evaluation of the learning capacity of a variety of species under a variety of conditions. The ability of animals to discriminate between different stimuli could also be measured. For instance, the sound of the conditioning stimulus could be made progressively fainter or higher in pitch until the trained dog no longer salivated to the signal alone after it had been presented several times together with food.

These findings favored the view that animals are primarily stimulus-response mechanisms, and that the connections in the nerve circuitry mediating their behavior are established anew in each individual by its experiences. This view seemed particularly applicable to man, who enters this world in a state of greater helplessness than most other mammals and has to learn a large part of the information enabling him to cope with his environment. Using Pavlovian

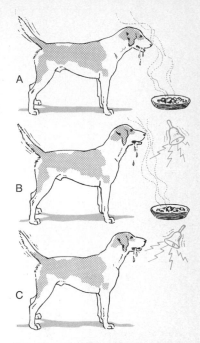

Figure 1–8 Conditioned reflex: At A the dog salivates on being presented with food. At B the sound of a bell is associated with food. At C the bell stimulus alone induces salivation.

conditioning, and later instrumental conditioning developed by B. F. Skinner, psychologists have made great advances in understanding the mechanisms of learning and in extending our knowledge of the sensory capabilities of many vertebrates in comparison with those of man.

Behavioristic psychology gained early support from the work of Loeb, who concluded that animal behavior was composed of a matrix of reflexes, a simple example of which are the spinal reflexes. This left no room for spontaneous behavior—actions not precipitated by an immediate external stimulus. Watson held similar views, and believed that all behavior could be explained as the elaboration of conditioned reflexes in such a system.

Nature or nurture?

The above views were widely held 25 years ago. If they are compared with those held by ethologists of the same period, it will be seen that they are diametrically opposed. This led to a bitter, wordy and, as it now appears, futile controversy over "nature or nurture." Is an animal endowed with nerve connections ordained by its genetic makeup, and, in accordance with ethology, does this determine the way it behaves? Or is its nervous system at first a *tabula rasa*—a blank page—on which, in accordance with behavioristic psychology, each individual experience registers the nerve connections that favor the animal's survival? Of course, both views stated so simply are extreme, but they led to a great many profitless attempts to prove one or the other correct.

At the present time this debate has died down because it is apparent that both views have their place. A relatively simple creature such as the honeybee can learn *certain things* at *certain times* with great speed and facility, yet most of its behavior unfolds automatically in the course of its development. At one stage of its adult life the honeybee acts as a "nurse" to bee larvae; later it flies out of the hive to gather nectar and, still later, pollen to provision the colony. At the other end of the animal kingdom man acquires most of his social behavior, that concerning interactions with his fellows, from individual experiences during his formative years. Yet below this cultural veneer lies a core of little-understood urges concerned with the avoidance of harm, the acquisition of food, and the propagation of his species. These urges he shares with other animals. If he did not he would not now exist. Sometimes these built-in urges run counter to man's learned social behavior. A serious conflict between the two may warp either aspect of his nature, and a happy compromise is reached in a well-integrated person.

The resolution of this controversy enabled most ethologists and psychologists to talk the same language. The two groups of students of behavior now differ mainly in their methods, the ethologists preferring to observe and experiment under conditions as close to natural ones as possible, the psychologists generally choosing carefully controlled conditions in the laboratory. And even that is changing. Ethologists are cautiously controlling certain factors in the environments of their subjects and psychologists are beginning to look at "nor-

pterodactyl forelimb

bat forelimb

bird forelimb

Figure 1–9 Insects, here represented by a giant dragon fly of about 300 million years ago, invaded the air about 40 million years earlier during the Mississippian Period. They were followed by flying reptiles, bats (mammals), and birds about 150 million years ago. Notice the close structural similarity in the forelimbs of the three vertebrate species shown in the diagrams.

mal" man and other species in relation to their natural surroundings. Methodological differences such as these are much more likely to generate new knowledge than is a futile controversy over nature or nurture.

MAN'S PLACE IN NATURE

In a recent lecture Tinbergen said that "Man is a unique creature, but then all creatures are unique. Perhaps man is uniquely unique." What he meant is that most species adapt slowly to gradually changing environments. General changes in their structure may take millions of years. As they partially adapt to the changing conditions the form and behavior of each species evolve in a unique direction. The sea, from which life is thought to have sprung, has been reinvaded a number of times, notably by turtles, penguins, seals, and whales. Each invasion was separate, and each group adapted to its new environment by means of unique modifications, but invasion of the sea was not in itself a novel event. The air has been invaded at least four separate times: by insects, birds, bats, and an extinct group of reptiles. Each of these groups evolved a unique way of flying (Fig. 1–9), but the invasion of the air was not in itself unique. Even the tendency to form social groups extending beyond pair formation and the family, a universal human characteristic, has occurred many times and at various levels of the animal kingdom.

Why, then, is man "uniquely unique" among living things? It is because his power of speech has enabled him to communicate ideas and information to other men rather than merely to express his moods through nonverbal behavior. Not only is verbal behavior completely novel among living things, but it has made possible man's cultural evolution at a pace many times faster than the rate of his organic evolution. In 10,000 years—even in 1,000 years—man's way of life in civilized countries has changed more than it did for his immediate ancestors over a span of more than a million years. And the enormous *rate* of change at which, through his technology, man is altering the environment (Fig. 1–10) occupied by his own species and many other organisms shows no sign

Figure 1–10 Through his technology, man has enormous impact on the environment. With bulldozers, bombs and shells, as evidenced by the devastation of Quangtri, the United States has made wasteland of much of Indo-China.

of stabilizing or slowing down. At the same time, man's rate of organic evolution seems to be similar to that of many other mammals, his anatomy and physiology being much more closely akin to that of a chimpanzee than the form of an ant is to that of a cockroach. Man's aggressive and territorial urges, his appetites for food and mates, and his sense of self-preservation seem to have kept pace with his organic evolution and are probably not very different from those of his prehistoric ancestors. However, his power to satisfy these urges has largely kept pace with his social evolution, and is immeasurably greater than that of his prehistoric forebears. This disparity in the rates of man's organic and social evolution seems to be at the root of his present predicament.

Everyone, today's youth in particular, is aware of the problems created by man's unique uniqueness. The matter is all the more urgent because the pace of social evolution not only far outstrips the pace of our organic evolution, but is clearly accelerating. Life has changed much more during the 20th century than it did during the 19th century. Attention has been drawn to this by a number of authors, notably Konrad Lorenz (*On Aggression*), Desmond Morris (*The Naked Ape*), and Robert Ardrey (*The Territorial Imperative, The Social Contract*). Their attempts to extrapolate from man's past, although tentative, are not particularly encouraging.

Cultural developments have given us more and more impressive technological advances, but wherever these clash with our basic biological properties they meet with strong resistance. The fundamental patterns of behavior laid down in our early days as hunting apes still shine through all our affairs, no matter how lofty they may be. If the organization of our earthier activities—our feeding, our fear, our aggression, our sex, our parental care—had been developed solely by cultural means, there can be little doubt that we would have got it under better control by now, and twisted it this way and that to suit the increasingly extraordinary demands put upon it by our technological advances. But we have not done so. We have repeatedly bowed our heads before our animal nature and tacitly admitted the existence of the complex beast that stirs within us. If we are honest, we will confess that it will take millions of years, and the same genetic process of natural selection that put it there, to change it. In the meantime, our unbelievably complicated civilizations will be able to prosper only if we design them in such a way that they do not clash with or tend to suppress our basic animal demands. (D. Morris, *The Naked Ape*)

The ever-recurrent phenomena of history do not have reasonable causes. It is a mere commonplace to say that they are caused by what common parlance so aptly terms "human nature." Unreasoning and unreasonable human nature causes two nations to compete, though no economic necessity compels them to do so; it induces two political parties or religions with amazingly similar programs of salvation to fight each other bitterly, and it impels an Alexander or a Napoleon to sacrifice millions of lives in his attempt to unite the world under his scepter. We have been taught to regard some of the persons who have committed these and similar absurdities with respect, even as "great" men, we are wont to yield to the political wisdom of those in charge, and we are all so accustomed to these phenomena that most of us fail to realize how abjectly stupid and undesirable the historical mass behavior of humanity actually is. (K. Lorenz, *On Aggression*)

On the brighter side, it must be noted that the major vehicle of man's rapid social evolution has been communication, first by word of mouth, then in song and legend followed by writing and printing, and now by telecommunication and rapid transportation. At the present time, word of a new idea, discovery, or event is potentially capable of reaching most members of our species within a few seconds. So in spite of its size and worldwide distribution, the human species is now capable of being much more closely knit, in touch, and sensitive to local perturbation than any other species has been. This reactivity has its dangers, as history has repeatedly shown, but it means that we are also capable of reacting rapidly to ideas that are for the general good. Good ideas, of course, are useful only to persons who are aware of the problems and their origins. This is the aim of education.

QUESTIONS
FOR REVIEW

1   What are some differences between ethology and behavioristic psychology?
2   What are some advantages of the study of animal behavior advocated by behavioristic psychology?
3   In what ways might plants be regarded as "behaving"?
4   Can you think of further examples of nonverbal communication in man?
5   Reread the quotation from Tinbergen at the beginning of this book. In the context of what you have read in this chapter, elaborate on the last part of what he says about man.

SELECTED READINGS

Throughout this book we have selected readings which the beginning student should find interesting and challenging. The usual pattern will be to list only a few books—not necessarily the best or best-known, but good references for the student to turn to for more detailed discussion. Here in Chapter 1 we will be more comprehensive.

RECENT TITLES THAT EXAMINE THE NATURE OF HUMAN BEHAVIOR

The following books have been widely read, quoted, and debated. A useful exercise for the student would be to select two or more of these titles, read them with a critical eye, and then examine some of the reviews that appeared later. What types of arguments do these authors make? How does the position taken by Skinner compare with that of the other authors? What major criticisms have been raised by the book reviewers you read? (For an excellent summary of the issues and criticisms involved here, read "Man and Beast" by Morton Hunt, *Playboy*, July 1970.)

Ardrey, Robert. *African Genesis*. New York: Dell Publishing Company, 1961.
———. *The Social Contract*. New York: Dell Publishing Company, 1971.
———. *The Territorial Imperative*. New York: Dell Publishing Company, 1971.

Lorenz, Konrad. *On Aggression.* New York: Bantam Books, Inc., 1967.

Morris, Desmond. *The Human Zoo.* New York: Dell Publishing Company, 1971.

————. *The Naked Ape.* New York: Dell Publishing Company, 1967.

Skinner, B. F. *Beyond Freedom and Dignity.* New York: Alfred A. Knopf, Inc., 1971.

Tiger, Lionel and R. Fox. *The Imperial Animal.* New York: Holt, Rinehart and Winston, 1971.

SOME DELIGHTFUL BOOKS ABOUT BEHAVIOR BY ETHOLOGISTS

Carr, Archie. *Windward Road.* New York: Alfred A. Knopf, Inc., 1955.

Lorenz, Konrad. *King Solomon's Ring.* New York: T. Y. Crowell, 1961.

Mowat, Farley. *Never Cry Wolf.* New York: Dell Publishing Company, 1963.

Schaller, George B. *The Year of the Gorilla.* Chicago: University of Chicago Press, 1964.

Tinbergen, Niko. *The Herring Gull's World.* New York: Harper and Row, 1971.

Van Lawick-Goodall, Jane. *In the Shadow of Man.* Boston: Houghton Mifflin Company, 1971.

FOR THE FASCINATED STUDENT . . . SOME HEADIER BOOKS

Eibl-Eibesfeldt, I. *Ethology: The Biology of Behavior.* New York: Holt, Rinehart and Winston, 1970.

Hinde, Robert. *Animal Behavior.* 2nd ed. New York: McGraw-Hill, 1970.

Klopfer, Peter H. and Jack P. Hailman. *Introduction to Animal Behavior: Ethology's First Century.* Englewood Cliffs, New Jersey: Prentice-Hall, 1967.

Kutscher, Charles. *Readings in Comparative Studies of Animal Behavior.* Lexington, Massachusetts: Xerox College Publishing, 1971.

Lorenz, Konrad. *Studies in Animal and Human Behavior.* Vols. 1 and 2. Cambridge, Massachusetts: Harvard University Press, 1970 and 1971.

Marler, Peter R. and W. J. Hamilton, III. *Mechanisms of Animal Behavior.* New York: John Wiley & Sons, 1966.

McGaugh, James L., N. M. Weinberger, and R. E. Whalen, eds. *Psychobiology: The Biological Bases of Behavior.* San Francisco: W. H. Freeman and Company, 1967.

Thorpe, William H. *Learning and Instinct in Animals.* Cambridge, Massachusetts: Harvard University Press, 1963.

SMALLER OR EASIER, BUT GOOD

Barnett, Samuel A. *Instinct and Intelligence: Behavior of Animals and Man.* Englewood Cliffs, New Jersey: Prentice-Hall, 1971.

Dethier, Vincent G. and E. Stellar. *Animal Behavior.* 3rd ed. Englewood Cliffs, New Jersey: Prentice-Hall, 1970.

Manning, Aubrey. *An Introduction to Animal Behavior.* Reading, Massachusetts: Addison-Wesley, 1967.

Otten, Charlotte M., ed. *Aggression and Evolution.* Lexington, Massachusetts: Xerox College Publishing, 1973.

Tinbergen, Niko. *Animal Behavior.* New York: Time-Life Books (Life Nature Library), 1965.

————. *The Study of Instinct.* Oxford: Oxford University Press, 1969.

Van der Kloot, William G. *Behavior.* New York: Holt, Rinehart and Winston, 1968.

Part 1
BASES OF BIOLOGY

In Part 1, we take a large view of organisms—how life may have arisen on Earth, how the continuity of life is maintained through inheritance from parent to offspring, how new species evolve, and how they have become adapted to a vast range of habitats.

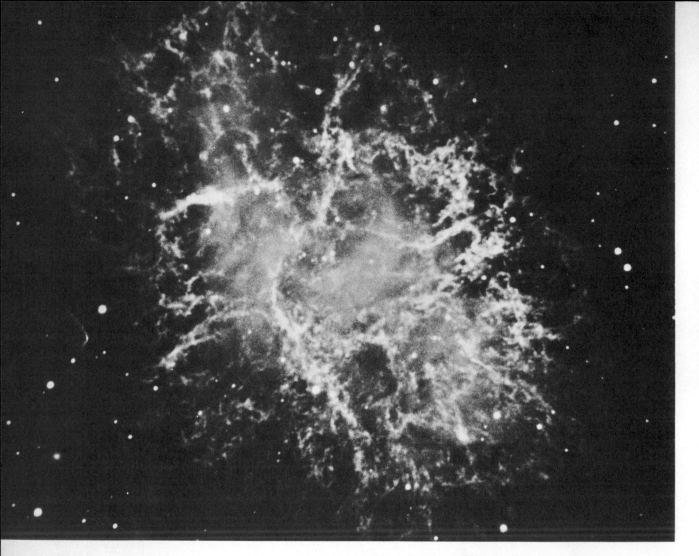

Figure 2–1 Order out of
chaos: This cloud of gas some
42 light-years in diameter was
produced by a star that
exploded in A.D. 1054. New
stars are formed from the
second-hand matter of such
exploding stars. The matter is
reorganized and is capable of
achieving that level of order we
call life, here represented by
biology's simplest unit, the cell,
in this case the ameba.

(CRAB NEBULA: LICK OBSERVATORY
PHOTOGRAPH. AMEBA: CAROLINA
BIOLOGICAL SUPPLY HOUSE.)

2

ORIGINS AND ORGANIZATION OF LIFE

IN THE BEGINNING

An age for Earth

When we ask how life arose on this planet we are asking a question that has occupied men's minds for thousands of years. However, only in recent decades have biochemists been able to investigate possible conditions and chemico-biological pathways along which inorganic matter might have evolved into living systems. While laboratory investigations supporting the idea are fairly new, the notion that life arose from nonliving materials is not. The ancient Babylonians, Greeks, and Egyptians, among others, all had mythologies claiming that through supernatural or divine intervention life originated out of nonliving materials.

Until the 1920s, the major obstacle to an understanding of how life originated was biochemists' inability to see how **organic** molecules—those that contain carbon atoms and are essential to life—could be produced outside of living systems. However the Russian biologist A. I. Oparin, in his book *The Origin of Life on Earth,* suggested biochemical pathways that enabled chemists and biologists to investigate the problem through experimentation.

Although today we can imagine processes responsible for organizing the precursors of the first life forms out of a primordial chemical broth, we hunger for more details of that recipe of synthesis that organized certain molecular aggregates into that fundamental biological unit, the cell.

Some of the very atoms making up your body and the pages of this book had a long history before they were organized as part of the third planet in the Solar System. Through a process called radioactive dating (explained in any introductory geology text) geologists are able to say that the oldest Earth rock formations discovered so far are on the order of 3.8 billion years old. Because Earth's crustal rock is continually subjected to chemical and physical change through weathering and erosion, it is impossible for us to know how many changes a particular rock formation underwent before it evolved into its present form. Although the mountains seem ageless, they are continually being eroded away, their remains washed down to the sea as sediments that are pressed deeply into the ocean floor and millions of years later thrust up as new mountain chains. Because Earth's crustal rocks had a geological prehistory going back considerably longer than 3.5 billion years, we are unable to say how much older than 3.5 billion years the planet is by studying its rocks alone.

Lunar rocks have been dated at about 4.6 billion years, but neither does that age take us back as far as we must go, for the Moon also had a geological prehistory. The large number of stony and iron meteorites that have been dated show a mean age of 4.7 billion years. That, for the present at least, is the oldest age geologists can come up with by direct means of age determination. But surely there was a time when the meteorites, along with the planets, their satellites, and the Sun itself, were very different from what they are today. "No single thing abides," the Roman philosopher–poet Lucretius tells us.

Most astronomers now agree that some time between 4.5 and 5.0 billion years ago the Solar System formed out of a dense cloud of hydrogen gas, and of molecular debris collectively called "dust." The diameter of the cloud may have been some 9.3×10^9 miles, or about 100 times Earth's distance from the Sun. While most of the material was hydrogen, small amounts of the heavier elements also were present. Over hundreds of millions of years the gaseous cloud contracted in upon itself, due to the mutual gravitational attraction of its particles, and flattened into the shape of a disk as the system gained rotational velocity. The central hub of material consolidated into a sphere that became the Sun, while the disk material formed aggregates that evolved into the planets and their satellites, comets, and other space debris.

Heavy elements from the stars

But we still have not accounted for the origin of elements heavier than hydrogen—carbon, nitrogen, and oxygen among them—that began the process we call life. We must turn the clocks back several billion years more, to a time when the Galaxy was a dark place consisting mostly of hydrogen atoms; the stars had not yet formed. Local concentrations of hydrogen atoms formed particularly dense clouds here and there, the astronomers tell us, each cloud giving rise to one or more stars (Fig. 2–2). As any particular sphere of hydrogen compacted itself around the core region, temperature, pressure, and density in the core would all increase. When temperatures reached 10,000,000°K or

Figure 2–2 In the first stage of the formation of stars, dense concentrations of gas and dust may form within a nebula (cloud of gas and dust). These are proto-stars (A). As a proto-star rotates, its surrounding gas and dust spread out in a disk-shaped volume of space (B). Local concentrations of disk material then condense into planets and their satellites (C).

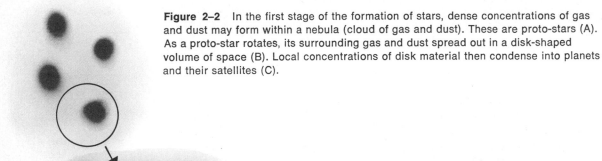
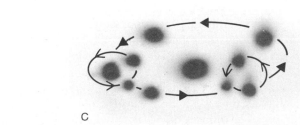

more, hydrogen nuclei would begin to fuse and form the nuclei of helium atoms. It is through just such a process of nuclear fusion that stars like the Sun are thought to radiate energy.

If the temperature and pressure within the cores of stars are raised still higher, the nuclei of helium fuse and give rise to the formation of carbon nuclei; at still higher temperatures and pressures carbon nuclei fuse and form nuclei of oxygen and iron. In this way, the process of nuclear fusion in the cores of stars can account for the synthesis of heavier and heavier elements. Stars, then, are the element factories of the Universe.

During its life span of several billion years, a typical star emits great quantities of matter into space. From time to time certain stars blow themselves to bits, such as the Guest Star observed by Chinese astronomers in A.D. 1054 and shown in Fig. 2–1. Such stars are rich suppliers of heavier elements. Stars like the Sun are second-generation stars in that they have been formed out of the debris emitted by aging or dying stars. Had the Sun and its planets been formed early in the life of the Galaxy, they would not have contained heavier elements. Only because they were formed relatively late did they inherit "second-hand" materials suitable for the development and evolution of life as we know it in our minute corner of the Universe.

And let there be life . . .

One hypothesis of Earth's formation takes us back to the time when the planets and their satellites were condensing out of the solar disk material. Gradually, according to this idea, Earth was built up from smaller bodies, called **planetesimals**, composed of a mixture of silicates, metallic iron, water, and ammonia. Heat generated by gravitational energy and by radioactive heating may have caused the young planet to heat up fairly rapidly to a temperature of about 1,200°K. As a result of such heating, the denser materials (iron, for example) would melt and migrate toward the core region while lighter materials (silicates, for example) would tend to float toward the surface. During some such process of separation, a variety of gases would be vented through the newly formed crustal rock and collected as a primitive atmosphere. Among the new atmospheric materials would have been large quantities of hydrogen (H), water vapor (H_2O), nitrogen (N_2), methane (CH_4), hydrogen sulfide (H_2S), and ammonia (NH_3).

By this time in the young planet's history, a number of other events were occurring and shaping its future. At first, heavy downpours of rain falling on the hot crustal rock vaporized on contact, but as the crust gradually cooled, the torrential rains formed ever-enlarging pools that became the proto-seas. Meanwhile, photochemical reactions in the upper atmosphere were breaking down water vapor to oxygen and hydrogen. Most of the free hydrogen in the atmosphere was too light to be held gravitationally captive by the planet and was lost to space. The heavier gases, such as O_2, CH_4, NH_3, H_2S, and others, were retained. The loss of hydrogen caused the atmosphere to become oxidizing; that is, NH_3 was being broken down to molecular nitrogen (N_2) with the subsequent loss of hydrogen, and CH_4 was being converted to carbon dioxide (CO_2). In short, Earth's primitive atmosphere was very different from the atmosphere that we know today. It may seem ironic that if an oxygen-rich atmosphere similar to the one we have now had existed some three billion years ago, life as we know it might never have evolved. In the presence of an abundance of oxygen, the large organic molecules that were the precursors of living systems probably would not have been formed. Such molecules are extremely unstable in the presence of oxygen.

Hence, an atmosphere consisting mainly of CH_4, NH_3, and H_2O, with gradually accumulating amounst of CO_2 and N_2, composed the substance out of which at first complex molecules, then living matter, were to evolve. But a source of energy was needed to drive the chemical reactions. There were several such sources. Among them, ultraviolet energy must have reached the young planet's surface as intense radiation since there was no ozone (O_3) layer —as there is today—to filter it out. There were also meteoric impacts, electrical discharges in the form of lightning, ionizing radiation, and heat. Given such materials and energy sources, what were the molecules synthesized?

THE SYNTHESIS OF AMINO ACIDS AND PROTEINS: In 1953 a graduate student named Stanley Miller, working with Harold C. Urey at the University of Chicago, designed an experiment to find out what the primitive organic molecules were. He circulated H_2, CH_4, NH_3, and H_2O through a closed system of glass tubing and then subjected the gases to electric discharges to simulate lightning in Earth's primitive atmosphere. Gradually the water vapor condensed out as "rain" and the other gases went into solution. After a week, Miller examined the solution and found that a number of organic molecules had been synthesized, among them **amino acids** (Fig. 2–3). These are the building blocks of proteins, which may sometimes contain tens of thousands of separate amino acid molecules.

With the use of chemical notation, we can actually visualize the composition of amino acids. The structural formula for an amino acid is shown on the left in Fig. 2–3. Amino acids are made up of an —NH_2 (amino) group, a —COOH (carboxyl, or acidic) group, and a variable R group, all attached to a carbon. There are about 20 different R groups found commonly in living things, so there are about 20 different amino acids. One such R group is shown in the second color on the right in Fig. 2–3 and forms the amino acid known as glutamic acid. The amino acids linked together as a protein molecule are joined by. a carbon–nitrogen bond occurring between the NH_2 group of one amino acid and the COOH group of another. This bond, called a **peptide** bond, is made possible by the removal of one hydrogen atom from the NH_2 and the removal of one hydrogen atom and one oxygen atom from the COOH, the released atoms combining as a molecule of water. Two amino acids so linked are called a **di**peptide; when many are linked they are referred to as a **poly**peptide.

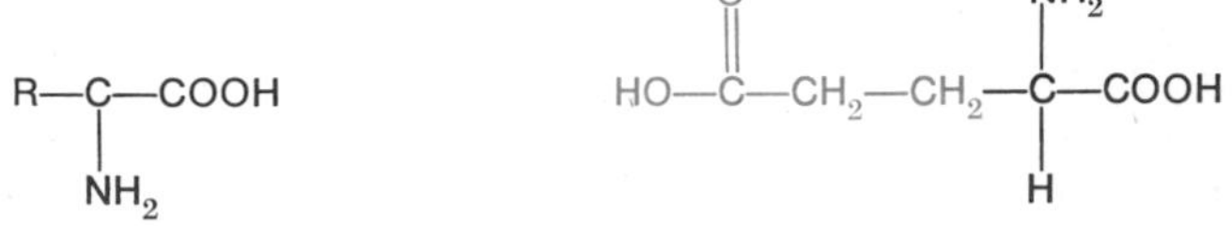

Figure 2–3 The generalized structural formula for an amino acid (left) and the amino acid known as glutamic acid (right).

We can imagine such synthesis of low atomic weight molecules occurring in "some warm little pond with all sorts of ammonia and phosphoric salts, light, heat, [and] electricity," as Darwin imagined the scene. But these relatively simple molecules were a far cry from anything that we could call "living." Larger and more complex molecules were needed, such as purines and pyrimidines (Fig. 2–4), which are the building blocks of **nucleic acids** and of complex proteins and protein-like molecules.

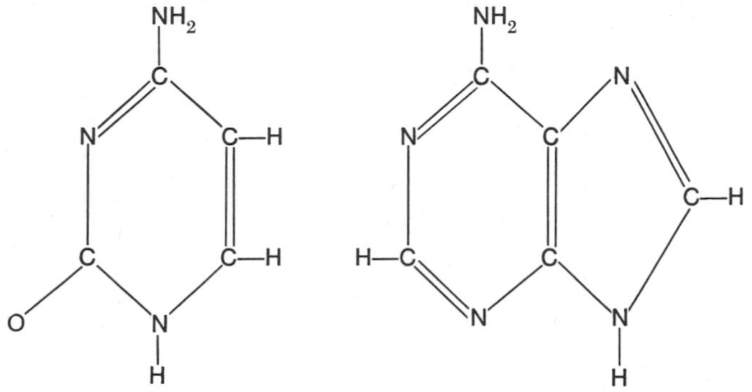

Figure 2–4 At left is the pyrimidine, known as cytosine, present in DNA. At right is the purine adenine, also in DNA.

In 1957, Sidney W. Fox presented a paper in which he suggested how the prebiochemical formation of the first protein molecules might have occurred. In brief, he suggested that rains would have washed to Earth various kinds of amino acid molecules present in the atmosphere. Those coming in contact with rock surfaces that were still warm would have dried and combined as complex molecules of proteins and protein-like structures, after which they would have been washed into the newly forming seas along with a variety of salts and other materials leeched from the rock crust. So a variety of complex new molecules would have evolved and become denizens of Darwin's "warm little pond." In addition to proteins, there would have been fats, lipids, sugars, and nucleotides, the latter of which formed nucleic acids.

SELF-REPLICATING MOLECULAR SYSTEMS: At this stage of prebiochemical evolution, we can imagine a kind of chemical natural selection taking place. Those molecules that were stable would tend to remain, but those that were unstable would tend to be degraded, their components being made available to enter into new synthesis reactions. We can imagine such a state of affairs existing some three to four billion years ago. But the evolutionary gulf between proteins and a metabolizing cell is immense. During an interim, of how many years we shall never know, molecular structures much more complex than those mentioned so far had to evolve. A mixture of salts and diverse organic molecules including polypeptides and nucleic acids is not something that characterizes the high degree of order of a healthy metabolizing cell. Oparin has suggested that the next stage of prebiochemical evolution might have been a relatively elaborate assemblage of new and more complex molecular aggregates called **coacervates** (from the Latin word *acervatus*, meaning "clustered"). When a protein molecule is dissolved in water, parts of it become **ionized**, or acquire an electrical charge. Once charged, those parts attract and establish bonds with water molecules, in the process becoming encased in a shell of water.

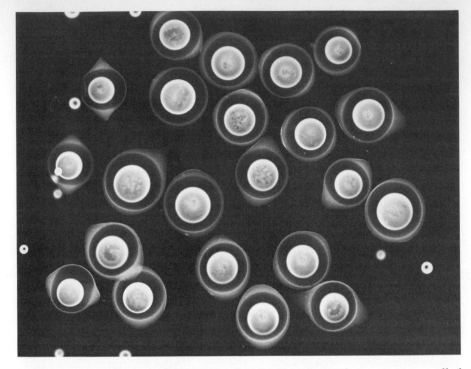

Let's take a closer look at these fascinating molecular structures called coacervate droplets (Fig. 2–5). Several individual protein particles may clump and form a droplet. The water molecules forming the surrounding shell are not randomly arranged but are oriented with such precision that a clearly definable interface exists between the water shell and the substance it encloses. That interface functions as a membrane that tends to isolate the coacervate droplet from the external environment. One of the properties of coacervate droplets is their ability to attract and incorporate into themselves certain materials from the external environment. The fact that their interface membrane enables them to draw on outside materials selectively accounts for another property of the droplets: The internal molecules composing a droplet are not randomly arranged, but are highly ordered structurally and tend to maintain that order as they incorporate on a selective basis raw materials from the outside. By definition we could describe this process as "growth," growth accompanied by a still greater tendency toward order through the development of a more elaborate membrane at the interface, which makes the droplet even more selective.

There must have been many different kinds of coacervate droplets in the primordial seas, some more stable than others. Those that were chemically successful and survived would tend to have the higher degree of physico-chemical organization and be surrounded by an abundance of inorganic "nutrient" materials. We can imagine the more successful droplets growing at the expense of the external environment and eventually reaching a size that made them unstable. We can further imagine such droplets breaking into component parts that were smaller versions of the large unstable droplets. Subsequent growth and eventual fragmentation of such coacervate droplets might represent self-replicating molecular systems on the precellular level.

A number of investigators have suggested that those droplets most successful at self-replication, survival, and growth would have been those with certain "genetic" controls that would lead to the production of successful "offspring" by successful "parent" droplets. At this stage we can do little more than make intelligent guesses and wonder about the chemical selection pressures that produced certain sequences of nucleotides in nucleic acids and certain other sequences of amino acids in proteins.

How can we classify these prebiological "cells" with a selectively permeable membrane that enabled them to grow at the expense of the external environment and that were capable of reproducing more of their kind? They were primitive cells of a sort, but were they *living* cells? If not, at what stage did the first living cells evolve? Here we run the risk of semantic snares, for the difference between the simplest living system and the most marvelously complex system of the type just described is a matter of definition and is better left to philosophers. As Oparin has said, "There is no fundamental difference between a living organism and lifeless matter. The complex combination of manifestations and properties so characteristic of life must have arisen in the process of the evolution of matter."

PREBIOLOGICAL HETEROTROPHS: Still there is an immense gulf between the most complex prebiological organism and the simplest organism known to us today, and perhaps we shall never fill in the details of how those extremes were linked except in the broadest of outlines. The self-replicating coacervates just described were **heterotrophic**; that is, they relied on certain compounds in the external environment as a source of energy to drive their intercellular chemical machinery. An increasing abundance of self-replicating heterotrophs would soon cause a serious drain on the nutrient materials required by these prebiological cells and laboriously synthesized abiotically—that is, by the combining of inorganic materials—over millions of years. As the nutrient supply continued to be depleted, competition among the heterotrophs would become more severe. Somewhere along the line natural selection could have favored certain of those cells with an ability to produce alternative nutritional substances on their own. Enzymes, which are protein catalysts, would be required for such an event, but the amino acids necessary for the synthesis of enzymes were available. The phosphate-containing compound abbreviated ATP would be required as an energy source. It, too, was available since it could have been synthesized abiotically from nucleic acids in Earth's primitive atmosphere.

No matter what elegant levels heterotrophy might have achieved, a universe of heterotrophic cells could not have survived long, for the depletion of nutrients eventually would have outpaced their production.

PHOTOSYNTHETIC AUTOTROPHS: Another dramatic sequence of events in our broad outline must have occurred and given rise to cells capable of producing food out of inorganic materials. Such organisms are called **autotrophs**. Respiration among the heterotrophic cells would tend to cause a build up of CO_2 in the atmosphere, and chemical conversion of the CO_2 along with H_2O would release molecular oxygen (O_2) to the air. The result would be a screening out of high wavelengths of radiant energy from the Sun. Ultraviolet radiation is one such source of energy required initially for abiotic synthesis. It was largely screened out. Selection pressure favored the survival of those mutant cells capable of synthesizing their own nutrients by using the wavelengths of energy down in the visible-light region of the electromagnetic spectrum. In other words, certain cells capable of photosynthesis evolved and autotrophy became the rule, such cells being capable of synthesizing carbohydrate out of the inorganic compounds CO_2 and H_2O, as here:

$$CO_2 + H_2O \rightarrow [CH_2O] + O_2$$

As their numbers increased, the photosynthetic autotrophs changed the environment in significant ways. For example, by releasing large quantities of free oxygen into the atmosphere, they changed the atmosphere from a reducing one to an oxidizing one. Examples:

$$CH_4 + 2O_2 \rightarrow CO_2 + 2H_2O$$

$$4NH_3 + 3O_2 \rightarrow 2N_2 + 6H_2O$$

$$O_2 + 2O_2 \rightarrow 2O_3$$

Aerobic respiration, respiration involving oxygen, became the rule among autotrophs and among the complex heterotrophs to be. By this time, some three billion years or so ago, chemical evolution had given way to biological evolution and the stage was set for the marvelously varied pageant of multicellular life.

Origin of the cell theory

According to the cell theory, all plants and all animals are made up of cells and cell products; further, the cell is the smallest structural unit of living things.

In 1665, the English scientist Robert Hooke contributed the word "cell" to biology on observing a slice of cork under a microscope and seeing box-like structures that reminded him of monks' monastery cells. During the 1800s, other investigators evolved the cell theory. In 1824, the French biologist Dutrochet suggested that all living things might be composed of cells, although he and other biologists had difficulty resolving in animal tissue structures as prominent as the box-like plant cells so readily observed.

The breakthrough came about 16 years later in Germany. The zoologist Theodor Schwann and the botanist M. J. Schleiden independently and at about the same time suggested that the contents, not only the shape, of cells should be emphasized. Animal cells clearly lacked the box-like structure of plants, but every living cell they observed contained a sphere-shaped structure, the **nucleus**, surrounded by a watery substance, **cytoplasm**, all enclosed within a membrane. Later in the century, the German physician Rudolf Virchow made another extremely important contribution to our knowledge of cells by saying that only cells produce other cells.

There is enormous diversity in cell structure and function in plants and animals alike. For our present purpose of introducing cells, we will imagine a

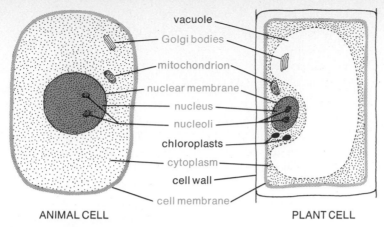

vacuole
Golgi bodies
mitochondrion
nuclear membrane
nucleus
nucleoli
chloroplasts
cytoplasm
cell wall
cell membrane

ANIMAL CELL   PLANT CELL

Figure 2–6 Those structures occurring in both plant and animal cells are identified by colored type. All living cells have a number of structures—and functions—in common.

"typical" plant and animal cell, although no such typical cells exist. Our imaginary cells will, however, permit us to describe some of the major products of cells (Fig. 2–6).

The nucleus can be regarded as the control center of the cell and may contain one or more **nucleoli**, which are concerned with protein synthesis, along with a thread-like substance called **chromatin**, which organizes itself into chromosomes during cell division. Surrounding the nucleus is the **nuclear membrane,** which separates the nuclear material from the cytoplasm but at the same time selectively allows passage of certain materials into and out of the nucleus. The **cell membrane**, also called the **plasma membrane**, functions in a similar way for the entire cell. Plants have in addition a stiff skeleton-like **cell wall**. Within the cytoplasm are structures called **mitochondria**, associated with energy requirements of the cell. **Golgi bodies**, also found in the cytoplasm of most cells, seem to have something to do with cell secretions. **Vacuoles**, often seen to occupy most of the volume of a plant cell are waste "storage tanks." The cells of green plants, particularly the leaves, contain many **chloroplasts**, which contain the green pigment **chlorophyll**. All the components of a healthy living cell are fully integrated as a smoothly functioning unit of organized material.

A question we must now ask is whether all "living" things fit the cell theory. The answer is no. Viruses, for instance, are regarded by some biologists as precursors of living cells. Whether they are termed living or nonliving is pretty much a point of view. The more than 300 varieties of viruses consist simply of a core of nuclear material (nucleic acid) wrapped in a coating of protein; cytoplasm seems to be totally lacking. Viruses behave as inactive molecules when they are on their own, but when inside a cell they behave as living agents and produce replicas of themselves.

There are other exceptions to the cell theory. Certain algae and fungi are composed of several nuclei embedded in a mass of cytoplasm, all retained within a wall. Are they single cells or multicells? Whatever we choose to call them, they do not fit the stereotype cells shown in Fig. 2–6. It really doesn't matter, however, any more than it matters whether we regard viruses as cells or noncells. What does matter is that we recognize such exceptions as having lost characteristic cellular organization, or in the case of viruses, possibly never having attained that level of complex organization.

PATHWAYS OF EVOLUTION

Of life "out yonder"

Although there are glaring omissions in our biological *Genesis*, some such broad outline like the one just described seems reasonable, and as time passes laboratory experiments—such as those of Oparin, Miller, Fox, Melvin Calvin (who synthesized glucose out of primitive Earth atmospheric gases), and many others—confirm the broad outline as they supply new details. At one time from his anthropocentric view, man looked on life on this planet as an exception in the Universe. Most biologists now agree that given the right conditions, the right association of matter and energy, life of some sort is inevitable as a natural consequence of the ways matter and energy are altered over periods of hundreds of millions and billions of years. But what of life *as we know it*?

It would be unreasonable to expect that evolution on other planets, even one other planet, has followed the same course that evolution has taken on this planet. The biochemist Isaac Asimov and his coauthor Stephen Dole discussed this point in their book *Planets for Man*.

When it comes to living things [of] other planets, of course, these might differ widely, depending on the precise course that evolution happened to take in each special circumstance. Even so, on each planet one would expect to find organisms carrying on photosynthesis and creatures capable of invading practically every conceivable corner of the environment: marine forms, fresh-water creatures, land creatures, aerial forms, cave organisms, and so on. In spite of differences in detail, certain basic kinds of life forms would be expected to display some common characteristics. Thus, fast-swimming marine forms would be streamlined. Land animals would typically have legs, and fast-moving aerial forms would have wings. There must of necessity be autotrophs, and one would also expect to find heterotrophs.

On no other planet, however, would we expect to find any of the actual phyla of plants or animals with which we are familiar on the surface of Earth. From the smallest virus to the largest whale, the Earthly life forms are unique products of Earth. Each planet on which living things have evolved must have its own peculiar classification of organisms, and this in itself should present the human race in general and biologists in particular with endless realms of new wonder and experience.

Evolution through natural selection

Earlier it was said that the process of evolution through natural selection must have operated on a chemical level before living cells were established. Darwin, and Alfred Russel Wallace after him, independently developed the concept of evolution through natural selection, an idea that enables us to view life over the ages in a behavioral as well as a genetic context.

CONTINUITY OF LIFE: Once it began, life flourished on Earth and maintained a continuity that was not broken. Cells living today are but transient links in a complex chain that originated some three billion years ago and continues to acquire more and varied links through evolution. As you saw earlier, continuity on the molecular level depended on the ability of certain macromolecules to replicate themselves, both within coacervates and in the external environment. On higher, biological levels replication also had to become the rule if life was to continue unbroken. Although individuals are mortal, *life* seems to march along a road of immortality.

Continuity implies unity, but it also implies diversity and change. During Darwin's time in the mid-1800s, the then popular theory of Creationism dominated the thinking of most scholars. According to the Creationists, God created each species so that it was perfectly adapted to the environment, the polar bear to the Arctic cold, the cod to salt water, and so on. Although the Creationists readily admitted that there was variation among the individuals of a species, they maintained that all such variations were departures from the "perfect" condition of the species created by God and must, therefore, be of negative value to the unfortunate individuals.

The geological and biological observations Darwin made during the voyage of the *Beagle* (see color section facing page 48) enabled him to see the fallacy of such an argument. Facts based on direct observation: Variation exists among the individuals of any species of plant or animal. Fossil evidence shows that species have become extinct. Fossil evidence of a given extinct species and observation of certain living species show structural similarities so striking that they could not be coincidental. Darwin's conclusion: Species are not created anew and immutable but in some way change. Although Darwin was able to observe such changes in the controlled breeding of pigeons, dogs, and other domestic animals, in nature the process operated far too slowly to be readily observable.

THE FUNCTION OF ADAPTATION: The facts led Darwin and Wallace to the same conclusion. Over the years a major change in the environment—an ice age, the formation of a vast inland sea, or whatever—might be so severe that no individual members of a species would be able to survive, and the species would become extinct. In other cases, where the environmental change was less severe, certain individuals with favorable variations would, quite by accident, be well adapted to the new environment. Those individuals with adaptations—a longer neck, a swifter gait—enabling them to cope with a new condition in the environment survived to reproductive age and were able to pass on the favorable trait(s) to their offspring. Those without the adaptation were doomed. Extinction of species is the rule in evolution, survival the exception. At least 99.9% of all species that have ever lived on Earth are now extinct!

The sensitivity of natural selection to favorable variations cannot be overstated as the process through which evolution works. Earlier we said that evolution helps us view life in a behavioral context. While many instances supporting that statement will be given in Chapter 5 when the adaptedness of behavior is discussed, one instance may be of interest here.

Fossilized tracks of certain groups of marine worms show an evolution of feeding behavior through time. The older tracks show a meander pattern resembling a child's scribbling. Such a poorly organized search pattern for food—one in which the organism inadvertently goes over much of the same ground twice or more often—would do in times of plenty, but during a period of food scarcity such an unsystematic search pattern could prove disastrous, and apparently did. For later on better organized feeding track patterns appear, tracks organized in nonoverlapping rows similar to those of a garden. Still more highly organized feeding behavior emerges later on. It would seem clear that those variant individuals with the genetic material responsible for the more efficient feeding behavior were selected for survival and lived to pass that behavior on to their offspring. The less efficient behavior was selected against and lost.

Their lack of knowledge about genetics was only one reason why 19th century biologists could not fully appreciate the subtle ways in which natural selection operates. During Darwin's time, and even into the present century, there was still belief in the notion that acquired characteristics could be inherited—that a parent who exercised and developed exceptional muscles, for instance, would pass on that character to his offspring. According to such thinking, evolution occurs not through natural selection of the fittest individuals but through a process whereby the characteristics of each generation are determined (acquired) largely by the characteristics inherited and acquired by the parent generation. Cultural and social evolution surely operate in that way, but most modern biologists reject the notion that biological evolution operates through the inheritance of acquired characteristics.

If a species is to evolve successfully biologically, each generation must contain individuals with adaptations favorable enough to assure survival in the face of change. Mutants with a swifter gait enabling them to avoid an increased number of predators represent a small, but important evolutionary factor, and natural selection singles them out for survival. **Adaptation**, then, is a vital function that has its roots in genetic materials of individuals, and by enabling individuals to cope with changes in the environment it ensures continued survival of the species.

We can demonstrate just such a process of evolution through selection pressures in the laboratory by working with the bacterium *Staphylococcus aureus*. If we add a small amount of the antibiotic streptomycin to a population of the bacterial cells, most of the cells are killed. However, certain genetic factors enable about one in a million cells to survive. Chance genetic variation has selected them for survival with the result that they flourish and produce more of their kind, among which will be other chance variations. If we now keep adding streptomycin to the culture medium, each time increasing the dosage, the majority of the surviving population dies each time. Eventually we stop increasing the concentration and test the cells. The tests show that we have been dealing with a mixed community of two populations—one that was resistant to the antibiotic and survived, and one that was not only resistant but had come to depend on the antibiotic as a nutrient and would not survive when deprived of it. Here is a clear example of evolution, since both populations of bacterial cells present at the end of the experiment had genetic factors significantly different from the cells of the original culture. Although the selection pressures in the laboratory example are artificial in that they were imposed and controlled by man, they are every bit as real functionally as the selection pressures operating in nature.

Evolution through geologic time

Evolution through natural selection seems entirely satisfactory as a means of accounting for the continuity, unity, and diversity of life arising out of self-replicating, nonliving aggregates of matter. Because the fossil record of organisms constituting the unbroken chain of life through geologic time is so frustratingly incomplete, our view of life's pageant is bound to be fragmentary. It is like trying to watch a parade that is proceeding south along one street, while you the observer are riding a bus proceeding north along a street run-

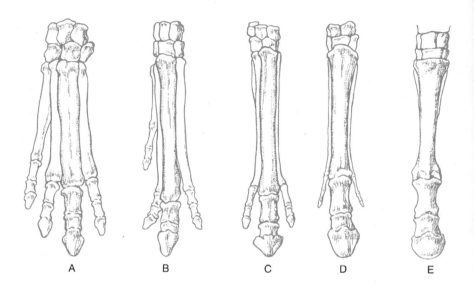

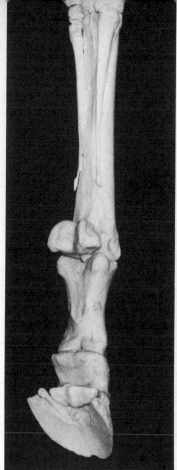

ning parallel to the parade route. You get a brief glimpse of the marchers only when the bus crosses an intersection and you are able to look along the block toward them.

Fragmentary though our view may be, we can clearly read the trend of evolution in the fossil record (Fig. 2–7). The first "living" organisms most likely were marine unicellular individuals, sometimes classified as **protists** rather than being designated as either plants or animals (see Appendix for classification schemes). During this time, some two to three billion years ago, life probably was restricted to marine environments, the land being completely barren. By the later Precambrian, Cambrian, and Ordovician, there were multicellular algae and fungi among plants, and a profusion of invertebrates, such as mollusks, crustaceans, coelenterates, arthropods, and echinoderms. The first vertebrates we know of appeared during the Ordovician. The geological time chart (Fig. 2–8) and evolution tree (Fig. 2–9) sketch in the remainder of the fossil evidence. Again, it is important to remember how incomplete that record is. For instance, man's earliest known ancestors, the chordates, appear suddenly during the Ordovician with no traces of evolutionary links with the past. Is it that paleontologists have yet to discover those fossils, or are they lying misinterpreted and incorrectly labeled in some musty forgotten drawer?

Figure 2–7 The trend of evolution is revealed in the evolution of the forelimb of the horse: (A) *Eohippus*, of the Eocene epoch, was a four-toed animal the size of a collie. (B) *Mesohippus*, of the Oligocene and larger in structure, developed hooves. The fourth toe was no longer used and there was a reduction in size of the side toes. (C) By the Miocene, the fourth toe of *Miohippus* had nearly disappeared. (D) Mid-Pliocene *Protohippus* had a much enlarged hoof with further reduced side toes. (E) Late-Pliocene *Pliohippus* was a true one-toed horse with mere splints representing the original side toes. The photograph shows the foreleg of *Equus*, the modern horse.

GEOLOGICAL TIME CHART

ERA	PERIOD	THE LAND	THE SEA	BIOLOGICAL EVENTS
CENOZOIC *(from the Greek words kainos, meaning "recent" and zoe, meaning "life")*	**QUATERNARY** *(meaning "fourth")* Present to 1.7 million years ago	The Cascadian Disturbance deformed the Coast Ranges of the west coast of North America and caused widespread volcanic activity. This disturbance probably is still going on today.	Continental glaciers developed on the continents of North America, northern Europe, and Antarctica while valley glaciers formed in the high mountain regions. There were four glacial and three interglacial ages. The heights of the sea varied with ice formation.	Modern horses appeared at the beginning of this period. Of the several man-like animals that developed, only one species (*Homo sapiens*) survived and occurs in great numbers today. Glaciation caused the extinction of many mammals and trees.
	TERTIARY *(meaning "third")* 1.7 million to 65 million years ago	There was widespread volcanic activity in the western United States. Mounts Shasta and Rainier were formed, as was the great Alpine–Himalayan mountain chain. There was also volcanic activity in the North Atlantic region, in East Africa, and in the Mediterranean region.	Most of the inland seas left the continents, and by the end of this period the continents had the same general outlines that they have today.	Grasslands were widespread. Mammals became the dominant land animals; primitive mammals disappeared. By this time cats, monkeys, whales, elephants, kangaroos, and birds were well established. The first anthropoid apes appeared. This period saw the modernization of flowering plants.
MESOZOIC *(from the Greek words mesos, meaning "middle" and zoe, meaning "life")*	**CRETACEOUS** *(from the Latin word creta, meaning "chalk")* 65 million to 136 million years ago	The Rocky Mountains of North America and the Andes of South America were formed as a result of the Laramide Disturbance.	Cretaceous seas covered most of Europe, much of Asia, and nearly half of North America. The Gulf of Mexico received nearly 11,000 feet of sediments during this period.	Flowering plants were common, as were giant sequoias. Sharks again became abundant. Snakes made their first appearance. The last of land. Primitive mammals appeared.
	JURASSIC *(named after the Jura Mountains)* 136 million to 195 million years ago	A period of relative quiet. The Sierra Nevada Mountains were formed. Geosyncline downsinking took place along the western edges of both North and South America. In a way, the Jurassic was a stage-setting period for activity during the Cretaceous.	Jurassic seas changed little from the Triassic (see below). Seas continued to cover the western borders of North and South America.	Among plants, cycads, ferns and scouring rushes flourished, and the first true pine trees appeared. Dinosaurs were numerous. The first lizards arose. Pterodactyls and feathered birds appeared, as did small mammals. Plesiosaurs, marine reptiles, grew 20 feet long.

Period	Geology	Seas	Life
TRIASSIC (*referring to a three-fold division of rock in southern Germany*) 195 million to 225 million years ago	Extensive igneous activity took place during the Triassic, which includes the formation of the famous Palisades of New Jersey, and similar rock in South America, southern Africa, Australia, and Antarctica.	Seaways continued to cover the western edges of North and South America, and some parts of Europe and Asia.	Due to cooler seas, or for some other reason, many marine creatures such as sharks did poorly during this period. Thecodonts, ancestors of the dinosaurs, arose, as did turtles. Crocodiles also made their appearance along with marine reptiles such as ichthyosaurs.
PALEOZOIC (*from the Greek words palaios, meaning "ancient," and zoe, meaning "life"*)			
PERMIAN (*named after the Province of Perm in the Ural Mountains of Russia*) 225 million to 280 million years ago	The Appalachians south of New England were formed from the Appalachian Geosyncline. The Ural Mountains were also formed. Along the west coast of North America there was widespread volcanic activity. The reddish sedimentary strata of Monument Valley, Utah were laid down.	The western United States was still covered by shallow seas during this period. In other parts of the Northern Hemisphere seas were drying up and leaving vast deposits of salt and potash.	Conifers increased, while the giant scouring rushes died out. Trilobites, some corals, and some amphibians also became extinct. A generally drying climate caused many plant and animal species to become extinct, but favored the success of reptiles.
PENNSYLVA-NIAN (*named after the coal regions of Pennsylvania*) 280 million to 310 million years ago	The Ouachita Mountains (see below) were altered many times during this period. Uplifting of sea beds in the Northern Hemisphere produced new low-lying land. In the Southern Hemisphere there was widespread glaciation.	Some areas of the land sank, producing vast lakes, swamps, and brackish lagoons, but in general the inland shallow seas of the Northern Hemisphere were not so widespread as they were during the Mississippian.	About half of the world's workable coal was formed during this period, mainly from giant scale trees. Amphibians, some of them 15 feet long and resembling salamanders, ruled the land. The first reptiles arose during this period. Conifers (cone-bearing trees) and 40-foot-high scouring rushes were common.
MISSISSIPPIAN (*named after the limestone area near the junction of the Mississippi and Missouri Rivers*) 310 million to 345 million years ago	The Variscan Disturbance raised extensive mountains in western Europe. The Ouachita Mountains of Oklahoma and Arkansas were formed.	Clear, shallow seas were still widespread in the Northern Hemisphere. The Appalachian Geosyncline, formed during the Cambrian Period, collected extensive deposits of sandy and muddy sediments from the rivers. Limestone was the most common sediment in the shallow seas covering the mid-continent region.	Sharks were abundant during this period, and amphibians made their appearance as the major land animal. Hundred-foot-high scale trees grew on the edges of pools, shallow lakes, and swamps. Winged insects appeared for the first time, one with a wing-span of 29 inches (Meganeura).

Period	Life	Seas and Land	Earth Movements
DEVONIAN *(named after Devon, England)* 345 million to 395 million years ago	A bewildering variety of fish arose during this period. Plants were plentiful and included giant tree ferns 40 feet high. Late in this period lobefinned fish began to establish themselves on the land.	Most of North America continued to be covered by shallow seas during most of the Devonian.	A land disturbance (called the Acadian Disturbance) raised high mountains in New England, Quebec, and Nova Scotia. The Kanimbla Disturbance raised mountains along east Australia.
SILURIAN *(named after the Silures, an ancient tribe living in Wales)* 395 million to 440 million years ago	The trilobites began to decrease in numbers during this period. Eurypterids, or "water scorpions," were quite common. The first land plants—ferns and psilopsids—appeared, and the first air-breathing animals.	Most of the present-day land area of the Northern Hemisphere was under water during this period. Extensive salt deposits, such as those of western New York and Michigan, were formed.	There was much volcanic activity in Maine, New Brunswick, and eastern Quebec. The Caledonian Disturbance gave rise to a 4,000-mile-long mountain range from Wales through Scandinavia and westward to northern Greenland.
ORDOVICIAN *(named after an ancient Celtic tribe, the Ordovices, living in Wales)* 440 million to 500 million years ago	This was a rich period for marine life. Trilobites were numerous, as were bryozoans, graptolites, cephalopods, and crinoids. Jawless fish also arose. First vertebrates (fish) appeared. Algae were dominant.	About 70 percent of the present-day Northern Hemisphere was flooded during this period.	Later during the Ordovician Period the crust of the Earth extending from Newfoundland to the Carolinas of the United States was affected by granitic intrusions, metamorphism, and folding, giving rise to mountains of this Taconic Disturbance.
CAMBRIAN *(Roman name for Wales)* 500 million to 570 million years ago	The shallow Cambrian seas abounded with many forms of life, including sponges, trilobites, brachiopods, graptolites, and other animals without backbones. Algae were dominant.	Shallow seas periodically advanced and withdrew over the land, covering much of the United States, Europe, Asia, Australia, and South America.	In North America, Europe, and Asia great troughs in the land (called "geosynclines") were filling up with sediments. Near the end of the Paleozoic Era, this sedimentary "fill" was thrust up as mountain ranges, including the Rocky Mountains and Appalachians.
PRECAMBRIAN 570 million to 4,500 million years ago	The first living things may have come into being about 3,000 million years ago. Rare fossils of algae-like and fungi-like plants have been discovered. Fossil imprints of jellyfishes, worm burrows, and, recently, brachiopods have also been found.	Sometime during this era the seas formed. But these early seas and oceans did not have the shape of our seas and oceans of today.	The Sun and planets were formed out of gas and dust. Earth went through a molten phase, developed a solid crust and a primitive atmosphere of methane, ammonia, and hydrogen.

Figure 2–8 The Cenozoic era is divided into six "epochs" as well as two periods. From older to more recent, the Tertiary consists of the Eocene, Oligocene, Miocene, and Pliocene epochs. The Quaternary period consists of the two epochs Pleistocene and Recent. (Chart adapted, by permission, from *Discovering Rocks and Minerals*, by Roy A. Gallant and Christopher J. Schuberth; Natural History Press.)

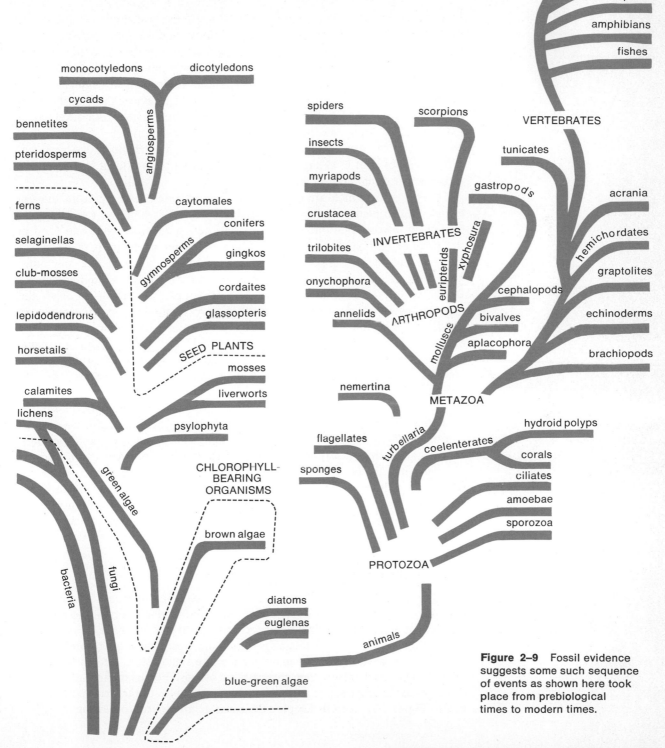

mammals
birds
reptiles
amphibians
fishes

VERTEBRATES

monocotyledons   dicotyledons

cycads

bennetites

pteridosperms   angiosperms

spiders   scorpions

insects   tunicates

myriapods   gastropods   acrania

caytomales

ferns

crustacea   INVERTEBRATES   xyphosura   hemichordates

conifers

selaginellas   gymnosperms   gingkos   trilobites   euripterids

graptolites

club-mosses   cordaites   onychophora   ARTHROPODS   cephalopods

lepidodendrons   glassopteris   annelids   bivalves   echinoderms

molluscs   aplacophora

horsetails   SEED PLANTS   brachiopods

mosses

calamites   liverworts   nemertina   METAZOA

lichens   psylophyta   turbellaria   hydroid polyps

flagellates   coelenterates   corals

green algae   CHLOROPHYLL-
BEARING
ORGANISMS   sponges   ciliates

amoebae

sporozoa

brown algae   PROTOZOA

bacteria   fungi

diatoms

euglenas

animals

Figure 2–9 Fossil evidence
suggests some such sequence
of events as shown here took
place from prebiological
times to modern times.

blue-green algae

FUNCTIONS OF LIVING MATTER

"Function" as a framework for defining life

In our search for a clear distinction between living and nonliving things we must avoid certain pitfalls. For instance, suppose that we defined living matter as something capable of capturing energy and materials from the external environment and incorporating both within its own internal environment with resulting growth and a capacity for reproduction. Mechanical engineers have, in fact, designed and constructed purely mechanical devices that satisfy those criteria and by that definition would qualify as living matter. But surely such mechanical systems, no matter how elaborately contrived, are not *alive*. Neither are the coacervates and other prebiological chemical systems described earlier. But if we are to exclude them from the world of the living, we must further qualify our definition of life.

Green plants, which are photosynthetic autotrophs, take up from the external environment a variety of inorganic compounds and use the energy of sunlight to incorporate those materials into new plant tissue and into food in the form of carbohydrate, some of which the plant uses for its own growth and some of which it stores in the form of starch. Cows, people, and other heterotrophic organisms eat green plants, and carnivores eat other heterotrophs. In either case both classes of heterotrophs are taking in from the external environment carbohydrate that they themselves are incapable of producing. The mineral elements—iron, magnesium, phosphorus, and many others—taken in by green plants and animals are termed plant **nutrients**. Animal nutrients include not only minerals but the carbohydrates, which animals, fungi, and most bacteria cannot manufacture for themselves and must obtain from an organic source. These and the proteins and fats are the special class of nutrients that we call food. When the carbohydrate consumed by heterotrophs is taken into the internal environment of the animal, it is decomposed chemically, in the process providing energy for the organism and a source of building materials used for growth and the replacement of worn or damaged parts. This process of breaking down nutrient molecules with the subsequent release of energy is called **respiration**. To further qualify a living thing, we can add (to energy capture and reproduction) respiration as a necessary function. And under the heading **metabolism** we can include the total chemical activity involved in nutrition, respiration, and synthesis.

Homeostatic regulation

Another characteristic of living things is the tendency to maintain a more or less steady state, with nutrition, respiration, and synthesis operating not randomly and independently but regulated in relation to each other. **Homeostasis** (from the Greek *homoios*, meaning "like" and *stasis*, meaning "standing") is the term used to designate the maintenance of a steady state. Living organisms have special mechanisms that ensure homeostasis. For example, some vertebrates sweat in response to an increase in temperature of the external environment (Fig. 2–10), thereby keeping their own temperature from rising.

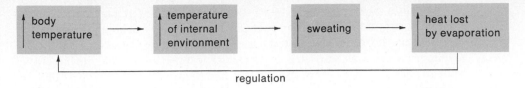

regulation

The above figure is an example of a **feedback** system, which has many analogs in electronics; for example, the thermostat that regulates the air temperature in your living room and the various servo mechanisms that guide a spacecraft to the Moon, or a missile toward its moving target. The kind of feedback involved in sweating is called **negative** feedback because it negates (regulates) a change (increased body temperature) that tends to upset the steady state of the system.

There are numerous examples of homeostatic regulation operating on a behavioral level. For instance, an animal eats because it is hungry and it gets hungry in response to an empty stomach. As it eats—even if it is fed non-nutritive bulk—its filled stomach triggers a stimulus that causes the animal to stop eating. In a species of small fish called the stickleback, the male serves as watcher over the eggs deposited in a nest by the female. During his guard over the eggs the male swims in an interesting behavioral pattern, directing water over the eggs by a fanning motion of his fins. It turns out that without being ventilated the eggs die. The fanning keeps richly aerated water circulating around the eggs, providing them with the oxygen they need and removing the CO_2 they expel.

In general, homeostatic regulation functions by enabling the individual to respond to changes in the external or internal environments that threaten to alter the steady state condition. Hence it is a negative feedback system. It is not always easy to identify precisely the mechanisms responsible for homeostatic regulation, for they are many and varied. When you feel chilled you draw your chair closer to the fire, a conscious regulatory response involving the brain. But many regulations are required to maintain a steady state within the human organism and the brain does not direct all of them. Most, therefore, are carried out automatically. Reflex actions are one example of automatic regulation. If you hold your hand too close to a flame you jerk it away even before you realize that you have been burned. Rather than traveling all the way to the brain and back, nerve impulses follow a short-cut route to the spinal column and directly back to the hand. This route is called the **reflex arc** and saves precious fractions of a second during which a large number of cells could be destroyed. Figure 2–11 shows an example of homeostasis operating automatically on the glandular level. It also operates on the cellular level, for instance when a cell takes in or expels various molecules by diffusion. Homeostasis serves the individual organism in many ways.

Figure 2–10 Sweating is an example of negative feedback in homeostatic regulation. As the air temperature on a summer day rises, the body maintains a steady state of temperature in the internal environment through increased sweating. Water loss at the skin surface removes heat by evaporation.

Figure 2–11 Homeostasis operates on the glandular level when the concentration of glucose in the blood becomes too high. A homeostatic regulator, the pancreas, secretes insulin, which causes glucose utilization by the body tissues, thus regulating the blood sugar concentration.

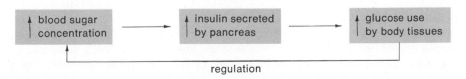

regulation

The notion of an organism having the capacity for self-regulation so that it maintains harmony with its environment has fascinated scholars through the ages. When the term homeostasis was first coined in 1939 by Walter B. Cannon, its use was restricted to homeostatic regulation occurring in living animals, but in recent years the concept has been applied to areas as diverse as population genetics, embryology, and ecology, as you will find in later chapters of this book. At this point we will consider, if only briefly, two additional examples of homeostasis.

HOMEOSTASIS IN PLANTS: Plants also have mechanisms enabling them to maintain a steady state. One example is the functioning of certain cells found in great numbers at the surface of green plants' leaves. They are paired, sausage-shaped cells capable of becoming turgid and losing turgor in such a way that each pair serves as a window leading to the interior of the leaf where photosynthesis takes place. When the cells, called **stomata**, lose turgor due to water loss the window closes; when they become turgid due to water pressure within the cells the window opens. These important regulators of a green plant's internal environment respond to three factors—the plant's water supply at a given moment, the amount of CO_2 in the air around the leaves, and the amount of light reaching the plant.

When the stomata are closed, water loss from the plant is reduced, as are the release of oxygen (a product of photosynthesis) and the intake of CO_2 (required for photosynthesis). The general pattern of the stomata is to open at daybreak, with resulting water loss and an increase in the rate of photosynthesis as it gets lighter. Around midday, the stomata tend to close due to lack of turgor through water loss during the morning. Continued intake of water by the roots soon makes up the water deficit and the stomata tend to open again, thus permitting an increase in the rate of photosynthesis. By evening the stomata have again lost turgor and they remain closed throughout the night. By opening when there is light, the stomata admit CO_2 to the leaves when it can be used for photosynthesis, and by remaining closed at night and at midday they regulate water loss. Although the activity of stomata is actually more complex than we have indicated, their function as homeostatic regulators is evident in this brief description of their activity.

Darwin and his son Francis investigated the response of plants to light, a response called **phototropism** (from the Greek *phot-*, meaning "light" and *tropos*, meaning "turn"). Their work eventually led other investigators to the identification and isolation of a class of plant growth hormones called **auxins**. Auxins play a number of growth regulation roles in plants. For example, green plants tend to bend toward the light and display their leaves in such a way that each leaf receives the optimum amount of light for photosynthesis. It is also common knowledge that the stems of most flowering plants tend to grow straight up rather than parallel to the ground. If, for example, you tip a potted geranium on its side and leave it in that position with the stem parallel to the floor, before long the stem will turn up at a right angle as it continues to grow. Auxin collects on the underside of the stem. Since it is a growth promoter in the stem, the cells along the bottom surface of the stem divide at a more rapid rate than those in the growth region of the stem's upper surface, with the result that the stem turns upward. The general rule in the plant world is that stems grow upward, roots downward.

In some way that plant physiologists do not yet fully understand, light shining on the exposed surface of a vertically oriented stem causes about twice as much auxin to be present on the shaded side of the stem as on the illuminated side. The shaded surface of the stem then grows at a more rapid rate than the surface in direct sunlight, with the result that the stem bends toward the light. Again, auxin is serving the stem as a growth promoter; and as a homeostatic regulator auxin is helping maintain the steady state by keeping the plant oriented toward light.

Auxin also serves as a growth regulator in roots. If for some reason a root deviates from its downward direction of growth and begins to grow horizontally, auxin tends to collect along the bottom surface of the root, just as it does along the bottom surface of a stem growing horizontally. But instead of taking a turn upward as the stem does, the root begins to grow downward in response to the auxin. It turns out that while auxin is a growth promoter in stems, it acts as a growth inhibitor in roots when its concentration exceeds normal. Because cell division at the bottom surface of the root tip is inhibited, the top surface cells elongate more rapidly than those on the bottom surface, with the result that the root maintains a downward growth trend. This particular response is termed **geotropism**.

HOMEOSTASIS IN ECOLOGY: Our model of homeostasis also serves us well when we apply it to biological systems larger than a single organism. Chapter 7, which deals with population dynamics, will have much to say about regulators on the ecological level. One brief example will serve here to demonstrate the existence of dynamic interrelationships among a mixed population of different species.

A simple dynamic relationship between a predator and prey species is that of the lynx and snowshoe hare in the region around Hudson Bay. In the early

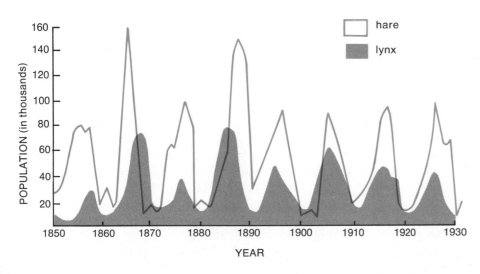

Figure 2–12 In such a simple predator–prey relationship the two populations never peak in phase with each other. The peaking of the predator species' population always lags behind the peaking of the prey species' population.

1800s, the Hudson Bay Company began to keep records of the number of hare and lynx pelts it purchased from trappers. One thing the data show is that while the population of each species peaked and declined in smooth cycles, they never peaked in phase. As the curves in Fig. 2–12 show, whenever the hare population reached a peak the lynx population began to increase from its depressed point. As the lynx population continued to increase and then peak, the hare population declined, and so on through cycles occurring rhythmically every 9 to 10 years. The general rule is that in any such simple predator–prey relationship there is a lag between the times the two populations peak. Here again is an example of homeostatic regulation occurring as a feedback system (Fig. 2–13).

Figure 2–13 An example of negative feedback operating to regulate the populations of a predator and prey species.

When the regulator is removed from such a simple community, what happens? Without predators to keep it in check, the population of a hypothetical prey species eventually would tend to reach an exponential growth rate, but the population could not continue to increase indefinitely. At some point other regulatory factors would come into play and the population would crash. Starvation, disease, psycho-physiological ailments due to overcrowding, and other factors would cause the population to decline, either gradually or with a sudden reduction in numbers.

As individual cells and complexes of cells on the level of organisms function, so a mixed community of organisms functions as a larger biological unit. In nearly any mixed community *many* variables characterize even the simplest food chains, with the result that various feedback mechanisms are operating simultaneously. In many complex communities there is a tendency toward stability, toward the steady state, but that is not always so. This notion will be amplified in Part 2 when "food webs" and the ways they affect populations are discussed.

Before turning our attention from the ways living matter functions to the ways in which it is structured, we should try to see that complex of adaptations collectively called homeostatic regulators in a framework of evolution, which will help emphasize the point that there are integral relationships between behavior, homeostasis, and evolution.

In general, lower organisms of a low order of specialization tend to operate along a wider spectrum of environmental conditions than more highly specialized organisms do. The trend in evolution clearly has been toward a higher degree of homeostatic precision to keep the more complex machinery of highly specialized organisms functioning within a relatively narrow range of deviation from a norm, or the average condition we call the steady state.

Elsewhere we have mentioned that light-sensitive, homeostatic regulator called the "red spot" in *Euglena*. The red spot enables a single-celled *Euglena* to respond to light intensity in such a way that the organism orients itself with respect to light for optimum photosynthetic activity. Although *Euglena's* "eye" is efficient enough to assure the organism of optimum photosynthetic activity, it would be an extremely inefficient light-detecting organ for an animal as complex as a bird or mammal, whose requirements of a light-detection organ are enormously more varied and demanding than those of *Euglena*.

It is difficult to know whether a particular homeostatic regulator evolved first along behavioral lines or along physiological lines. For example, behavioristic psychologists have shown that if goldfish are given the opportunity to respond to changes in the water temperature of their tank in such a way that they themselves are able to regulate the temperature, they invariably maintain the temperature at a value suitable for optimum growth. And if they are placed in a large tank with different local temperatures, they also respond behaviorally by seeking out that same optimal temperature.

Fish tend to seek out optimum temperatures in their environment by behavioral means and lack physiological homeostatic regulators enabling them to tolerate a wide environmental temperature range. Reptiles and other cold-blooded organisms also rely on behavioral techniques, such as body orientation with respect to the Sun's position, to maintain body temperature within a tolerable range. Mammals and birds, more highly specialized physiologically, are equipped with complex internal regulators that maintain a steady-state temperature within a range that is remarkably narrow when compared with that of fish, reptiles, and amphibians. In general, birds maintain a temperature that does not vary by more than a degree, although there are a number of exceptions. Man's temperature rarely varies by more than a couple of degrees.

The evolutionary pathways of homeostasis are clearly indicated when we compare man as a warm-blooded animal with other mammals and birds. Man has many sweat glands; most other mammals have few, and birds lack them entirely. Most mammals have fur or hair that can be raised or lowered hair-by-hair, thus regulating heat loss. Although man as a mammal has retained the ability to raise and lower each individual hair on his body, all it does is produce goose pimples since man long ago lost his hairy coat.

While we have approached homeostatic regulators pretty much as behavioral adaptations, in Part 3 we will examine them in detail from a physiological perspective. It is now time to focus our discussion on the structure of living matter in order to see how it is organized on still another level.

STRUCTURE OF LIVING MATTER

A hierarchy of order

When we speak of the way something is structured, we mean the ways in which its matter is organized. We might also add the way in which its matter and energy are organized. At the lowest level in the hierarchy of structure shown in Fig. 2–14 are the subatomic particles composing atoms—electrons, protons, and neutrons. On the next higher level are atoms, which can be thought of as organized systems of subatomic particles. Locked in a structural complex, six randomly selected electrons, six protons, and six neutrons become

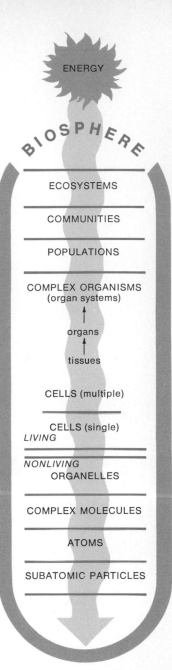

ENERGY

BIOSPHERE

ECOSYSTEMS

COMMUNITIES

POPULATIONS

COMPLEX ORGANISMS
(organ systems)

↑
organs
↑
tissues

CELLS (multiple)

CELLS (single)
LIVING

NONLIVING
ORGANELLES

COMPLEX MOLECULES

ATOMS

SUBATOMIC PARTICLES

Figure 2–14

a new substance—the one we call carbon—with new properties, properties that those dissociated components do not have. The atoms that most concern us in the context of living systems are those of carbon, hydrogen, nitrogen, and oxygen, along with sulfur and phosphorus.

At the next higher structural level are complex molecules, such as those described earlier in this chapter. Compared with the smaller molecules of H_2O and CO_2, **macromolecules** are enormous structures, usually occurring in long chains of thousands of atoms. Four such molecules are especially important in living systems: 1. proteins, which are groupings of smaller amino acid molecules; 2. lipids, composed mainly of fatty acids; 3. polysaccharides, composed of sugar molecules; and 4. nucleic acids, composed of smaller molecular aggregates called nucleotides. Much more will be said about these substances later.

If we bathe a cell in a certain kind of solution the cell bursts its plasma membrane and spills its contents into the external environment, including its various organelles (see page 25), which are made up of the macromolecules just described. When placed in a suitable medium, some of these organelles continue to carry on certain functions for a while. For example, they ferment sugars and continue the routine task of constructing new molecules, but none will carry on for long, for each kind of organelle has come to depend on the presence of certain other organelles for continuous functioning. Outside the cell, the organelles are not able to carry on and reproduce more of their kind. While they are on the border line separating the living from the nonliving, they do not qualify as fully living matter. Although at one time in the history of living things certain organelles may have existed independently before taking up residence inside primitive cells, over a period of time both the primitive cell and the organelles came to depend on each other for survival, since each contributed something needed by the other. Such a biological condition is called **mutualism** and is a common behavioral feature among plants and animals.

When we reach the level of cells, we are dealing with a matter–energy complex that is fully alive, for on this level we find organized matter capable of adaptation, in addition to having the ability to metabolize and reproduce. New cells are created out of the stuff of living cells; they are not the product of simple synthesis, as were the first primitive cell-like structures. Life, and only life, gives rise to new life. When cells have divided and reproduced themselves, the two resulting daughter cells are fully metabolizing units of matter and, as you found earlier in the case of bacterial cells, are capable of adaptation. But many cells are incapable of reproducing more of their kind once they have taken on a special function, and if isolated they die. Each organelle performs a certain task. Deprive a cell of an organelle and you alter the complex pattern of its internal functions with the result that the steady state of the cell is drastically upset. Biochemical order can no longer be maintained and we say that the cell is dead.

Multicellularity and specialization

At the level of multicellular organisms not only does matter become more complex structurally and functionally, but far greater amounts of energy are required to maintain the organism, although on a per cell basis multicellular organisms require less energy than do unicellular organisms. We can make another generalization as well: At each level upward in the hierarchy, more complex structures are able to carry on not only the functions of the structures lower down, but also new functions that the simpler structures are not capable of. For instance, consider the marvelous ability of DNA compared with the more restrictive characteristics of the nucleotides of which DNA is composed. This holds true all along the upward climb from simpler to the more complex levels of structure. In all unicellular organisms—including bacteria, algae, and protozoa—each cell must carry on all of the functions required to keep the organism alive. At the level of multicellular organisms that is no longer true. Because different cells have different structures and functions, we say that they are **specialized**. An ostrich egg, which is a reproductive cell, may be more than 10 cm in diameter while a human egg cell is only about 0.1 mm. This difference in structure between the two egg cells is attributed to a difference in cell function. The bulk of the ostrich egg is yolk, stored food that maintains the developing embryo. Because the developing human embryo derives its food from its mother, it needs no such adaptation for food storage.

On the multicellular level there are more striking differences in cellular structure and function than on the unicellular level. Take one of the simplest multicellular organisms known, the green alga *Volvox*, which is a colony of from hundreds to tens of thousands of cells (Fig. 2–15). Each cell composing *Volvox* is equipped with two flagella, a chloroplast, a nucleus, cytoplasm, and a light-sensitive spot. If one such cell were leading an independent life and its

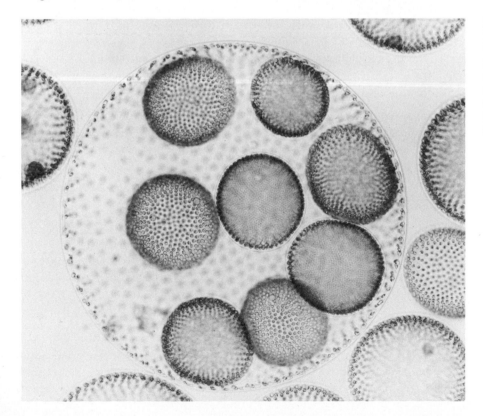

Figure 2–15 Although *Volvox* is usually described as a "colony" of cells, it can be regarded as a simple multicellular organism since some of its cells are specialized to carry out the function of reproduction. (CAROLINA BIOLOGICAL SUPPLY HOUSE)

cell wall were punctured, the cell would die. Life takes on a larger meaning on the multicellular level than on the unicellular level. In a *Volvox* colony when one of the cells is punctured beyond repair, *Volvox* does not die. Somewhere along the path of evolution, selection pressure operated in favor of colonial aggregates because the survival value of a colony was greater than that of an individual cell. A closely related and equally interesting alga is *Pandorina*. The problem we face with *Pandorina* is whether to call it a colony, and if so, then how do we define a *Pandorina* individual? *Pandorina* is a ball of cells enclosed in a gelatinous sheath. When the ball is pressed through a fine mesh the individual cells are dissociated, with the remarkable result that each cell regenerates a complete *Pandorina* ball.

In order for a multicellular organism to function, cooperation among its cells, rather than independence, must be the rule. For example, *Volvox* rotates as it moves forward through the water, similar to the motion of a football in a forward pass. If each cell of *Volvox* moved its flagella independently of neighboring cells, *Volvox's* motion would be random rather than coordinated. The effect would be that of the oarsmen of a skull crew rowing in different directions and out of phase, not uniformly and cooperatively.

Volvox displays another feature of interest: The cells at the aft "end" of the organism are somewhat larger than those at the forward end. The rule in biology is that a difference in structure goes hand in hand with a difference in function. These larger cells in *Volvox* may be specialized to carry out the task of reproduction. A smoothly functioning multicellular organism depends on the ability of its individual cells to function cooperatively, which implies a level of order more complex than that on the next level down in the structural hierarchy. It also implies a higher (more complex) level of behavior. We have yet to discover the biochemical magic that produces cell specialization.

From tissues to organism

Groupings of cells specialized to perform a single task are called tissue. Under magnification the cross section of a rose stem reveals a variety of tissues arranged in concentric circles (Fig. 2–16). The vascular system, for example, includes phloem tissue that is specialized for the transport of sugar, principally, throughout the plant. Cells forming certain connective tissue in animals give rise to tough fibers that connect the skin to underlying muscle tissue, but the fibers are flexible enough to permit the skin and muscle to slide against each other. **Tissue**, then, can be thought of as a group of cells all of which cooperate in the performance of one or more particular functions. Blood is a tissue.

At the next higher level, **organs**, such as leaves and roots in green plants and the heart, liver, and lungs in certain animals, can be thought of as assemblages of a variety of tissues all of which work cooperatively by bringing about a group function. The rhythmic and uninterrupted beating of a healthy heart is an example of numerous tissues functioning cooperatively. A system of organs, which works cooperatively and is maintained in a steady state, brings us to the level of **organisms**, but organ systems made up of numerous organs occur only in the most advanced animals and plants. Many multicellular systems are relatively simple. Among plants, liverworts are so simple that they are down

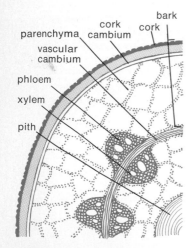

Figure 2–16 This cross-sectional view of a typical woody stem shows organized tissue specialized to perform a variety of functions, including protection (bark), growth (cambium tissue), conduction, (phloem and xylem), and food storage (pith).

parenchyma
vascular cambium
cork cambium
bark
cork
phloem
xylem
pith

on the level of cells and tissues; among animals, the hydra is barely above the cell-tissue level.

Earlier we said that life takes on a larger meaning on the multicellular level. Parts of us are "dying" from the moment we are born, but from our anthropocentric view our most meaningful perspective on life is not on the level of cells but on the much higher level of complex organ systems. What does it matter that epidermal cells or certain liver cells die from day to day? Even though they are a living part of us, it would be ludicrous to mourn their passing. They are replaced by new cells and neither the structure nor the function of the organ or tissue is altered. The organism continues to live. But if a vital organ such as the heart fails, or if cells of certain tissues die faster than they are replaced, or, as in the brain, they die and are not replaced at all, the steady state of the organism eventually is so drastically upset that the organization of matter and energy decays. Science can come to grips with living matter, but "life" is too elusive to be included in the scientist's lexicon.

When we carry discussions of living things to levels higher than that of individual organisms, we become involved in abstractions such as species, populations, communities, and so on. But living matter activated by energy functions cooperatively on those levels just as surely as it does on lower structural levels. From a cell's point of view, perhaps "life" of the complex organism of which the cell is a part would also be considered an abstraction! What is happening is that at each higher level in the hierarchy we are changing our frame of reference. At any one level the living matter is able to do everything that the living matter at each lower level can do; but in addition it can do other things, and those other things make each higher level of living matter radically different from the various systems lower down.

Higher biological systems

It is a huge step from the realms of molecular and cell biology to those higher levels of behavior included in the ecologist's world of populations, communities, and ecosystems. As the cell is the biologist's basic unit, populations are the ecologist's basic unit. An ecologist may speak of the **population** of buttercups on a Colorado hillside, such a population consisting of interbreeding individuals of a single species sharing the same area at a given time. As unicellular and multicellular individuals have certain structural characteristics, so are populations structured, and the particular ways in which they are structured determine their future course. For instance, on page 189 five diagrams show the effects of various age structures of a human population.

As an organ is an aggregate of tissues, a **community** is an aggregate of populations. The homeostatic regulators operating at this level of the structural hierarchy include climate, local weather, the availability of mineral nutrients and other abiotic (nonliving) factors. They also include the number, density, and variety of living organisms making up the biotic (living) part of the community. These myriad interrelationships are the community regulators. All of the plant and animal organisms of a community are mutually sustaining and interdependent. Every moment of their lives from birth to death they are fixing, using, and dissipating energy. Energy is moved into the community not only by sunlight but also through birth and immigration, and out of it through death and emigration. And after death the complex organic molecules are broken down by the decomposers of the soil and again made available as inorganic compounds for use by living members of the community.

An **ecosystem** is a still higher structural unit composed of an aggregate of communities. Whether aquatic or terrestrial, an ecosystem has two basic substructures: autotrophs, which use the Sun's energy and various inorganic substances and fix energy in the form of manufactured food; and heterotrophs, which rely on the food-energy made available by the autotrophs.

Finally, that all-encompassing zone of our structural high-rise (Fig. 2–14) is the **biosphere**, which includes land, water, and air capable of supporting organized matter that can metabolize, reproduce, and adapt to changing conditions. That, then, can serve as our working definition of living things, arrived at within a framework of function and structure; but it is not a hard and fast definition since it excludes those specialized cells of a multicellular organism that are unable to reproduce. No matter what definition we come up with, it seems, there are bound to be exceptions.

The last section of this book focuses on biological–cultural man in many of his behavioral aspects. When you finish reading those pages, and with the present chapter as background, you may begin to wonder if "man" of some sort exists in biospheres beyond the cozy one we inhabit. And if so, what kind of physiological and behavioral costume does he wear? As far-fetched as such a question may seem, it is a relevant and real concern of biologists. As Loren Eiseley has so eloquently put it in his book *The Immense Journey*:

> Life, even cellular life, may exist out yonder in the dark. But high or low in nature, it will not wear the shape of man. That shape is the evolutionary product of a strange, long wandering through the attics of the forest roof, and so great are the chances of failure, that nothing precisely and identically human is likely ever to come that way again. . . . Nowhere in all space or on a thousand worlds will there be men to share our loneliness. There may be wisdom; there may be power; somewhere across space great instruments, handled by strange manipulative organs, may stare vainly at our floating cloud wrack, their owners yearning as we yearn. Nevertheless, in the nature of life and in the principles of evolution we have had our answer. Of men elsewhere, and beyond, there will be none forever.

1   Explain the thought behind these two seemingly contradictory statements: "New life can arise only from living matter." "Life originated out of non-living matter."

2   Which of the following functions can we associate with living things? With a mechanically contrived system? With both? Metabolism (including synthesis, respiration, and nutrition), reproduction, growth, homeostasis, adaptation.

3   Cite several examples of the following generalization: Living organisms are continually exchanging matter and energy with the environment.

4   Explain how natural selection might have operated in a prebiological environment, and how it operates on the species level.

5   Elaborate on this statement: "Life takes on a *larger* meaning as one moves from the level of unicellular organisms to the level of multicellular organisms."

SELECTED READINGS

Darwin, Charles. *The Origin of Species by Means of Natural Selection*. This timeless book is available in many editions and was first published in 1859. It represents the essence of Darwin's thinking about evolution through natural selection and is highly readable. It is a classic in the literature of science.

Ehrensvard, G. *Life: Origin and Development*. Chicago: University of Chicago Press, 1962. This book is a clear treatment of the problem of deducing the pathways along which life originated on Earth. It is a less technical treatment than Oparin's *The Origin of Life on the Earth*.

Gallant, Roy A. *Charles Darwin—The Making of a Scientist*. Garden City, N.Y.: Doubleday & Co., 1972. A most favorably received introduction to Darwin as humanist and scientist and to the process of forging his theory of evolution through natural selection during the voyage of HMS *Beagle*. This is a good prelude to reading Darwin's own accounts of the voyage.

Galston, Arthur W. *The Life of the Green Plant*. Englewood Cliffs, N.J.: Prentice-Hall, Inc., 2nd ed. 1964. This paperback edition is a concise treatment of the physiology of green plants and contains many interesting excursions into the physiological bases of plant behaviors such as phototropism, geotropism, and others.

Harrison, R. J. *Man, the Peculiar Animal*. Bàltimore, Md.: Pelican Paperback, 1938. The emphasis of this book, in keeping with one of the major themes in the present chapter, is on the structures and functions of humans as contrasted with other animals.

Figure 3–1 Folklores of the Middle Ages describing highly imaginative crossbreeds have their origins in antiquity when various "strengths" of different species were combined in an imaginary individual. The stone work here is of a colossal winged, human-headed lion from the palace of Ashurnasirpal II, king of Assyria from 883 to 853 B.C. (THE GRANGER COLLECTION)

3 TRANSMISSION OF LIFE

HEREDITY AND REPRODUCTION

One of the characteristics of living things is that they are capable of making rather faithful copies of themselves. By doing so, they have maintained an unbroken continuity of life for some two to three billion years. We cannot duplicate a house simply by cutting it in half; to preserve and replicate its structure and contents, we must return to the architect's plans and build anew by supplying a quantity of materials equal to the original quantity, and finally by organizing a duplicate set of furnishings.

Similarly, we cannot divide a man, a butterfly, or most other living organisms in two and expect to end up with two new individuals, although in certain unusual instances—in the case of that remarkable flatworm known as the planarian, for example—individuals can be duplicated that way. But it is not the rule in nature. Within each of us there is an architect's plan of sorts. Every living cell contains a set of plans that are units of inheritance known as genes, which are arranged in linear fashion on structures called chromosomes. Guided by this material, a single cell may begin to synthesize new material and then reorganize itself in such a way that it divides, producing two replicas of itself. What happened to the original cell is a question we might better leave to philosophers, for it no longer exists, yet it did not die.

The term we use to denote duplication of living things when new life arises from one parent only with a single set of inheritance plans is **asexual reproduction**. A new plant that grows from a bulb asexually develops faithfully in accordance with the inheritance plans of its uniparent.

In **sexual reproduction**, which is the rule among the great majority of living organisms, two cells combine and give rise to a new individual, so two parents with two *different* sets of inheritance plans contribute to the character of the offspring. While the continuity of life is thus preserved, the new individual arising from *two* parents stands an excellent chance of having at least some characteristics uncommon to either parent, although he will have many characteristics common to both. So sexual reproduction is a means of building variety, or **variation**, into new generations of living things.

A matter of difference

One way we learn about the world is by observing and noting differences; this is particularly true in the study of **heredity**, the transmission of characters from parents to progeny. If we were to study a species of fish in which the markings and behavior of every male were identical, we would be hard pressed to account for the uniformity. However, if we were able to recognize a general similarity in behavior and markings of the males, but at the same time noticed that certain individuals varied in behavior, or varied in markings, and if we found that those variations were passed from parents to offspring, we would be in a much better position to search for rules governing not only the individuals with abnormal variations, but the "normal" individuals as well.

Although the Babylonians and ancient Egyptians were well aware of the advantages of crossbreeding and inbreeding as a means of improving the vigor of crops and domesticated animals, they were unable to account for the mechanisms that brought about desirable differences. By the Middle Ages, folklores of several cultures, unrestrained by rules governing inheritance, described highly imaginative crossbreeds resulting from interspecies union (Fig. 3–1). Russian legend, for instance, describes its "Goliaths" as the male offspring of women who were crossbred with bears. Approximately A.D. 1256, St. Thomas Aquinas had described the inheritance of mental defects, but he was unable to account for their transmission on a mechanistic level, nor was he able to derive any rules governing inheritance. Early students of heredity were as much in the dark about just what characters could be transmitted from parent to progeny as they were about the means of transmission. Certain behavioral characters, temperament for example, were often dissociated from the body, as was "mind," and regarded as part of the soul. The soul, being created quite separately from the body, supposedly did not contain in its makeup characters that were heritable. Curiously enough, language, presumably as part of "mind," *was* regarded as a heritable character. There are a number of accounts of "experiments" performed to find out what language a child would speak if reared in isolation from language. According to one pious researcher, a Scottish lad so reared emerged from isolation speaking "God's language," Hebrew. Various cultures have their own versions of this story. The capacity for language is indeed heritable, but our predilection for Swahili or Sanskrit is culturally determined. It was left to investigators of the late 19th century to conduct systematic inquiries into the transmission of characters and formulate rules based on statistical criteria.

MENDELIAN INHERITANCE

At the time Darwin was writing *The Origin of Species* in the mid-1850s, the Austrian monk Gregor Mendel was experimenting with pea plants in his monastery garden. The results of those experiments were to become the foundation of modern genetics. To his dying day, Darwin expressed frustration at not being able to discover mechanisms of heredity that could account for natural selection. The then-popular theory of **blending inheritance** seemed entirely unsatisfactory to Darwin, a notion holding that if, for example, one crossed an animal having black fur with a member of its own species having white fur all of the progeny would be gray and none of the future generations of the gray animals, no matter how they were crossed with blacks, whites, or other grays, would ever give rise to black or white progeny. Once blended, the inheritance material from two different types could never be segregated.

text continued on page 49

VOYAGE OF THE *BEAGLE*

When HMS *Beagle* put to sea two days after Christmas in 1831 for a five-year surveying voyage around the world, "a new chapter in the history of science began," as Sir Gavin de Beer has put it. Aboard her was a young amateur naturalist named Charles Darwin, freshly down from Cambridge where he had been preparing for the ministry after an unsuccessful two-year bout in medical school at Edinburgh University. In nineteenth-century England natural history was considered a fitting and proper occupation for a clergyman, for God revealed His handiwork in marvelous ways through the laws of nature. The *Beagle*'s voyage seemed tailor-made for a young naturalist and country gentleman of means.

Commanding the *Beagle* was an intense young man of aristocratic birth, in his mid-twenties and three years Darwin's senior. Captain Robert FitzRoy of the Royal Navy had two compelling reasons for wanting a ship's naturalist

HMS *Beagle* in Murray Narrow, Beagle Channel, as painted by Conrad Martens, the ship's official artist during the latter part of the voyage. Martens replaced the original ship's artist, Augustus Earle, at the end of 1833 in Montevideo. (Photo © George Rainbird Ltd., reproduced by courtesy of the Royal College of Surgeons of England)

This watercolor of Darwin was painted by George Richmond in 1840, when Darwin was 31 years old, and four years after the *Beagle* returned from her five-year voyage around the world. (Photo © George Rainbird Ltd., reproduced by courtesy of the Royal College of Surgeons of England)

on board. For one, he had been unable to evaluate a number of unusual geological formations, possibly of mining interest, during an earlier surveying voyage of the *Beagle* around South America, and consequently "I could not avoid often thinking . . . that if ever I left England again on a similar expedition, I would bring along a person qualified to examine the land." FitzRoy's religious zeal provided the second motive for wanting a man versed in science on the voyage. FitzRoy believed in the literal truth of the Bible, particularly in the creation story in the Book of Genesis, and he made it perfectly clear to Darwin that he expected the young naturalist's observations of plants, animals, and fossils to prove once and for all the "scientific" truth of Genesis. At the time Darwin seemed comfortable enough with his assignment.

This oil painting of FitzRoy was done by Francis Lane when FitzRoy was promoted to the rank of Vice Admiral. Although he had a brilliant career as a young man, his later life was a very unhappy one and was to have a tragic ending. (Photo © George Rainbird Ltd., 1969, reprinted by permission of the Admiral President, Royal Naval College, Greenwich)

Catastrophism and creationism

In the early 1800s, geology was not the highly sophisticated science it is today. Darwin found a champion in the enlightened English geologist Charles Lyell and soon came to realize that an ability to read the geological record accurately was essential to an understanding of the fossil record. Two notions widely held among early nineteenth-century scientists and clergy alike were catastrophism and creationism. Observation clearly showed that crustal rocks everywhere were stratified, and further that each distinctive stratum contained a characteristic assemblage of fossils. Baron Cuvier advanced the idea that from time to time in Earth's history geological catastrophes occurred abruptly: "The dislocation and overturning of older strata show without any doubt that the causes which brought them into the position which they now occupy were sudden and violent. . . . The evidences of those great and terrible events are everywhere to be clearly seen by anyone who knows how to read the record of the rocks."

During each catastrophic upheaval all the animals and plants then living were destroyed, the remains of some being preserved as fossils. According to the Creationists, God then created an entirely new assemblage of animals and plants, whose species survived until the next catastrophe obliterated them. Lyell, whose writings were to influence Darwin so much, contended that species became extinct gradually as the environment underwent slow alterations over vast stretches of time. He did not attempt to account for the fact that new species arise; and when it came to man's origin as a species, Lyell turned to the Bible.

With a passion for collecting, Darwin littered the *Beagle*'s decks with specimens brought up in his tow nets. At each island stop, and ashore for weeks at a time on the South American mainland while FitzRoy was off surveying, Darwin collected by the hundreds insects, small mammals, reptiles, plants, anything that could be preserved for shipment to Cambridge for further study and classification. Meanwhile, he recorded his observations in meticulous detail and maintained a running narrative to John Henslow, his botany teacher and close friend.

At Punta Alta, overlooking the harbor of Bahia Blanca, Darwin made his first important find when he pried out fossils of an extinct giant rodent (*Toxodon*) resembling a hippopotamus, and another extinct giant (*Megatherium*) related to the sloth. Darwin wondered why these extinct species should so closely resemble species living today.

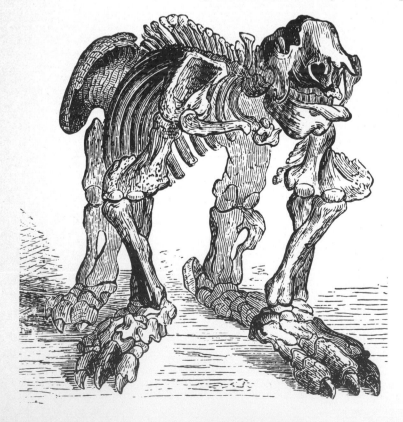

LEFT   This reconstruction of *Megatherium* was based on bone fragments discovered by Darwin on the east coast of South America. An extinct giant, *Megatherium*, with its great claws, resembled the much smaller South American sloths living today and only about three feet high.

RIGHT   The toco toucan (*Ramphastos toco*), here in a painting by John Gould, was typical of the countless exotic bird species that delighted Darwin. (Photo © George Rainbird Ltd., 1969)

This painting by John Gould shows the cactus-feeding finches *Cactornis scandens*. Twenty-five of the 26 species of birds observed by Darwin on the Galapagos occurred nowhere else. (Photo © George Rainbird Ltd., 1969)

The "magic" of adaptation

The more he observed and marveled over the close relationships between the dead and the living, the clearer it became to Darwin that species evolved. But how? He did not realize during those early years of the voyage just how close he was to an answer whenever he sensed renewed amazement over the "magic" of adaptation. Everywhere he looked he found life in splendid variety. "We may well affirm," he wrote, "that every part of the world is habitable! Whether lakes of brine, or those underground ones hidden beneath volcanic mountains, or warm mineral springs, or the wide expanse and depths of the ocean, or the upper regions of the atmosphere, and even the surface of perpetual snow—all support living things."

Four years after setting out from Plymouth, the *Beagle* arrived at the Galapagos. As FitzRoy carried out his surveying mission from one island to another, Darwin had an opportunity to observe and collect. One aspect of the behavior of marine iguanas particularly interested him and served as an important lesson in natural selection. Dissection and examination of the stomach contents of several of the animals revealed their diet of a species of seaweed that was common along the sea floor a hundred yards or more offshore, but not along the shore itself. At first Darwin could not understand why the animals spent almost all of their time on the land and were extremely reluctant to stay in the water any longer than was needed to feed. This behavior " . . . may be accounted for," Darwin reflected, "by the fact that this reptile has no enemy whatever on shore, whereas at sea it must often fall a prey to the many sharks. Hence, probably, urged by a fixed instinct that the shore is its place of safety, *whatever* the emergency may be, it there takes refuge."

Darwin observed 26 species of birds on the Galapagos, 25 of which were found nowhere else in the world. Not until later did he understand the significance of that fact. He was particularly interested in the 13 species of finches he saw on the islands. As he collected specimens for shipment home, he kept all the birds from James Island in one bag, those collected on Chatham Island in another bag, and so on. The general features of all the finches were similar—body shape, shortish tails, they all built the same kinds of nests and laid the same number and color eggs, and they resembled the finches of the South American mainland. However, there was a dramatic difference in beak structure from one species to another (Fig. 4–16).

Darwin described the land iguana (*Amblyrhynchus demarlii*) of the Galapagos in these words: "Like their brothers of the sea-kind, they are ugly animals, of a yellowish orange beneath and of a brownish red colour above. . . . When not frightened, they slowly crawl along with their tails and bellies dragging on the ground. They often stop and doze for a minute or two, with closed eyes and hind legs spread out on the parched soil."

One day the Vice-Governor of the Galapagos mentioned to Darwin that one glance at a tortoise was enough to tell him on which island the animal had been caught. "I did not for some time pay enough attention to this statement," Darwin later recalled, "and I had already partly mixed [my bird collections] from two of the islands. I never dreamed that islands about fifty or sixty miles apart, and most of them in sight of each other, formed of precisely the same rocks, placed under a quite similar climate, rising to a nearly equal height, would have different kinds of animals. . . . To my astonishment, I discovered that all the finches from Charles Island belonged to one species and [had the same shape beak]; all from Albemarle Island belonged to another species; and all from James and Chatham Islands to still other species. [Could it be that here on these islands remote] both in space and time we seem to be brought somewhat near to that great fact—that mystery of mysteries—the first appearance of new beings on this earth?"

The *Beagle* returned home on October 2, 1836. For the next 20 years Darwin carefully built his case for evolution through natural selection and early in 1856 began to write "pretty fully" on the subject. He wanted his book, tentatively entitled *Natural Selection*, to be as comprehensive as possible, a tome, and to include so much hard evidence that it would be impossible to deny that species evolved. Then it happened. In 1858 he received the famous letter and "little essay" from Alfred Russell Wallace, who quite independently had developed the idea of evolution through natural selection. Darwin had to get into print fast. At the urging of Lyell and others, he abandoned all plans for his highly detailed *Natural Selection*, which would have taken him years to document, and for the next 13 months and 10 days wrote *The Origin of Species*, which was published in November, 1859 and became the *Principia* of biology. The first printing of 1,250 copies sold out the first day and turned the whole science of biology upside down.

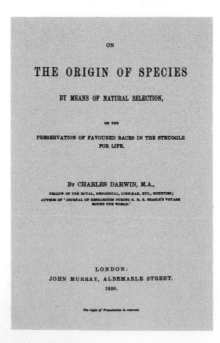

The publication of *The Origin of Species* was, perhaps, biology's greatest moment in history. Sir Gavin de Beer has said of Darwin: ". . . By his proof of the fact of evolution [Darwin was] the Copernicus, and by his discovery and establishment of the principle of natural selection, was the Newton of the realm of living things."

There were a number of reasons why Darwin could not accept this idea. For one, blending suggested that there would be a general trend toward uniformity among a species, variations becoming less and less pronounced as their inheritance material become increasingly diluted. Darwin also dismissed the theory on the grounds that his observation of controlled breeding of pigeons, livestock, and plants led to a reappearance of the original parental **phenotype** —physical characters or appearance—after several generations of progeny. Such **reversion** to original parental appearance would not be possible if blending were the rule. It was with that very topic that Mendel's experiments were concerned.

The segregation of characters

The pea plants Mendel worked with were all of the same species but had very different and easily observed characters. As Table 3–1 shows some had round

CHARACTER OF PARENTS (P)	FIRST FILIAL GENERATION (F_1)	SECOND FILIAL GENERATION (F_2)	F_2 RATIO
seed color: yellow + green	all yellow	6,022 yellow:2,001 green	3.01:1
seed shape: round + wrinkled	all round	5,474 round:1,850 wrinkled	2.96:1
pod shape: inflated + constricted	all inflated	882 inflated:299 constricted	2.95:1
stem length: tall + dwarf	all tall	787 long:277 dwarf	2.84:1
flower color: red + white	all red	705 red:224 white	3.15:1
flower position: axial + terminal	all axial	651 axial:207 terminal	3.14:1
pod color: green + yellow	all green	428 green:152 yellow	2.82:1

seeds, others wrinkled seeds; some seeds were yellow, others green; some of the plants were tall, others dwarfed. Before Mendel began his experiments he made certain that each variety of pea plant bred true; that is, that when plants that produced yellow seeds were self-pollinated, progeny of all future generations produced yellow seeds, and that red-flowered plants kept giving rise to more red-flowered plants generation after generation when the plants were self-pollinated. Next he began crossing the different varieties as shown in the table, cross-pollinating round-seeded plants with wrinkled-seeded plants, red-flowered plants with white-flowered plants, and so on. A detailed look at one such cross will show the significance of Mendel's results and how he was able to begin to formulate his laws of inheritance.

Each time Mendel crossed a tall plant with a dwarf plant—tallness and dwarfness being called **traits** in the parent generation (P)—all members of the first filial (F_1) generation were tall (Fig. 3–2). The dwarf trait never appeared. Tallness, then, is **dominant** (T) while dwarfness is **recessive** (t). At this stage in our account, we should remind you that those units of heredity we call genes were unknown in the 1800s. Nevertheless, Mendel imagined some substance in each pure-bred parent sex cell (called a **gamete** and being either an egg cell or sperm cell) controlling either tallness or dwarfness. He called that imagined substance simply a "factor." To avoid a confusion of terms,

Table 3–1 Statistical methods such as those shown here, and used by Mendel, gave biologists a new way of looking at living things.

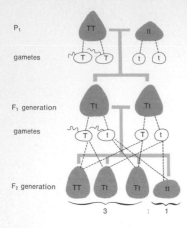

P₁

gametes

F₁ generation

gametes

F₂ generation

3 : 1

Figure 3–2

however, we will use the term genes to designate those factors controlling various heritable traits. All Mendel could say at this point was that the gene governing dwarfness in one parent became lost or obscured in the F_1 generation.

In an attempt to find out what happened to the gene, Mendel next allowed each plant in the F_1 generation to pollinate itself. The table shows what happened: Of a total of 1,064 plants self-pollinated, 787 exhibited the dominant trait (T) while 277 exhibited the recessive trait (t), a ratio of very nearly 3:1 (Fig. 3–2). Note the ratios for all of the other crosses. What is apparent from these ratios? Mendel could say that the gene for the recessive trait (t) dwarfness was not lost. He deduced that each parent has two genes for a given trait and that when a gamete is formed it is given one gene factor. So when two gametes combine as a new individual, the resulting **zygote** contains a pair of genes for a given trait, one contributed by each parent. Mendel could further say that genes can be shown to appear in succeeding generations in predictable ratios. This conclusion of Mendel's came to be known as the **law of segregation**.

The fact that apparently "lost" traits did reappear in the F_2 generation struck a death blow to blending inheritance. If genes blended, then we would expect F_1 generation plants to be intermediate in height, not all tall, and we would expect all subsequent F_2 generation plants also to be intermediate in height rather than tall to dwarf in a ratio of 3:1.

Carrying the experiment further, Mendel next allowed each plant in the F_2 generation to self-pollinate itself. The segregated tall plants (Tt) bred segregated tall exactly as had the segregated tall plants in the F_1 generation. The pure tall (TT) bred pure tall and the pure dwarf (tt) bred pure dwarf.

Mendel's thoroughness as an investigator caused him to carry out still another experiment, called a **test cross**, to test his hypothesis that two different genotypes of tall plants existed in the F_2 generation. This particular test is

A MATTER OF TERMS

A cross involving only one pair of traits such as tall *vs.* dwarf, red flower *vs.* white flower, and so on is called a **monohybrid cross**. Mendel also experimented with two pairs of traits, such as seeds that were yellow *vs.* green, and round *vs.* wrinkled. This is called a **dihybrid cross**. When we speak of the physical appearance of an individual—the redness of a flower or the tallness of a woman—we are talking about the individual's **phenotype**. When we speak of the genetic factors leading to that redness or tallness, we are talking about the individual's **genotype**. The (TT) individuals mentioned earlier are said to be **homozygous dominant** for tallness, while the (tt) type is said to be **homozygous recessive**, and the (Tt) type is **heterozygous**. A gene existing in two forms, such as (T) and (t), is said to consist of two **alleles** (singular, **allele**).

extremely important to plant and animal breeders who want to be certain that they are dealing with homozygous individuals that will breed true, thus repeating a certain desirable trait. Mendel selected the two tall (TT) and (Tt) F_2 plants in turn, the phenotypes of which were identical. By crossing each with a dwarf type (homozygous recessive), he would get the following results. If the genotype of the test plant happened to be (TT), then the cross would turn out as shown in Fig. 3–3. On the other hand, if the genotype of the test plant happened to be (Tt), then the cross would turn out as shown in Fig. 3–4. In the latter test, the two kinds of progeny exist in a 1:1 ratio, indicating that the test plant will not breed true. The cross test also confirmed Mendel's conclusion that a recessive trait (t) that is "lost" when crossed with a (T) reappears in the following generation when crossed with another (t).

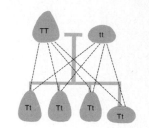

Figure 3–3

Law of independent assortment

Mendel also experimented with dihybrid crosses, plants with two pairs of traits, such as seeds that were yellow (Y) or green (y) and round (R) or wrinkled (r). This was a more complex task than determining the law of segregation in a monohybrid cross. Before proceeding, Mendel had learned that each new character in the two pairs of characters he was testing for simultaneously followed the law of segregation when tested for separately.

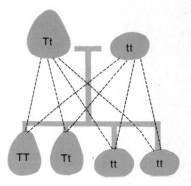

Figure 3–4

As Table 3–1 shows, Mendel had discovered that yellow was dominant over green and that round was dominant over wrinkled. Further, he knew that, as in tallness–dwarfness, there were three possible genotypes expressing themselves as two phenotypes for each pair of characters. For seed color there would be (YY) homozygous dominant for yellow; (Yy) heterozygous for yellow; and (yy) homozygous recessive for green. For seed coat there would be (RR) homozygous dominant for roundness; (Rr) heterozygous for roundness; and (rr) homozygous recessive for wrinkled. According to the law of segregation for monohybrid crosses, Mendel suspected the dominant traits yellowness and roundness to appear in the gametes of each individual of the F_1 generation, as shown in Fig. 3–5. Notice that during gamete formation (meiosis) the alleles segregate and all the gametes of plants homozygous for yellow, round seeds (YYRR) are (YR). They never produce (RR) gametes or (YY) gametes.

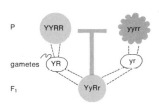

Figure 3–5

At this stage Mendel could not be certain about the distribution of alleles in the F_2 gametes when an F_1 generation plant (YyRr) was allowed to pollinate itself. Would there be two or four kinds of gametes, as follows?

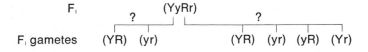

Notice that in the P gametes in Fig. 3–5 the two dominant alleles are associated in one gamete and the two recessive ones in another. If they were always associated that way, then there could never be more than two kinds of F_1

gametes as shown above. If the alleles were assorted independently, however, each allele of an (Rr) and (Yy) pair going their separate ways, then the F_1 gametes would repeat the pattern of the P gametes (Fig. 3–5) but in addition exhibit two new combinations, thus giving rise to four genotypes expressing themselves as four phenotypes. When Mendel carried out the experiment, as before he planted the seeds of the F_1 generation of yellow-round phenotype (YyRr) and then allowed each plant to pollinate itself. The ratio of traits turned out to be 9:3:3:1, as shown in Fig. 3–6, the Punnett square (named after the British geneticist L. C. Punnett, the first to use this method of showing genetic distribution). In actual count, the F_2 progeny numbered 315 yellow-round; 106 yellow-wrinkled; 108 green-round; and 32 green-wrinkled. Mendel called his second law the **law of independent assortment**. In keeping with his model of genetic inheritance, Mendel could say that inherited traits in organisms are controlled by a variety of gene pairs. He concluded further that the sperm cell of the male parent contributes one gene of each pair inherited by the progeny and the egg cell of the female parent contributes the other member of the pair. Each unpaired genetic factor entering a newly forming gamete does so independently of its allele.

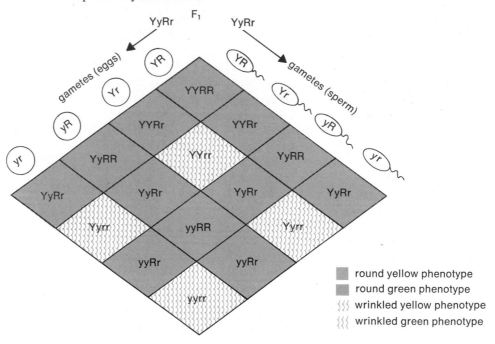

Figure 3–6 Mendel began by crossing round-yellow with wrinkled-green. In the F_2 generation how many new phenotypes appeared, phenotypes unlike either P or F_1 individuals?

THE CHROMOSOME THEORY

By 1900, Mendel's work gained the attention it deserved but never received earlier. While Mendel was still alive, biologists had recognized sperm cells and ova for what they are, and nine years before Mendel died a German biologist actually observed the union of sea urchin gametes. You will recall that Darwin rejected the theory of blending in explaining the mechanisms of heredity. In frustration, he turned to the theory of **pangenesis** as an explanation of the transmission of inherited traits. This theory was particulate in that small units of matter called "gemmules" were imagined to migrate from various parts of the body, one part each from the "location" of each physical or behavioral trait to be transmitted. Once in the gametes, the gemmules were destined to determine the characteristics of the progeny after fertilization.

"Gemmules," as pangenesists termed them, "factors," as Mendel termed them, and "genes," as they are now called, were regarded as particles of matter. As such, surely they must occupy space within each cell. But where were investigators to look for them? The tiny sperm cell was practically all nucleus; perhaps one should look there, and perhaps one should also look to the nucleus of the much larger egg cell as well. Yet the nucleus seemed very unstable as a "control center" since it was seen to break up during cell division, as anyone with a microscope can observe. It all seemed very puzzling.

Something else was puzzling as well. During the late 1800s, many advances in optics were being developed, as were staining techniques in the study of cells. Staining often brought several rod-shaped structures into view in the nuclei of cells. They were called **chromosomes** (meaning "colored bodies"). The significance of these structures eluded biologists for several years. Today we know why chromosomes stain so well. They are bearers of **genes**, which are made up of an acid (DNA) that combines strongly with certain dyes. Eventually, biologists came to realize that the **somatic cells**—all specialized, or body cells except the germ cells—of different organisms had different numbers of chromosomes, the number in any given species being nearly always constant: in man, 46; houseflies, 12; corn, 20; and so on. Fig. 3–7 shows the chromosomes in a normal human male. The two sets of chromosomes in somatic cells are identified by the **diploid** ($2n$) number, or double number. Some organisms are triploid ($3n$), tetraploid ($4n$), and so on; these collectively are said to be **polyploid**.

Mendel, remember, had contended that each germ cell, or gamete, had only one chromosome of the original pair to contribute to the zygote (called the **haploid** ($1n$) number). What happened to the "missing" gene of the original pair? By postulating that in some way unknown to him, a reduction process caused a newly formed gamete to have a single gene rather than a gene pair for a given trait, Mendel anticipated a process that came to be called meiosis. Some such process of chromosome number reduction during cell division was required, otherwise an individual of each succeeding generation would accumulate twice as many chromosomes as its parent generation. Before continuing our account into the first decade of the 20th century, and into non-Mendelian genetics, we should find out what investigators just before 1900 were discovering about the distribution of genetic material during cell division.

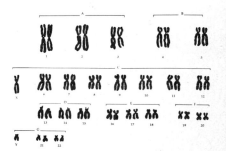

Figure 3–7 Normal human males have 22 paired chromosomes, called autosomes, each pair being distinctive and identified by an assigned number. The remaining two single chromosomes, making a total of 46, are the X and Y sex chromosomes. Human females have an XX pair instead of one X and one Y chromosome.

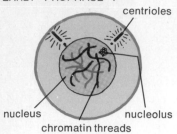

centrioles

nucleus

nucleolus

chromatin threads

LATE PROPHASE

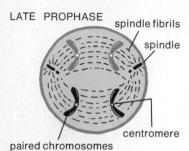

spindle fibrils

spindle

paired chromosomes

centromere

METAPHASE 2

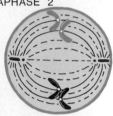

EARLY ANAPHASE 3

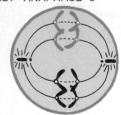

LATE ANAPHASE

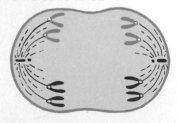

ASEXUAL REPRODUCTION AND MITOSIS

As mentioned earlier, improved resolution in optical microscopy and improved staining techniques allowed late 19th-century investigators to become increasingly familiar with the goings-on within cells. They came to understand that the nucleus with its chromosomes was indeed the cell's control center. They had observed cell division in unicellular organisms and in onion root tips, for instance. One cell divided and gave rise to two **daughter cells** with the same kinds and numbers of chromosomes as the parent cell. In observing cell division of this type, called **mitosis**, experimenters saw the chromosomes split along their length and migrate in a way that suggested an equitable distribution of genetic material to each daughter cell.

Figure 3–8 MITOSIS

1 PROPHASE: At this stage, chromatin threads, which had replicated themselves before mitosis began, double up in pairs, each member of a pair being called a **chromatid**. As the paired structures shorten through successive orders of coiling, they thicken and take form as the chromosomes. By late prophase the nucleoli have broken down and disappeared, as has the nuclear membrane.

2 METAPHASE: At this time the paired chromosomes line up along the cell's equator, as shown. Meanwhile, structures called **centrioles** have moved to opposite ends of the cell and formed structures called the **spindle poles.** Spindle **fibrils**, consisting of chains of protein molecules, extend from the spindles and become attached to the chromosomes (B of Fig. 3–9) at their pinched **centromere** region. During metaphase, the chromosomes of every cell have developed distinctive and characteristic shape and size, as in Fig. 3–7.

3 ANAPHASE: The centromere holding together each chromatid pair of a chromosome divides and releases the chromatids as individual chromosomes. As the protein spindle fibrils appear to contract, a complete set of chromosomes is drawn toward each spindle pole. As shown in C of Fig. 3–9, anaphase is completed with the arrival of the chromosomes at the poles. Each pole now has a complete and identical set of genetic materials.

4 TELOPHASE: The chromosomes uncoil and lose their individuality, becoming long, tangled strands again. Nucleoli are reformed, the spindle disappears, and a nuclear membrane begins to enclose the material at each pole. In animal tissue, two new daughter cells are pinched off by a **cleavage furrow**; plant cells develop a **cell plate** that grows in such a way that it completely partitions the cell, thus giving rise to two daughter cells.

TELOPHASE 4

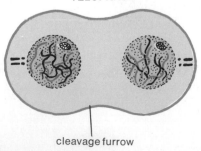

cleavage furrow

INTERPHASE

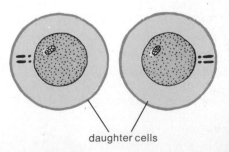

daughter cells

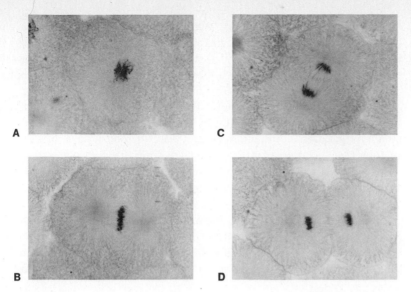

Figure 3–9 Cells of a whitefish embryo can be seen in various phases of mitotic division here: (A) prophase, (B) metaphase, (C) anaphase, and (D) telophase. (OMIKRON)

Mitosis and daughter cells

Cytologists still have much to learn about what prepares a cell for division. The process sometimes begins when the cell goes through a period of stepped-up synthesis, during which the amount of nucleic acid in the nucleus doubles. This can happen early during a stage called **interphase**, at which time the nucleus exhibits granular **chromatin**, which is organized into chromosomes. One or more small spherical bodies called **nucleoli** are also distinguishable during interphase. In addition, animal cells have two structures called **centrioles**. Located just outside the nucleus, the centrioles later migrate to opposite poles of the cell, where they form what is called the spindle apparatus.

The remaining four stages in the division process, **prophase**, **metaphase**, **anaphase**, and **telophase**, are described in detail in Fig. 3–8. The process is also shown photographically in Fig. 3–9. From beginning to end, mitosis is continuous and without pause between stages and may be accomplished in as short a time as 20 minutes in bacteria or in about a day in plant and animal cells; the time varies from one type of animal (or plant) cell to another. Within two or three hours after completing mitosis, a cell may replicate its chromosomes. If it does, it is destined to divide again; if it does not, under normal circumstances it becomes differentiated for a special function and does not undergo mitosis again. At this point you should thoroughly study Figs. 3–8 and 3–9 and their captions before reading on.

One thing the illustrations do not show is the remarkable way in which the chromatin threads condense into short, stubby structures. A chromosome is essentially a string of DNA molecules. A bacterial chromosome is a relatively simple affair 20 Angstrom units wide (0.000 000 02 cm) and about a millimeter long, shaped as a closed loop. Now a set of human chromosomes contains about 6×10^{-12} g of DNA. This tiny mass contains the entire plan for a human being. Stretched out as a single thread of molecules 20 Angstroms wide, the DNA chain would be about 200 cm long! The problem, at least to us, is to pack that length of DNA into a nucleus only a few micrometers in diameter

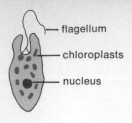

flagellum

chloroplasts

nucleus

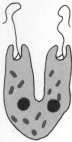

(1 micrometer = 0.000 1 cm). What seems to happen is that the chromatin threads form tight coils, thus causing a shortening and thickening of the original material, and that those coiled strands form further coils so that successive orders of coiling produce the stubby structures visible during prophase.

VEGETATIVE REPRODUCTION: There are two main types of asexual reproduction, one vegetative and the other by spores. An entire new plant can be generated by vegetative reproduction from a piece of root, a piece of stem, or a leaf. In such cases, certain plant cells that are specialized to perform one function —cells specialized to divide and give rise to new cells, for example—have the ability to produce daughter cells capable of taking up new functions needed for the survival of the plant—cells specialized for the transport of water and minerals from roots to leaves, for example. Several years ago botanists wondered if a single plant cell had the morphogenetic potential of generating an entire new plant. They isolated a single cell from a carrot plant and watched it divide and soon produce masses of undifferentiated cells. The undifferentiated

Figure 3–10 The diploid protist *Euglena* prepares for division by mitosis first by feeding and growing larger. As a new flagellum grows, the nucleus begins to divide. The organism then splits lengthwise, one new nucleus and half the amount of remaining cell material migrating into what become two new diploid daughter cells.

Figure 3–11 Budding is a form of vegetative reproduction in animals, typical of *Hydra* shown here. Each bud that develops on *Hydra* becomes a new free-living individual genetically identical to its uniparent. (OMIKRON)

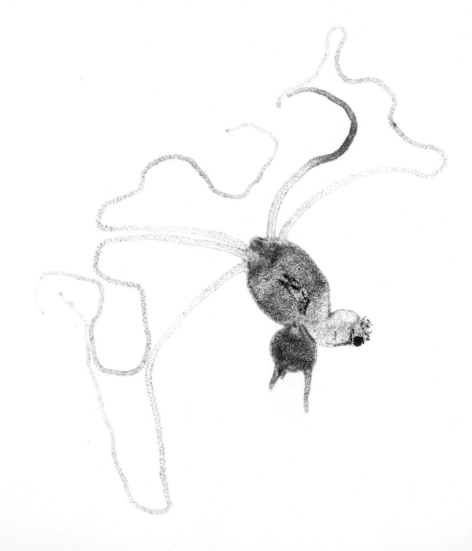

cells eventually specialized and gave rise to all the differentiated organs (roots, stem, leaves) of a healthy plant. This ability of a single plant cell to regenerate an entire plant now seems to be the rule rather than the exception.

Vegetative reproduction is not restricted to plants only, although it is much more common in plants than in animals. It is also common among those unicellular organisms sometimes classified under the separate kingdom Protista, and among certain multicellular organisms. Figure 3–10 shows the one-celled autotrophic organism *Euglena* undergoing mitotic division by **binary fission**, while Fig. 3–11 shows the animal *Hydra* undergoing vegetative reproduction through a process called **budding**. A "bud" develops on part of the organism and grows into a complete new organism, at which time it detaches itself and takes up life independently. Bulbs of onions and tulips, potato tubers, and strawberry runners are all vegetative reproductive organs. The essential feature of vegetative reproduction is that a portion of the uniparent organism develops into a whole new individual genetically identical to the parent.

SEXUAL REPRODUCTION AND MEIOSIS

In Chapter 2 we spoke first of prebiological "cells" and then of living cells populating the primordial seas through some simple process of division, which depended on the cell's ability to capture and incorporate into itself energy and materials from the external environment. Asexual reproduction was and still is the rule among unicellular organisms. But somewhere along the way sexual reproduction developed and became the rule for multicellular organisms.

We will now pick up and develop a thought mentioned earlier in the chapter: Sometimes it could be very troublesome if a cell divided by mitosis. The essence of sexual reproduction is the union of a sperm cell with an egg cell. If each of those gametes were diploid, the F_1 zygotes formed out of the union would have twice the number of chromosomes of the P generation, and F_2 zygotes would have twice the number of chromosomes of the F_1 generation, and so on approaching infinity. This simply would not do. While somatic cells tend to be polyploid, sex cells tend to be haploid. Thus the accumulation of chromosomes at an exponential rate from one generation to the next is avoided. Mendel, you will recall, predicted some sort of reduction–division process that tends to keep the number of chromosomes constant from parent to progeny.

Meiosis and reduction–division

Put quite simply, **meiosis** is that process of cell division that reduces the diploid ($2n$) number of chromosomes in the parent cell to a haploid ($1n$) number in the daughter cells; hence, it is called a reduction–division process. In all animals that are multicellular, meiosis takes places at the time gametes are produced. As in mitosis, there are five recognizable stages in meiosis, but as you can see in Fig. 3–12, there are two sequences of division in meiosis. As before, you should study the accompanying illustrations and their captions thoroughly before reading on.

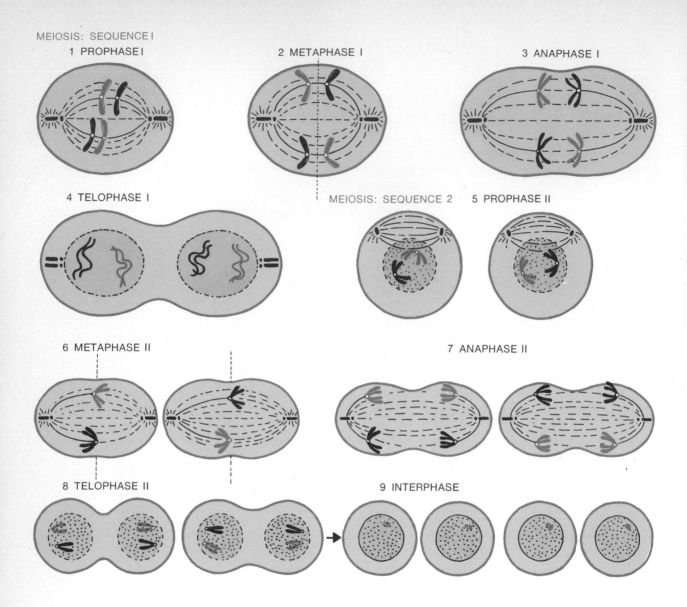

MEIOSIS: SEQUENCE I
1 PROPHASE I

2 METAPHASE I

3 ANAPHASE I

4 TELOPHASE I

MEIOSIS: SEQUENCE 2 5 PROPHASE II

6 METAPHASE II

7 ANAPHASE II

8 TELOPHASE II

9 INTERPHASE

Figure 3–12   MEIOSIS: SEQUENCE 1

1   PROPHASE I: Chromosomes appear as fine threads and contract as they form homologous joined pairs. At mid-prophase each chromosome of a pair does not appear to be double-stranded (as they do at mid-prophase mitosis) but they are, and they reveal their double-strandedness at late prophase. By the end of prophase, the nucleus has dissolved, the nucleoli have disappeared, and the spindle has formed. The chromosomes are now oriented on the spindle fibrils and are moving toward the cell's equator.

2   METAPHASE I: In mitosis each chromosome consisting of two chromatids is attached to a fibril by its centromere. In meiosis each homologous pair of chromosomes, consisting of two chromatids each, is attached to the same spindle

fibril by its own centromere. By the end of metaphase, the chromosome pairs have taken up a position along the cell's equator, each member of a pair being equidistant poleward from the equator.

3 ANAPHASE I: The chromosomes now move poleward, but the centromeres of each pair do not divide as they do in mitosis. During migration toward the poles, the homologues are freed from each other along their length. Each chromosome now consists of two chromatids separated along their length, linked only at the centromere. In meiosis, only half as many chromosomes have migrated poleward as in mitosis.

4 TELOPHASE I: As in mitosis, a nuclear membrane forms around each set of chromosomes and a membrane wall, which eventually separates the two daughter cells, is formed in certain meiotic cells. By the time the chromosomes fade from view in mitosis, they are single strands of matter; in meiosis they are double strands. The two daughter cells formed in first telophase of meiosis are haploid since they contain only half the number of chromosomes of the parent cell. In mitosis, the daughter cells are diploid.

MEIOSIS: SEQUENCE 2

The stages in the second meiotic division are very similar to mitosis. Interphase is short and the cells go into PROPHASE II almost at once. At PROPHASE II the chromosomes are just the same as they were at ANAPHASE I, meaning that each chromosome consists of two chromatids, also meaning that this time the chromosomes *did not* replicate themselves during interphase. The spindles form, the nuclear membranes decay along with the nucleoli, and at METAPHASE II each pair of chromatids attaches itself to a spindle fibril by its common centromere. By the end of METAPHASE II each centromere has divided, and during ANAPHASE II each set of chromosomes is drawn to each cell's poles by the contracting fibrils. Nuclear membranes form around the chromosomes during TELOPHASE II and the two cells complete the division and become four daughter cells. Each daughter cell is now haploid, like the nuclei formed in TELOPHASE I, but unlike the daughter cells formed in mitosis. In certain organisms, the daughter cells become sperm or ova, which on union with an opposite sex cell produce diploid zygotes.

Conjugation as sexuality

Again, the general rule is that *cells* divide by mitosis and that *sex cells,* or gametes, are produced from somatic cells by meiosis. There are exceptions, however, one of which we will consider simply to show just how complex affairs can become in "simple" organisms.

Among the many protozoans some, such as amebas and *Euglena,* do not have sexual cycles but occur as diploid cells that divide by mitosis and give rise to diploid daughter cells. Other protozoans, however, do have sexual cycles, which enable individuals to exchange genetic material. Among them is one of the most common laboratory organisms, *Paramecium.* During times when there is no environmental stress—overcrowding or a shortage of food— paramecia commonly reproduce by binary fission. However, during times when there is environmental stress, certain individuals occur in mating pairs, but the "purpose" of the mating is not to produce progeny; genetic material is exchanged instead. The probability is that during a period of environmental stress a diploid individual of homozygous genotype (AA) or (BB) is less fit than an individual of heterozygous genotype (AB). Figure 3–13 shows how sexuality without reproduction can give rise to hardier genotypes.

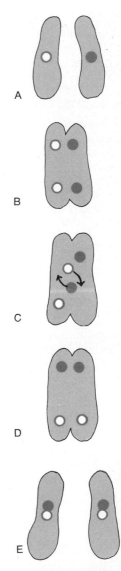

A

B

C

D

E

Figure 3–13 Sexual conjugation in *Paramecium.*

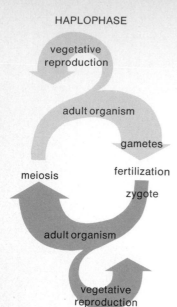

HAPLOPHASE

vegetative
reproduction

adult organism

gametes

fertilization

meiosis

zygote

adult organism

vegetative
reproduction

DIPLOPHASE

Figure 3–14 A great number
of organisms, including animals,
plants, and protists, have
reproductive cycles involving
both sexual and asexual
reproduction. The generalized
cycle shown here illustrates
how an imaginary organism
might spend half of its time in
diplophase (with a diploid
nucleus) and half in haplophase
(with a haploid nucleus).

HAPLOPHASE

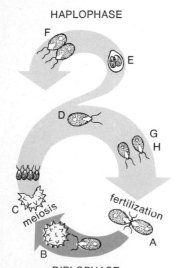

F

E

D

G
H

C

meiosis

fertilization

A

B

DIPLOPHASE

Figure 3–15 The reproductive
cycle of *Chlamydomonas.*

At A two potential mates of different genotype pair and in B fuse their cellular material in what is called **conjugation**. The micronucleus in each cell has undergone meiosis, after which three of the four haploid nuclei in each cell degenerate. The fourth divides by mitosis and produces two haploid sex nuclei in each organism. At C and D the organisms exchange haploid gamete nuclei, and at E the two micronuclei fuse as the conjugated cells separate. Fertilization has made each organism more fit genetically, but has not produced offspring. At a later time, of course, each diploid individual may reproduce by mitotic division, but again the "purpose" of the sexual conjugation was not reproduction; instead a mixing of genetic material took place.

Reproductive cycles

With an understanding of mitosis and meiosis and of the essential differences between asexual and sexual reproduction, you will be able to see that there are fundamental similarities between the reproductive cycles of most plants and most animals. The one major difference is that in animals the haploid cells (gametes) rarely develop beyond their gamete status. As one biologist has put it, the male sperm cell does not develop into a yacht, it remains a haploid gamete with an outboard motor. Nevertheless some adult animals—bees and wasps, for example—are haploid organisms. In plants, however, the rule is for the haplophase to develop further, sometimes into a new and complete multicellular organism. Figure 3–14 shows a generalized reproductive cycle that can be followed in the light of what has just been said.

The evolutionary significance of haploidy and diploidy will become apparent if we briefly examine two life cycles in the plant kingdom, one during which the haplophase is predominant, and another in which the diplophase is predominant. As you will find, asexual and sexual reproduction occur in both.

HAPLOTONIC CYCLES: Figure 3–15 shows the life cycle of a one-celled photosynthetic organism known as *Chlamydomonas,* which is **motile**, or free-moving. At A fertilization takes place with the union of two haploid gametes, which produces a diploid zygote (B). The zygote encases itself (C) and quickly undergoes meiosis, producing four haploid cells of a new generation (D). A mature haplophase cell (E and F) may take the vegetative reproduction path and produce two new individuals by mitosis (G), or the cells may act as gametes (H) and engage in sexual reproduction (A). This **haplotonic** life cycle, so called because adults spend most of the time in haplophase, is very primitive, being common to all primitive organisms such as bacteria and one-celled organisms, and most likely gave rise to all other reproductive cycles.

DIPLOTONIC CYCLES: Figure 3–16 shows the life cycle of a typical flowering plant. We can start at A in the diplophase with the mature plant complete with sex organs. The plant can take the vegetative reproduction route (B) and propagate asexually, and it can reproduce sexually. A haploid sperm nucleus contained in pollen grains from the same plant (self-pollination), or from another plant (cross-pollination), migrates down through a tube (C) grown by the pollen grain and fuses with a haploid egg nucleus (D), at which time fertilization takes place. In relation to diplophase, haplophase in flowering plants is as brief as diplophase is in *Chlamydomonas*. At E a second sperm nucleus is shown. This nucleus, also haploid, unites with a diploid "fusion nucleus," the union of which two nuclei gives rise to a triploid cell that divides by mitosis and produces a mass of material called **endosperm**. The seed (F) is a diploid zygote that develops into a mature plant. In lima bean and corn seeds endosperm forms the bulk of the seed and serves as food for the tiny seed plant within.

We could show many more life cycles among both plants and animals, but most would be variations of the two shown here. While the continuity of haplotonic life cycles has been maintained in many organisms since primitive times, natural selection came to favor the survival and proliferation of diplotonic cycles as well. There seem to be certain adaptive advantages to diplotonic life. For instance, if an organism spends most of its life as a diploid individual it has two sets of genes. If one of the genes in a cell is damaged by radiation or in some other way, the surviving gene still carries the inheritance plan. This is not true of a haploid cell, and the longer the time an organism spends in haplophase, the more susceptible it is to genetic damage. Even in what could be called a "compromise situation," as in ferns, which have a sporophyte (diplophase) generation alternating with a gametophyte (haplophase) generation, the haploid gametophyte plant is relatively short-lived.

Like ferns, many other plants have a reproductive pattern that is an **alternation of generations**. Such a reproductive cycle assures the plant the best of two worlds, so to speak. On the one hand, it has the advantages of asexual reproduction, during which spores give rise to many new individuals that can be widely dispersed; on the other, sexual reproduction gives the plants' offspring genetic variation, thus increasing the species' survival potential through an increased potential for adaptation.

Figure 3–16 The reproductive cycle of a typical flowering plant. A plant may reproduce asexually (B), but sexual reproduction (A) is the rule. Put simply, sexual reproduction involves the nuclei of a pollen grain fusing with nuclei in the ovary to produce a seed. Pollen from stamens of the same or another plant is deposited on the stigma. A mature pollen grain contains three haploid nuclei, two of which (the sperm nuclei) are active in fertilization. They germinate and produce a pollen tube (C) through which the sperm enter the ovary. Within the ovary are three functional nuclei—one egg nucleus (D) and two polar nuclei. One sperm nucleus fuses with the egg nucleus to form a diploid embryo. This zygote gives rise to the new plant. The other sperm nucleus fuses with *both* polar nuclei to produce the fusion nucleus, which gives rise to the endosperm—that starchy part of the seed (F) that supplies nourishment to the young plant.

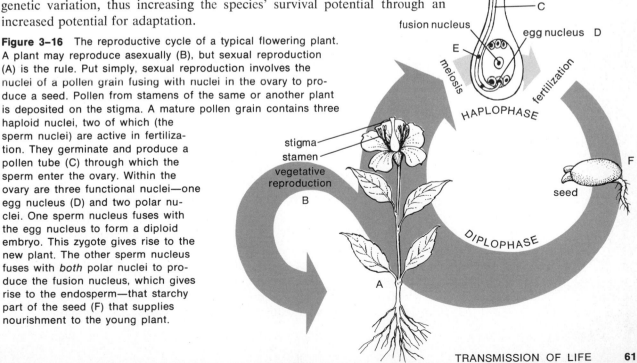

Sexual reproduction and variation

If we consider all living forms, life carries on quite competently by asexual reproduction. Sexual reproduction is not simply an embellishment, nor is it primarily a means of producing more organisms. The advantage of sexual reproduction is that, through segregation and **recombination** of chromosomes in the zygote, it produces genetic variation. Without this variation species would be unable to adapt to environmental change and would be doomed to early extinction.

Mendel had observed that two plants, one homozygous for the single gene pair (TT) and the other for (tt), produced only (TT) and (tt) progeny by asexual means. As long as the two plants reproduced asexually, each one would breed true to its genotype. Sexual reproduction, however, could give rise to progeny of three different genotypes (TT), (Tt), and (tt). Now suppose that we have two F_1 individuals that are heterozygous for two pairs of genes: (RrYy) and (RrYy), deriving from P genotypes (RRYY) and (rryy). The F_2 generation would exhibit not three but nine genotypes: (RRYY), (RRYy), (RrYY), (RrYy), (rRyy), (RRyy), (rrYY), (rrYy), and (rryy). While this variety of progeny may seem impressive at first glance, it becomes even more impressive when you realize that a human being, for example, with 46 chromosomes, carries not two but thousands of pairs of genes! The full impact of genetic variation thus becomes apparent, and we can see that its implications for the adaptation of populations are profound. No matter on what level it occurs, asexual reproduction is an inhibitor of variation; sexual reproduction promotes variation of individuals and so increases the survival potential of a species. Is it any wonder, then, that sex is as popular as it is? Sexual reproduction has remained the rule among organisms for the simple reason that the variation it fosters ensures the survival of a given population amid environmental change. It is, in short, a superb adaptation.

CHROMOSOMES AND THEIR GENES

Sex determination

Since we have been talking about sex cells, sometimes calling them germ cells and other times gametes, it is time that we come to grips with what endows a cell with maleness or femaleness. Although a mammalian embryo has all of the physiological equipment required to develop into either a male or a female, its course of development as one or the other was committed at the moment of fertilization. By about 1900, the hereditary basis of sex had been established.

Normal human males and females have 46 chromosomes. In females there are 22 pairs of chromosomes termed **autosomes**, and one pair of sex chromosomes identified as *XX*. As Fig. 3–7 shows, males also have 22 pairs of autosomes, but they lack the *XX* pair. Instead, there is one *X* chromosome plus a smaller one called the *Y* chromosome. During meiotic formation of gametes, the paired chromosomes separate, each haploid daughter cell receiving one complete set. An egg cell then has 22 autosomes plus one *X* chromosome.

During the production of sperm cells something different occurs because of the presence of the *Y* chromosome. The male diploid cell undergoing meiosis produces two kinds of haploid sperm cells. While one has 22 autosomes plus an *X* chromosome, the other must necessarily be left with 22 autosomes plus the *Y* chromosome. Throughout the entire class of mammals, the chromosomal makeup of ova is identical, but there are two different kinds of sperm, one carrying an *X* chromosome and one carrying a *Y* chromosome. So after fertilization, as Fig. 3–17 shows, the resulting diploid zygote may have $44A + XX$, or $44A + XY$. If it has the *XX* pair, it develops into a female; if it has the *XY* pair, it develops into a male. That is what we observe to happen in mammals. So it would seem that there is something about the genetic contents of the *Y* chromosome (although it is small and has far fewer genes than either the *X* chromosome or the autosomes) that in some way we have yet to discover promotes maleness or inhibits femaleness. Possibly it operates through the hypothalamus.

The situation is more complex than the above description indicates. For example many animals, including grasshoppers, do not have a *Y* chromosome at all. And butterflies, moths, birds, some fishes, and some reptiles and amphibians have a sex chromosome arrangement that is the reverse of the one we have been discussing: Males are *XX,* and females are *XY.*

Although Japanese investigators have shown that the presence of the *Y* chromosome in silk moths is important to sex determination, it has long been known that the *Y* chromosome carried by male *Drosophila* is not important. In *Drosophila,* the autosomes play a significant role. For example, when the chromosome ratio of *X:A* (autosome) is 1:2 (0.5), normal males are produced. For a number of years some geneticists suspected that this ratio of *X* chromosomes to autosomes in *Drosophila* also applied to humans and hence the human *Y* chromosome did not play a significant role in human sex determination. However, we now know that the theory does not apply to man. Evidence presently indicates that the *Y* chromosome in humans does indeed carry genes with male sex-determining properties. As one investigator has summarized it: "In a [human] female cell the feminizing effect of the two *X* chromosomes outweighs any masculinizing influence the autosomes may have; and in a male cell, the masculinizing effect of the *Y* chromosome (and probably also the autosomes) outweighs the feminizing influence of the single *X* chromosome." The fact is that we have much more to learn about what happens at the genetic level, and until we do there are bound to be different interpretations.

Sex-linked heredity

The sex chromosomes' role is not limited to sex determination. When certain genetic characters, such as color blindness, are associated with sex chromosomes we say that the character in question is **sex-linked**. An example will show how sex linkage works in humans and certain other animals.

In the early 1900s, the American geneticist T. H. Morgan carried out many important experiments with the fruit fly *Drosophila melanogaster.* One day he noticed that one of his bottle cultures of flies included a fly with white eyes.

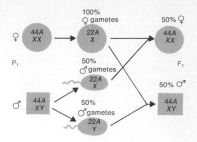

Figure 3–17 Because the female has two *X* chromosomes, all ova carry a single *X* chromosome. Because the male has one *X* and one *Y* chromosome, half of the sperm cells will be haploid for *X* and half will be haploid for *Y*. A diploid zygote resulting from the union of an ovum and sperm has a 50/50 chance of being *XX* or *XY*.

Figure 3–18 shows the result of a cross of a red-eyed female (WW) with a white-eyed male that carries a mutant gene for eye whiteness on his *X* chromosome. The (WW) beneath the paired *X* chromosomes of the female indicates that she is homozygous for the dominant trait of red-eyeness. The (w) beneath the male *X* chromosome indicates white recessiveness. The hooked chromosome is the *Y* chromosome. **Figure 3–19** shows the result of a cross of a white-eyed female (ww) with a red-eyed male (Ww). Again the mutant genes for eye whiteness are carried on the sex chromosomes. The (ww) beneath the paired *X* chromosomes of the female indicates that she is homozygous for the recessive trait of whiteness. The W beneath the male *X* chromosome indicates red-eye dominance. The hooked chromosome is the *Y* chromosome.

Normally the eyes are red. After obtaining a strain of true-breeding white-eyed flies, Morgan carried out experiments showing that the transmission of the white-eyed trait was sex-linked.

Figure 3–18 shows the P generation consisting of a homozygous red-eyed female (WW) crossed with a white-eyed male (w). The F_1 generation contains only individuals with red eyes. This shows that red is dominant over white. In the F_2 generation, however, the recessive white-eyed phenotype reappears in Mendel's 1:3 ratio, but with an important difference from what occurs when we make a cross involving autosomal genes. In the case of the white-eyed phenotype, only males—not females—have white eyes in both F_1 and F_2 generations. Notice also that the F_2 generation contains females of two genotypes, some homozygous (for red) and some heterozygous. If we continue to breed F_2 heterozygous females with white-eyed males, the resulting progeny are half red-eyed phenotypes and half white-eyed phenotypes. This means that the heterozygous female must contain (w) in a recessive state. Further breedings are needed, however, to reveal the heterozygosity.

Now look at Fig. 3–19, which shows what happens if a female homozygous for white-eyes (ww) is crossed with a red-eyed male (Ww). The results are surprisingly different. The first difference is that in the F_1 generation all females have red eyes while all males have white eyes. So the dominant phenotype appears only in the females. When members of the F_1 generation are bred, the F_2 generation consists of phenotypes in a 1:1 ratio in both sexes. Now again, if we cross an F_2 red-eyed male (W) with a (ww) female, all of the male progeny will be white-eyed. The two reciprocal crosses illustrated here clearly

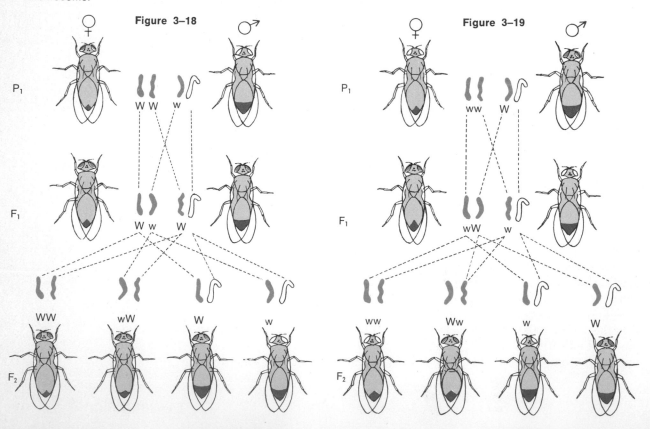

show that whenever a sex-linked trait is passed from one generation to the next it is important to the progeny whether the male or the female parent carries the trait. Let's consider a common case in man, red-green color blindness, which is a recessive trait.

A color-blind male passes on his color blindness through his daughter to his grandson, but not directly to his sons. This can be seen if you follow the genetic routing in Fig. 3–18. But, as Fig. 3–19 shows, a color-blind mother passes the trait on to her sons and daughters alike. In order for a daughter to be color blind, as opposed only to being a carrier of the trait, she must inherit the trait from *both* male and female parent. In order for a son to be color blind, he must receive the trait from his mother, who herself may be color blind (homozygous) or a carrier (heterozygous). From this it is clear that male members of a population stand a significantly higher chance of inheriting a sex-linked trait than females. Color blindness, as it turns out, is present in about 8% of white American males, but in only about 1% of white American females. In Negroes the figures are 4% for males, and 0.8% for females.

Linkage and crossing-over

LINKAGE: It was established earlier that there are far too few chromosomes in organisms to account for the many heritable traits, and that each chromosome must bear many, many genes. The eight chromosomes of a fruit fly, for instance, have several hundred genes that we know and can locate on the chromosomes. We can imagine the genes on a chromosome to be aligned like birds on a telephone wire, each bird representing an individual gene. A chromosome bearing a string of genes is actually a DNA molecule with varying nucleotide sequences linked to each other and representing individual genes. Any two or more genes on a given chromosome that segregate together without changing their positions relative to each other are said to be **linked**. When all of the linked genes on a given chromosome segregate as an entire group, the segregation is termed **complete linkage**.

Mendel, remember, did not know about chromosomes or genes. He imagined two pairs of hereditary *factors* in each parent segregating and recombining in the F_1 generation in a 9:3:3:1 ratio. In the first decade of the 1900s, investigators working with sweet pea plants that had two pairs of characters (one had purple flowers and long pollen while the other had red flowers and round pollen) were surprised to find that F_2 plants did not follow the 9:3:3:1 ratio. When they next tried a test cross, and according to Mendel's principle of segregation should have found a ratio of 1:1:1:1, they found instead a ratio of 7:1:1:7. Clearly something that Mendel had not observed, or something that he had observed but did not report, was upsetting the "expected" results. Four years later, Morgan, during his work with fruit flies, worked out an explanation of anomalous ratios. It has come to be called crossing-over.

CROSSING-OVER: The genetic fate of the progeny of the two improbable parent mice shown in Fig. 3–20 demonstrates the results of the crossing-over of chromosomes. At A in the diagram we show that each mouse has a pair of heritable characters. One is short-eared and spotted, while the other is long-eared and striped. Now if the chromatids of each homologous pair of chromosomes always separated cleanly during the first division of meiosis, the progeny here could be of only two varieties—short-eared spotted (CGcg) and long-eared striped (cgcg). This is so because the genes governing short ears and spots are on one chromosome (1), while the genes governing long ears and stripes are on a different chromosome (2). During the first division sequence in meiosis when the chromatids of each homologous pair of chromosomes split, as seen in B, the inner two chromosomes wrap around each other, or **crossover** (3), (4), (3a), and (4a). When they separate, each chromosome of a crossed-over pair may break, each retaining some part of the other when separation is complete (5), (6), (5a), and (6a). As you can see in 5, the gene sequence has been altered from A–B–C–D–E–F–G to A–B–c–d–e–F–G. In other words, as a result of the cross-over, the gene for short ears (C) now occurs on one chromosome while the gene for spots (G) occurs on a different chromosome. Similarly, the gene for long ears (c) occurs on one chromosome (6) while the gene for stripes (g) occurs on a different chromosome (5). As C of the diagram shows, progeny resulting from such a cross-over may be short-eared and spotted (CGcg), long-eared and spotted (cGcg), short-eared and striped (Cgcg), and long-eared and striped (cgcg). It is not difficult to see that the increased number of genetic combinations resulting from crossing-over adds significantly to variation in any population of organisms

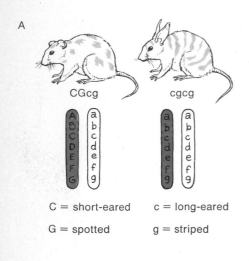

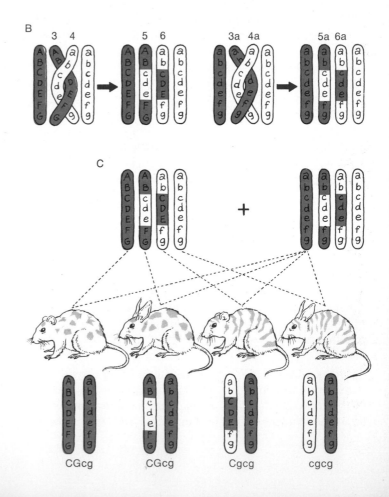

Figure 3–20 Crossing-over, as these diagrams show, adds significantly to the genetic variation in any population of organisms that reproduce sexually.

that reproduce sexually. And variation in turn provides a greater potential for adaptation, thus increasing the species' survival potential.

Chromosome mapping

Crossing-over provided geneticists with a valuable new way of looking at the chromosome. For one thing, it was strong evidence that genes were not arranged haphazardly along a chromosome, as were our birds along the telephone wire. This was suggested by the fact that certain traits resulting from crossing-over showed up in individuals of a population at a certain frequency, which meant that a given pair of genes had a given and predictable rate of crossing-over. One of Morgan's associates used this information to devise a way of mapping the positions of genes on a given chromosome. The greater the distance between two linked genes on a chromosome, the greater the probability of their crossing-over; the shorter the distance, the less the probability of a cross-over, because the greater the space between any two genes, the greater the number of opportunities for the chromatid to break. Hence, crossing-over between Gene A and Gene B at right is about five times as likely as a cross-over between Gene B and Gene C; and a cross-over between Gene D and Gene E is twice as likely as a cross-over between either B and C or C and D.

The percentage of times a given cross-over took place, represented here by 25, 5, 5, and 10, became the distance units on a chromosome map, indicating *relative* distances of genes from each other. It also became possible to establish the correct sequence of genes on a chromosome. For instance, suppose that we introduce Gene X with a cross-over frequency of 12% with Gene B. Does Gene X lie to the right of B or to the left? We measure the cross-over frequency of Gene X with Gene C and find a cross-over frequency of 15%. Where must Gene X be located on the chromosome? Figure 3–21 is a photomicrograph of giant chromosomes found in the salivary gland of *Drosophila*. (Ordinary somatic body cells have chromosomes smaller than this one by a factor of about 100.) The clearly defined lines are gene positions and were found to match almost perfectly chromosome maps worked out earlier for this particular chromosome.

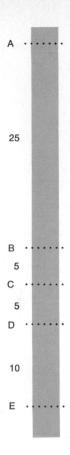

MUTATIONS AND VARIATION

Mutations have been described as the "raw materials" of biological variation and, therefore, of evolution. If there were not some mechanism by which genes became altered, there would be no variation among the individuals of a given population. For example, in an imaginary diploid organism with a total genetic makeup of the homologues (AA) and (aa), the offspring forever after could occur only as the genotypes (AA), (Aa), or (aa) if the individuals were not subject to variation. There would be no other possibilities, and without such possibilities the species would cease to evolve. Evolution can be regarded as a change in the genetic makeup of a population. And the total variety of genes present in the population is what biologists call the **gene pool.**

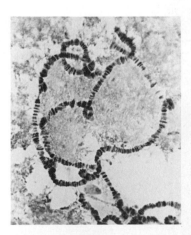

Figure 3–21 Giant chromosomes occurring in the salivary gland of *Drosophila*. (OMIKRON)

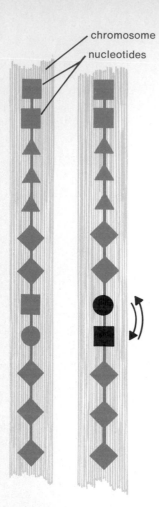

chromosome

nucleotides

Figure 3–22 Genes can be thought of as nucleotides occurring in certain sequences along a chromosome (A). When a chromosome replicates itself, an "error" may be made and result in a change in nucleotide sequence (B). Such errors produce mutant (abnormal) genes, which are usually harmful and sometimes lethal.

Sources of mutation

The DNA molecules composing chromosomes are made up of paired nucleotides, which are the genes (Fig. 3–22). The nucleotide pairs occur in a certain sequence, a particular number and sequence being characteristic of a certain gene. If, during the process of replicating itself, a chromosome in some way alters the nucleotide sequence of a gene, we say that a gene **mutation** has occurred. There are a number of ways mutations are brought about. For example, one nucleotide may replace another and thus lead to a gene carrying new instructions. Biochemical "accidents" during chromosomal replication in meiosis is another cause of mutation, and radiation is a third. The high-energy subatomic particles emitted as gamma radiation may score a direct hit on a chromosome and alter or destroy parts of a given gene. X rays and ultraviolet radiation, natural background radiation from Earth's crust, and radiation released into the environment by nuclear weapons tests, nuclear power plants, and their "hot" wastes are additional sources.

Mutations also occur when a cell acquires an abnormal number of chromosomes during meiosis, when homologous pairs separate, or fail to separate and migrate into the daughter cells as defective parts. If a human male cell gains an extra *X* chromosome and becomes *XXY* instead of the normal *XY* type, the individual is said to have Klinefelter's syndrome, a condition in which the normal male phenotype is altered, exhibiting small testes, not much body hair, and enlarged breasts. The lack of one *X* chromosome in a human female, giving her an *XO* genotype, instead of the normal *XX,* results in Turner's syndrome, a condition characterized by low-set ears, a webbed neck, underdeveloped breasts and ovaries, and other abnormalities. If the small, number 21 chromosome in humans occurs in a triploid rather than in a diploid state, Down's syndrome (mongolian idiocy) results.

Rate of mutations

Although we know relatively little about the rate at which mutations occur in humans, we know enough about mutation rates in other organisms to make the generalization that each gene appears to have a characteristic mutation rate. In corn (*Zea mays*) the *R* gene, which is a compound gene, has a mutation rate of 492 per 10^6 gametes, but the *S* gene's rate is only 1 per 10^6 gametes. In humans, the mutation causing dwarfism has a rate of 41 per 10^6 gametes; that for albinism, 28 per 10^6 gametes; and that for complete color blindness, also 28 per 10^6 gametes.

When we make some educated guesses, it seems possible that every somatic cell in a human body has a new mutation, but the somatic cells are not involved as the carriers of heritable traits. Of the germ cells, which are the carriers, it seems possible that one out of every 100 gametes carries a new mutation. These, then, are the "raw materials" of variation and evolution. One biologist has estimated that if a given species has as few as 1,000 heterozygous genes, the number of possible combinations ($2^{1,000}$) exceeds the number of atoms in the universe!

Mutations occur at random and the great majority of them are deleterious.

Rarely does a mutation turn out to be advantageous. The fact that this is so helps explain why mutant forms tend not to be common in a population. Selection pressures tend to weed out the less fit and remove them from the reproductive group of individuals who contribute to the gene pool. Or a mutant zygote may never develop; or if it does, the individual may never live to reach reproductive age; or if the individual does, he or she may be sterile or may fail to find a mate. If the individual does find a mate and reproduce, what is the genetic future of the progeny?

Suppose that a mutation occurs and it turns out that the mutant allele is dominant. When the individual mates with a normal individual, all of the offspring have phenotypes of the heterogyous-dominant parent. The F_2 generation will contain individuals that can then be bred true for the trait. This is also true of recessive mutants. Such mutations that prove beneficial and that are perpetuated are rare, but they do occur from time to time. For example, twice that we know of a mutation has produced a ram (Ancon) heterozygous for short legs. When the ram is mated with a normal ewe homozygous for long legs, all of the F_1 progeny have phenotypes of the male. With such a genotype, individuals could be bred true for the mutant trait short-leggedness. In nature it is virtually certain that selection pressures would eliminate this short-legged variety of sheep, for the obvious reason that short-leggedness is disadvantageous to sheep living in the presence of predators. As domestic animals, however, the mutation actually proved advantageous; the short-legged sheep could not jump fences.

In order for natural selection to eliminate mutant genes from the gene pool of a population, the mutant gene must express itself as a phenotype. Only then can the individual carrying the mutant gene be eliminated from the population. If the gene is recessive, then for as long as it occurs in the heterozygous state—that is in a genotype as opposed to a phenotype condition—the gene can be carried by individuals in succeeding generations and so continue to remain within the gene pool. But if two individuals carrying the recessive gene mate, one-quarter of their progeny will carry the gene in a homozygous state and will express the mutation in the phenotype condition. Since the occurrence of a given genetic defect will be common within a given family, it is not difficult to see why inbreeding is risky business. The probability that a brother and sister or first cousins will mate and produce progeny with phenotypes of a given mutation is astronomically greater than the probability that two members of different families both possessing the deleterious recessive allele in a heterozygous state will mate at random and produce progeny with phenotypes of the mutation. Explain why this should be so.

SICKLE-CELL ANEMIA: This dreaded disease common among African Negroes, but less common among American Negroes, is an interesting example of a mutation that can be advantageous to some but lethal to others. Sickle-cell anemia is a mutation that has upset the hemoglobin molecule by chemically altering a single amino acid in the molecule's two chains of about 150 amino acids each. The result is a change in the shape of the red blood cells to that of a sickle with filaments (Fig. 3–23). The abnormal structure of the cells causes them to clog in the small blood vessels. Among the symptoms

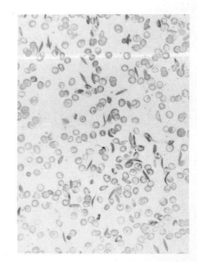

Figure 3–23 A person suffering from sickle-cell anemia has red blood cells shaped in the form of a crescent. The cells tend to rupture, causing anemia, and to clog in the small blood vessels. (CAROLINA BIOLOGICAL SUPPLY HOUSE)

of the disease is severe anemia, caused by the frequent rupturing of the red cells. Death almost always occurs before age 30 for persons who are homozygous for the mutation.

Interestingly enough, individuals who carry the mutant gene in a heterozygous condition nearly always survive, and the disease symptoms they exhibit tend to be mild. The fact that the mutant gene for sickle-cell anemia occurs in the gene pool of Negroes in the United States at relatively low frequency compared with that of Negroes of certain parts of Africa is another interesting fact. The gene occurs in 30% or more of some African populations. The question we might ask is why selection pressure did not eliminate the sickling gene long ago. Here is an excellent example of the misleading oversimplification of some classical geneticists' belief in the idea "one gene–one character." The sickling cell condition, it turns out, prevents attack by the malaria parasite, which explains why its occurrence in a heterozygous state is beneficial in malaria-infected parts of the world and why selection pressure has not weeded the gene out of the gene pool of these populations. This one instance (and there are others) shows that a phenotypic change may be accompanied by beneficial as well as detrimental physiological effects. In this sense one gene may control several characters just as several genes may influence one character.

Variation among organisms, then, is not as simple as Mendel had pictured it. Modern genetics recognizes that a gene can have more than only two alleles—one expressing dominance and the other recessiveness; **multiple allelism** within a population is the rule, although a given individual may have only two allelic forms of a given gene under ordinary circumstances. Investigators have found that three different forms of one gene govern whether mice will have black, yellow, or barred fur. *Drosophila* has about 20 allelic forms of a gene affecting eye color. In humans, the four blood types A, B, AB, and O are determined by three alleles of a single gene, identified as L^A, L^B, and L^O. The genotypes shown at the left produce various phenotypic blood types.

Another idea of Mendel's that has been revised is that of complete dominance. Because genes interact, or tend to be influenced by the action of other genes, a blending of characters, or **incomplete dominance**, is possible. In one species of fowl, two alleles of one gene operate together and give rise to a phenotype different from the phenotypes produced by either allele alone.

In addition to there being multiple alleles, there is also a multiplicity of genes affecting a single trait. *Drosophila* has nearly 100 different pairs of genes, all in the same cell, that affect eye color. In humans, skin color and stature are characters determined by **polygenic inheritance**—several genes interacting and giving rise to a single trait. Crop yield in plants is also determined by polygenic inheritance. Within a given population, then, natural selection operates on phenotypes that are determined not only by multiple alleles of a given gene, but by polygenes as well, both influenced by mutation.

Clearly, mutation underlies our notion of the continuity of living things. It is the ultimate source of variation among individuals of a species, and it is the source of adaptation since the ability of a species to adapt to environmental changes depends directly on variation among its individuals. Finally, mutation is the source of evolution through natural selection.

GENOTYPE	PHENOTYPE
L^A L^A (or L^A L^O)	A
L^B L^B (or L^B L^O)	B
L^A L^B	AB
L^O L^O	O

1   Considering the deleterious effects of mutations, as a rule, explain why it seems likely that natural selection has favored diploidy over haploidy.

2   Tuberculosis and malaria are two among many diseases that man has brought under control. How might continuing the reduction of malaria on a global basis affect the occurrence of the sickling gene in the world's gene pool?

3   What are sex-linked characters? Explain how sex-linked characters are transmitted by discussing the recessive trait red–green color blindness in humans. First, assume that the male parent is color blind and that the female parent is normal. Diagram the F_1 and F_2 generations, showing where color blindness occurs and with what frequency. Next, assume that the female parent is color blind but the male parent is not. Diagram the F_1 and F_2 generations, as above. What condition is necessary for an F_2 female to have the phenotype of color blindness?

4   Explain how crossing-over increases the potential for genetic variation.

5   Try to obtain some literature reviewing potential genetic damage to organisms, including humans, located near nuclear power plants, radioactive waste disposal areas, or high radioactive areas like some parts of Colorado. The public utilities and the Atomic Energy Commission, both promoting wide-scale construction of nuclear power plants as if such plants were the only means of meeting power shortages in certain regions, speak of the "clean power" produced by the plants. Find out just how "clean" nuclear power plants are.

6   As our ability to work out chromosome maps for humans increases, man will be in a position to alter man quite deliberately within certain limits, by suppressing or replacing defective genes, for example. What is your attitude toward genetic engineering in humans? Do you see it as a moral issue? For instance, if one goal of genetic engineering were to remove "undesirable" behavior tendencies, who would decide what "undesirable" behavior is?

SELECTED READINGS

Auerbach, C. *Genetics in the Atomic Age*. New York: Essential Books, Inc., 1956. If you want more detail about radiation as a cause of mutations, this relatively easy discussion of chromosomes and genes will be helpful.

Dobzhansky, Theodosius, *Genetics of the Evolutionary Process*. New York: Columbia University Press, 1970. This book is a classic up-to-date version (continuation would better describe it) of Dobzhansky's *Genetics and the Origin of Species* published in 1937. The book is a highly detailed treatment of several topics in Part 1 of this text. With genetics as his focus, Dobzhansky includes in his discussion the unity, diversity, continuity, and evolution of life.

Simpson, G. G. *Horses*. New York: Doubleday & Company, Inc. The Natural History Library, 1951. Genetics as a theme underlying the larger topic of evolution comes across in a grand way in this highly readable book, an account of perhaps the most thoroughly known history of an organism attained through a study of its relatively complete fossil record.

Figure 4–1 Those species well adapted to their environment are selected for survival, tend to live to reproductive age, and produce more of their kind. That evolution proceeds through such a process of natural selection is undeniable and is the unifying principle of biology. Cryptic coloration, here dramatically shown in a female white-tailed ptarmigan and her young, is one such adaptation.

4 EVOLUTION OF LIFE

EVOLUTION BY NATURAL SELECTION: THE UNIFYING PRINCIPLE OF BIOLOGY

The major principle that unifies all of biology—from molecular and cellular biology to populational biology and behavior—is Darwin's concept of evolution by the natural selection and accumulation of small heritable variations. The result of natural selection and adaptation—evolution—is a fact, but certain ways in which evolutionary change is brought about are best considered theories.

For example, there is extremely good evidence among plants and animals for the adaptation of populations to their environments and for speciation, but the genetic mechanisms and the roles played by isolation and selection are far from fully understood. However, the many examples of adaptation, speciation, and adaptive radiation we will examine in this chapter and elsewhere represent, when taken together, an overwhelming body of evidence in support of evolution by natural selection (Fig. 4–1).

Lamarckism

In 1809, Jean Baptiste de Lamarck proposed a theory of evolution, which in essence stated that evolution proceeds by the inheritance of acquired characteristics. Lamarck was an evolutionist in his own right, and he suggested that individual organisms evolve into new organisms, in effect, because they try harder! That is, individuals improve on their normal behavior and way of life and so change through exercise or continued use of an appendage or other part of the body. He assumed in turn that this *acquired* characteristic would be inherited. Thus, he viewed evolution as a process of "increasing perfection" of organisms, and adaptation as a consequence of accumulation of inherited traits due to responses to environmental stimuli.

Figure 4–2 shows an application of Lamarckian evolution to a hypothetical species whose survival potential was increased as a result of its members "improving" themselves by growing longer and longer antlers. First (top) all members of the species have short antlers, but because longer antlers are more efficient for defense and so have greater survival value, Lamarck postulated that individuals lengthened their antlers by intensive use. The progeny (middle) have inherited somewhat longer antlers than those possessed initially by their parents and in turn pass on to their own progeny (bottom) still longer antlers.

Figure 4–2 According to Lamarckian evolution, antlers grew longer with use in the individual animal's lifetime, for the "purpose" of improving defense against predators. Hence increased antler length was presumed to be an acquired characteristic that was also passed on from parent to progeny.

Figure 4–3 According to Darwinism, long-antler variation existed among short-antler and medium-antler members of the species (top). Because the long-antler individuals had an advantage over the others, the longer-antler individuals tended to avoid predation more successfully and gradually became more numerous than short- and medium-antler individuals (middle). Eventually, most short-antler and medium-antler individuals were selected against, leaving a predominantly long-antler variety (bottom).

Contemporary evolutionists such as George Gaylord Simpson and Ernst Mayr have said that given the pre-Mendelian, pre-Darwinian status of biology during Lamarck's time, his theorizing contained some good conceptual elements, if not scientific validity. For example, there is some logic in thinking that acquired behavior is passed from one generation to the next. This is particularly true in the case of cultural inheritance and the transmission by learning of behavioral information from the old to the young in humans. Nevertheless, Lamarck's concept was a hypothesis that failed. Although Darwin and Mendel's thinking struck a ruthless blow to Lamarckism, there were other reasons for doubting it. For example, consider protective coloration in insects. How could an insect by exercise or behavior simulate or mimic in color or form a plant leaf or the bark of a tree? Also, Lamarck's hypothesis was based on pangenesis. The rise of Mendelian inheritance in the late 19th and the 20th centuries put the final lid on all concepts of pangenesis, and thus was disproved the Lamarckian mechanism for the inheritance of characters acquired by "perfecting" organisms.

Darwinism

Darwin's *The Origin of Species* is a superb presentation of the case for evolution by natural selection of inherited variations and is a book that every person who considers himself educated should be familiar with. The history and particulars of Darwin's genesis of the concept of evolution by natural selection during the voyage of the *Beagle* are documented in the color section facing page 48.

Darwin's concept of evolution by natural selection was based on the idea that there are variations among the offspring of parents, and that the variations are inherited. Those individuals whose variations are more in harmony with the environment are "selected," and they reproduce and give rise to more offspring than their counterparts, who are not in harmony with the environment and are "selected against." Darwin visualized the following sequence of events in this process of adaptation, or evolution:

1 Organisms produce far more offspring than can ever survive.
2 Because the populations of most species are essentially constant, there must consequently be a high death rate.
3 Individuals of a species are not identical. They vary in their morphological and behavioral characters.
4 Those individuals that "fit" their environments are favored over those less fit. By inheritance, the favored individuals preferentially pass their characters on to the next generation.
5 The following generation of individuals continues to improve on the adaptations inherited from their ancestors.

Darwin understood fully, following the writings of the English economist Thomas R. Malthus, that while plant and animal species in nature have a remarkable potential for increase in numbers, in reality their numbers remain fairly constant from one year to the next. He thus concluded that natural populations tend to remain in balance as a consequence of "recurrent struggles against other species or against external nature." One can hardly improve on Darwin's own account of the survival of the fittest:

> As many more individuals of each species are born than possibly survive; and as, consequently, there is a frequently recurring struggle for existence, it follows that any being, if it varies however slightly in any manner profitable to itself, under the complex and sometimes varying conditions of life, will have a better chance of surviving, and thus be naturally selected. From the strong principle of inheritance, any selected variety will tend to propagate its new and modified form.

Both Darwin and Alfred Russell Wallace emphasized the differential mortality of individuals as the primary manner in which natural selection resulted in evolution.

In a simple way, Fig. 4–3 summarizes how Darwin would explain the evolution of the long-antler individuals in our hypothetical species in contrast to Lamarck's explanation. Darwin would say that there is always variation in antler length among the members of the species. Better able to defend themselves, those members with longer antlers tend to be more successful in escaping predation and thus are better fitted for survival and reproduction. Since these variations are inherited, those variants with longer antlers are favored and produce more offspring of their own character. Accordingly, over a series of generations, the average antler length increases as a favorable adaptation. Darwin's writings clearly indicate that he believed selection rewarded (or discriminated against) the *individual* and that the cumulative effects of this selection resulted in the adaptation or evolution of populations or species.

Three other aspects of Darwin's concept of evolution should be clarified:

First, Darwin envisioned the inherited (today we say genetic) variations to be small, and the process of adaptation usually to involve the slow but steady accumulation of these small but favored variations. So time becomes extremely important to the evolution of species in nature. For example, Fig. 2–7 shows the change in the structure of the foot of the horse, correlated with geologic time. Paleontologists have now described countless examples of historical change in the structure and form of plant and animal species. Usually these changes reflect increasing complexity with the species becoming increasingly adapted to an ecologically more narrow or specialized way of life. The continued adaptation of a species during geologic time is frequently referred to as **phyletic evolution**.

Second, in *The Origin of Species* Darwin took advantage of many examples of the artificial selection man has applied to certain plant and animal species for domestic purposes. Figure 4–4 shows how the original wild rock pigeon gave rise, through selective breeding by man, to three different varieties of a pigeon identified as Jacobin. The principle of artificial selection shown here is essentially the same as that of natural selection, the only difference being that man rather than natural forces exercised the selection of those variations to be encouraged to breed and produce offspring of a "favored" form and behavior.

Finally, the examples of natural and artificial selection cited indicate another aspect of Darwin's explanation, one that is of fundamental importance. Species are not immutable. On the contrary, they undergo variations

wild rock

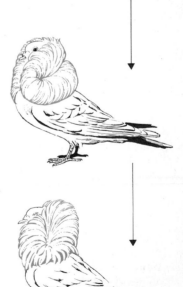
Jacobin

Figure 4–4 Through selective breeding of offspring of the wild rock pigeon, man controlled the selection of the varieties shown here.

in time and space. This point clashed violently with the religious belief that species were instantaneously created by God and thus immutable. With the publication of Darwin's *The Origin of Species*, the floodgates were opened for a confrontation between biology as a science and religion as dogma and a rigid social force.

GENETICS, NATURAL SELECTION, AND ADAPTATION

We have stated that genetic variation is the raw material on which selection acts. What are the sources of genetic variation within natural populations? Clearly, mutation and recombination produce new genotypes in populations. The new phenotypes arising from these genotypes are then subject to selection pressures. The primary sources of genetic variability in natural populations can be summarized as follows:

MUTATION
> genetic mutation
> chromosomal mutation

RECOMBINATION
> heterozygosis as the product of homozygous parents
> random assortment of genes
> genetic cross-overs between chromosomes

GENETIC DRIFT

GENE FLOW FROM OTHER POPULATIONS

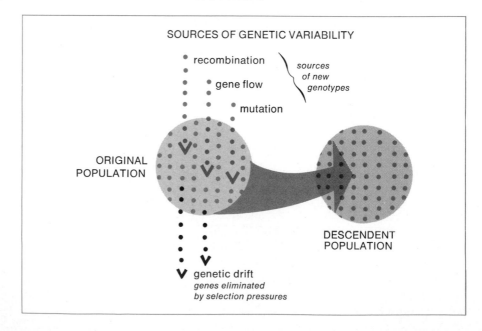

Figure 4–5 Sources of genetic variability within natural populations are shown here: mutation, recombination, genetic drift, and gene flow. Selection pressures eliminate genes of unfit individuals with the result that the evolving descendent population is better adapted to the environment.

Gene flow and genetic drift

In the previous chapter we discussed the roles of mutation and recombination in producing genetic variation. Gene flow and genetic drift are also important factors contributing to the gene pool of a population. **Gene flow** results from the dispersal of individuals to and from a given population. For example, individuals of a population adapted to one environment sometimes disperse to another population that happens to be adapted to a somewhat different environment. When immigrant individuals interbreed with the resident individuals, new genes or gene combinations are introduced into the population by heterozygosis.

Genetic drift also contributes to genetic variation within populations, particularly those that periodically fluctuate in numbers and reach a small size. Sewall Wright in particular has emphasized the genetic consequences of genetic drift. Genetic drift is a result of the effects of "sampling error" in small populations. For example, a population of butterflies breeding in the alpine habitat of a mountain top might consist of several hundred individuals. A late spring freeze or other aspect of a harsh environment conceivably could kill all but 10 or so individuals. Many genes or gene combinations would be lost by chance, and the atypical genes or gene combinations of the surviving 10 or so individuals would be the basis of the gene pool of the population as it built back up to a greater size in subsequent generations. Figure 4–5 summarizes various phenomena that contribute to genetic variability within natural populations. These are the genetic sources of phenotypic variations available to natural selection, and without them there would be no adaptation and thus no evolution or life as we now know it.

With the foregoing as background we can now pin down a concept of species. According to Simpson, a **species** is

> a population or group of related populations . . . whose anatomical and physiological characteristics are simply the total of those characteristics in the individuals making up the population. The pattern of characteristics is neither a real individual nor an idealized abstraction of the characters of an individual. It is a frequency distribution of the different variants of each character actually present at any given time. Species are populations of [interbreeding] individuals of common descent, living together in similar ecological relationships and tending to have a unified and continuing evolutionary role distinct from that of other species.

Variation and its fate

When we consider genetics at the level of populations—called **population genetics**—as opposed to the level of individuals, we are much closer to the mechanisms that bring about species change through natural selection. The variety of traits—eye and skin color, wing length, blood type, or whatever—in a given population is an expression of the total number of genes in the population's gene pool. It does not take a trained biologist to inform you that the distribution of genes in two populations of a given species is different. Skin color, eye color, and mean height differences between a population of African pygmies and one of Scandinavians does not need elaboration. When we want to compare the distribution of genes within the gene pools of different populations we use the term **gene frequency**, which is the ratio between the alleles that determine a given trait. The frequency of the gene controlling B type blood gradually increases from 4% in London to 15% in Kharkov, Russia. The fact that gene frequency does change from one population to another related one has led geneticists to ask if gene frequencies within a population tend to remain constant.

HARDY–WEINBERG PRINCIPLE: In 1908, at about the time biologists were rediscovering the ideas of Mendel, the British mathematician G. H. Hardy and the German physician W. Weinberg independently published papers suggesting that gene frequencies within a random-mating population do tend to remain constant.

Consider a hypothetical population whose individuals have but a single gene (A) and its allelic form (a). We are working with what biologists call a single-gene model. Suppose further that mating among individuals is random, that mutations do not occur, and that selection pressures and gene flow are entirely absent. In short, we have an idealized population with genetic stability. Mendelian inheritance tells us that there can be only three possible genotypes in our population (AA), (Aa), and (aa). Hardy and Weinberg showed that as a consequence of random mating the proportion of these three genotypes reaches an equilibrium and remains constant for all future generations. It is important to note that the frequency of these two alleles—(A) and (a)—reaches equilibrium after the first generation of random mating. The Hardy–Weinberg equilibrium describes the way in which these alleles are distributed in the three possible genotypes.

The proportion of individuals carrying each of the three genotypes at equilibrium is given by the formula:

$$p^2 + 2pq + q^2 = 1$$

where p^2 is the proportion of (AA) individuals, $2pq$ is the proportion of (Aa) individuals, and q^2 is the proportion of (aa) individuals. We can understand why this is so if we consider the gametes of these individuals. Since each gamete carries only one of these alleles, the genotypes of the progeny depend only on the frequency of the alleles carried by the gametes of our randomly mating population. The proportion of gametes carrying (A) is p and the pro-

		SPERM	
		(A) p	(a) q
EGGS	(A) p	(AA) p^2	(Aa) pq
	(a) q	(Aa) pq	(aa) q^2

Figure 4–6

portion carrying (a) is q. The frequency of the offspring genotypes is shown in Fig. 4–6. From this we can calculate the proportion of the various genotypes of the progeny—p^2 (AA) individuals: $2pq$ (Aa) individuals: q^2 (aa) individuals.

It can be shown that the frequency of (A) (that is, p) equals the frequency of all the (AA) individuals plus one half of the (Aa) individuals. Likewise the frequency of (a) (that is, q) equals the frequency of all (aa) individuals plus one half of the (Aa) individuals. Because (A) and (a) comprise all the alleles in the population, the sum of their frequencies ($p + q$) must equal 100% or 1.0. Squaring each side: $(p + q)^2 = 1^2$ and expanding: $p^2 + 2pq + q^2 = 1$ mathematically predicts the distribution of the genotypes which we found above.

Natural selection and gene frequency

The fact is that populations do not *always* follow the Hardy–Weinberg principle. Mutation and migration for example, are two factors capable of altering gene frequency. Natural selection, of course, is the major factor. Here is one example. In a species of the fly *Drosophila polymorpha* occurring in Brazil, the males have three types of coloration on their abdomens, indicated as genotypes (EE), (Ee), and (ee). In nature, the frequencies of the three phenotypes are relatively constant from one generation to the next, with the "light" genotype (ee) being the rarest. A. Brito DaCunha crossed homozygous individuals (EE) and (ee) in the laboratory and obtained in the F_2 generation the observed frequencies of genotypes shown below. The observed frequencies

	(EE)	(Ee)	(ee)
observed	1,605	3,767	1,310
expected	1,670.5	3,341	1,670.5
relative adaptive values	0.85	1.0	0.70

were significantly different from those expected according to Hardy–Weinberg equilibrium. There are fewer homozygotes and more heterozygotes than expected. DaCunha accordingly concluded that flies heterozygous for the portion of the chromosome containing the (E) gene have an adaptive advantage over the homozygous condition. Here, then, is a case of heterozygote superiority. Can we not conclude that a deleterious gene is thus maintained in the population? This gene is buffered, so to speak, against extinction due to selection as a consequence of the superior fitness of the heterozygote. Can you recall a similar situation described in Chapter 3?

How does natural selection increase or decrease the frequency of a gene in a population? The unit of selection in nature is nearly always the individual.

In modern terms, if that individual is more successful in producing offspring than its fellow individuals, in the next generation a greater proportion of individuals will carry the DNA of our "favored" individual.

By now it should be obvious that adaptation is a populational phenomenon, even though the individual is the unit of selection. Individuals do not adapt; populations and species do. The genes passed from one generation to the next provide the inherited individual variations on which natural selection operates. The work of geneticists such as S. Wright, R. A. Fisher, and J. B. S. Haldane in this century has clearly indicated that gene substitution or selection is the unit process in population adaptation. That is, one gene is favored by selection

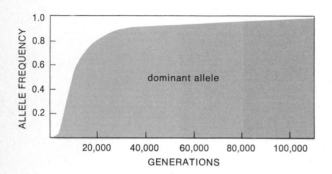
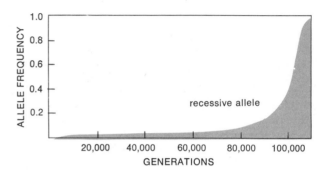

Figure 4–7 These curves show the rate of change in frequency of a new allele that has a small selective advantage over the old allele. It is assumed that individuals carrying this new allele produce one-thousandth more offspring in each generation than do the same number of individuals having the old allele. If the new allele is dominant, it is favored in both the heterozygous and homozygous state and its frequency increases rapidly (figure at left); if it is recessive, it is selected for only when homozygous, so its frequency increases slowly at first (right).

over its allelic counterpart. So in the next generation that gene occurs more frequently in the population. Conversely, its allelic counterpart, being selected against, occurs less frequently. The time it takes for selection pressure either to increase or decrease the frequency of an allele in a population is clearly an important factor here. In Chapter 3 the phenomenon of dominance of one gene to its allelic recessive counterpart was discussed. Population geneticists have shown that if time is measured in generations, the rate of increase in frequency of a gene or an allele is strongly affected by whether or not it is dominant. Figure 4–7 describes the rate of change in frequency per generation of a pair of alleles in a Mendelian population. Both alleles have the same small selective advantage, but one is recessive and the other dominant. As you can see, both alleles increase more rapidly when their frequencies in the population are medium (say, from 0.4 to 0.8). However, at low frequencies (say, from 0.1 to 0.2) it is clear that the dominant allele increases far more rapidly than the recessive one. Since most mutants in nature are recessive and deleterious, if not lethal, what does this example say about the rate of evolution of new genotypes appearing as a consequence of mutation only?

In what manner or through what pathways does selection alter the statistical character of a natural population? This is an important question that evolutionists and geneticists have confronted in recent years. In fact, George Gaylord Simpson in 1953 defined selection as anything producing a systematic heritable change in a population between one generation and the following one. Simpson's definition implies a direction in the operation of selection.

Figure 4–8 shows schematically what may be the only three basic types of selection. In the case of **stabilizing selection,** the average phenotype is favored, and the extremes are selected against. By **directional selection,** an extreme or nonaverage phenotype is favored, and the average and remaining extreme phenotypes are at a disadvantage. In the case of **disruptive selection**, selection pushes the phenotypes of a population into two separate classes, each away from the population mean. We shall see below some classic examples of these types of selection, but keep in mind that stabilizing selection is the most common in nature and usually maintains the *status quo* of populations in genetic equilibrium at an optimum peak of adaptation to their environments, whereas

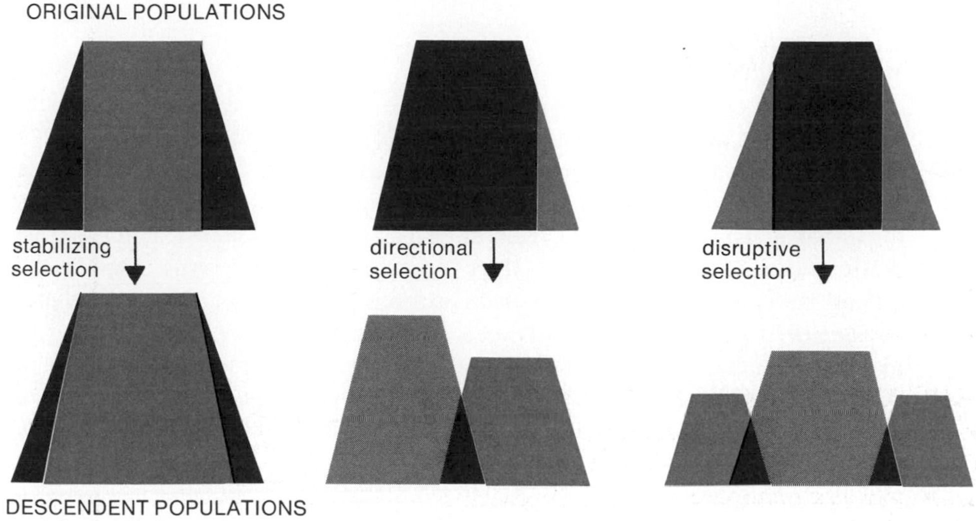

ORIGINAL POPULATIONS

stabilizing selection

directional selection

disruptive selection

DESCENDENT POPULATIONS

Figure 4–8 Three types of selection—stabilizing, directional, and disruptive—are shown as they operate at the level of populations.

directional selection is less frequent but of fundamental importance. It occurs when the environments of populations change or when populations change from an old to a new environment. This is the type of selection that leads to progressive adaptation and evolution. Disruptive selection is not fully understood, but it is thought to play a key role in novel and important instances of adaptation.

CLASSIC EXAMPLES OF POPULATION ADAPTATION

Stabilizing selection

Since stabilizing selection removes deviant or extreme phenotypes from the population, the population or mean phenotype remains essentially constant, so we rarely notice this type of selection operating against less fit phenotypes. A famous example of stabilizing selection is that of the fate of a flock of common house sparrows in a severe snow storm in New England in 1899. H. C. Bumpus collected the immobilized individuals of the flock and measured the wing lengths, weights, and certain other characters of the individuals that died and of those that survived. He obtained good evidence that the surviving sparrows shared a relatively narrow range of variation compared with a larger range of variation shared by those birds that died. In general, those individuals with abnormally long or abnormally short wings died. Presumably this is an example of a well-adapted species whose deviations from the average or optimal phenotype of size are removed by stabilizing selection in a suddenly harsh environment.

Directional selection

MOTHS AND COLORATION: In England since the 1840s, a variety of species of Lepidoptera have become dark in their coloration in industrial areas where the terrain and vegetation have been darkened by soot and other air-borne pollutants. This response of insects to environmental pollution is known as **industrial melanism**. H. B. D. Kettlewell has made a detailed study of one moth species, *Biston betularia*, which is preyed upon by birds. During the second half of the 19th century in industrialized urban regions of England, dark-colored or melanistic individuals of this species began to occur with increasing frequency. This was especially true for populations of *betularia* in the vicinity of factory centers. One of the first black specimens of *betularia* was found in Manchester in 1848. By 1895, about 98% of the *betularia* population around Manchester was dark in coloration. Because the species lives for only one year, we can conclude that within about 50 generations a genotype of less than 1% frequency shifted to a frequency of 98%. Various calculations indicate that the darkening of the environment by pollution increased the selective advantage of the dark phenotype to 30% over that of the light phenotype. In other words, dark moths produce about 30% more surviving offspring than do light moths. This change in genotype frequency is greater than can be expected from recurrent mutation.

Presumably the dark mutants were originally at a selective disadvantage resting on their light backgrounds of lichen-covered trunks. With increased pollution of local vegetation by industrial soot, the dark mutant gained superiority in fitness due to its protective coloration (Fig. 4–9). In this way, frequencies of the two genes were altered by selection. The gene controlling light coloration decreased, and the gene operating for melanism increased. The gene for melanism is dominant to its allelic counterpart. This is one reason why the frequency of the dark mutant in the population has been altered so rapidly. Kettlewell, in fact, showed that the rise in frequency of the mutant form in an industrial population was rapid. The rise was similar to the rapid rise in frequency of a dominant allele compared to a recessive one, as shown in Fig. 4–7.

Kettlewell captured and released individuals of both forms of *betularia* and discovered the selective advantage of protective coloration. From 1953 to 1955, he examined survival values for the two phenotypes of this species in

Figure 4–9 The selection effects of industrial melanism are clearly evident in this photograph of black and pepper-marked moths shown against a dark background.

both a polluted and a "clean" region of England. In both regions he released dark and light forms of *betularia*, recaptured them, and determined the respective frequencies of the two forms among the recaptured individuals. His data show that the light phenotype has a higher survival value in the unpolluted regions than the melanistic one, and that the dark phenotype has a higher survival value in the polluted or industrial areas of England.

For about 50 years, or 50 *betularia* generations, a dominant mutation has possessed a selective advantage as a consequence of change in the population's environment. Natural selection caused by birds preying upon conspicuous phenotypes has altered the genotype and phenotype of a moth species. *Direction* of selection is involved here, and the average phenotype of the population has shifted from a light-colored one to a melanistic one involving a dominant gene.

It is ironic to think that knowledge of industrial melanism is one of the few good consequences of the undesirable pollution of our world's environment. Indeed, now that the English have controlled their release of factory smoke and soot into the air, the vegetation is becoming cleaner and the tree trunks, along with their associated lichens, are less dark in appearance. In the last several years, Kettlewell has obtained evidence for a reversal in the previous trend of adaptation. Where trees are becoming lighter, the light phenotype of *betularia* is now on the increase! This is in keeping with his model for adaptation in the species. Industrial melanism is a perfect example of the directional nature of natural selection in the rapid adaptation of a population at the single-gene level.

HOUSE SPARROWS AND BODY WEIGHT: Still another good example of adaptation caused by selection is that of the house sparrow, which was introduced into North America in 1852 and represents a case of natural selection that is both rapid and directional. This species has now spread throughout nearly all of North, Middle, and South America. Its rapid adaptation has been studied by R. F. Johnston and R. K. Selander, who analyzed geographical variations in this species. Among their findings was that the average weight of sparrow populations increases with the decrease in average winter temperature and increase of latitude (Fig. 4–10), that is with the increase in winter coldness.

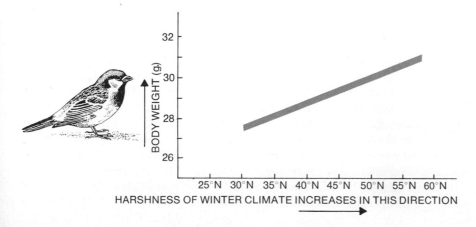

Figure 4–10 This graph shows a correlation between harshness of winter climate and increase in body weight of 14 populations of the house sparrow, *Passer domesticus*, as reported by Johnston and Selander.

This geographical trend for increase in size in the northern and colder regions has apparently been generated by selection on the sparrow populations in about 100 years following its introduction into North America. All the New World individuals of this species are descended from the few individuals originally introduced. Johnston and Selander also found that a character such as plumage color for this introduced species is more intense or dark in humid geographical regions, and that appendage length such as that of the tarsus of the leg decreases in the colder regions of the north. Although the genetic basis of these intraspecific variations in the house sparrow has not been studied, Johnston and Selander have made a good case for the rapid evolution of the morphological characters in this introduced species.

Disruptive selection

A good case has been made for disruptive selection in the African swallowtail butterfly, *Papilio dardanus*. Throughout most of Africa, the males of this species are monomorphic, but females are unlike the males in appearance. They do not have hind wings or wing "tails." Many of these females are mimics of females of species distasteful to predators. In Madagascar, the females are monomorphic, sport "tails," and essentially have the same appearance as the males. Of special interest is that in the Abyssinian region of Africa the majority of females are nonmimetic, have tails, and in general look like the males. A minority of the females, however, are tailless and have mimetic patterns similar to the females of *P. dardanus* throughout the rest of Africa. In a series of elegant investigations, C. A. Clarke and P. M. Sheppard have presented convincing evidence for the role of disruptive selection in the Abyssinian populations of this butterfly species.

Figure 4–11 is a frequency histogram of tail length in hybrids of the South African males crossed with either male-like females or mimetic females obtained from Abyssinia. Note the bimodal distribution of the tail length. In fact, there is an "antimodal" region of potential tail length (about 6.5 mm), which females do not show. Tail lengths are clearly greater or less than 6.5 mm. Clarke and Sheppard have made a convincing case that in Abyssinia, but not elsewhere in Africa, disruptive selection operates on the females of *P. dardanus*. They have shown, both by observing individuals obtained in nature and by crossing and inbreeding in the laboratory, that the bimodal nature of the observed phenotypes of the females is genotypic.

Accordingly, Clarke and Sheppard conclude that in Abyssinia, a situation roughly intermediate between the South African and Madagascar populations of the species, disruptive selection rewards the mimicking females who reduce the length of their tails, but also rewards the male-like, nonmimetic females for increased tail length. Clearly, females with an intermediate tail length of, say, 6.5 mm would be at a selective disadvantage. Finally, we may add that the effectiveness of disruptive selection in nature could, theoretically at least, lead to complete reproductive isolation between the extreme forms within a population, and to the evolution of new species. There is presently little evidence for a "sympatric speciation," as this sort of speciation is called, but it is considered in more detail later in this chapter.

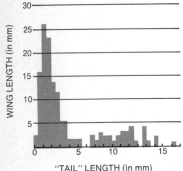

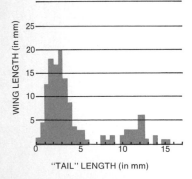

Figure 4–11 Frequency histogram of "tail" length in the offspring of crosses of South African and Abyssinian individuals of *Papilio dardanus*: mimetic females below and male-like females above.
(AFTER CLARKE AND SHEPPARD)

VARIATION, REPRODUCTIVE ISOLATION, AND SPECIATION

Although Darwin fully realized the importance of natural selection in the origin of species, he was understandably at a loss to explain how one species gives rise to another. Part of the difficulty was the absence of the Mendelian concept of genes and gene flow in relation to reproductive isolation. We now know that wide-ranging species, or species whose distributions include ecologically diverse areas, break up into biologically distinct—or morphologically different—subspecies, or races.

Five subspecies of the deermouse are distributed through North and Middle America. There is an increase in subspecies of the populations occurring in the ecologically diversified western North America, where high mountains and vast deserts occur side by side. The song sparrow, also of North and Middle America, exhibits the same tendency for geographical variation and fragmentation. Many more examples of variation between populations of plant and animal species could be cited, but the problem at hand is to explain *how* one species gives rise to another.

Reproductive isolation

Obviously, if one species gives rise to another the two are closely related. Frequently two morphologically similar plant species or two morphologically and behaviorally similar animal species derive one from another, or from a parental third species. This is particularly true for **sympatric species**; that is, species that are closely related and either co-exist or have co-extensive breeding distributions. Figure 4–12 shows the song sparrow and Lincoln sparrow, which are sympatric in North America. They are virtually identical in external phenotype, but do not inbreed, hybridize, or exchange genes. Two common maple species, the red maple and the sugar maple, are widely sympatric in North America, but neither do they hybridize nor exchange genes. Here we are dealing with reproductive isolation between sympatric species. It is evident that there must be barriers, isolating mechanisms we call them, that prevent the species from exchanging genes.

Isolating mechanisms may be extrinsic or intrinsic in operation. **Extrinsic isolating mechanisms** are agencies of the environment (rivers, oceans, mountain ranges) that prevent gene exchange between isolated species or races by restricting the species to separate geographical areas. Such species or races are said to be **allopatric** in distribution. **Intrinsic isolating mechanisms** are adaptations or biological differences that prevent individuals of different species from interbreeding; or, if interbreeding occurs, they prevent the successful production of offspring. G. Ledyard Stebbins has categorized the most important intrinsic isolating mechanisms that separate species along the following lines.

PREZYGOTIC MECHANISMS: Although populations of two related species may occupy the same region, the fact that they are adapted to different habitats

song sparrow

Lincoln sparrow

red maple

sugar maple

Figure 4–12 "Sympatric" species are here represented by two related but distinct species of sparrows and by two related but distinct species of maple trees.

keeps them isolated. Seasonal or temporal forces may interfere with inter-breeding of the two species because the individuals reach sexual maturity at different times. Still another isolating mechanism, in animals, may be incompatible mating behavior. And finally, there may be mechanically restrictive forces at work, such as incompatible male–female reproductive organs in both animals and plants. In all of the above cases, fertilization is prevented.

POSTZYGOTIC MECHANISMS: If fertilization does take place, resulting in hybrid offspring, the interbreeding population may maintain their species identity for the following reasons. The resulting hybrid zygote does not survive because it is inviable or intrinsically weak. Or if the zygote does survive, the hybrid adult may be sterile. F_1 hybrids may be sterile because of deficient gonads, because meiosis is interrupted before completion, or because of abnormal chromosome (and gene) segregation. Although the F_1 progeny of interbreeding individuals may be fertile and vigorous, the F_2 progeny may contain among them many sterile or weak individuals.

There is no need to consider examples of each inhibitory mechanism that maintains the separation and separate identity of the gene pools of related species. However, you should realize that there are many examples of natural selection strengthening isolating mechanisms of two sympatric species or of two allopatric species in a zone of sympatry. Consider the populations of two rock nuthatches in Asia Minor. The two birds are mostly allopatric, but in Asia Minor their ranges overlap and populations of the two species co-exist. Selection has varied their bill structures so that the species now take different sized food in their zone of sympatry. Further, their facial plumage characters, important in mating behavior, have diverged. Presumably, a variety of morphological and behavioral characters in the two species have been altered by selection. These can be considered isolating mechanisms strengthened by natural selection. We should not lose sight of the fact that isolating mechanisms, both in plants and animals, nearly always have a genetic basis, so the mechanisms are subject to selection whenever not to exchange genes is a selective advantage to a population.

Behavior as an isolating mechanism

Gene exchange between closely related species is often prevented by isolating mechanisms that involve courtship behavior patterns. Often these courtship patterns are very complex, and nearly always they are species-specific; and the differences in courtship behavioral patterns between two related species may be quantitative rather than qualitative.

For instance, two sibling species of *Drosophila* (*D. melanogaster* and *D. simulans*) use the same basic male–female courtship patterns, except that they perform their behavioral activities at different speeds. These quantitative differences are species-specific and are sufficiently different that synchronization for mating rarely occurs between a male and a female of the different species. Males of both species perform the same three behaviors—orient their body toward the female, display their wings, and stick out their tongue and lick the female—but at different frequencies. Thus if females of *D. melanogaster* are put in a cage with males of *D. simulans*, the females are not induced to sexual receptivity by the males' courtship attention. The same is true if the experiment is done in reverse, with the females of *D. simulans* caged with the males of the other species.

The isolating mechanisms here favored by selection include not only the courtship behavior of the male, but also the female's sexual receptivity or sexual inhibition. A. Manning and others have shown that if the female's antennae (which respond to the male) are activated by the wrong set of male stimuli, inhibition of sexual receptivity continues. However, artificial removal of the female's antennae causes a removal of the inhibitions, and thereafter a male of a different species has no difficulty in copulating with the female! Such is the complex and quantitative nature of certain isolating mechanisms.

We are all familiar with the evening spring chorus of toad and frog mating calls. Selection pressures operating in zones of both hybridization and sympatry tend to differentiate vocalization patterns with the result that conspecific matings are the rule. A classic example is that of the cricket-frogs *Acris gryllus* and *A. crepitans* in North America. *A. crepitans* is found throughout most of the United States east of the Rocky Mountains. *A. gryllus* lives in the southeastern United States, occupying coastal regions from Florida west to Louisiana and Mississippi, and from Florida north to Virginia.

W. F. Blair and his students have studied the vocalizations of the two species in their zones of allopatry (Texas and southern Florida), and in their zone of sympatry (southwest Mississippi). Those individuals allopatrically distributed never or only very rarely interbreed in nature, and they have similar mating calls. Where individuals of the two species occur together in sympatry, however, there is a pronounced difference in their mating calls (Fig. 4–13). Blair concluded that "where the two species occur together in southwestern Mississippi, their calls differ in every measurable characteristic." Again, we see an example of the evolution of a behavioral isolating mechanism. Selection has undoubtedly operated in a way that reduces or prevents hybridization, the adaptations having been achieved by the evolution of vocal behavioral characters that involve increasingly precise and specific call differences.

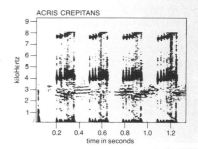

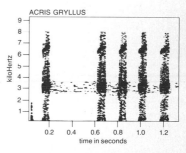

Figure 4–13 Behavior as an isolating mechanism is evident in these sonagrams of related species of cricket-frogs. The calls, seen against a faint background of calls of other species, are different in that the calls of *A. gryllus* lack the pulsations evident in the calls of *A. crepitans*, which makes each call species-specific. (COURTESY OF W. F. BLAIR.)

Speciation

One of the major advances of evolutionary biology in the mid-20th century has been insight into ways plant and animal species arise. Theorists for plant species (Stebbins and V. Grant) and for animal species (Simpson, Mayr, and Th. Dobzhansky) have reached some common grounds on the topic, and it is their thinking that we shall follow here. One conclusion is that allopatric speciation is the usual (but not the only) mode of speciation and probably is the most common among animal species, particularly the higher vertebrates.

By **allopatric speciation**, we mean that a population or a group of populations fragment off from a parental group, so an extrinsic barrier is erected between the parental species and the new **isolate**. Since the new isolate will nearly always have an environment different from the parental species, in time the isolate populations will adapt to the new environment through selection pressures.

As new gene combinations and genotypes are formed, the isolate gradually develops its particular phenotype. By that time it has diverged from its parental species and is an incipient species. The theory states that eventually the isolate or incipient species will diverge so much that its gene pool is substantially different from that of the parental species. Then if the two species—the old and the new—come back together, there will be sufficient genetic and phenotypic differences between them to prevent interbreeding and an exchanges of genes. So to speak, by passing the "test of sympatry" they demonstrate that they are now "good" species. These ideas are summarized schematically in Fig 4–14.

GENE FLOW IN SPECIATION: It is important here to consider the role of gene flow in speciation. Most modern evolutionists consider gene flow to be a conservative and retarding factor with regard to isolate divergence and speciation. After all, the role of the extrinsic factor in allopatric speciation is to prevent gene exchange between the parental species and the isolate. A commonly accepted point here is that blockage of gene flow from the parental species *permits* the isolate to undergo adaptation to its new environment, free of genetic "swamping." That is, the gene pool of the isolate can make a more complete adaptation to the new environment if it is not annually swamped by the arrival of new genes (carried by dispersing individuals) from the parental species' population. It is in this context that Mayr has argued so strongly, in considering allopatric speciation in animal species, that small, peripherally isolated populations are important in evolution.

Do isolates always give rise to new species? The answer is no. In fact, usually the isolate merges back with the parental species. Either the extrinsic barrier to gene dispersal breaks down too soon, or the environment of the isolate is

Figure 4–14   The possible fates of an isolate population are shown here: At A the isolate population has attained complete separation from the original parent population, an extrinsic barrier preventing union of the two. The barrier breaks down, however, resulting in reunion of the two populations at B with no genetic differentiation; at C is a reunited population, but one with hybridization of some individuals, which show partial genetic differentiation; and at D complete genetic differentiation has occurred with the result that a zone of sympatry occurs where the populations overlap.

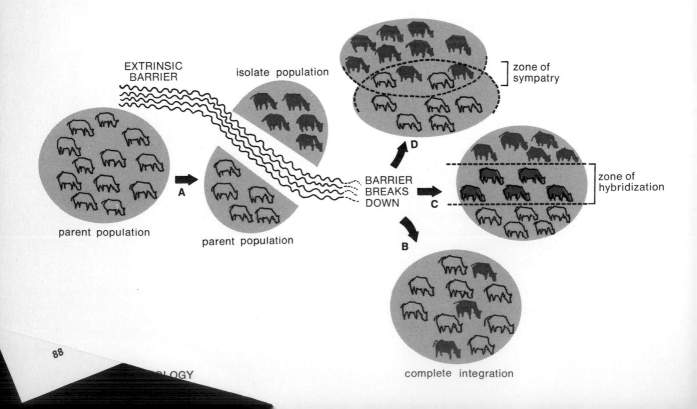

OLOGY

so similar to that of the parental species that the isolate's gene pool does not differentiate sufficiently for the acquisition of intrinsic isolating mechanisms. Sometimes the isolate merges with the parental species when the isolate is, so to speak, only half way along the road to speciation. Again, Fig. 4–14 summarizes the various fates that may befall an isolate, depending on its stage of evolutionary divergence during allopatric isolation.

SYMPATRIC SPECIATION IN ANIMALS: While most animal species seem to have evolved as a result of geographical isolation, some may have evolved from a single ancestral species without the influence of physical or spatial isolating achieved by extrinsic barriers. This is **sympatric speciation**, a well known precedent for which occurs among plants when a chromosomally sterile hybrid of two species in some way has its chromosome number doubled. This instantaneously produces a fertile species, free of the hybrid sterility problem. The hybrid origin of species is a common method of speciation among plants, but among animals the role of sympatric speciation in evolution is uncertain. However, let's imagine a hypothetical butterfly species that does evolve by sympatric speciation and then consider one possible case from the archives of nature.

Suppose that the caterpillars of our imaginary species feed on only one species of plant. Suppose further that a few individuals of the species accidentally lay their eggs on a different species of plant and that the new caterpillars develop normally as they eat the leaves of the new plant. Also suppose that the butterflies that develop from the caterpillars that ate the new food plant prefer to mate with butterflies that fed on the same leaves. If the behavior of laying eggs on the new food plant and mating between individuals that develop on the same type of food is subject to genetic control, it is theoretically possible that the gene pool of the original species might become separated into two distinct gene pools. Two new species would have evolved in the same geographical area in the absence of environmental boundaries.

So much for theoretical aspects of sympatric speciation among animals. The question is does it actually occur? Perhaps the best case for it is a plant pest species of the genus *Rhagoletis* that occurs in both North America and Europe. In Europe, the species has never been known to parasitize apple trees. In 1866, about 200 years after apple trees were introduced into North America, individuals of *R. pomonella* (the apple maggot) were observed to be infesting apples. Previously in North America, this species infested the fruit of the native hawthorn (*Crataegus*). The species also uses the species of American roses (*Rosaceae*) as a plant host. Recent studies performed by G. L. Bush suggest that in the 100 years since the introduction of apple trees into North America, *R. pomonella* has shifted its host preference from hawthorn to apples, *and* has developed an earlier breeding season and the larger ovipositor required to penetrate the thicker skin of apples for the egg-laying process. The degree of genetic exchange, or the extent of genetic isolation, between the two host races of *R. pomonella* (the hawthorn race and the apple race) is presently unknown. However, this is a good possibility of sympatric speciation, and the available evidence is in agreement with the hypothetical example given in the preceding paragraph.

ADAPTIVE RADIATION: THE MAJOR TREND OF EVOLUTION

Paleontologists studying the fossil record, and biologists studying the distribution and relationships of living species, have described many examples of adaptive radiation. In reality, **adaptive radiation** is no more than accelerated speciation and associated evolutionary divergence. It is the evolution of adaptations that enable an organism to take on a new role in the environment. The diversity among marsupial (or pouched) mammals of Australia and among the placental mammals of Europe, Asia, and North America serves as an excellent case for adaptive radiation. In both groups, species such as the Tasmanian (marsupial) wolf and the North American (plancental) wolf have exploited a similar way of life. As a result of their adaptation to that common way of life, the two species have many similar phenotypic characters. Also compare the flying phalanger of Australia with the flying squirrel of North America. Here is an additional example of convergence in evolution (Fig. 4–15).

Darwin's finches

A fascinating example of adaptive radiation is that of Darwin's finches, which were briefly mentioned in the color section facing page 48. The sight of these finches of the Galapagos Islands was a seminal factor in Darwin's reaching the

Figure 4–15 Convergent evolution can also be seen operating in these three related marine forms: extinct ichthyosaur (top), shark, and porpoise. How has one specific environmental factor played a role in establishing morphological similarity in these species?

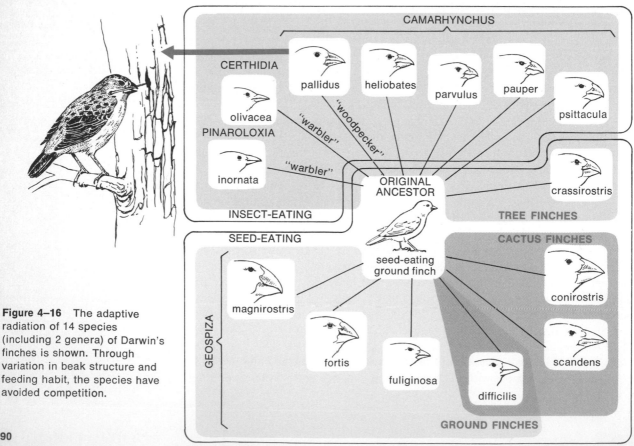

Figure 4–16 The adaptive radiation of 14 species (including 2 genera) of Darwin's finches is shown. Through variation in beak structure and feeding habit, the species have avoided competition.

conclusion that species originate through natural selection. The adaptive radiation of these finches is a consequence of evolutionary opportunity and ecological opportunity.

The Galapagos are volcanic in origin, and, of particular importance, they have never been connected with South America or any other major land mass. Hence probably all the terrestrial plant and animal species occurring there have reached the islands by overseas dispersal of some sort. Beginning with the work of Darwin, and continuing through the classic studies of the ornithologist David Lack in the 1940s, it is evident that this group of finches is descended from one founding species, which sometime in the historical past inhabited the islands, probably coming from the South American mainland. As a consequence of speciation, there are now about 14 species in the archipelago, each of which uses the resources of the islands in a different way. Figure 4–16 shows the different species of the Darwin finches and illustrates the various ways in which they feed in different habitats and on different foods. Here it is clear that the species have evolved adaptations (isolating mechanisms) enabling them to avoid interspecies competition. Of the 14 species shown in Fig. 4–16, three feed on seeds on the ground, two feed on cactus, one feeds on cactus and on the ground, and the others feed on trees in different ways. One species (*Camarhynchus pallidus*) feeds on tree trunks, as a woodpecker does. However, it gets its food from the tree trunks by use of a cactus spine probe, a behavioral adaptation. The probe forces insects out of cracks and crevices in the bark. This is a rare instance among birds of the regular use of a tool for feeding. The behavior rather than a morphological structure such as the bill has been the agent of adaptation, so presumably here is a case where natural selection has favored behavior.

What factors of speciation and pressures of the environment are responsible for this case of adaptive radiation? Lack and others have suggested that soon after reaching the Galapagos the original stock of finch individuals colonized all or most of the islands by dispersal. In time, because some of the islands are relatively far apart, isolates developed and gave rise to new species. Most likely, this occurred on the smaller and outer islands. The dispersers of the new species, in turn, the theory continues, would reach other islands. This cycle of "isolation–speciation–dispersal" would continue to the present day, when we find about 14 species in the Galapagos, with as many as 10 living in sympatry on the larger islands forming the core of the archipelago. Lack has made a good case for the thesis that interspecific competition has provided selection pressures that have intensified the pre-existing differences between the species. So today we find on Albemarle Island, for instance, 10 species in sympatry, with each obtaining the environmental resources necessary for breeding and production of offspring in a manner that is not seriously impeded by the presence of a related species.

The salient features of the explanation of the adaptive radiation of these finches are evolutionary opportunity and ecological opportunity. In other words, there must be first an opportunity for allopatric isolation for the formation of new species, and second an opportunity to obtain a new habitat or ecological niche, vacant with regard to a competing species or group of species. With more than 16 islands in the archipelago, some being as far as 30 miles from their nearest neighboring island, the opportunity for allopatric speciation is evident. Given the isolated and oceanic position of the volcanic islands composing the archipelago, and given the relatively few birds and other terrestrial animals that occur there, one can make a good argument for an ecological opportunity for adaptive radiation. In other words, the two prerequisites for an adaptive radiation of Darwin's finches were present in the Galapagos Archipelago: isolation and vacant ecological niches.

There are many other examples of adaptive radiation. The references at the end of this chapter contain many interesting cases of adaptive radiation, such as the honey-creepers and *Drosophila* in the Hawaiian Archipelago, the progressive specialization of either the odd-toed or even-toed herbivorous mammals from the Eocene to the present, and the sequential differentiation and extinction of aerial penguins from the Miocene to the present (loss of wings).

If you take a broad view, the evolution of all the plants and animals occurring on Earth today is a result of one large adaptive radiation. This represents no more than the sequential, progressive evolution of species, during which the descending species gradually have exploited the available "non-living" environment of Earth. Parasites can even be considered to have adaptively radiated in host plant and animal species, a "living" environment, as it were.

If we glance at the historical record of the vertebrates (Fig. 4–17), we find dramatic sequential exploitation over time of the world environment. Bony fishes gave rise to the amphibians, which exploited the terrestrial environment. Reptiles took over from the amphibians as the ruling land animals and continued the exploitation of the land. The reptiles, in turn, radiated and gave rise separately to two groups of warm-blooded vertebrates: birds and mammals. The mammals, particularly in the Cenozoic, underwent a massive radiation. Primates then radiated, and one line gave rise to *Homo sapiens*. In the past,

Figure 4–17 The relative abundance through time of the vertebrates is shown by the shape of their "corridors."

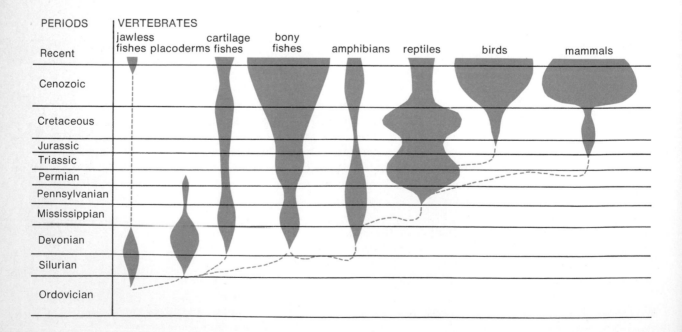

different varieties of man have adapted to different environments—to Arctic, tropical, and alpine habitats, for instance. Man is now evolving *nongenetically* as a consequence of his behavior, behavior (including intelligence and its use) that is passed on by learning and culture from one generation to the next.

Today, not by evolving to occupy new niches but by carrying his own niche with him, man is exploiting the environment to an extent never achieved by any other animal species. What more evidence is needed than our scientific exploration of the deepest ocean trenches, the Moon, and planets? Perhaps one day far in the future our species will succeed in colonizing the planets of other star systems.

QUESTIONS FOR REVIEW

1　What are the primary sources of genetic variation responsible for the evolution of natural populations?

2　Explain why adaptation occurs on the level of species and populations, but not on the level of individual organisms.

3　Why should stabilizing selection be the most common in nature (more common than either directional or disruptive selection)?

4　Explain how industrial melanism operates as an example of directional selection.

5　Cite one example of how an extrinsic isolating mechanism might lead to speciation. Cite an example of how an intrinsic isolating mechanism might lead to speciation.

6　Explain how the evolution of Darwin's finches is an example of adaptive radiation.

7　In the light of what you have learned in the present chapter, how would you answer Question 6 at the end of Chapter 2?

SELECTED READINGS

Huxley, Julian S. *Evolution: the Modern Synthesis*. New York: Harper and Row, 1943. A classic and comprehensive survey of the facts and theories pertaining to the theory of evolution by natural selection. This is one of the first neo-Darwinian reviews with particular emphasis on the morphological and systematic data relevant to our knowledge of adaptation.

Mayr, Ernst. *Animal Species and Evolution*. Cambridge, Mass.: The Belknap Press of Harvard University Press, 1963. A monumental work. This is the most comprehensive and detailed account of isolation, genetics, and ecology of speciation in animals published in the 20th century. The last chapter on the evolution of man is particularly recommended.

Simpson, George Gaylord. *The Major Features of Evolution*. New York: Columbia University Press, 1953. The first major neo-Darwinian synthesis of the facts and theories of evolution. Evolution is considered at all levels, from populations to species to the origin of the higher taxonomic categories.

Stebbins, G. Ledyard. *Processes of Organic Evolution*. Englewood Cliffs, N.J.: Prentice-Hall, Inc., 1966. One of the better paperbacks concerned with adaptation and speciation. It is certainly the best elementary account of evolution in plants and animals.

5

ADAPTIVE DIVERSITY OF LIFE

MORPHOLOGICAL AND PHYSIOLOGICAL DIVERSITY

In the preceding chapter, we spoke of the diversity of plant and animal life on Earth as the result of a sequential, progressive evolution of species. About 1,200,000 species of animals and nearly 500,000 species of plants have been described by biologists, and each year another 15,000 new species are added.

The remarkable diversity of these species—ranging from certain aquatic bacteria that thrive at temperatures above the boiling point, to massive sea-going mammals, to plants that survive in a constantly below zero environment—is a reminder that in the course of evolution life has invaded nearly every habitat available to it. As Darwin observed,

> We may well affirm that every part of the world is habitable! Whether lakes of brine, or those underground ones hidden beneath volcanic mountains, or warm mineral springs, or the wide expanse and depths of the ocean, or the upper regions of the atmosphere, and even the surface of perpetual snow—all support living things.

The types of adaptations that have evolved, and that account for the existence of almost two million species on Earth, may be **morphological** or structural, **physiological** or functional, or **behavioral** (Fig. 5–1). By morphological, we refer to such genetically controlled features of an organism as size, symmetry, shape, coloration, and composition and placement of the skeleton (Figs. 5–2 and 5–3).

We have already seen how the shape of a finch's beak can be adaptive to a particular habitat. Each one of Darwin's finches has a specialized bill that evolved from a generalized form, exploiting a different food source and a different environment. Similarly, the enormous size of the blue whale, the shell (exoskeleton) of a lobster or snail, the protective coloration of a bobwhite, the spherical shape of an ameba, and the jaws of a predatory jaguar have evolved as morphological adaptations ensuring survival of the species. If the environment remains fairly constant—as in the case of sea-dwelling animals—the physical form of an organism may also remain fairly constant over millions of years. The indomitable horseshoe crab is one such example. On the other hand, if the environment changes rapidly—recall the industrial melanism in the previous chapter—the adaptations of form that had been so nicely in harmony with the environment will be tested suddenly through natural selection. As we have seen, it is genetic variation within the population that allows

Figure 5–1 Egrets and herons, although closely related, show remarkable variation in the way they capture their food. Here a snowy egret simply stands and waits, a common method of foraging. (OMIKRON)

NATURE'S ENDLESS VARIETY

Figure 5–2 Adaptive diversity exists on many levels, the most obvious being diversity in physical form, here represented by six widely differing organisms: A, whale; B, armadillo; C, talons of an owl; D, snapping turtle; E, crab; and F, walrus. What physical features of these organisms appear to be highly adaptive, having been selected for in the organism's evolutionary past?

A

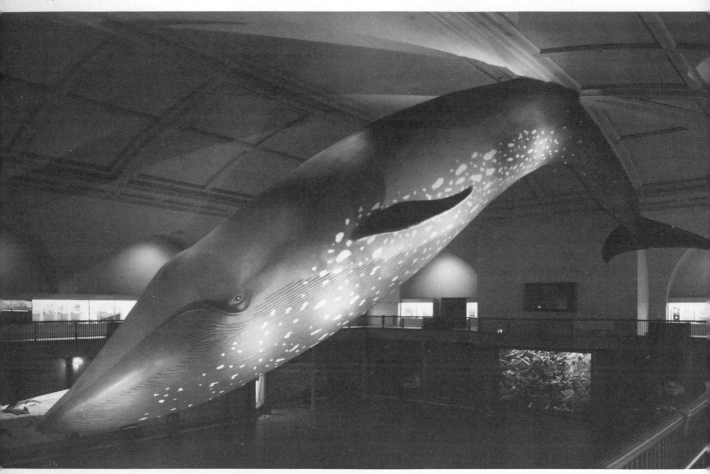

B

C

OMIKRON

D

E

F

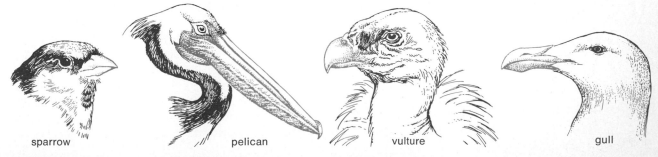

sparrow   pelican   vulture   gull

Figure 5–3   The diversity in beak structure among birds reflects a diversity of function (feeding habit).

97

the population to adapt to a new set of environmental pressures. The form that survives, such as the dark form of *B. betularia* in polluted forests, is the one best adapted to the changed environment.

Physiological diversity

Adaptation may also be functional or physiological. By physiological, we refer to such regulatory and supportive activities of an organism as temperature control, conservation of water, control of metabolic rate, hormonal balance, gas exchange, and internal transport. The fact that life has invaded every imaginable habitat—from Equator to poles and from desert to sea bottom—implies wide adaptive variation on the physiological level. Yet in spite of its ubiquity, life tends to avoid extremes and to cluster comfortably where conditions are about midway between extremes in temperature, pressure, and moisture.

Figure 5–4 Adaptations of form and function in this "gigante" cactus of El Salvador include a tough, waxy cuticle that reduces water loss by evaporation, and needle-like leaves that reduce water loss by transpiration. The small black objects are seeds being released by the open fruiting body.

MOISTURE: Plant and animal cells are unable to live without water, which they need as a medium for chemical reactions. Too much water, like too little, can be disastrous. Various organisms have evolved physiological adaptations that enable them to maintain a more or less steady state of water supply. The fleshy stem of cactus plants serves as an organ specialized for water storage so that the plant meets its water needs during times of drought. The thin spine-like leaf of cactus plants is another adaptation that reduces water loss through excess transpiration, as is a waxy cuticle coating that reduces water loss through evaporation (Fig. 5-4). The leaves of the creosote bush are similarly protected against water loss. Growth inhibitors present on the coats of certain desert plant seeds must be washed away by vigorous washing before the seed will germinate. Mild washing by a gentle rain is not enough to remove the inhibitor, thus preventing the seed from germinating at a time when there would not be enough water available to maintain the seedling.

Kangaroo rats have a number of physiological adaptations that permit them to thrive in the desert environment. For example, they have solved the water problem by being remarkably conservative. Their entire water needs are met by water released through the digestion of the food they eat (called "metabolic water"). Further, their kidneys do not require large volumes of water to wash away nitrogenous wastes in the form of ammonia, which is toxic. The kangaroo rat's urine is so concentrated and so free of water that it solidifies moments after it is excreted. Unable to regulate water loss so economically, a man soon dies of desiccation when lost in the desert and deprived of drinking water.

Most terrestrial insects, like many plants, have an impermeable cuticle a few micrometers thick that minimizes water loss. In addition, the **spiracles** (air passageways for breathing that lead from the body to the external environment) of most insects are fitted with tiny valves that open only during respiration. Without such a physiological adaptation, water loss through the tracheal system would be increased manyfold.

Earlier we said that an excess of water in the body can be as disastrous as too little water. Adult members of the mosquito genus *Aedes* have an ingenious physiological adaptation that guards against internal drowning. From time to time adult males and females drink water, although metabolic water serves their needs most of the time. When they do drink, the water does not go directly to their mid-gut, where digestion takes place. If it did, absorption of water into their circulatory system would take place so rapidly that blood dilution would prove fatal. So instead of going directly to the mid-gut, water is diverted to two cuticle-lined storage tanks that are part of the foregut. From there it is delivered gradually to the mid-gut on demand, with the result that there is no flooding. Interestingly enough, when the female takes her blood meal, the blood taken up is not diverted, but goes directly to the mid-gut. Apparently, she has some mechanism for distinguishing the quality of various liquids she takes in, diverting some to the storage tanks but delivering others directly to the mid-gut.

TEMPERATURE: Among all living organisms, only mammals and birds are **homeotherms** (meaning "same temperature"), or warm-blooded. All other animals are cold-blooded, or **poikilotherms** (meaning "variable temperature"), the temperature of their internal environment tending to vary according to temperature fluctuations of the external environment. Various physiological adaptations enable plant and animal organisms alike to tolerate temperature extremes. Extremes in air temperature range over 150 Celsius degrees—from about the 60°C of tropical deserts to about −90°C found in Antarctica.

Hibernation in some animals and dormancy in certain other animals and in some plants are physiological adaptations enabling the organisms to tolerate extreme cold or drought conditions (Fig. 7–19). Certain plants, for example, have growth inhibitors that prevent the plant from breaking dormancy, or that prevent a seed from germinating, until it has been subjected to a sufficiently long period of cold. With the passage of a sufficiently long cold period the growth inhibitor is destroyed. It is not difficult to understand how this adaptation is advantageous to the plant. An unseasonably warm period might occur in February or early March in the Northern Hemisphere. If the plant responded by germinating or breaking dormancy, it might fail to survive during resumption of the cold period.

Certain **thermophilic** (meaning "heat-loving") bacteria thrive at temperatures only eight Celsius degrees below the boiling point. Several species of algae abound in hot springs where the water temperature is 70°C. Physiological adaptations enable other species of algae to thrive on the surface of snow, turning it red in many parts of the world. Certain bacteria and fungi have been known to grow normally at 12 Celsius degrees *below* the freezing point, and others at 4 Celsius degrees *above* the boiling point.

In a number of instances, man has shown ability to undergo physiological change in response to extreme environmental conditions. The adaptedness of Eskimos to the harsh climate of the Arctic, and of the Fuegians to the southern tip of South America as observed by Darwin, demonstrate various ways a species may respond to specific environmental conditions. Many of the adaptations are physiological—for example, a higher basal metabolic rate than people living in temperate climates have, which gives an Eskimo the advantage of being able to generate more heat, and a higher rate of blood flow to the fingers and other extremities.

Figure 5–5 This photograph, taken at a depth of 5,282 meters, shows the track of some unknown marine animal.

Several populations of Peruvian Indians live in villages at altitudes of 4,650 to 5,580 meters in the Andes. Visitors to the villages complain of blurred vision, faintness, shortness of breath, and headache. At an altitude of 5,580 meters the atmospheric pressure is only 380 mm Hg (7.34 pounds per square inch), or half the value found at sea level. Since the partial pressure of oxygen in the lungs is reduced, people accustomed to sea-level pressure suffer **hypoxia**, or oxygen deprivation. The Peruvian Indians have largely overcome such physiological problems. Over centuries of living at high altitudes these mountain people have developed certain adaptations to the lower atmospheric pressure. They have larger chests, considerably greater lung capacities, and more capillaries in the oxygen-absorbing tissues of their lungs. Also, their hearts reportedly are 20% larger than those of people living at sea level, and they have about two more quarts of blood. Living at high altitudes has, however, made these people particularly susceptible to respiratory diseases common at sea level.

Temperature, moisture, and atmospheric pressure are only three of many abiotic environmental factors that have given rise to physiological diversity. Not long ago biologists frowned on the idea that living organisms could exist on the deep-sea floor, but in recent years several forms of animal life have been discovered there (Fig. 5–5). Physiological and morphological adaptations enable such organisms to survive in a world of perpetual darkness and withstand 1,400 times the pressure at the sea's surface. At a depth of 10,000 meters an organism must be able to endure pressures exceeding one ton per square inch of body surface. Still other organisms have adapted to an atmosphere totally lacking in molecular oxygen, to the extent that a trace of oxygen is toxic to the organism. The bacterium that produces botulism (acute food poisoning) is one such example.

BEHAVIORAL DIVERSITY

Before we take up behavioral adaptations, let's look at one organism, a termite, that offers an excellent example of how morphological, physiological, and behavioral adaptations interact.

Although termites eat wood, their digestive systems are incapable of digesting cellulose, the main ingredient of wood. Some termites rely on bacteria living in their gut to digest cellulose and convert it into a product that the termite can process and assimilate and from which it derives nutritional benefits. Like other insects, termites shed their skin from time to time in the process of growth. Similarly, lobsters, crayfish, shrimp, and other crustaceans shed their exoskeletons from time to time as they grow. When a termite sheds its skin (a morphological or structural adaptation), the hindgut—and wood-digesting bacteria along with it—is also shed (a physiological or functional adaptation). The termite regains its "digestive system" by eating its shed skin (a behavioral adaptation)! A behavioral adaptation also provides a newly hatched, "uncontaminated" termite with the bacteria it needs and lacks at birth. The young termite simply licks the anus of a nearby adult termite.

An organism *behaves* when it responds to some change in the external environment (for example shivering as a result of the cold), or to some change

in the organism's own internal environment (hormonal activity, for instance, that induces ovulation in the female of many species). Behavior, then, can be regarded as an organism's ability to make responses. The response may involve action or temporary inactivity: An animal remaining inactive and hidden on the approach of a predator is "behaving" every bit as much as the animal on the prowl. If the responses of an animal tend to be "correct"—because they have been selected for during the species' evolution and have proven useful— the organism survives and transmits the behavior to its offspring. If the responses tend to be incorrect—a wrong signal cue in a sequence of courtship display, for example—the organism may survive but does not contribute its "defective" gene(s) to the gene pool.

A basic assumption of most ethologists when they observe and record an organism's behavior is that the behavior pattern is the result of a series of evolutionary changes that have perfected and refined the behavior. However, some behavior patterns than animals perform seem so minor that how they increase the adaptedness of the species is not immediately obvious. A good example of such behavior was studied by Tinbergen and his colleagues. The black-headed gull (Fig. 5–6), which nests on the ground, invariably moves the shells from the nest an hour or so after the chicks have emerged. This seemingly unimportant bit of behavior is, however, highly adaptive. Tinbergen was able to show that predators on gull eggs use the presence of cracked pieces of eggshell as a cue to look for young chicks or unbroken eggs nearby. Removing this cue from the vicinity of the camouflaged, unhatched eggs increases the probability that they will not be seized by a predator.

If the environment of a species changes, natural selection begins to mold new adaptations to the altered conditions. In animals with long lifetimes, such as large mammals, natural selection proceeds slowly. In long-lived species, however, natural selection is greatly aided by behavioral adaptations to a changing environment. Certain behaviors can be learned and may increase an animal's chances of survival; morphological and physiological adaptations cannot be so acquired.

The behavior of other species of animals is coupled with and controlled in part by morphological adaptations. For instance, visual displays play an important role in the courtship behaviors of some species of fish (sticklebacks, for example), but we would hardly expect to find such a reliance on vision in the courtship behavior of blind cave fish. Both morphology and behavior can be considered as a part of the phenotype of an organism. In fact, studies of behavior have revealed that what was thought to be one species turned out to be two or three.

Morphology and behavior develop together during the evolution of a species. The similarities and differences between kittiwakes (a species of gull), which nest on cliff faces, and other gulls that nest on land are discussed in detail in Chapter 9. Kittiwakes also differ from other gulls in having a bright orange mouth interior, an adaptation they use extensively in a series of threat postures. In all these displays the mouth is opened widely. The evolution of such a morphological character (a bright orange mouth) and a specific set of threat postures using the morphological character apparently are a response to a specific environmental challenge—cliff nesting. The limited horizontal space on cliff ledges severely restricts the amount of movement possible as part of the display. The species has adapted to these conditions by integrating alterations in both its morphology and its behavior.

Adaptations in plants

Although we sometimes tend to think that only higher animals "behave," single-celled organisms (the protozoans) exhibit numerous behaviors. *Euglena*, a single-celled photosynthesizing organism (claimed as an animal by zoologists), has a red spot that is sensitive to light. *Euglena* can respond to a light stimulus by moving toward it or away from it. Clearly this response is a behavioral adaptation enabling the organism to function photosynthetically at an optimum level. In a sense, all living cells of multicellular organisms can be regarded as behaving as they continually exchange materials with the external environment in the process of maintaining a more or less steady chemical state.

Multicellular plants, although lacking a nervous system and incapable of locomotion, also exhibit a number of behavioral adaptations. A plant's response to light (phototropism), its response to gravity (geotropism), and the related function of auxin were mentioned in Chapter 2. Certain plants, among them some that supplement their nutritional needs by functioning as heterotrophs, exhibit even more complex behavior. Bladderworts, found in freshwater ponds, trap and feed on water fleas and mosquito and other insect larvae (Fig. 5–7). The plant consists of a main stem with branches supporting thin leaves, so the plant functions photosynthetically. Attached to the branches are tiny traps shaped like a bladder, around the opening of which are hairs that serve to guide an approaching insect toward the mouth of the trap. The trap of one species of bladderwort has a small door with trigger hairs. If an investigating insect is unfortunate enough to brush the trigger hairs, the door snaps open inwardly, drawing in water and the insect. One estimate of the plant's response time is only a thirty-fifth of a second from the time the trap door opens until it snaps shut again. Enzymes break down the trapped insect's soft parts, which once in solution are absorbed by the plant. The Venus's-flytrap is another plant that functions both as autotroph and heterotroph.

How can we account for such adaptations in certain plants? Since the plants are able to carry out photosynthesis, why do they seem to need a supplementary diet of animal tissue? The plants have been grown under laboratory conditions in their native soil and water. Deprived of insect food, they grow and produce flowers and seeds quite normally, so insects are not essential to their diet. However, when the plants are given a supplementary diet of insects, they grow better. They also grow better when deprived of insects but when nitrogen is added to the soil in which they grow. Habitats where such plants occur tend to be relatively poor in certain minerals required by the plants; furthermore, the root systems of such plants appear to be less well developed than other plants for taking up minerals from the soil. It would appear that the leaves of such plants have taken on part of the function of the roots, an adaptation enabling the plants to thrive in a mineral-deficient environment.

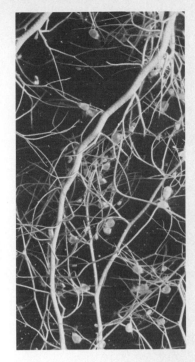

Figure 5–7 The bladderwort, an insectivorous plant, functions partly as a heterotroph by engulfing insects, thus supplementing its nutritional needs.

Tracing the evolution of behavior

One of the most difficult problems in behavior study is determining the evolutionary history of a particular behavior pattern. Behavior does not become fossilized, at least not in the usual way; hence historical documentation of behavior is relatively hard to obtain. Since morphology and behavior often go hand in hand, however, biologists can gain a fair amount of information about the behavior of fossil forms from a study of footprints, horns and antlers, and the like. Fossil *Gopherus* (tortoise) males had a "battering ram" on their shell just as do males of living species, and no doubt they used them in the same way in male–male combat and to stimulate females during courtship. In addition, comparison with closely related species affords a wealth of indirect evidence that at least points the way to the evolution of a particular behavior.

The first task is to establish that several species exhibiting a similar behavior are more or less related. Once such a relationship has been established, the next task is to describe the similarities and differences in the behavior from species to species. Then the biologist must try to determine the evolutionary sequence of the behavior. If the behavior is genetically determined, he can form hypotheses about which species are older and which more recent. In certain cases an arrangement of the behavior from the simplest to the most complex (or vice versa) may suggest the evolutionary chronology. Figure 5–8 will serve as an example. The question we want answered is how did the elaborate courtship behavior of the carnivorous balloon fly shown in Stage F of the diagram evolve, in which the male presents the female (who is usually cannibalistic) with an empty silken balloon? While she is occupied with the balloon, the male mates with her. We can imagine the behavior evolving something like this: (A) An empty-handed male attempting to mate may be attacked by the female and is less likely to leave offspring. (B) The male of a related species presents his prospective mate with a food gift, which diverts her and makes mating more likely. (C) The male of another species wraps silken strands around the food gift. (D) The male of another species presents his food gift wrapped within a silken balloon which further diverts her attack. (E) At this stage the package (balloon) has become more important than the food inside. (F) In the last (most recent) stage, the male presents the female with an empty balloon, which engages her interest while he mates with her.

CATEGORIES OF BEHAVIOR

Science always begins with a description of phenomena that later are subject to experimental analysis. Zoologists have been describing the kinds of animals found on our planet at least since the time of Aristotle, and they continue to do so today. The study of behavior also begins with a description of the behavior of an organism. The cataloging of all the behavioral patterns of a species results in an **ethogram**, which is an inventory of its behaviors. However, as with the cataloging of books in a library, several systems have been proposed. If behaviors are classed together because they are all affected by, or are responses to, a single underlying stimulus, the system of classification is said to be causal. For example, many behaviors may be a result of the stimulus hunger or of the presence of sex hormones in the circulatory system. These behaviors would be classed respectively as food getting–eating behaviors and as sexual behaviors. Behaviors may also be classified according to their evolutionary source, or they may be classified as learned or inherited.

Figure 5–8 Sometimes we can trace the possible evolution of a particular behavior by studying the behavior in several closely related species. The evolution of courtship behavior of the balloon fly is illustrated here. (AFTER A. J. MEYERRIECKS)

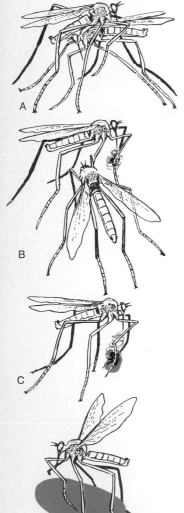

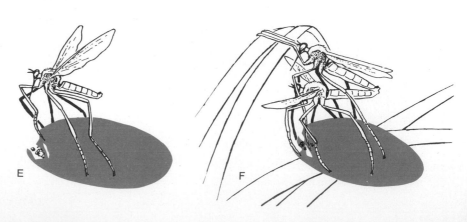

A MATTER OF TERMS

Types of adaptive behavior

John Paul Scott has broken behavior down into nine categories of function, which are summarized here: **Eating behavior** ("ingestive behavior," as Scott terms it) consists of the gathering and intake of food for nourishment and includes hunting and killing prey. Examples of **shelter-seeking behavior** include the roosting of birds in locations and arrangements for optimal protection, the construction of lodges by beavers, the selection of and retreat to dens by bears for dormancy and by certain small mammals, amphibians, and reptiles for hibernation. **Agonistic behavior** includes the aggressive actions between two animals involved in a territorial dispute or any adaptation involving any hostile encounters between animals. **Sexual behavior** (which also may be termed **reproductive** behavior) includes all those behaviors from seeking a mate up to and including courtship and copulation. **Care-giving behavior** ("epimeletic behavior") includes all those parental behaviors that result in care of the young from the time of egg laying (in the case of some species) to the time the offspring are able to fend for themselves. This type behavior is also applied to ants and bees. **Care-soliciting behavior** ("et-epimeletic behavior") includes all those behaviors of offspring indicating to the parents that the young are in need or want of something. The cheeping of nestlings for food and the cry of a human infant because of pain or discomfort or hunger are examples. Care-soliciting behavior in some species occurs not only between offspring and adult, but also between one adult and another. **Eliminative behavior** includes the different ways in which various species keep their areas clear of feces and urine. Young birds of certain species deliver their feces and urine in pellets enclosed by a membrane, which the parents can then lift out of the nest. Dogs characteristically deposit their feces away from their own home territories; cats bury theirs. Monkeys are notoriously hard to house-break because eliminative behavior is practically zero if you happen to be adapted to living in a tree. The use of feces and urine as territorial markers is common among many species of mammals. **Mutual-mimicking behavior** ("allelomimetic behavior") is characterized by geese in making their V-formation flights, by schooling fish, and by buffalo and certain other grazing animals, among whom each individual tends to do what other members of the group are doing. During his study of mountain gorillas in Africa, George Schaller observed that the individuals making up a gorilla group tended to nap at the same time, feed at the same time, and bed down for the night and get up in the morning at the same time. **Investigative behavior** is exhibited by many animals on being placed in a strange environment. A rat sniffs out its new surroundings when first placed in a cage or moved from one cage to another. This exploratory behavior is also shown by dogs, cats, and small boys. Any kind of sensory investigation of the environment, according to Scott, qualifies as investigative behavior.

Most of the categories of behavior mentioned in the box involve two or more individuals of the species. Interactions of this sort lead us to a larger category of behavior called **social behavior**. Much of the behavior of most animals occurs in a social context. Now that you have seen a number of ways behavior can be categorized, let's turn to several specific examples of behavioral adaptations.

HOW TO AVOID BEING EATEN

No animal species has evolved a foolproof way to avoid being eaten, either by predators or parasites. Even the largest mammals such as elephants and whales are preyed upon by man and by parasites. The tendency toward an ecological balance in nature dictates that there be a rough, though fluctuating, balance between the numbers of predator and prey individuals: Some prey individuals are eaten while others survive, some predators are well nourished while others die of hunger. Therefore, the relation between a predator species and its prey species has the aspect of a game that has been played for millions of years and in which both parties have repeatedly evolved small improvements in their equipment and tactics. In the course of time, some of these "games" have become very subtle.

Evasive action

Escape is probably the oldest and most general way of avoiding being eaten. Speed and agility are important to a rabbit if it is to out-maneuver the predator's strike or pursuit. These qualities, in turn, depend on sense organs capable of detecting the predator when or before it springs from ambush. The well-developed senses of smell, vision, and hearing and the fleetness of some rodents and antelope species are examples of these forms of protection. Speed in communication in the prey's nervous system is also of prime importance since a fraction of a second may separate "the quick from the dead." This means that often the neural circuits concerned with evasion have become direct and simple. A minimum of information is all that is needed and there is no time for decision-making.

A classic battle of milliseconds is played by the cold-blooded praying mantis and its prey, which are other insects. The mantis remains in ambush motionless on a plant stem and strikes with its pincer-like front legs when an insect alights within reach. An interval of 50 to 70 milliseconds elapses from the instant the mantis begins its strike and gives its position away until it hits the target. If we measure the time taken by a fly to begin flying or a cockroach to begin running after it has detected some slight movement nearby, the interval also turns out to be between 50 and 70 milliseconds. Natural selection has pared the response times of both parties to a minimum of less than 0.1 second, which is very similar to the startle response times of a wide variety of animals, including man. In many animals, the continuous selection pressure that has bettered response time has led to the evolution of special fast-conducting giant nerve cells.

Examples of evasive action are numerous. Flocks of starlings tend to get strung out when in flight, and the peregrine falcon tends to go after the stragglers. As a falcon dives for the kill, the starlings suddenly bunch up into a compact mass and make twisting movements as a group to left and right, an action that appears to deter the falcon. Similar evasive behavior has been observed in cedar waxwings in response to the attacks of a Cooper's hawk. When a bald eagle approaches a flock of coots, the coots very quickly gather into a huge mass of birds on the water, then they point their bills at the eagle and also flap their wings and beat the water. The whole effect, which deters the eagle from its attack, is that of a giant black wheel in the water with thousands of coots milling and thrashing about in the wheel.

Figure 5–9 Cryptic behavior in the Indian leaf butterfly *Kallima inachis*, whose wing undersurfaces are a highly realistic representation of the mid-rib and branch veins of a purplish-brown leaf.

Cryptic behavior

Remaining hidden is probably the second most common way of avoiding being eaten. It is the antithesis of evasive behavior in that it consists of moving as little as possible. When danger threatens, the potential prey ducks and freezes, aided in its concealment by patterns or colors that break its outlines (Fig. 5–9) and blend its appearance into the surroundings. This behavior is common in the young of a great many birds and mammals, which frequently have dappled or camouflage patterns in their fur or feathers. Some fish, lizards, and crustaceans can also change their body coloration on short notice so that it blends with the background on which they happen to be. These specialized structural characteristics must be accompanied by appropriate behavior, which usually is complete immobility. Many animals, like the puff adder and opossum, also simulate being dead.

Crypsis takes the most elaborate forms in insects (see color section facing page 112). The forewings of many nocturnal moths commonly mimic the texture of the tree trunks where they rest during the day, and this may include greenish patterns that simulate the algal growths commonly found on tree bark. Other moths mimic bird excreta, a product not particularly attractive to potential predators.

Startle displays

Many insects combine cryptic behavior with startle displays. When at rest some moths fold their dully mottled forewings over a brightly colored pair of hindwings. When disturbed as they sit on a tree trunk, they suddenly raise the forewings and expose red or varicolored hindwings. These bright colors often are embellished or replaced by "eye spots" (Fig. 1–7). The eye spots range all the way from black dots to large and incredibly perfect representations of the vertebrate eye, some even including a white fleck indicating the highlight or reflection from the cornea. When the moth is poked, it suddenly flashes a pair of owl-like eyes at the aggressor. This defense seems to be successful since eye displays have evolved in many different insect groups. Many cryptically colored caterpillars display eye spots when disturbed. Some insects have gone overboard and display not merely a single pair of eyes but a dozen or more.

Biologists have long been enchanted by the detailed perfection of line and color found in some of these eye mimics, and there has been much speculation about the selective pressure that must have caused them to evolve to this level, and how effective they may have been when at a much more rudimentary stage of evolution. Since the spots are flashed abruptly at an intruder, there seems little doubt about their protective value. David Blest has answered some of these questions. He raised small insectivorous birds in captivity on a diet of mealworms. Behind the dish of mealworms was a screen on which patterns could be projected. When natural eye mimics or even crude figures consisting merely of concentric circles were suddenly displayed on the screen just as a bird was about to take a mealworm, the bird hesitated and drew back. This happened even though the bird had been hand-raised and had never been confronted with the face of a natural predator. This suggests that in nature the prey either would not be touched or would have at least a split-second chance to escape while the predator hesitated. Startle displays can be acoustic as well as visual. Many palatable insects make hissing noises when disturbed. These sounds are commonly produced by rubbing parts of the body together or by forcefully expelling air through the spiracles.

Warning displays

Many animals are marked distinctively—brightly or vividly colored. Unlike startle displays, warning displays are on view at all times. Sometimes such markings function for species recognition and courtship, but often they serve as a warning of unpleasant qualities to prospective predators. Examples of such warning, or **aposematic**, displays include the distinctive markings of skunks, the bright colors laid out in very simple, contrasting patterns of certain poisonous reptiles, and the black and yellow banding on the abdomens of common wasps. Many caterpillars and day-flying butterflies are also decked out in vivid and contrasting patches and bands of color, commonly red, black, and yellow. Warning coloration is associated, directly or indirectly, with an unpalatable or poisonous quality such as a bite or sting, a poisonous secretion, or a nauseating taste. An experienced vertebrate predator will usually reject prey having such markings. Lincoln and Jane Brower have shown that a naive jay or toad rapidly learns to reject vividly colored food when the food is found to be distasteful on first experience. They also demonstrated that certain colored butterflies owe their unpalatability to retention of certain nauseating and toxic substances ingested from the larval food plant by their caterpillars.

Like startle displays, warning displays can be auditory in nature. Nocturnal bats locate and track their flying insect prey in darkness by means of **echolocation**—emitting sound pulses and then locating an object by interpreting the echo of the sound rebounding from the object. Some moth species belonging to the family Arctiidae (their caterpillars are the familiar woolly bears) make a series of high-pitched clicks as soon as they detect the sound pulses made by an approaching bat. D. Covalt-Dunning has shown that this acoustic signal apparently serves to warn the bat that the prey it is tracking is highly distasteful. Bats break off their attack on hearing the clicks and cannot be persuaded to eat this species, dead or alive. Closely related to warning behavior is mimicry, the subject of the photo essay facing page 112.

Figure 5-10 This young pelican and its parent exhibit a feeding behavior called the "reverse gape," during which the young sticks its head inside the parent's mouth to feed.

FEEDING BEHAVIOR

Eating behavior, like behavior enabling an organism to avoid being eaten, offers many examples of adaptive diversity. Cuttlefish feed on shrimp, but to do so they must first locate their prey, which spend much of their time hidden just beneath the sediments of the sea floor. An essential part of the cuttlefish's feeding behavior as it cruises along just above the bottom is its periodic ejection of a jet of water. The jet disturbs the top layer of sand or other sediments and from time to time exposes a shrimp. The shrimp responds by wiggling in an attempt to cover itself again, an action that attracts the attention of the cuttlefish, which immediately projects tentacles and snatches up the shrimp. Here is a case of an adaptation for defense (the shrimp's rapid motion to re-conceal itself) seemingly working disadvantageously. The fact is that the cuttlefish is not the only animal preying on shrimp—and apparently not the most successful of their predators—so we can conclude that the scurrying action of the shrimp to regain cover works to its advantage most of the time. The water-jet adaptation of the cuttlefish is equally advantageous.

If we examine patterns of feeding behavior in nestling birds, we find examples of care-giving behavior as well. The nestlings of American robins, for example, gape and the parent bird responds (the bright coloring of the interior of the nestlings' mouth seems to serve as a stimulus for the parent) by stuffing food into the nestling's mouth. The young of certain other birds, brown pelicans, for instance, exhibit a reverse gape, the young sticking its head inside the mouth of the parent (Fig. 5-10). Pigeons feed their young by pumping food into the throat of the young in response to their gaping. The herring gull chick is stimulated to peck at a red spot on the parent's bill, and this pecking stimulates the parent to regurgitate food for the chick (Fig. 5-11). In other species, such as herons, the young stimulate the adult by grasping the base of

Figure 5-11 The colored spot (actually red) on the bill of the herring gull is pecked at by the chick, a stimulus that causes the parent to regurgitate food, which is then eaten by the chick.

the parent's bill, an act that stimulates the parent to regurgitate food into the mouth of the young.

Foraging by herons

Feeding among adult herons provides several examples of behavioral adaptations. U.S. Route 1 in Florida extends in an arc from Homestead on the mainland to Key West about 100 miles out in Florida Bay and the Gulf of Mexico. This road crosses numerous mangrove-covered islands—the famous Florida Keys—as well as the brilliantly colored waters of the bay and gulf. If you take a boat to one of the keys out in the shallows of Florida Bay away from the noise and bustle of the main highway, you will travel past turtle-grass-covered flats or shoals that extend from one key to the next, or reach from the edge of a key well out into the waters of the bay. Drop anchor near such a flat and you will soon be witness to a fine example of evolutionary ecology.

The actors in this drama are herons and egrets, those long-legged, long-necked, fish-eating, wading birds. There are about 60 different species of these waders in the family Ardeidae, the heron, egret, and bittern family. Of this number, 13 kinds are found in Florida, and on a good day in the Florida Bay area you may see upward of nine species foraging on the same flat. Herons are primarily fish eaters, and the long legs and long necks are clearly structural adaptations for wading in water and reaching out to seize their aquatic prey. Additionally, most herons and egrets have a long dagger-like bill, another adaptation used for seizing food. Most of us have seen one kind of heron or another, and perhaps we know that these birds do in fact feed on fish; few realize, how-

ever, that herons and egrets show a remarkable diversity in how they go about capturing their fish food (Fig. 5–12).

All herons, so far as we know, have a basic method of foraging, a behavior pattern called "stand and wait." The heron or egret does just that—stands and waits in the water for some unsuspecting minnow to swim by and be promptly seized, held momentarily between the tips of the bird's long bill, and tossed down its gullet. This was probably the fundamental foraging stance from which the various modifications evolved as we see them today. An obvious first modification would be simply to wade or walk about slowly in search of suitable prey, especially if the motionless posture failed. Again, so far as we can tell, all heron and egret species show this first evolutionary change in their foraging repertoires. Some heron species, such as the great white heron, wade slowly in rather deep water in their search for food; others, such as the small green heron, are restricted in their wading to rather shallow water since their legs are relatively small.

When using this foraging technique, the heron wades slowly until it sees its prey, then it stops and remains motionless until its quarry is within striking range. With a very rapid forward and downward strike of the neck and bill, assisted by some modifications of the neck vertebrae, the heron seizes its food scissor-fashion between the tips of its long bill. A variant of this method is called "head-tilting." Here, the wading heron angles its head and neck to one side, at times to an extreme degree. This variation is most often seen on days when there is much surface glare on the water. Perhaps by moving its head and neck in this way, the foraging bird can see its victim better.

A major evolutionary change came when herons began to pursue their prey.

Figure 5–12 Diversity in foraging among egrets and herons is shown here. At far left is a yellow-billed egret on a cape buffalo's back. The egret captures insects flushed into view by the buffalo's grazing movements. The reddish egret's raised wings cast a shadow into which fish swim for "cover" when disturbed by the bird's wading, and become easy prey. At near left a Louisiana heron walks slowly until it spots prey and then, at right, prepares to strike.

Much of this behavior can be categorized as "disturb-and-chase" foraging. When behaving in this way, the forager actively disturbs the habitat of its food organisms; then, when the prey has revealed itself, the heron actively chases it. Some remarkable kinds of behavior are shown by different species when using this technique. For example, the Louisiana heron runs rapidly through the shallows with one or both wings extended fully to the side. Undoubtedly the shadow cast on the water disturbs the heron's prey into revealing themselves, at which time the heron suddenly stops and strikes. At times a foraging Louisiana heron will pirouette in place with one wing raised; as with head-tilting, the bird seems to use this technique when there is surface glare because it tucks its head under the raised wing as it whirls about.

The reddish egret is the most active forager of all the heron species found on the Florida Bay turtle-grass flats. The bird dashes through the shallows, flicking first one wing and then the other, whirls about, stops, changes direction, then wing flicks once more. Suddenly it stops with both wings widespread then slowly forms a canopy over its head with the extended wings. Small fishes disturbed by the egret's erratic running through the water are duped into entering the false refuge under the wings of the egret. As soon as a number of fish have entered the shadows cast by the bird's wings, the egret strikes. An African species, the black heron, takes such "canopy feeding" one step further. A foraging individual of this species forms a canopy with its wings just as the reddish egret does, but the African form actually places the tips of its flight feathers into the shallow water.

During foraging, the cattle egret takes advantage of another animal's activities. It regularly associates with a variety of animals—in particular hoofed mammals—that act as "beaters" for the egrets since this heron species feeds largely on the insects disturbed by the grazing movements of the egret's associate. However, cattle egrets can and do feed in typical heron fashion, even though they are most famous for their association with cattle, rhinos, and the like. At times, cattle egrets act as their own beaters when they engage in "leap-frog feeding," a most interesting kind of behavior in which a large flock of cattle egrets begins to spread out over some suitable pasture or grassland. The birds at the rear of the group fly up and over the foragers in front of them, and as they land at the front they stir up insects, which are quickly seized by the nearest birds. In this way, the birds move across the area helping each other as they forage. Recent studies have shown, however, that cattle egret foraging efficiency is at its highest when they associate with some hoofed mammal, lowest when they forage by themselves.

Since herons and egrets are primarily fish-eaters, these diverse patterns of behavior have evolved with a resulting reduction in competition for food among the different species occupying the same niche. If all fed on the same prey, and did so by using the same technique, competition would be most keen and the number of species that could co-exist in the same habitat would be greatly reduced. Since these birds feed on different species of prey and do so with varied foraging techniques, a given habitat can support many more different kinds of herons and egrets. The evolution of diversity in foraging behavior has "permitted," so to speak, the co-existence of a large number of species foraging on the same turtle-grass flat at the same time.

text continued on page 113

MIMICRY AND CAMOUFLAGE

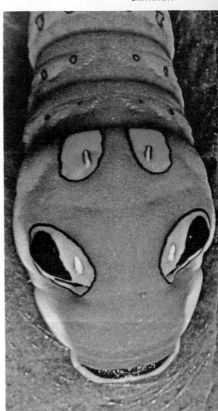

Mimicry

Among the most fascinating examples of the work of natural selection are adaptations known as mimicry and camouflage. Mimicry is defined as a close resemblance between two or more organisms that is advantageous to at least one of the species involved. If you live in the arid regions of the southwestern United States you are undoubtedly familiar with a beetle often called the stink bug. When this animal is disturbed, it stands on its head and emits a foul smelling, black secretion from glands in its abdomen. It is usually left undisturbed by small boys and other predators alike. A morphologically similar beetle which belongs to a different genus but is found in the same geographical area has adopted the "bottoms-up" behavior of the stink bug even though it possesses no defensive secretion. Predators of these beetles have apparently learned to flee from the stink bug in response to its "bottoms-up" behavior. The mimic beetle has taken advantage of the response of the predators and its morphological similarity to the stink bug through the evolution of a similar behavior pattern. Such behavioral mimicry would not have evolved in this beetle had it not been for the presence of a "real" stink bug in its territory.

False "eyes" in a number of insects are a form of mimicry, an adaptation that tends to protect an individual from predators, usually birds. Above is the caterpillar of a swallowtail butterfly displaying enormous false eyes. Its real head is small and tucked out of sight. At left are beautifully elaborate false eyes—complete with pupil "highlights"—on the rear wings of a moth.

Polymorphic females in *Papilio dardanus:* In regions such as Madagascar and Ethiopia, where distasteful models are absent, *P. dardanus* females are scarcely distinguishable from *P. dardanus* males (top). However, in many regions of tropical Africa, and well into southeast Africa, there are several unpalatable potential models. In association with such models, *P. dardanus* females will, through natural selection, evolve resemblances to as many as four such models in a single area. In this photograph three *P. dardanus* female mimics (at right) are shown in association with their models (at left). From top to bottom the models are *Niavius dominicanus, Amauris jacksonsi,* and *Bematistes poggei.*

BATESIAN MIMICRY: There are few children or adults who will attempt to disturb a wasp or yellow jacket, for we all know how painful the sting can be. Other harmless insects, many of them flies, have copied the black and yellow patterning of many wasps and derive protection from their similarity to the wasp. Another example of this sort is the bee-fly, which looks like a large bumble bee when flying. Examining it carefully, however, we find only one pair of wings—not two as is characteristic of bees.

The study of mimicry traces its beginnings to the writings of Henry W. Bates, who spent some 11 years in the forests of Brazil in the mid-19th century. Among his many other contributions to our knowledge of tropical forest life, Bates observed that some species of butterflies which were not closely related often had very similar color patterns. Such species are often very brightly colored, fly slowly, and should be easy prey for insectivorous birds. Since they are *not* attacked, Bates reasoned that they must be distasteful to birds. The similarity in color patterns between unrelated species probably allows palatable species to be protected by their similarity to unpalatable species. **Batesian mimicry** is the term applied to this phenomenon.

Some of the most remarkable and best studied examples of mimicry occur among various species of the swallow-tail butterfly in Africa and Asia. As is often the case in mimetic butterflies, only the females are mimics; the males, which are morphologically quite different, never mimic unpalatable species. The reasons for this phenomenon are not clear although a number of hypotheses have been proposed. Females of the species *Papilio memnon* have a pattern of coloration and morphology that resembles several different and unpalatable species of butterflies of the genus *Atrophanura*. Caterpillars of this genus feed on distasteful plants and as a result the adults are not preyed upon. Female *Papilio memnon* have several different morphological types or morphs, each of which mimics a different unpalatable species of *Atrophanura*.

The morphological differences are often as extreme as the presence or absence of a "tail" on the hind wings. That such examples of mimicry should occur is fascinating. That different females of the same species should mimic different unpalatable species is truly remarkable—yet understandable. A species will be a successful Batesian mimic only if the distasteful model species is more common than the mimic. If the mimic species becomes too common, predators (usually birds) will soon discover that most butterflies are edible and the advantage of the mimic will be lost.

Experimental proof that Batesian mimicry involves an association between an unpalatable model species and a palatable mimic species has been obtained by Jane and Lincoln Brower. Batesian mimic butterflies were fed to caged Florida Scrub Jays that had not had previous experience with the distasteful model. In every case the birds ate the mimetic butterflies with relish. Next the birds were presented with the model, which they strongly avoided after the first taste. After a large number of tests with the unpalatable model, the mimic butterfly was presented. It was consistently avoided by the birds. Similar tests with nearly identical results have been performed using toads as the predator.

MÜLLERIAN MIMICRY: The observation that predators on butterflies occasionally make errors and attempt to eat distasteful species led another early naturalist, Fritz Müller, to propose yet another class of mimicry now termed Müllerian mimicry. Müller reasoned that if several species of butterflies were protected by their unpalatability, it would be of mutual advantage if all such species within the same area resembled one another. If this were the case, predators would only need to learn one color pattern and/or morphological shape in order to avoid eating distasteful prey. Since the effectiveness of Müllerian mimicry requires that each predator in a given area learn the pattern to be avoided, we would not expect to find examples of sexual dimorphism and the existence of several different morphs within a prey species. This expectation is in fact borne out for most species involved in Müllerian mimicry associations.

Some of the best examples of both Batesian and Müllerian mimics are among species of coral snakes found in the New World. The conspicuous color pattern of coral snakes—red, black, yellow, or white alternating bands—

At left below is an eastern coral snake (poisonous) brightly colored with highly contrasting banding. At right is a nonpoisonous scarlet king snake, a mimic of the true coral snake.

has long been assumed to be a warning device since many coral snakes are highly poisonous. However the existence of so-called false coral snakes that are not poisonous has led herpetologists such as R. Mertens to propose that the some 75 species of two separate families which exhibit the "coral pattern" include examples of both Müllerian and Batesian mimics. Those poisonous forms which look alike are examples of Müllerian mimicry, while the non-poisonous forms are Batesian mimics.

PREDATORY MIMICRY: Some of the more bizarre and wonderful examples of the action of natural selection are revealed by various adaptations that some species use to capture their prey. Species of praying mantids are famous mimics. Many species are cryptically colored, often resembling a dried twig or part of a leaf. One Malaysian species is a bright pinkish red and when settled among the red flowers of a Malay orchid seems to blend into the plant and become yet another flower. This insect simply waits until unsuspecting flies alight to feed on the nectar of the flowers. The flies are quickly captured and eaten. The coloration of these mantids may also serve to protect them from predators such as birds and lizards.

Another example of this sort is provided by behavioral mimics of fireflies, which are really beetles belonging to the family Lampyridae. The flashing of fireflies on warm summer evenings is actually a stage in the courtship of these beetles allowing the two sexes to locate each other. The flashing patterns of

Coloration and immobility—one a morphological and the other a behavioral adaptation—provide protection against predation for the praying mantis.

various species are quite different, and often the two sexes of a single species show different patterns. It is clear that the two sexes are signaling each other. The females of one species of firefly take advantage of male fireflies of another species by mimicking the flashing pattern of their females. The deceived male signals to the mimicking female who signals back until the male alights beside her. The male is then grasped and eaten.

PARASITIC MIMICRY: The concept of mimicry also extends to associations between parasites and their hosts. Several bird species have adopted the behavior of laying their eggs in the nests of other species. These brood parasites depend upon the abilities of foster parents to hatch and raise their progeny. Cuckoo birds are the best known species to use this method of raising a family. Since the host bird species are usually able to recognize and eject from their nests eggs of a different color or pattern from their own, cuckoos have evolved egg colors and patterns which closely mimic those of their hosts. Since cuckoos usually parasitize bird species of a smaller size than themselves, they have also evolved a much smaller egg size than they would normally have or than non-parasitic species show.

The range of egg patterns and colors mimicked by various cuckoo species is remarkable, but the fact that some cuckoo species lay their eggs in the nests of several different host species having quite different eggs is astonishing. The European cuckoo, for example, parasitizes at least four species. One of these host species is a warbler whose eggs are blue-green with speckled areas of brownish-yellow. Another host species is a redstart whose eggs are light blue with no markings. Since individual females of the European cuckoo always lay similarly colored eggs, they must select the correct host species (the same one in whose nest they were raised) before depositing their egg. If an incorrect choice is made, the parasitic egg will quickly be ejected from the host nest.

MIMICRY IN PLANTS: Mimicry of other organisms is by no means restricted to animals. Plants provide some of the most extraordinary examples of this phenomenon. Many plant species are pollinated by insects who are rewarded for their task by nectar the flowers produced. Some species of orchids do not produce nectar but are nevertheless pollinated by insects. These orchid species have evolved modified flower parts which often resemble a hovering or stationary bee or wasp. This artificial bee attracts male bees that attempt to copulate with the simulated female. During the process of attempted copulation, pollen from the flower becomes attached to the deceived male bee. The bee soon flies off and often attempts to copulate with a second simulated "orchid-bee" and transfers pollen grains sticking to his body. Remarkably enough, the similarity between the artificial bee and real females extends beyond gross morphological resemblance. Male bees will not attempt copulation if the dummy female is too large or if it lacks the proper tactile stimuli provided by hairs on the flower that simulate the real female's bristles.

Among Hymenopterans (bees, wasps, and ants) some females use chemical stimuli to attract males. The orchids that rely on these species for pollination have even managed to extend their mimicry of female Hymenoptera to the

Like the European cuckoo, the American cowbird parasitizes other birds by laying its eggs in the nest of a foreign species. Six cowbird eggs have been laid in the nest of a woodthrush shown here. The woodthrush's eggs are blue.

development of chemical substances that mimic the attractive odors of real females. Indeed it may well be that these odors initially attract males to the orchids.

FISH MIMICS: While morphological and behavioral mimics are most common among insect species, they are also found among higher animals. Wolfgang Wickler has reported that some 42 species of marine fish have a unique method of obtaining food. These species act as cleaners of other species of fish. Using a rather specialized swimming motion, the cleaner fish moves over the surface of its "customer" removing attached parasites, pieces of fungus, and dead tissue. The fish which is being cleaned appears to "enjoy" the whole process and even actively cooperates with the cleaner fish. The customer remains as immobile as possible and allows the cleaner fish to swim behind its gill covers and even into its mouth to perform its task. The cleansing activities of the cleaner fish are apparently quite important to the health of their customers; such fish kept in aquaria without their cleaners develop abscesses and patches of fungus that may even cause death.

OMIKRON

Camouflage among ground-nesting birds is an extremely important morphological adaptation, an example being the near invisibility of this woodcock on its nest.

Remarkably enough, a third species of fish with an external appearance almost identical to that of the cleaner fish takes advantage of the docile behavior customer fish show when they are being cleaned. This cleaner mimic swims up to its unsuspecting "customer" and removes and eats a chunk of its fin! When the customer turns around in surprise the nonchalant cleaner mimic remains in position, apparently protected by its external appearance. The customer fish may become suspicious after some time, but the ruse works.

Camouflage

Organisms that mimic their natural background or attempt to go otherwise unobserved by mimicking common and usually inedible objects in their environment are said to be camouflaged. Nearly everyone has watched chameleons change from green to brown to match their background.

The evolutionary development of camouflage coloration in the peppered moth in England and Europe is one of the best demonstrations that natural selection is the factor responsible for camouflage (Fig. 4–9).

Another example of camouflage, this one in a mammal, is the seasonal variation in coat color of snowshoe rabbits (also called varying hares).

OMIKRON

Certain bottom-living fish, such as the flounder shown here, change color to an unusual degree in response to the color and texture of the background. The sequence of three photographs here shows a flounder against two contrasting natural backgrounds and against an artificial checkerboard background.

Some animals have achieved a really remarkable degree of coloration. Many species of flatfish are able to adjust their coloration to match the light and dark patterns of the sandy substrate where they rest. When fully camouflaged they are very difficult to spot even for a human actively searching for the fish. The cryptic coloration of preying mantids has already been discussed, but they are far from being alone as masters of camouflage among the insects. Some species of tropical Katydids have wings that closely resemble green leaves. The resemblance extends to the presence of leaf veins, notches in the margin where other insects have chewed, and other markings on the surface of the leaf. Many species of caterpillars have evolved various kinds of mimicry and camouflage. The twig caterpillar attaches itself to a real branch of a tree and then extends itself in a rigid pose. In this position the coloration of the body makes it appear to be just another dead twig attached to the tree. Most species of organisms that are subject to predation and do not have a ready and potent means of defense have evolved protective coloration of one sort or another. That this statement by no means applies to all species is demonstrated by the examples of Batesian mimicry discussed earlier. The apparent contradiction of a defenseless organism adopting a bright and dazzling color pattern to attract attention to itself is just another example of the "creativity" of natural selection.

REPRODUCTIVE BEHAVIOR

In most groups of animals, successful reproduction depends on the precise integration of behavioral and physiological processes. Reproductive behavior is an adaptation that ensures that fertilization takes place and that the zygote formed is provided with nutrition and protection while it develops. This sequence, of course, involves a number of rather complex behavioral components, not all of which are present in every species. One of the initial functions of reproductive behavior is to ensure that individuals of opposite sexes congregate in the same area, thus enhancing mating. A variety of different behavioral mechanisms have evolved toward this end, and many of them are discussed in detail in the later chapters dealing with social behavior.

Reproductive adaptations of frogs and toads

If the question of how frogs reproduce were posed to most of us, we would probably relate some elements of the breeding pattern found in a common North American species such as the bullfrog *Rana catesbeiana*. This largely aquatic form breeds in the spring and summer; the males bellow their *jug-o'-rum* call while floating in shallow water in a pond or marshy area. Those females ready to breed move toward the calling sites of the males where they are promptly seized in a pectoral embrace. As the female extrudes her eggs they are fertilized externally by the clasping male.

The egg clutch is finally deposited as a huge (1 to 2 meters) disc-shaped aggregate of 10,000 to 20,000 eggs. The mass may float on the surface of the pond, or the eggs may be laid among a variety of aquatic plants. No parental care is given the developing eggs and eventually a larval stage—the polliwogs of our youth—hatches from the egg. The tadpole finally undergoes a transformation (**metamorphosis**) into a smaller replica of the adult. This pattern of aquatic breeding—little or no courtship, external fertilization, floating egg mass, total lack of parental care, and a developmental life history that includes a tadpole stage—would in all probability represent the frog and toad method of reproduction to most people.

While many species of frogs and toads do show this mode of reproduction, these tailless amphibians exhibit a remarkable diversity in their breeding behavior. For example, reproduction may entail lengthy migrations to and from the breeding sites; the risk of exposure to a variety of enemies; loud and persistent vocalizations; active defense of a potential breeding place; internal as well as external fertilization; the laying of eggs or the production of live young; growth stages that may include the familiar tadpole *or* direct development into a miniature version of the adult; and parental care ranging from no care at all to the extreme of taking developing eggs and placing them inside the body of the adult where full development follows.

The vocalizations of frogs and toads appear to be of great importance in their breeding biology. For example, such sounds may assist in establishment of a male calling site, in sex recognition, and in stimulation of the female prior to actual mating. Additionally, distinctive mating calls may prevent hybridization between different species that aggregate in the same pool or marsh. For

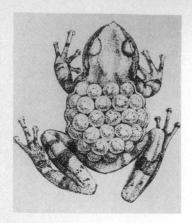

Figure 5–13 Like *F. goeldii*, the *Pipa* frog also carries its eggs in pockets on its back.

example, as many as 14 species of frogs and toads may congregate for breeding in the same pond, necessitating rather sharp discrimination on the part of the assembled forms.

Let's look at some evolutionary modifications of the "classic" mode of breeding described above. The so-called "tailed frogs" of the family Liopelmidae include species distributed as far apart as New Zealand and the northwestern United States. The "tail" of the American tailed frog contains an extension of the reproductive ducts and is used by the male as an intromittent organ. Fertilization is internal in this inhabitant of swift mountain streams; otherwise the sperm would be swept away from the eggs before they could be fertilized. Furthermore the adults seem to be voiceless, a corollary to their noisy habitat. The eggs of the tailed frog are attached in strings to the underside of rocks, an adaptation that keeps them from being swept downstream. A New Zealand relative lays its eggs under stones or logs, and the life history lacks a tadpole stage.

Great variability is shown not only by frogs and toads as a group, but also in the breeding behavior of closely related species classified in the same family. For example, some tree frogs of the family Hylidae may lay masses or strings of eggs in water in typical frog fashion, but some members of the family have adaptations that further ensure the survival of the eggs without recourse to the production of thousands of them. For example, *Flectonotus goeldii* females carry their eggs (perhaps as many as 20) around on their backs, held in a hollow surrounded by a rim of clear skin (Fig. 5–13). The male marsupial frog, *Gastrotheca marsupiata*, assists the female in placing the fertilized eggs in a pouch of loose skin on her back. Shortly afterward, the edges of the pouch seal themselves and development begins. Later, when the young are ready to emerge, the female helps them by raising her hind foot and extending one toe, which she uses to pull apart the slit-like opening left in the pouch. A common Brazilian member of this family constructs a large mud nest for breeding purposes. The female lays her eggs in the center of this protective device.

Several species of the genus *Scaphiopus* live in the deserts of the southwestern United States, in what seems to be most unsuitable habitat for an amphibian. The problem, of course, is to find water for breeding. These toads are ready to breed at any time during warm weather a few hours after rain has fallen. The tadpoles of several such species show some incredible behavioral adaptations to life in such a harsh environment. Just before they are able to leave a pool that is rapidly drying, the tadpoles aggregate in a non-feeding group and rapidly sweep the bottom of the disappearing pool. This behavior results in the construction of a slight depression into which the very last of the water will flow. Now, each tadpole scoops out a little vertical hole for itself into which it backs. The depression he has created reduces surface area for water evaporation, and the protected tadpole gains enough time—in some cases a single additional hour is all that is needed—for transformation to take place.

One of the most remarkable examples of extreme parental care in frogs is shown by *Rhinoderma darwini*, a South American species classified in a family by itself. This native of Argentina and Chile was first made known to science by Darwin during his voyage on the *Beagle*. When a female lays her eggs—

from 20 to 30 of them—several males gather about them and guard the egg cluster for from 10 to 20 days until the eggs are about ready to hatch. Then each male takes several eggs up with his tongue and inserts them into his vocal pouch. This is remarkable in that the male's vocal pouch extends from the buccal cavity back to the groin, then alongside the flanks and forward to the underside of the male's chin. The little frogs metamorphose while still in the male's vocal pouch and finally emerge as small froglets!

These are but a few of the many remarkable aspects of frog and toad reproduction. We can see how in the course of evolution progress has gone from the basic broadcasting of masses or clusters of eggs in suitable aquatic habitats to greater insurance of egg survival by the construction of trenches, nests, and similar devices to the amazing placement of the eggs inside the body of the adult for subsequent development.

In some invertebrates, such as marine annelid worms, mating by physical contact does not occur. The gametes are shed into the water. For this mechanism to work effectively, individuals of opposite sex must spawn about the same time if there is to be a sufficiently high probability that a sperm and an egg will unite. A chemical signal that spreads rapidly in the water stimulates simultaneous spawning, or **epidemic spawning**, in a number of species. Most fish use external fertilization. This means of reproduction is, of course, relatively inefficient since a large number of gametes must be released to ensure the union of at least two. A big step in the efficiency of reproductive behavior was achieved with the evolution of internal fertilization. The probability that two gametes will meet is greatly increased in animals that have internal fertilization. However, the problems of identifying members of the opposite sex may still be present.

Chemical signals and behavior

Certain behavior patterns, including identification of the opposite sex, of most animals are triggered by olfactory stimuli. Chemicals produced by animals and serving as olfactory signals are called **pheromones**. Pheromones may be released into the air or water or deposited onto or near the ground by animals when they are in certain behavioral states. Pheromones then generate complementary behavior when they are detected by other members of the species. These chemical signals play a part in behavior comparable to that played by hormones as chemical messengers between different groups of cells within the body.

Best known are the chemical markers serving to bound the territories of individual animals. A great many mammals produce a "personalized" secretion from anal or facial glands that is rubbed onto trees or rocks (see page 209). Cat and dog species generally urinate to mark the edges of their territory. These markers play the same role as the hedge marking the boundary of a house lot. Any incursion into the territory evokes a response. The reaction of your pet male dog is almost inevitable when he finds that a foreign object such as a package or a strange automobile has been "deposited" within his territory. Marking of this kind serves to stabilize the individual territories of the species and to reduce territorial squabbles.

Figure 5–14 The photograph of the Cecropia moth shows the size of the antennae in relation to the rest of the moth, while the magnified view of a luna moth antenna shows details of antenna structure.

Equally familiar are the chemical signals released by female mammals when they are in heat. Our human noses are mostly insensitive to such signals, which to many other species are potent and species-specific. They may be carried long distances downwind, a fact well known to the owners of female dogs and cats by the number of "suitors" that gather round the house at certain times.

Other striking examples of the potency of sex pheromones are the sex attractants released by virgin female moths of many species, including the silkworm moth and the gypsy moth. These pheromones, which have been chemically identified and synthesized, are secreted by special glands on the female abdomen and are detected by receptors on the male antennae (Fig. 5–14). A "calling" female releases minute amounts of the sex attractant, which is then carried downwind. When it is detected by males, often miles away, it induces flight activity and a tendency to travel upwind in a search pattern for as long as they can detect the odor. These built-in instructions bring the males close to the calling female. When we realize that the abdomen of a female silkworm moth contains a total amount of only 1.5×10^{-6} g of pheromone and that only a fraction of this amount is diluted in an air stream that may be miles in length, the extreme sensitivity of the male moth's olfactory sense is not surprising. Dietrich Schneider estimates that a male moth will react when 40 out of 40,000 receptors on the antennae receive one strike of a pheromone molecule per second. Gypsy moth caterpillars are serious defoliators of broad-leaved trees in many parts of the United States. Their pheromone has been used to control this pest by placing the chemical in traps that kill all the males attracted to the sex pheromone.

The best known and most elaborate systems of chemical communication are found in social insects such as the termites, ants, bees, and wasps. Honeybees and ants are thought to have up to a dozen different **exocrine** (externally secreting) glands, each producing chemicals that elicit specific forms of behavior in nest mates.

Beekeepers are well aware of the fact that if one bee stings, many others will attempt to. An alarm substance (isoamyl acetate) is left with the stinger of the bee in the wound. It diffuses into the air and excites other bees to aggregate and sting. When their colony is threatened, ants produce various kinds of alarm substance that cause aggregation, excited running, and readiness to attack. An ant returning from a rich food source touches her stinger to the ground every few steps, leaving a chemical trail that is followed by other ants who in turn reinforce the trail on their return to the nest. Oleic acid is formed in the decomposing corpses of dead ants. This chemical causes a live ant to pick up the source and carry it out of the nest to the nearby refuse pile. Oleic acid smeared on a live and healthy ant will make its nest mates "dump" it repeatedly in spite of strenuous efforts of the "corpse" to return to the nest.

The unity and stability of these insect colonies are reinforced by mutual licking and a continuous interchange of material regurgitated from the crop. This is called **trophallaxis** and serves as a social bond by distributing a common "nest flavor" among nest mates. The queen honeybee sustains her monarchy in the hive by distributing keto-decenoic acid from a special gland. This inhibits the worker bees in the manner of a hormone, preventing ovarian development and the raising of other queens in the hive. The effect of this pheromone disappears a few hours after the queen's death, releasing queen-raising behavior in the worker bees.

Courtship behavior

Chemistry is not the only way for a species to differentiate mating types or identify opposite sexes. Animal species have evolved a broad range of behavioral as well as morphological mechanisms that serve to identify the sexes. Male mosquitoes of the species *Aedes aegypti*, for example, are remarkably sensitive to the buzzing of females. The male's antenna vibrates at a frequency very similar to that of the female's wing beat frequency. If a tuning fork vibrating at a frequency similar to that of a female's wing beat frequency is held next to a cage containing *Aides* mosquitoes, males will rapidly congregate at the point of the cage wall nearest the tuning fork.

Many species of birds have developed dramatic and intricate behaviors that are used as a prelude, and in some cases a postlude, to mating. Most male bowerbirds use sticks to build a courtship playground called a bower. The male decorates his bower with colored berries, stones, pieces of string, and other bright objects, which it uses to attract the female. Those bowerbird species with the drabbest plumage have evolved the most complex bower-building behavior—an excellent example of how the physical appearance of a species (plumage) and its behavior (bower building and posturing with "artificial plumage") interact. The bar-headed goose, among other species, has a vigorous post-copulatory display. Possibly it induces ovulation in the female and so increases the probability of fertilization. Further, natural selection would favor the evolution of this display if it helped preserve a bond between the mated pair, thereby increasing the probability that offspring would result from the mating.

COURTSHIP BEHAVIOR OF THE GREEN HERON: Andrew J. Meyerriecks has studied the courtship behavior of the green heron (Fig. 5–15), and the following account appeared in his Biological Sciences Curriculum Study pamphlet entitled *Courtship in Animals*:

Figure 5–15 Various courtship behaviors of the green heron. (AFTER A. J. MEYERRIECKS)

migration

skowing

snap display

full forward display

flap flight display

stretch display

twig passing

migration

The green heron, *Butorides virescens*, is a rather small, dark, wading bird broadly distributed in North America. For the most part the two sexes look alike. After the breeding season green herons move south to their wintering quarters in northern South America, the islands of the Caribbean, and along the Gulf coast of the United States. At this time the species is strictly solitary. In late winter and early spring, stimulated by a complex interaction of external and internal factors, these herons begin to move northward toward their breeding grounds. Some move alone, while others migrate in small flocks, including members of both sexes.

Once they have arrived at the potential nesting sites, two features stand out: The color of the birds has changed from that of the wintering period, and the behavior of the sexes is radically different. Males and females are rather drab-colored in their wintering grounds, with rather dull, yellowish-green legs and feet, and a patch of bare skin of the same color in front of the eyes. However, at the end of the northward migration the color is quite different. The legs and the feet are now colored a brilliant coral orange, while the skin in front of the eyes is a dark blue-black. Also, the feathers on the back are long and lance-shaped. Though the color and feather shape of both sexes change, the differences are more striking in the males.

The males are extremely aggressive shortly after their arrival, and territories are established very quickly. The females are more quiet; they head for the neighboring feeding grounds (ponds, lakes, streams, or vast tidal bays). At first the territory of a male is rather large, and he patrols its boundaries regularly, pausing now and then at a favored spot to call—a rather harsh, low-pitched *skow*. This call of the male is functionally similar to the songs of other birds in that it signals to other males that the territory holder is in residence and ready to threaten or attack any intruders, including females. If neighboring males intrude on one another's territories, threats and fights soon follow (Fig. 5-15). The resident first crouches low, raising his dark crest and fine back feathers. If this threat doesn't work, he opens his bill and utters a rasping call. This usually suffices to intimidate an opponent, but in the case of a particularly aggressive trespasser, the owner then flies to the attack. Rarely does a resident bird lose such an encounter.

Thus occupied for a number of days, the males gradually establish the boundaries of their respective territories. Now the females begin to drift back from the foraging grounds, attracted by the *skows* of the males, and circulate among the different territory holders. The first response of a male to the appearance of a female on his territory is a hostile one—he threatens her as he would another male, and drives her from his defended area. The female usually leaves and flies to the territory of another male, typically one that is *skowing*. Soon the males permit the females to perch on the very edges of their areas, but if one approaches too close she is chased away.

During this early period, the male has selected a nesting site, sometimes a nest that has survived from a previous breeding season. If he has chosen an old nest, he starts to gather sticks and make repairs; if he has a new site for the nest, he starts to build its foundation. The female is very much interested in the nest-building activities of the male and tries to approach the nest, but still she is repulsed.

Eventually a change occurs in the behavior of the male: He permits the female to remain on his territory . . . and he no longer defends the edges of his initial territory. Then by means of a series of distinctive aerial displays, the male begins to shift from hostile behavior to sexual behavior. He flies in a circle about his territory, brightly colored legs dangling, crest raised, returning to his nest at the end of each display. Soon the female joins the male in mutual display flights. By this time the defended territory of the male is much smaller. Now the female may even land in the nest tree, and though the male is still wary, his hostility is usually little more than symbolic.

The first clear signal that the male is ready to mate is shown by his beautiful "stretch display." The male stands in his nest, raises his bill straight up, erects the fine plumes on his back, and sways from side to side. During this part of his display, the male utters a soft, almost gurgling call, quite the opposite of the harsh, rasping calls that accompany his threat displays.

The moment of pair formation comes when the male allows the female to enter the nest and stand by his side. This is a very tense period for both birds, and a sudden movement on the part of either bird triggers a threat display by the male. This is understandable, because the male has been vigorously defending his area, especially the region around the nest, and now here is another green heron actually standing in the nest. This tense period lasts for a few hours to a day or so, but soon the birds are nibbling each other's plumage, and the male begins to bring nest sticks to his mate, who weaves them into the platform. Now the female shows stretch displays similar to those of the male, typically before the pair copulate. As soon as this stage is reached, neither sex *skows* any more. The territory is defended by both, and it has been reduced to the area immediately around the nest. The parental stages of the nesting sequence now begin.

A number of questions come to mind after such an initial descriptive study has been made: What is the meaning of the change in coloration of the "soft parts" (legs, feet, and bare skin in front of the eyes?) What role do the fine plumes on the back play in courtship? Would the male be successful in getting a mate if he lacked such plumes? Why does the male defend a progressively smaller territory? What are the physiological bases for the color changes? Can such color changes be induced in non-breeding birds? Are the courtship patterns truly innate, or does a young green heron learn to perform them? If so, how? How did such a complex behavior originate and evolve? Do other heron species behave similarly? If not, how do they differ, and why?

It should be clear by now that behavior is an adaptation, just as are the various morphological and physiological characteristics of a given species. Behavior is tailored for individual survival and the reproduction of progeny. That has been our larger message in the first part of this book. We will now look at organisms in the context of their environment, examine populations and their fluctuations, and take a detailed look at that category of behavior mentioned earlier as social behavior.

1 Cite several ways in which behavior is an adaptation essential to the survival of a species; to the survival of an individual.

2 Citing at least one example, explain the significance of this statement: Morphology and behavior develop together during the evolution of a species.

3 How do biologists attempt to trace the evolution of a particular behavior?

4 How is it possible for environmental change to induce a physiological adaptation? Give at least two examples.

5 Is it likely that understanding the behavior of an animal will change a person's attitude toward the animal? Toward another human? Can our attitudes change with understanding even when the behavior in question elicits a negative response in us?

6 Coral snakes are dangerous venomous snakes. Their bright red, yellow, and black markings seem to be mimicked by a few other species. How could such a relationship evolve if a naive predator were killed in its first attempt to capture the reptile?

7 In what way is an insectivorous plant's behavior as a heterotroph an adaptation favoring the species' survival?

8 Give one example each of the following behaviors: evasive action, cryptic behavior, startle displays, warning displays.

SELECTED READINGS

Bastock, Margaret. *Courtship: An Ethological Study.* Chicago: Aldine-Atherton, Inc., 1967. An excellent coverage, with numerous examples, of the evolutionary origins and physiological bases of courtship behavior, an area of behavior study that has intrigued biologists since the time of Darwin.

Evans, Howard. *Wasp Farm.* Garden City, N.Y.: Natural History Press, 1963. One of America's top entomologists and a first-rate writer tells of his numerous researches on wasps both social and solitary. Most informative and engagingly written.

Burkhardt, Dietrich, Wolfgang Schleidt, and Helmut Altner. *Signals in the Animal World.* New York: McGraw-Hill Book Co., 1967. This richly illustrated book was originally published in Germany in 1966. It includes contributions by 15 researchers on such subjects as sense organs, nerves and hormones, the animal in its environment, and animal language. A broad, highly recommended coverage with numerous examples.

RECORDS ON BEHAVIOR

Bogert, Charles M. *Sounds of North American Frogs. The Biological Significance of Voice in Frogs.* New York: Folkways Records, 1958. This record is accompanied by an excellent descriptive booklet.

Borror, Donald J. *Bird Song and Bird Behavior.* New York: Dover Publications, Inc., 1972. This record is accompanied by an excellent descriptive booklet.

Part 2

INTERACTION

So far in this book we have
emphasized what living organisms
are, how they change through
geologic time, and their diversity
in form and behavior.
In Part 2, we tighten our frame
of reference by examining the
interactions of organisms with each
other—as individuals and as
populations—and with nonliving
parts of the environment.
The two umbrella topics for Part 2,
then, are ecology and social
behavior. We'll begin with ecology.

Figure 6–1 Low tide in this salt-water cove reveals a habitat group that includes
 lobsters and the men who catch them, clams, oysters, mussels, sea stars,
seaweeds, periwinkles, marine worms, numerous species of insects and fish,
gulls, ducks, heron, plant and animal plankton, rats, and other organisms. All
are continually interacting with each other and exchanging matter and energy
with the environment.

6
THE ORGANISM
IN ITS ENVIRONMENT

WHAT IS ECOLOGY?

In the broadest sense, ecology is a science of relationships between living organisms and their environment (Fig. 6–1). The **environment** is the sum total of nonliving and living, or physical and biological, factors that may influence an organism. Until recently, ecologists have tended to concentrate on nonhuman organisms and "natural" systems for study, but the widespread environmental degradation caused by man's activities over the past century or so has forced us to realize that human beings live as a part of, not apart from, the environment. Man depends on and is as intimately connected with the environment as a caterpillar or kangaroo. Because man gradually has come to regard himself as a biotic component of the environment, over the past few years the word *ecology* has emerged from relative obscurity into prominence. The "ecological issue" is one of the few issues today that manages to bridge generation gaps and politics alike. Who among us today can afford to ignore the impact of this or that program on "the environment," be it the issue of oil on the Maine coast, the systematic destruction of a lake by a developer, or the fouling of the air and rivers by paper mills?

Despite its widespread concerns, ecology is a legitimate branch of biology, as are genetics, physiology, ethology, and embryology. As such, ecology is a scientific discipline with a rich heritage and an impressive and detailed reservoir of knowledge. It seeks to explain certain phenomena of biology by the usual methods of analysis, synthesis, and generalization. In doing so it has evolved its own vocabulary of terms, which have rather precise meanings. In earlier times ecology suffered from such an enormous proliferation of terms that it was once facetiously defined as "that phase of biology primarily abandoned to terminology." Fortunately, pathological proliferation of terms is a thing of the past in biology, so we will concern ourselves only with those terms that are necessary for a proper understanding of the basic tenets of the science.

Ecology through history

Naturalists of earlier centuries realized that plants and animals do not live independently of their surroundings, but that every phase of an organism's life is regulated by where it lives. Studies of plants and animals in their natural habitats were called natural history, and natural history emerged as a descriptive venture concerned with the sociability of organisms and associated

A MATTER OF TERMS

The **environment** has already been defined as the total of physical and biological factors that may influence an organism. A **population** is a group of similarly adapted, interbreeding organisms of the same species.

A **community** is made up of all populations occurring in a particular area. However, it is difficult to study every population of each species in any particular area. That is why community studies are often restricted to the species in an area that belongs to a particular taxonomic group. Therefore, we speak of the plant community, the foliage–insect community, or the small-mammal community. The interrelationships between such groups may then be considered on the level of the community as a whole.

An **ecosystem** is composed of the community (taken in the broad sense) plus the physical environment. Thus an ecosystem has two parts —the **biotic** (living) components and the **abiotic** (nonliving) ones.

The **biosphere** is the collective total of all living organisms on Earth. The **ecosphere** is the biosphere plus the nonliving components with which it interacts; in other words, it is the ecosystem on a global scale. A **habitat** is the place where an organism lives. For example, the habitat of a sucker is a stream. The **niche** of an organism is its "occupation," or what the organism does in a community. The niche of the sucker is grazing algae from rocks on the bottom of the stream.

As a science, ecology is concerned primarily with populations, including the human population, as constituents of a highly complex and interactive system.

environmental features. The descriptive approach was far from sterile, and many of the great biologists of the eighteenth and nineteenth centuries, such as Charles Darwin, Alfred Russel Wallace, and Henry W. Bates, were natural historians (Fig. 6–2).

About a century ago the German biologist Ernst H. Haeckel coined the term "oecologie" from two Greek words, *oikos*, meaning "home," and *logos*, meaning "discourse." In Haeckel's words, the study of oecology would lead to ". . . total knowledge concerning the economy of nature . . . the investigation of the total relations of the animal both to its organic and its inorganic environment." Haeckel's oecologie gradually came into common use as a word, although ecology and natural history as disciplines were essentially the same.

Ecology persisted as a descriptive science well into the twentieth century and began to split into two major taxonomic and methodological branches. Plant ecology tended to concentrate on the interactions of plant species in communities and the relations of plant communities and environments. This approach is often referred to as "synecology" (*syn* meaning "together").

Most animal ecology, on the other hand, concerned itself with the physiological responses of animals to the environment and became known as "autecology" (*autos* meaning "self").

More recently there has been general recognition that the division between plant and animal ecology is traditional and artificial, since it is impossible to understand the "economy of nature" without considering both animal and plant components. Ecology also gradually adopted quantitative techniques, stressing the importance of careful measurements, numerical data, and statistical analysis. Qualitative description alone was no longer enough.

Traditional definitions of ecology usually went something like "studies of the interrelations between living organisms and their environment" or "the study of the structure and function of nature" or simply "environmental biology." Consider, however, that more than 1,000,000 animal species and about 350,000 plant species have already been described, and that each year biologists add an average of about 10,000 new animal species and 5,000 new plants to the inventory. If one ponders the wide range of complex and varied responses that so many species of organisms can make to the ever-changing environment, the study of ecology seems to be beyond the scope of human understanding. Indeed, a generation ago traditional biology seemed to many to be little more than an endless chronicle of the diversity of life, and this approach to ecology led some to believe that it would never be possible to understand the complexity of nature. The best that science could do was to describe what was there.

In the last two decades or so, however, an intellectual revolution of sorts has shaken biology and has led to enormous breakthroughs in our understanding of life processes. Since many of these discoveries, such as the methods of gene action and the intricacies of cellular metabolism, have been made on the molecular level, there has been some feeling that the only "good" biology is molecular biology. The fact is that many meaningful and interesting biological questions cannot be framed or answered in molecular terms. In order to understand *all* of biology, we must view the living world as a hierarchy of levels of organization, each level having its own unique set of properties (see page 39). Included in the hierarchy are the sub-cellular (molecular) level, the level of the cell itself, the organism level, and the level of the population. This levels-of-organization approach to biology, which stresses uniformities in the living world rather than diversity, along with the acceptance of analytical methods instead of description, has been chiefly responsible for the biological revolution.

The level of organization most appropriate for ecological study is that of the population. This level has properties and characteristics that are not found at other levels of organization, and the population, not the individual organism, is the basis for evolution. Since it is the response of all the populations of a species to an environmental change that determines whether or not a species will persist, the study of evolution is intimately entwined with ecology. Therefore the best definition of **ecology** seems to be the study of biological systems at a level at which populations of organisms change within themselves and react to one another within an environmental matrix.

Figure 6–2 Naturalists of Darwin's era, concerned primarily with a descriptive approach to biology, were amazed by the variety and proliferation of life they found in the tropical forests of South America. The wood engraving here is from Bates' *The Naturalist on the River Amazon,* published in 1863. (THE GRANGER COLLECTION)

Figure 6-3 Since it is impossible to count the total number of organisms in a mixed community of plants and animals, ecologists take samples throughout the community and rely on statistical techniques to determine the significance of their data.

Ecology, or population biology, as we now have defined it, can be approached from two different perspectives, that of the study of individual populations and that of community, or multiple population, studies. The former perspective emphasizes the study of the evolution and variation of species, population genetics, distribution of species in space and time, population dynamics and regulation, population energetics and metabolism, and the environmental determinants of physiological and behavioral adaptation.

Multiple population studies include the classification and description of communities, measurements of the physical characteristics of habitat, the relationships between populations and their role in community structure, and the interrelations between communities and the physical environment. Obviously there are not clear-cut lines between these two approaches. It is also obvious that the study of the relationships of the human population to other populations and the effect of these relationships on the world ecosystem also falls within the province of ecology.

The nature and scope of ecological investigations

Since the number of individuals comprising a population may be extremely large, it is usually impossible to study a whole population, let alone an entire community. That is why ecological data are drawn from a sampling of a population or a community, and then the significance of the data is established by statistical techniques (Fig. 6-3). For this reason, the design of an ecological experiment is often quite different from the design of an experiment in other branches of biology, where "all-or-none" responses are often expected.

Ecological data are gathered either in the laboratory or in the field. The laboratory approach calls for establishing populations or simple ecosystems in a laboratory where most of the variables can be controlled. This approach has contributed a great deal to our understanding of population dynamics and simple inter-species interactions. However, this approach has a serious drawback. Organisms do not exist in nature under such "ideal" or restricted conditions, so we must be cautious whenever we construct general theory from such data.

Field studies, on the other hand, are conducted under natural or semi-natural conditions. Often it is possible to document changes that take place within a population or community if we make our observations and measurements with sufficient care. However, because of the very large number of uncontrolled variables that must be considered in a field study, it may be impossible to determine exactly the underlying causes of the changes.

A more recent approach to field studies is the field experiment designed to intensify certain conditions or interactions. For example, we might increase the supply of food in a certain area, or we might alter some physical factor in a controlled manner. We can then measure the response of populations to the changes we have induced. In general, ecological studies that combine laboratory investigation, field observation, and field experiments seem to be the most profitable ones.

The alteration of the landscape by man's activities may be thought of as a massive ecological "experiment." Unfortunately, the experiment may not be a repeatable one, and often there is not enough time to measure the base-line conditions before the alteration occurs.

Ecological investigations also differ in scale. We can study the interactions between protozoan species in a few milliliters of water in a test tube, or a single strawberry plant may be an adequate universe for the study of the interactions between two species of mites. While some investigators have considered fifty-gallon aquaria or quarter-acre ponds adequate for studying certain aspects of aquatic communities, other investigators have conducted extremely thorough and detailed studies on entire watersheds or mountain ranges. The scale of the study-universe is roughly correlated with the size and activity of the organisms to be studied. A single meadow may be adequate for a study involving voles or butterflies, but it may be necessary to cover hundreds of square kilometers to understand the ecology of the puma.

Often it is convenient—and meaningful—to let the boundaries of a field study be the boundaries of a certain type of habitat. Consider a pond, for example. It is clearly separated from surrounding habitats, and the water-land interface forms a recognizable boundary. Also, we can expect to find a characteristic assemblage of organisms within the confines of the pond. Although we would not expect to find fish in the adjacent field, or mice burrowing in the pond's bottom mud, we would expect to find certain organisms in each habitat, such as frogs and fishes in one, and garter snakes and mice in the other. In the case of the pond, we could be fairly confident that its inhabitants and the abiotic components of the pond form a cohesive, interactive unit, which enables us to make meaningful statements about a "pond ecosystem."

Some terrestrial habitats may appear to be equally well defined. Occasionally we do find bold breaks in the continuity of prominent vegetation, such as a field bordering on the edge of a forest (Fig. 6–4). Often such boundaries

Figure 6–4 More than 100 years ago, part of this forest was cleared for farm land. When the land was abandoned many years later, a field ecosystem was established. Here is an instance where we can speak of marked differences between adjacent ecosystems, each with a distinctive assemblage of plants and animals.

Figure 6–5 Life in an ecotone (that region where two ecosystems merge) tends to be more diverse than life in either ecosystem. Here, when a north coniferous forest ecosystem blends with a pond ecosystem, the result is a marshy area. What animals might be found using this particular ecotone?

mark the limits of reasonably self-contained ecosystems. Here certain organisms are characteristically found in the field and certain others in the forest, and we can speak with confidence about an old-field ecosystem or a forest ecosystem.

Where two recognizable ecosystems merge, forming an **ecotone**, we often find organisms characteristic of both sharing the overlapping area (Fig. 6–5), and life in the ecotone may be more diverse. However, the distribution of many plant and animal populations is quite independent of what human observers might intuitively recognize as different habitats. The butterfly *Erebia epipsodea*, for example, is found in equal abundance in both meadows and sagebrush flats in certain areas of alpine Colorado. Evidently these butterflies do not recognize habitat discontinuity in the same way that ecologists do. Nevertheless, many species often occur together in ecologically discrete areas.

When areas of vegetation are the object of study, stands so much alike that we do not bother to give them different names are referred to as **associations**. As with single populations, however, the distribution of animal communities may or may not coincide with plant associations. For example, soil arthropods usually are not distributed in relation to vegetation. Instead, their distribution is determined by subtle differences in soil moisture, although those differences in moisture have little effect on plant distribution.

Stands of one association often occur as separated patches, either due to the discontinuity of suitable habitat or through fragmentation by man's activities. All the land surface where the same association regularly occurs is referred to as a **vegetation zone**. Intervening areas consisting of other types of habitats are generally ignored when defining a zone. Vegetation zones are particularly distinct in the mountains of the western United States where differences in temperature and precipitation vary abruptly with elevation. Still larger units differentiated on the basis of predominant vegetation are called **biomes**. Biomes are named after their characteristic plant life (Fig. 5–5), such as the grassland biome or north coniferous forest biome. As with associations, the distribution of plants and animals within a biome may correspond with the boundaries of the biome, but often it does not. The reasons for such distributions are challenging questions for the ecologist.

Components of the ecosystem

Populations of organisms comprise the biotic parts of an ecosystem. Abiotic factors include energy, the ultimate source of which is the Sun, and various elements and compounds necessary to sustain life, such as water, carbon, and phosphorus. When populations of organisms interact with their environment, a reciprocating system is set in operation. The system functions by cycling and recycling organic and inorganic materials alike. Energy introduced into the system, however, flows along a one-way street. Unlike water, phosphorus, and other materials in the system, energy cannot be recycled or reconstituted.

Since the environment is such a complex affair, we try to look at it part by part, breaking it down into various categories such as water, temperature, light, gases, dissolved salts, pH, pressure, and so on. It is possible to measure many of these factors in isolation from other variables. When we do, however, we must be fully aware of the consequences and not fall into the trap of what has come to be called "one-factor ecology." While any one environmental factor may be critical to a population at any one time, one or more of the others may be critical also. It is essential to remember that altering any one factor invariably influences all the others. Thus, the environment may be thought of as "holocoenotic," or without walls between its various aspects.

The notion of the holocoenotic environment can be illustrated by contrasting a north-facing hillside with a south-facing one (Figs. 6–6, 6–7). The first things we notice are gross differences in vegetation. The north-facing slope has

Figures 6–6 and **6–7** Relatively dense growth (left) contrasted with a relatively open forest (right) can be accounted for, in part, by the direction in which the forest floor slopes, which determines the quantity of solar radiation the soil receives. Intensity and duration of solar radiation in turn trigger a chain of growth activities involving soil temperature and rates of evaporation.

denser vegetation, and perhaps the plant species growing there are quite different from those on the south slope. To discover the reason for these differences, we might first consider incoming solar radiation. Since this particular slope is in the north temperate region, the north side will receive less solar radiation and therefore will have, on the average, lower soil and plant temperatures than the south slope will. Low temperatures mean low soil evaporation rates, which in turn can mean high soil moisture content. More soil moisture generally leads to denser vegetation, which in turn reduces wind movement near the ground and solar radiation reaching the ground, but which leads to a greater evaporative surface area of the leaves and stems of the plants, and more accumulation of leaf litter. The more leaf litter there is, the less runoff there will be during heavy rains, which means less erosion and deeper soil. Rich leaf litter also contributes to better soil structure and fertility, which in turn leads to denser vegetation. The greater evaporative surface area resulting from denser vegetation leads to higher relative humidity, which in turn lowers water loss by plants and soil alike, which results in more soil moisture and denser vegetation.

As complex as these interrelationships may seem, the example is a simplified picture of what actually goes on. For instance, we have not taken into account the changes in species composition of the plants, and we have not considered the responses of the several animal populations that may be involved.

The biotic components of the ecosystem may be broadly classified on the basis of their niches, or functional roles within the system. The broadest and most general method for making such a classification is based on the way that the organisms acquire the energy they need for growth, maintenance, and reproduction. So every ecosystem has a structure—called a **trophic structure** —based on the energy acquisition of its organisms.

The anchor position, in the trophic hierarchy is occupied by the photosyn-

Figure 6–8 A typical terrestrial food chain consists of producers, (grass and shrubs, for instance), herbivores such as deer, primary carnivores such as mountain lions, secondary carnivores such as man, and finally the decomposers of the soil.

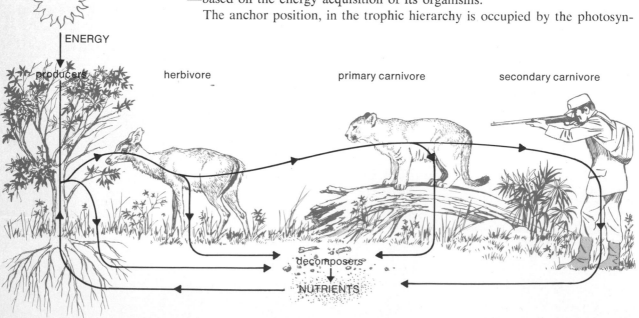

ENERGY

producers   herbivore   primary carnivore   secondary carnivore

decomposers

NUTRIENTS

thetic autotrophs, or **producers** (Fig. 6–8), which were discussed in Chapter 2. We call them "producers" because they are able to make their own food (carbohydrate) by using the energy of sunlight and in the presence of chlorophyll combining water and carbon dioxide from the air. (There are a few autotrophic bacteria that use the energy from other chemical reactions for the same purpose.) Photosynthesis carried out by green plants is the most important energy-fixing process taking place in the biosphere. Without it, almost all life would cease.

The next step in the trophic hierarchy is occupied by heterotrophic organisms, or consumers, which are mainly animals (Fig. 6–8). Those consumers that eat plants or plant products directly are called **herbivores**, while those that eat other consumers are called **carnivores**. Carnivores are further classified by their eating activities. Those that eat herbivores are primary carnivores. Those that eat primary carnivores are secondary carnivores, and so on. Some animal species always remain on a fixed trophic level. For example, most grasshoppers, voles, and deer are always herbivorous. Other animals may feed at several different trophic levels. Bears, as herbivores, may eat berries; as primary carnivores they may eat deer and ground squirrels; and as tertiary or even quarternary carnivores they may eat salmon. Obviously man is as flexible as the bear and is able to operate on several different trophic levels.

The end position in the trophic hierarchy is occupied by the **decomposers**, or the organisms of decay. Mostly bacteria and fungi, these organisms feed on the remains at all trophic levels. They are the planet's ultimate scavengers. They break down the organic substances into inorganic materials and release those materials to the soil as nutrients to be taken up anew by the producers and recycled.

In summary, in its simplest form our system for energy flow and material cycling works like this: Producers take in abiotic materials—and energy source (sunlight) and nutrients—and convert them into living materials. Primary consumers (herbivores) eat the producers. Higher level consumers (carnivores) next eat the herbivores. The remains of all organisms that die are then consumed by the decomposers. During this chemical breakdown essential nutrients are released to the environment and made available for use by the producers once again. In that way, the structure of an ecosystem is intimately related to its function: The flow of energy and the cycling and recycling of materials are as one.

ENERGY FLOW IN ECOSYSTEMS

Every ecosystem, whether a large and complex unit such as a biome, or a relatively small unit like a pond or a tidal pool, has a characteristic flux of energy. We can measure energy exchanges occurring in a local system rather accurately. Then by using data from geophysics and astronomy, we can calculate the energy budget of the entire ecosphere and estimate the total amount of life that Earth can support.

Biomass and productivity

Before we can discuss energy relationships in biological systems, however, we must introduce one more term. **Biomass** is the total quantity of material that makes up living organisms in a given area. The amount of biomass depends on the amount of solar energy fixed by autotrophic organisms. We can measure that quantity in terms of the production of new organic matter. Usually it is expressed in units of dry grams of organic material produced per square meter per year.

The conditions favoring life in one habitat over another are reflected in the habitat's productivity. For example, desert productivity ranges from 10 to 250 $g/m^2/yr$, while tropical rain forest productivity ranges from 1,000 to 5,000 $g/m^2/yr$ (Fig 6–9). Estimates of productivity of all of Earth's major

BIOME PRODUCTIVITY

Habitat	Area (10^6 km^2)	Net primary productivity per unit area (dry $g/m^2/yr$)	
		normal range	mean
Lake and stream	2	100-1,500	500
Swamp and marsh	2	800-4,000	2,000
Tropical forest	20	1,000-5,000	2,000
Temperate forest	18	600-2,500	1,300
Boreal forest	12	400-2,000	800
Woodland and shrubland	7	200-1,200	600
Savanna	15	200-2,000	700
Temperate grassland	9	150-1,500	500
Tundra and alpine	8	10-400	140
Desert scrub	18	10-250	70
Extreme desert, rock, ice	24	0-10	3
Agricultural land	14	100-4,000	650
Total land	149		730
Open ocean	332	2-400	125
Continental shelf	27	200-600	350
Attached algae, estuaries	2	500-4,000	2,000
Total ocean	361		155
Total for Earth	510		320

Figure 6–9 Productivity ranges for various biomes.

ecosystems show that the energy flux in the biological cycle is much greater —and much more efficient—than the sum total of man's energy transformations.

The first law of thermodynamics tells us that the amount of energy in the Universe is constant. This energy may be transformed into another form of energy or into matter, but the transformations do not involve any net gain or loss of energy to the system as a whole. Furthermore, when energy is transformed, part of it is changed into a type that cannot be transferred any further. That is the second law of thermodynamics. It may be convenient to remember these two laws as "You can't win" and "You can't even break even."

Yet, as you have seen, in the context of the ecosphere energy is continually renewed. Unlike the nutrients, which cycle, energy flows through the ecosphere along a one-way street. The source of 99.994% of the energy that flows through the global ecosystem is solar radiation. The rest comes from tides, meteorites, natural radioactivity, moonlight, and starlight.

Let's consider this energy source for a minute. Deep within the Sun, nuclear reactions involving the fusion of hydrogen nuclei into helium nuclei are converting relatively small amounts of the Sun's mass into relatively large amounts of energy. This process goes on at a constant rate. One gram-atomic weight of helium (4.0034 g) is produced from the fusion of four gram-atomic weights of hydrogen, each with a mass of 1.0081 g. But notice that if you multiply four times 1.0081 you get 4.0324, not 4.0034. The reason for the discrepancy is this: During the fusion of hydrogen nuclei something happens to 0.029 grams of mass. Einstein's equation $E = mc^2$ tells us that the mass is converted into energy, E. The amount of energy equals the mass lost (m) times the velocity of light (3.0×10^{10} cm/sec). Solving the equation turns up a remarkable fact—that 700,000,000,000 calories of energy, roughly equivalent to the heat produced by burning 100 tons of coal, are released during the production of only four grams of helium. The amount of solar energy reaching Earth per year comes to about 1.3×10^{24} gram-calories.

Although solar radiation consists of various wavelengths ranging from 0.01 micrometers to more than 100,000 micrometers, most of the Sun's energy reaches Earth in short wavelengths—mostly visible light and near-visible ultraviolet, the range being from about 400 to 700 micrometers for visible light (Fig. 6–10). During the daytime about 35% of this radiation is reflected back to space by clouds and dust particles in the air (Fig. 6–11). The reflected

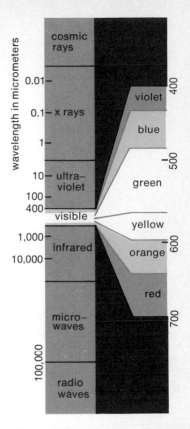

Figure 6–10 Visible light has wavelengths ranging from about 400 micrometers in the violet region to about 700 micrometers in the red region.

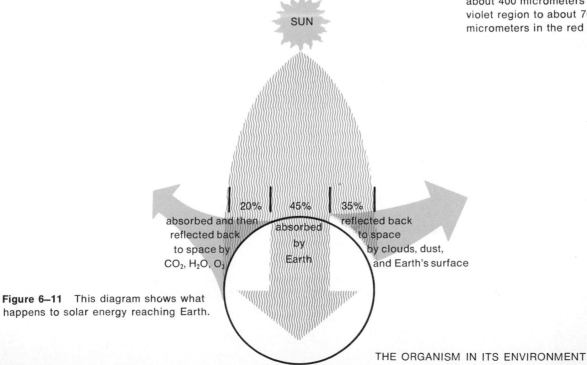

Figure 6–11 This diagram shows what happens to solar energy reaching Earth.

radiation is called the planet's **albedo**. About 20% of the incoming radiation is absorbed by carbon dioxide, water vapor, and ozone and is re-emitted to space. The remaining 45% is absorbed by Earth itself. Since the atmosphere is relatively transparent to this radiation, most of the energy is absorbed by the soil, surface rocks, surface water, and vegetation. Because Earth is relatively cool in relation to the Sun, the energy Earth reradiates from its surface is of the longer wavelengths, mostly in the infrared region of the spectrum. However, only part of this long-wave energy is reradiated into space. About half of it is absorbed by carbon dioxide and water vapor in the atmosphere and part of this is reradiated back toward the surface again. This heat-trapping action of the atmosphere is known as the greenhouse effect.

Since about 1870, there has been an 11% or 12% increase in the CO_2 content of the atmosphere. Although the causes for this increase are probably very complex, a great deal of the increase comes from our burning vast amounts of fossil fuels (coal, natural gas, and petroleum). Along with this rise in atmospheric CO_2, a gradual rise in the average temperature of our planet had been observed until the 1940s, presumably because of an increased greenhouse effect. However, the increase in particulate matter in the atmosphere—dust, pollution, and jet contrails—that has occurred since the 1940s has increased the albedo. So it appears that the increased greenhouse effect from CO_2 may have been offset.

Biogeochemical cycles

Certain elements and dissolved salts are essential to plants and animals alike. These nutrients, as they are called, are extremely important to an ecosystem. The paths the nutrients follow through the environment—through both the abiotic and living components of a community and back—are called **biogeochemical cycles**. However, not all the world's supply of nutrients is involved in this cycling. Great quantities of many essential elements are deposited in reservoirs that are unavailable to the living world. Some elements such as carbon, hydrogen, nitrogen, and oxygen are cycled mostly as gases. Others such as sulfur, potassium, calcium, and phosphorus are involved in sedimentary cycles. The elements we have just mentioned are referred to as macronutrients and are needed in relatively large quantities by all organisms. Equally essential, but required in smaller amounts, are the micronutrients such as iron, manganese, copper, zinc, sodium, molybdenum, chlorine, and iodine. Unfortunately, details of micronutrient cycling are not yet very well known.

CARBON CYCLE: The cycling of carbon parallels the flow of energy through the trophic structure of the ecosystem. It begins with the fixation of CO_2 during photosynthesis (Fig. 6–12). About 10% to 50% of the carbohydrate produced during this process is used by the plant in respiration. This process evolves more CO_2, some of which is again made available for use in photosynthesis. The rest is stored in plant tissues. Some of this plant material is eaten by consumers and the carbon is either respired as CO_2 or stored as consumer biomass. The plant material not eaten is eventually decomposed,

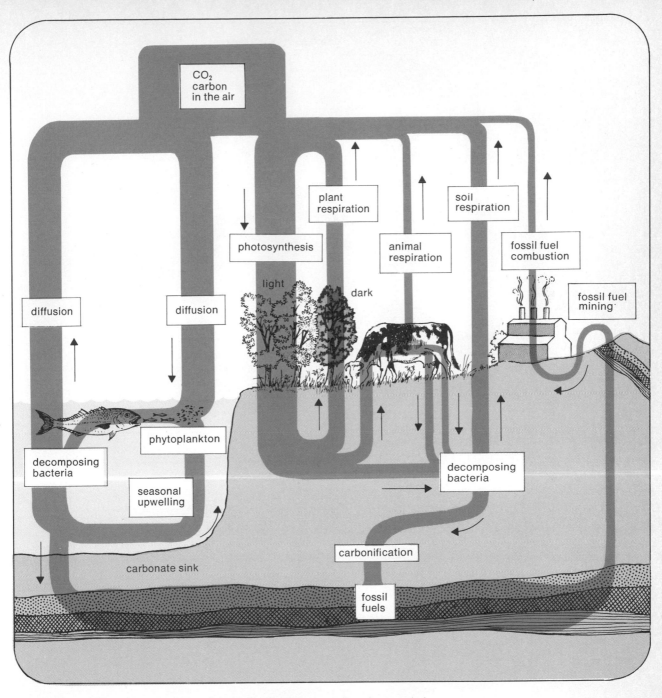

Figure 6–12 Like many other materials in the biosphere, carbon is recycled from the living to the nonliving and back to the living again.

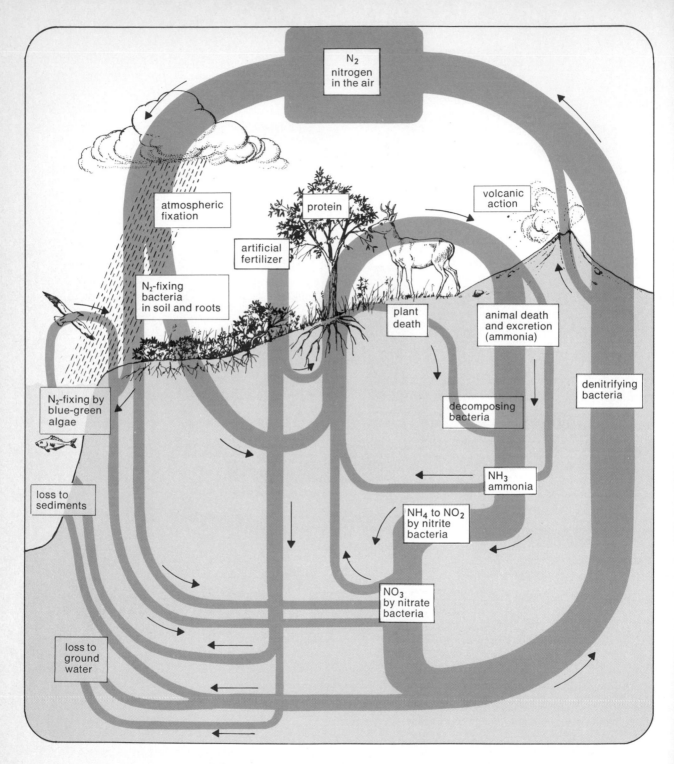

Figure 6–13 Nitrogen, like carbon, follows a variety of biochemical pathways.

along with the remains of dead consumers. That carbon is oxidized to carbon dioxide by the decomposers and released into the atmosphere, where it will be available to be recycled in the same way. Great quantities of fixed carbon were stored during the Pennsylvanian Period, some 300 million years ago, in the form of fossil fuels (coal, natural gas, and petroleum). Some has also been stored in deep ocean sediments as calcium carbonate ($CaCO_3$).

OXYGEN CYCLE: The oxygen cycle is closely related to the carbon cycle. Oxygen evolved during photosynthesis is used by plants and animals during respiration and is released as CO_2. Some free oxygen is produced from O_3 (ozone) and water vapor by ultraviolet radiation in the upper atmosphere, but most is produced during photosynthesis. Because oxygen is so reactive, much of it is tied up in mineral oxides as a result of weathering. Rusting, for instance, produces iron oxide.

An estimated 2.62×10^{15} grams of oxygen are produced by plants during photosynthesis every year in the United States. It has also been estimated that the consumption of oxygen in the United States—mostly through burning fossil fuels—is about 4.46×10^{15} grams annually. This means that we are consuming 70% more oxygen than we are producing. Obviously we in the United States depend on oxygen produced outside the country. Even though we "import" nearly half of our oxygen from other parts of the globe, no overall decline in the worldwide oxygen content of the atmosphere has yet been detected. So far, oxygen continues to make up 21% of the air, just as it has ever since man has been able to make that measurement.

Since in the United States every year at least one million acres of farm land are removed from production to make room for housing developments, shopping centers with their mammoth parking lots, freeways, and the other trappings of our culture, our reliance on outside sources of oxygen will continue to increase.

Some authorities estimate that about three-quarters of the world's oxygen supply is produced by phytoplankton (drifting, one-celled marine plants) in the ocean. Others contend that oxygen production by marine phytoplankton is much less. It is clear, however, that man's activities can only decrease this source of oxygen production, since various pesticides and industrial residues that we keep dumping into the ocean at a furious rate either inhibit or stop photosynthesis in many phytoplankton species. Possible long-term effects of this abuse are not difficult to imagine. But as with many other aspects of the game of ecological roulette man is playing, we cannot be sure of the outcome.

NITROGEN CYCLE: Although 78% of the atmosphere is nitrogen, this essential element is unavailable to living organisms in its molecular, atmospheric form (N_2). It must be "fixed" into nitrates (NO_3) before it can be used by the producers to make proteins (Fig. 6–13).

Some atmospheric nitrogen (about 2 lb/acre/yr) is fixed by lightning, and some (4 lb/acre/yr) is brought into the soil from other sources by rain. However, nearly all of the atmospheric nitrogen is made available to the biosphere by the activities of nitrogen-fixing bacteria and blue-green algae.

Some of these organisms are free-living and account for about six pounds per acre fixed per year. But the vast majority of nitrogen-fixing bacteria live in association with a few families of plants, especially plants of the pea family.

Dumbbell and rod-shaped bacteria of the genera *Rhizobium* and *Rhizobacter*, for example, live in small nodules on the roots of clover, alfalfa, and other legumes. They may be responsible for the fixation of 100 pounds of nitrogen per acre per year. These fixed nitrates are taken in by the producers in the system and may work their way up through the trophic levels. The nitrogen is returned to the soil either through animal excretion, as urea or ammonia, or through the action of the decomposers on the dead bodies of both producers and consumers.

The ammonia produced by the decomposers is converted to nitrites (NO_2) by the action of other soil microorganisms of the genus *Nitrosomonas*. They use the energy released in the conversion of NH_4^+ to NO_2^- as their sole energy source. The nitrites (NO_2^-) are further oxidized to nitrates (NO_3) by the action of still other soil bacteria, genus *Nitrobacter*. There are many kinds of soil bacteria that denitrify NO_3 and release N_2 back to the atmosphere where the cycle starts again.

Besides the activities of the denitrifying bacteria, nitrates are removed from the soil by leaching and erosion (7 lb/acre/yr), and by the action of nonleguminous plants (60 lb/acre/yr). Before the techniques of modern agriculture, the amount of nitrogen fixed and the amount lost through denitrification processes were in dynamic balance. However, massive applications of synthetic nitrogenous fertilizers have upset the cycle, and much more fixed nitrogen is now present in the ecosphere. Most of the fertilizer added to a field is not used by the plants; instead, it is washed off and ends up in surrounding waters. Because of the abundance of this usable nitrogen, smelly and unsightly algal blooms occur (Fig. 6–14). When the algae die, the decay process uses up the oxygen in the water, leading to the death of fish and other aquatic life. The unwanted nitrates also work their way into ground water and end up in domestic water supplies. Some California wells, for example, contain 113 parts per million of nitrates. That is 13 times the maximum tolerant dose for human consumption. Unfortunately, at the present time there is no economically feasible way to get nitrates out of natural waters.

The nitrate problem is further aggravated by the enormous production of manure by cattle. Ten thousand head of cattle produce 260 tons of manure each day. However, it is no longer economically profitable to sell this manure for fertilizer, so it too goes into the water supply and further increases the nitrate pollution already caused by the synthetic fertilizers. What the long-term effects of pesticides will be on soil microorganisms involved in the nitrogen cycle is still another unanswered question.

Figure 6–14 The algae bloom (a rapid proliferation of these photosynthetic organisms) in this body of water was caused by excessive nitrogen from fertilizer run-off.

PHOSPHORUS CYCLE: The phosphorus cycle is a good example of the movement of sedimentary nutrients through the environment (Fig. 6–15). Phosphorus occurs in adenosine triphosphate (ATP), a substance needed for energy transformations in living cells. Natural phosphates are found in such reservoirs as phosphate rock deposits, fossil animals, and bird guano.

Through the processes of weathering and leaching, phosphorus finds its way both into terrestrial and fresh-water ecosystems and into marine ecosystems. In varying degrees it then moves through the trophic levels. Some of the phosphates released by decomposers are recycled through the ecosystem, but a great deal becomes locked up as land deposits or is washed ultimately into the sea. Some of the marine phosphate is cycled through marine ecosystems by seasonal upwellings of shallow sediments. After a period of upwelling, the phosphate-enriched surface waters are conducive to phytoplankton growth. The population densities of these marine producers rise and are soon followed by the growth of herbivore populations. One way in which the phosphorus can be returned to terrestrial ecosystems is through sea birds acting as secondary consumers in this marine food chain. These birds leave large deposits of phosphate-rich guano. The guano can then be mined and the phosphates returned to land systems as fertilizer. Most of the marine phosphates, however, are stored over millions of years as ocean sediments. Eventually, they are returned to the land through geological processes leading to the formation of sedimentary rock. But in the context of human affairs, these processes are inexorably slow.

Figure 6–15 Phosphorus is an extremely important nutrient needed for energy transformations in living cells. Like carbon and nitrogen, phosphorus is recycled through terrestrial and aquatic ecosystems.

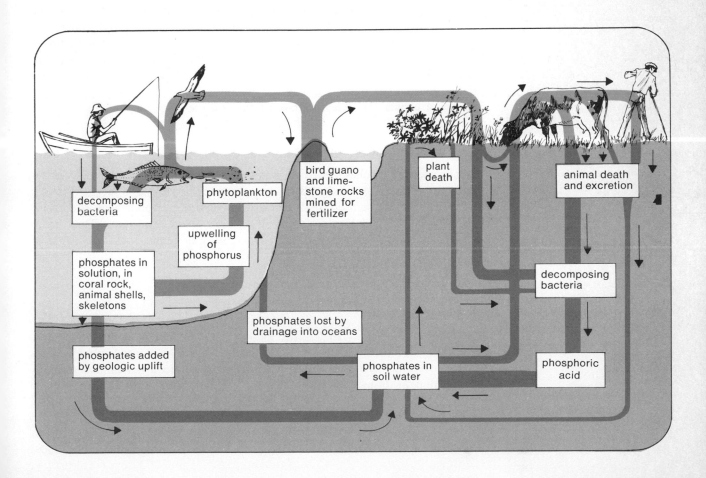

THE ORGANISM IN ITS ENVIRONMENT   139

Before man began to interfere with the natural recycling processes on a large scale, the slow return of phosphates to land ecosystems through geological processes was adequate. However, by depleting our natural phosphate reserves on land by mining phosphates for fertilizer and for use in industrial processes, it is quite possible that we have created a situation where the shortage of phosphates may become critically limiting, not only to natural ecosystems, but also to man-made agricultural ecosystems.

Man has brought about many other changes in natural cycles, both by adding large amounts of substances to active pools, and by adding to the environment new substances that enter biogeochemical cycles. Lead, which is poisonous, is one such substance. Since 1870 the lead content of the relatively remote polar ice has increased by a factor of 10 (from 20 mg/ton to 210 mg/ton). The release of lead into the atmosphere by industrial processes and by the burning of leaded gasoline is responsible for much of this increase. Hazardous isotopes, such as strontium^{90}, cesium^{137}, and krypton^{85}, which result from reprocessing fuel for nuclear reactors, or from residues from radioactive fallout, are new hazards that must also be reckoned with.

Sr^{90}, for example, behaves chemically very much like calcium and is readily taken up by plants from soil and water. As it moves up the trophic structure from one level to the next, it is found in increasingly high concentrations in the tissues of secondary and then tertiary consumers. Eventually it lodges in bone marrow and other blood making tissues. These tissues are extremely sensitive to radiation damage, and Sr^{90} is highly radioactive. When the ecosystem contaminated with Sr^{90} involves grass, cattle, and people, the reality of ecological cycles is driven home with somber emphasis.

The structure and dynamics of food chains

Solar energy reaches Earth's surface at an average rate of about 2.0 cal/cm^2/min. A maximum of only three-tenths of one percent (.003) is of a kind that can be used by the producers. However, even at that rate of use about 6.0×10^{17} kilocalories of energy are fixed per year. This figure represents the gross energy fixed. Remember that plants must use some of this energy (from 10% to 50%) for their own respiration. We can find the net annual production by using the equation:

$$GP - R = NP$$

Gross production (GP) less the amount used by plants in respiration (R) equals net production (NP). It turns out that net annual production is from 3.0×10^{17} to 5.0×10^{17} kcal, which translates into a net annual biomass production of from 150 billion to 200 billion metric tons of dry organic matter. Approximately two-thirds of this biomass is produced in terrestrial ecosystems, the remainder in the ocean.

What happens to all the energy that is fixed every year? Some is lost through rapid oxidation, or burning, and some is stored as living tissue.

The vast majority, however, is used by herbivores or by decomposers as the energy moves through the trophic levels. A straight-line movement of energy through an ecosystem is called a **food chain**. The amount of energy passed through the chain is an important regulator of the dynamics of the system, both at the abiotic and biotic levels.

Sometimes we think of food chains as beginning with the producers and ending with the last-link consumer, but there are also food chains at the decomposer level. Food chains are the simplest of trophic relationships within a community and may be as simple as four links, if we include the decomposers, but only three links if we don't:

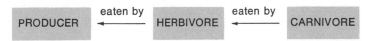

An example of such a short chain is found in the Arctic tundra, as follows:

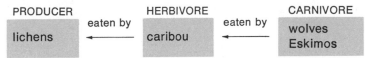

As more carnivores take part in the trophic structure, one or two more links may be added to the chain. However, food chains rarely exceed five links (including the producers but not the decomposers). We can find examples of a five-link chain in a fresh-water lake:

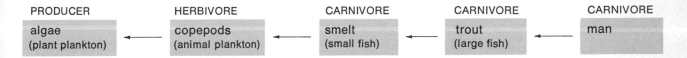

The reason for food chains being restricted to a maximum of five or six links becomes clear when we discover the efficiency with which its members use energy. In general, the efficiency of energy use of herbivores is quite low. At least 50% of the potential calories consumed by herbivores passes through their guts unused. When an herbivore's metabolism is operating at maximum efficiency, about 30% of the food it eats can be converted into living material. Energy from the rest is spent for maintenance of the animal. Thus, secondary production at the herbivore level in the food chain proceeds at about 15% *maximum* efficiency ($0.50 \times 0.30 = 0.15$). Furthermore, efficiencies approaching this level probably occur only in young, growing animals. Full-grown animals produce much less biomass. Certain kinds of herbivores have much lower efficiencies. For example, 90% of the food that aphids consume passes through these insects unused. So secondary production of aphid biomass proceeds at a maximum of 3% (0.10×0.30). An overall average figure for secondary production efficiency at this trophic level is probably somewhere in the neighborhood of 10%.

Carnivores (secondary, tertiary, and quarternary consumers) are somewhat more efficient users of the energy they take in. They may waste as little as 30%. A maximum of 70% efficiency times the 30% that can be incorporated into living material results in a 21% efficiency overall. Again, these figures estimate maximum use of caloric intake.

In that way we can quantify our simple lake food chain in terms of energy and biomass. In terms of energy, 100 kcal of algae produce 15 kcal of

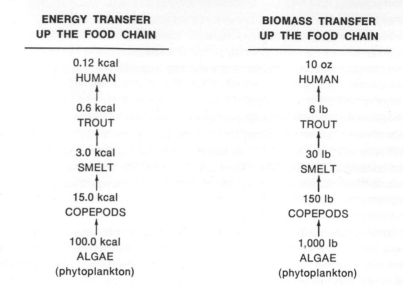

ENERGY TRANSFER UP THE FOOD CHAIN	BIOMASS TRANSFER UP THE FOOD CHAIN
0.12 kcal	10 oz
HUMAN	HUMAN
↑	↑
0.6 kcal	6 lb
TROUT	TROUT
↑	↑
3.0 kcal	30 lb
SMELT	SMELT
↑	↑
15.0 kcal	150 lb
COPEPODS	COPEPODS
↑	↑
100.0 kcal	1,000 lb
ALGAE	ALGAE
(phytoplankton)	(phytoplankton)

copepods. The 15 kcal of copepods produce about 3 kcal of smelt, which in turn provide energy for 0.6 kcal of trout. At the top link in the food chain 0.12 kcal could be tied up in human biomass.

In terms of biomass transfer, let's look at our food chain from the other direction. A nice six pound lake trout that you have just caught had to eat a minimum of 30 pounds of smelt to grow that large. Those smelt had consumed at least 150 pounds of copepods, which in turn had eaten more than 1,000 pounds, or one-half ton, of phytoplankton. After the trout has been cleaned, the edible meat may amount to three pounds. A young, growing child might be able to convert that to about 10 ounces of flesh.

Building an efficiency model

We can base a simple model on our efficiency data and find out why food chains rarely exceed five links. We will call the species involved in our hypothetical food chain S_1, S_2, S_3, and so on. By looking at our algae–smelt–copepod food chain, we can safely assume two things: first, that if S_1 is the producer in the system, then the numbers of S_1 will be greater than S_2, and that the numbers of S_2 will be greater than S_3, and so on. Second, we can also assume that the size of S_5 will be greater than S_4, and that the size of S_4 will be greater than S_3, and so on since predators generally are larger and less abundant than their prey.

Let's further assume that the body size at each level in the chain is five times the size of the next lower level. What can we predict about the size of the S_5 level individuals in relation to those on the S_1 level? How many individuals at the S_1 level are needed to support one individual at the S_5 level? Let's assume a realistic 10% efficiency overall. Some simple mathematics show that under these conditions, one consumer at the S_5 level will require the existence of 10,000 producer units at the S_1 level. If we can visualize a terrestrial system with the herbivore (S_2 level) being one inch long, and our size ratio is constant all the way up the food chain, a quarternary consumer will have to be more than ten feet long!

These relationships are often pictured as energy biomass pyramids. Howard T. Odum constructed a biomass pyramid for a thermal spring at Silver Springs, Florida (Fig. 6–16). This spring flowed at nearly a constant temperature of 22°C to 23°C all year, and mineral nutrients were continually renewed. The only major annual variable was day length. Odum was able to estimate the biomass at the various trophic levels and express it as a pyramid, with about 810 g/m² of producers at the base, mostly eel grass and some algae. There were 37 g/m² of herbivores on the next level, followed by 11 g/m² of carnivores. The top level of the pyramid was occupied by 1.5 g/m² of top carnivores (large fish). About 5 g/m² of decomposers (bacteria and crayfish) completed the system.

Odum was also able to construct a balance sheet showing energy flow through the system. On the income side of the ledger was primary productivity of 6,370 g/m²/yr of biomass and 120 g/m²/yr of bread thrown into the water by tourists as fish food. Outgo consisted of 6,000 g/m²/yr due to respiration, and 766 g/m²/yr exported downstream. As we would expect from the first law of thermodynamics, the income and the outgo were roughly in balance, totaling 6,490 g/m²/yr and 6,766 g/m²/yr respectively.

Figure 6–16 This pyramid shows an estimate of the biomass at various trophic levels for a thermal spring studied by Odum.

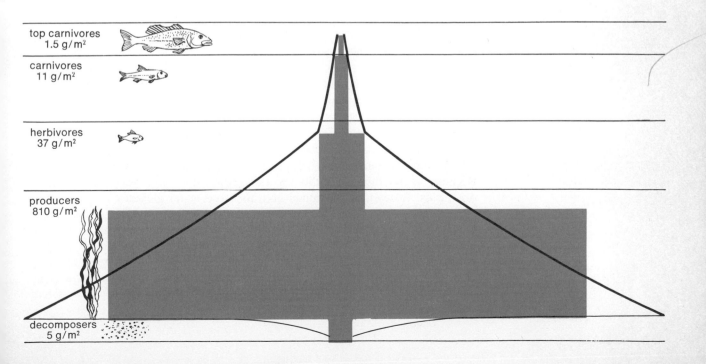

top carnivores
1.5 g/m²

carnivores
11 g/m²

herbivores
37 g/m²

producers
810 g/m²

decomposers
5 g/m²

Odum also estimated the number of kilocalories of energy fixed per year by the various trophic levels and calculated the efficiencies involved. Although the transfer of energy from the producer to the herbivore level was calculated at a rather high 16%, the efficiencies averaged about 10% at each level of transfer. Only about 1.2% of the energy fixed by the producers got to the top carnivores at the peak of the pyramid.

The 10% rule of efficiency also applies to man-made food chains. It takes at least 10,000 pounds of fodder to produce 1,000 pounds of beef. Obviously it would be far more efficient if human consumption were on the herbivore level instead of on the carnivore level. Surprisingly, some of our large-scale farming practices end up on the debit side of the energy ledger. LaMont Cole has estimated that the fossil fuels used by farm machinery during planting, cultivating, and harvesting operations on some of our large wheat farms contain more calories than are contained by the crops being harvested! Rather than living off the "interest" of fixed energy, we are spending our "capital," or savings, which has been stored in the form of fossil fuels. If the human population and environmental degradation continue to increase at the present rate, we will soon have to drop down a link in our food chains, meaning that we will be eating more vegetables and less meat. Further into the future, generations yet to be born may have to face the problem of harvesting increasingly more food without the benefit of petroleum-powered machinery.

Pesticides in the food chain

Another extremely important aspect of food chains is their ability to accumulate increasingly high concentrations of certain substances. DDT, DDE, and other pesticides classified as "chlorinated hydrocarbons" break down extremely slowly. DDT, for instance, has a half-life of 15 years. When these chlorinated hydrocarbons do eventually break down they usually form other substances that are equally toxic—or even more toxic than the original compounds.

In very small quantities neither the original compounds nor their breakdown products are particularly toxic to mammals or birds. However, insecticides of the chlorinated hydrocarbon type are extremely soluble in fats but not very soluble in water. Because they are fat soluble (lipophilic), the toxins are concentrated at successive trophic levels as they move along the food chain. For example, when DDT is sprayed over water for mosquito control, or on a field where it soon finds its way into water as it is washed off by rains, some quantity of the pesticide is taken in by phytoplankton. Because of its high solubility in fats, DDT does not pass out of these organisms. Instead, it is retained and dissolved in fat globules.

Let's consider a hypothetical example of a minute application of DDT that results in only 100,000 DDT molecules entering a body of water. If each individual alga in our five-link food chain took in 10 of these DDT molecules, all of the molecules would be concentrated in 10,000 algae. This number of algal cells would furnish food for 1,000 copepods, which in turn would be consumed by 100 smelt. The 10 trout that could be supported by this system would furnish food for one top carnivore. The top carnivore could receive the full dose of 100,000 DDT molecules.

Even though small quantities of these compounds are not toxic to vertebrates, by the time they have gone through the concentrating effect of food chains the quantities are no longer small. High concentrations of DDT have been found in many birds that occupy top positions in food chains. Examples include California brown pelicans, western grebes, and peregrine falcons. High concentrations of DDT and oher chlorinated hydrocarbons interfere with the calcium metabolism in these and other birds. The result is that contaminated birds produce thin eggshells that break during incubation. The overall result is that reproduction effectively stops. Populations of these birds that once were reasonably common in areas where there is heavy use of DDT are now pathetically small, some of the species nearing extinction.

The effects of DDT on human beings are not well understood. Only a fool or a pathological optimist would assume that large concentrations of a substance that has been shown to interfere seriously with vital physiological processes in birds are not harmful to humans. Even if all use of chlorinated hydrocarbon insecticides were stopped immediately, we would be able to observe its effects for many years to come. Because of its extremely slow breakdown time, more than half of the DDT that has ever been produced is still present in the global ecosystem.

Simple food chains, such as our algae–copepod–smelt–trout chain are relatively rare in nature. There are too many chances for catastrophe inherent in such a system. For example, if unseasonably dry weather prevented the smelt from entering streams to spawn during a particular year, the smelt populations in our lake would be seriously reduced the following year. Increased predation pressure by trout would further depress the smelt populations, and large numbers of trout would starve. Copepods, on the other hand, would become overabundant, overgraze the algae, and then experience a massive die-off because of a shortage of phytoplankton. Drawn as an open-ended feedback loop, we can picture the chain of events like this:

It is easy to see that a critical disturbance in one link in a food chain is likely to have catastrophic effects in other links. Communities in which resources are shared tend to be much less liable to catastrophe. In such situations food chains have become interlinked, forming food webs.

The structure and dynamics of food webs

As a general rule, herbivores usually are confined to that one trophic level. However, organisms higher up in the trophic hierarchy often operate at two or three levels at once. Even in a relatively simple community, such as the Arctic tundra, trophic levels become interlinked and form **food webs**.

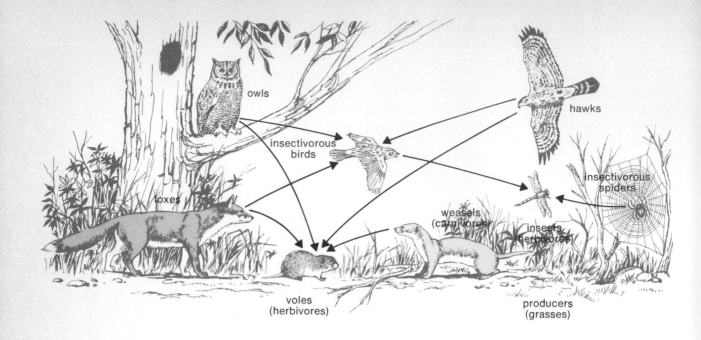

owls

insectivorous
birds

hawks

insectivorous
spiders

foxes

weasels
(carnivores)

insects
(herbivores)

voles
(herbivores)

producers
(grasses)

Figure 6–17 A typical food web consists of a variety of organisms operating on a variety of trophic levels. Various checks and balances tend to make food webs more stable than straight-line food chains. Why should that be?

To get some feeling for the way a food web operates, let's take a superficial look at another segment of the Arctic tundra community (Fig. 6–17). The producers in this system are grasses, which are eaten by herbivores, including insects, voles, and lemmings. (Lemmings are rodents famous for population explosions that occasionally end with dramatic mass marches into the sea.) The insects in this food web are preyed upon by spiders and by insectivorous birds. The birds also eat the spiders. Hawks and owls, as well as weasels and foxes, eat both the lemmings and the insectivorous birds. If the lemming populations crash for some reason or other, a few top carnivores are able to subsist on birds until the lemming populations build up again. Although it is oversimplified, this sketch of an Arctic food web at least illustrates the principle that checks and balances and divergent channels for energy flow make for much greater stability than straight-line food chains do.

Stability and succession in communities

STABILITY: The stability of a community and the amount of energy necessary to maintain it depend on the community's structure. The structure in turn depends on the number and relative abundance of species in the community, called its **species diversity**. There are many ways of measuring species diversity. The simplest is to count the number of species per unit area. Such an index is useful in a general sort of way. For example, it can tell us that there are perhaps 100 different tree species per square mile in a tropical rain forest, but only about 25 in a temperate forest. While such information is useful to us, it is also useful to know the relative abundances of species in a community. If we hope to find out about divergent channels of energy flow, we must know if the species are evenly distributed, or if there are one or two extremely abundant species and many rare ones.

For example, consider two communities each having five species. The percentage occurrence of species in the first community is 20–20–20–20–20, but in the second community it is 96–1–1–1–1. We would expect interactions between all species to occur frequently in the first community, but interspecies interactions would occur only rarely in the second. We could further predict that a catastrophe affecting one population in the first situation would not have as much of an effect on the community as a catastrophe occurring to the abundant species in the second. Conversely, the disappearance of one of the extremely rare species in the second community would have little effect on its complexity while the disappearance of one of the species from community number one would have relatively more effect.

The number of alternate pathways for energy flow in a community is considered to be a resource, just as energy, space, and matter are resources. Ecologists call this resource **information**. One way that the amount of information in an ecological system can be increased is an increase in **equitability**. In this context, equitability is a measure of the relative abundances of species in a system. For example, our previous example of a five-species community in which each species comprises 20% of the total is more equitable and contains more information than the community with the same number of species distributed 96–1–1–1–1. The second way that information can be increased in an ecological system is by adding more species to the system. Thus, a community with 20 species with relatively equal abundances is more diverse and contains more information than one with five evenly distributed species.

Because there are more channels for energy flow in ecosystems with high information content, these systems are less liable to catastrophe and hence are more stable. Furthermore, complex ecosystems—ecosystems with high species diversity and high information content—require less energy to maintain themselves than do systems with simpler structure, fewer species, less equitability, and low information. Newly established ecosystems tend to increase in complexity through time, so long as the environment is stable enough to allow this complexity to develop. Environmental stability does not necessarily mean constancy, incidentally, although a constant environment such as a wet tropical forest is indeed a stable one. Predictable environments, those that go through recognizable patterns of change such as seasonal variation, are also stable environments from a biological standpoint.

SUCCESSION: The patterns of change that occur as an ecosystem ages are called **succession**. Succession proceeds through a number of recognizable stages, called **seres**, which culminate in a so-called **climax community**. Early successional stages are characterized by a high flow of energy per unit biomass and low efficiency of energy use. Because photosynthesis goes on at a much greater rate than respiration (the P/R ratio is greater than 1), there is an increase in biomass. Early seres have low species diversity. Species characteristic of these early stages have fast generation times and high potential rates of increase, and they tend to be capable of living under a wide range of conditions (Fig. 6–18).

As succession proceeds and the system matures, the total biomass increases. The non-living components of the biomass increase as well. This two-fold development results in an increase in both the number and types of habitats available in the community, and, therefore, an increase in available niches. As new niches open up, more species can occupy the community, and species diversity increases (Fig. 6–19). As the system matures, gross production keeps

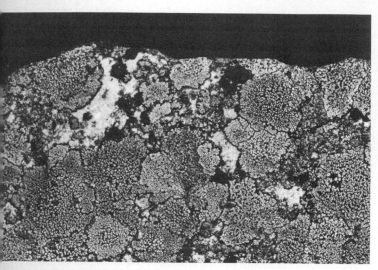 

Figure 6–18 A pioneer stage in succession is represented here by a community of lichens on rock.

Figure 6–19 A more advanced stage (continuing from that shown in Fig. 6–18) is represented by this mixed community of lichens, mosses, and seedlings taking root in the newly-formed soil.

rising, but after a time it reaches a plateau. Eventually gross production is balanced by respiration within the system (the P/R ratio $= 1$) and the accumulation of additional biomass ceases.

Since biological systems seem to evolve toward the most efficient use of energy, the climax community (Fig. 6–20) probably represents the most efficient community that can exist in a particular environment. A climax community of high structure and high species diversity has more trophic levels, and because energy flows through more diverse channels, the stability of the system is maximized. The species associated with climax communities tend to be less flexible and less adaptable to environmental changes than are species characteristic of earlier seral communities. Because of the increased number of niches available, the species of climax communities are faced with an array of different selective pressures, and evolution can proceed in different directions and at different rates. Because these species tend to be more specialized and less adaptable, they may be more prone to extinction by fairly mild perturbations in the system. However, as we have already seen, removal of one species from a complex community has fewer effects on the community than removal of a species from a simple community.

A drastic environmental change, however, either man-caused or natural, is a catastrophic event for a climax community. For example, if a forest is logged by clear-cutting, the environment is rendered completely unsuitable for climax species. The only way for a climax community to re-establish itself

Figure 6–20 The climax community, following the previous stages of succession shown in Figs. 6–18 and 6–19 is a north coniferous forest. Notice that in each of the three stages there is an increase in species diversity.

after it has been destroyed is for succession to begin anew. The time scale involved in succession for most terrestrial communities is a hundred years or so at the very least. More often thousands of years are necessary. Once a climax community has been lost, it is gone forever so far as man's life span is concerned.

As an example of succession, consider what happens when farm land is abandoned in the Piedmont uplands of the southeastern United States (Fig. 6–21). After one year, horseweed (*Erigeron*) grows in almost pure stands on

Figure 6–21 When farm land is abandoned in the Piedmont uplands of the southeastern United States, several stages of succession ranging over about 200 years are required before a stable climax community of oak, hickory, and other hardwoods is established.

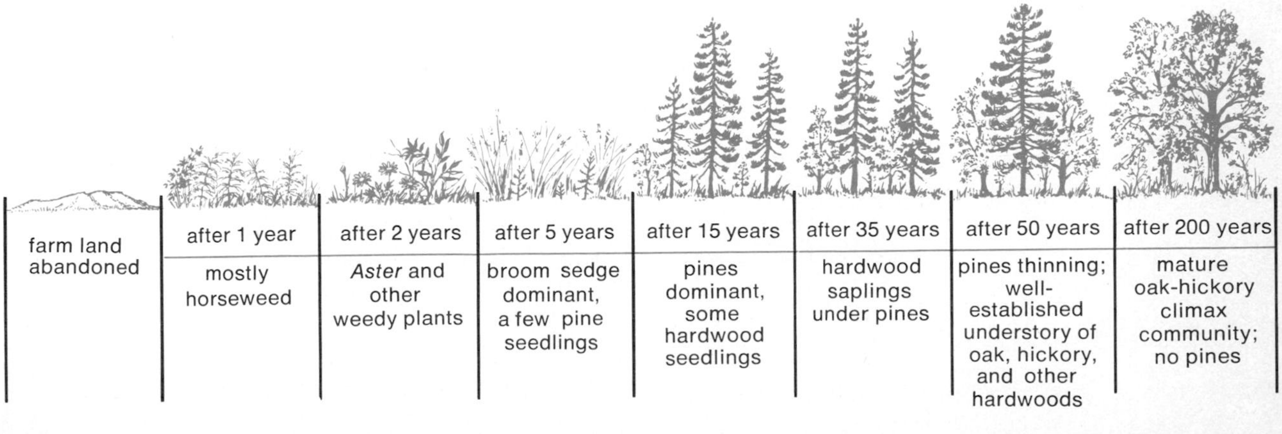

farm land abandoned	after 1 year	after 2 years	after 5 years	after 15 years	after 35 years	after 50 years	after 200 years
	mostly horseweed	*Aster* and other weedy plants	broom sedge dominant, a few pine seedlings	pines dominant, some hardwood seedlings	hardwood saplings under pines	pines thinning; well-established understory of oak, hickory, and other hardwoods	mature oak-hickory climax community; no pines

the field. Thus, the first seral stage in this successional sequence has a species diversity close to zero. The second year, species diversity is still low, but the horseweed has been replaced by a few other weedy plants, the most common of which is *Aster*. After five years, broom sedge (*Andropogon*) is dominant. There are a few scattered herbs and young pine seedlings begin to establish themselves. After 15 years the pines form a dense stand. All the field herbs have been eliminated. However, hardwood seedlings may be found growing under the pines. Thirty-five years after the field was abandoned saplings of many hardwood species can be found growing under the pines, and 50 years after the process began an understory of oak, hickory, and other hardwoods is well established under the now thinning pines. If there is no drastic disturbance to the environment, a fully mature oak-hickory climax community will develop on the site within 200 years.

Diversity and stability of a community or ecosystem are easily alterable by man's hand. From oil spills on a relatively small scale to the great "dust bowl" of the 1930s on a large scale, we have ample evidence that this is true. We still have much to learn about the long-term effects of man's tampering with the environment, but we do know that the net effects of man's activities result in simplification and loss of diversity and information. Most natural systems are rich in variety and complexity, but by comparison, man-made ecosystems such as cities or agricultural crops are extreme in their simplicity. Population explosions of rats, starlings, and pigeons provide monotonous evidence of the inherent instability of urban and suburban areas. The decimation of more than 10% of the 1970 corn crop in the Midwest by a blight attests to the fact that agricultural ecosystems are also terribly unstable. Even though thus far it has usually been possible for us to prevent pests from totally consuming our crops by massive applications of insecticides, and to produce high agricultural yields by applying large doses of fertilizer, the calamities that result when these practices stop remind us that any semblance of stability or regulation in man-made systems requires a huge input of energy under human control.

Man's activities are now affecting the few remaining natural systems, no matter how remote. DDT, smog, radioactive substances, and the leakage of various toxins into the biosphere are as effective as the bulldozer or chain saw in weakening climax communities by selectively removing species from them. As diversity declines, stability is also sure to decline as many divergent channels for energy flow are eliminated. Unfortunately, we do not yet have enough knowledge to predict the results of the elimination of 10 or 100 species from various ecosystems. Furthermore, the implications of such simplification and the reversal of long-term evolutionary trends toward complex, stable systems are also imperfectly known. One thing, however, does seem certain. The cost to mankind for turning most of the planet into an impoverished and unstable system cannot help but be immense.

1 Explain the meaning of "You can't win" and of "You can't even break even" as examples of the first and second laws of thermodynamics.

2 Give an example of a four-link food chain in a typical terrestrial habitat near where you live; also of a typical aquatic habitat. Why are food chains restricted to a maximum of five or six links?

3 Explain the meaning of the following statement made in this chapter: "Rather than living off the 'interest' of fixed energy, we are spending our 'capital,' or savings, which has been stored in the form of fossil fuels."

4 Explain the significance of a biogeochemical cycle by tracing one in detail. Amplify this statement: "When the ecosystem contaminated with Sr^{90} involves grass, cattle, and people, the reality of ecological cycles is driven home with somber emphasis."

5 Cite five examples of the following concept: *Living organisms are continually exchanging matter and energy with the environment.*

6 What is the significance of the following statement? "A man-made ecosystem, such as a large city, is extreme in its simplicity."

SELECTED READINGS

The Biosphere. A Scientific American Book. San Francisco: W. H. Freeman & Co., 1970. A fine collection of articles dealing with energy flow and nutrient cycling in the world ecosystem. The articles are well written, not too technical, and superbly illustrated.

Odum, Eugene P. *Fundamentals of Ecology.* 3rd ed. Philadelphia: W. B. Saunders Co., 1971. An encyclopedic book by a distinguished ecologist, who treats the subjects of this chapter in much greater detail.

Whittaker, Robert H. *Communities and Ecosystems.* New York: The Macmillan Company, 1970. A short but scholarly book, written from a plant ecologist's point of view. Somewhat technical but required reading for anyone interested in the organization of natural communities.

Figure 7–1 Two male moose compete for a mate. Competition for mates, for food, and for living space are all behavioral factors that influence the future course of animal populations.

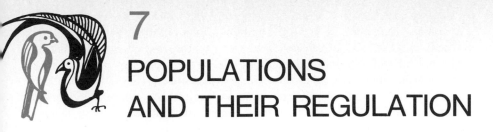

7
POPULATIONS
AND THEIR REGULATION

WHAT IS A POPULATION?

Individuals and populations

Remember that in Chapter 6 we defined a population as a group of similarly adapted, interbreeding organisms belonging to the same species. This means that a population functions as an evolutionary unit. Understanding how populations of organisms grow, interact, change, and become extinct is essential to an understanding of ecology (Fig. 7–1). Ecologists sometimes tend to overlook the fact that their basic units are populations; however, agreeing on what constitutes a proper population is not as easy as it might seem to be.

Sometimes it is even difficult to define individuals. As one drives through the Rocky Mountains, large stands of deciduous trees are often conspicuous among the conifers, which are the characteristic vegetation. These deciduous trees are quaking aspen (*Populus tremuloides*), relatives of birches, poplars, and cottonwoods. Studies of aspen groves show that often an entire grove consists of one genetic individual, meaning that each "tree" has the identical genetic makeup of all other trees in the grove, and all are connected through a common root system. The groves are a result of vegetative reproduction, in which roots give rise to aerial sprouts that form another tree. (Taking a cutting from one plant to start a new plant is another example of vegetative reproduction.)

In the case of the aspen, each tree may be considered an ecological individual despite the fact that it is only a small part of a larger whole. Although a biologist interested in the *genetics* of aspen trees must consider the entire grove as a single individual in a population that might include all aspen groves in the entire mountain range, an ecologist interested in the *productivity* of an aspen grove could justifiably treat one grove as a population consisting of many individuals.

A similar problem may occur in other types of forests. Roots of trees graft themselves to roots of other trees, either of the same species or of different species. Stumps of cut trees have lived for many years because of natural root grafts. The stump is kept alive through the photosynthetic activities of its neighbors. In this case it is clear that the two root-grafted trees are genetically different individuals, but how they function as individuals along ecological lines is not quite so clear.

Problems of defining individuals also occur in certain simple organisms, as discussed in Chapter 2 when *Volvox* and *Pandorinia* were described. We face similar problems in certain symbiotic relationships. **Symbiosis** is a condition in which the life histories of two or more organisms of different species are intimately related. Sometimes one of the organisms is harmed by the relationship while the other one benefits **(parasitism)** (Fig. 7–2). Or one benefits while the other one doesn't seem to receive any apparent advantage **(commensalism)**. Or perhaps both may benefit **(mutualism)** as with lichens (Fig. 6–18). All three situations may present problems when we try to seek out the "individual."

For example, certain species of *Hydra* (minute fresh-water relatives of

Figure 7–2 Parasitism, a common mode of life, is shown here by the squaw root, a coniferous plant that is parasitic on oak tree roots.

jellyfish) have symbiotic algae living in their outer layer of cells. It is clear that the algae benefit from the hydra since the algae are provided with a protective environment. The benefits that the hydra receive from this association are not so apparent, but there is evidence that under certain conditions hydra with algae function better than hydra without algae. So, what we would normally consider an individual hydra can be regarded as a hydra-algae complex forming one functional unit.

An even more striking aspect of this problem is posed by termites and the protozoans that live in their gut. Termites, like most other animals, do not have enzymes that can digest cellulose, a principal component of wood. The protozoans do have the enzymes, however, so by living in the guts of termites they are guaranteed a plentiful supply of cellulose. The protozoans partially digest the cellulose, converting it to a form that can be digested by the termites, so the association is clearly one of mutual benefit. Again, what we think of as an "individual" termite actually is a termite–protozoan complex. Without its protozoans, the termite is not a functional unit since it would starve to death within a mountain of food.

Furthermore, once defined, individuals comprising a single species are rarely if ever distributed uniformly. Since some areas within the range of a species usually are suitable for its survival and reproduction while other areas are not, a species is often fractioned into many populations, and each one then acts as an evolutionary unit. While one population adapts to one set of local conditions, a population elsewhere adapts to a rather different set of conditions. Eventually, the two populations diverge from each other. Most often, divergence of this sort is reflected in relatively small differences in gene frequencies between the populations. If more pronounced divergence occurs, the populations are sometimes called different subspecies.

Because the environment is a mosaic, sub-units of a population having many of the properties of the total population may occur on a local level. Because these sub-units are of a transient nature, they are not significant in an evolutionary sense. We can call these units **local populations** and define them as groups that exist as some sort of ecologically functional entities. Such a population is said to be **interspersed**.

As an example, let us consider wild populations of the fruit fly *Drosophila melanogaster*. Large local populations of these flies are commonly found in garbage cans, but those populations are almost certainly not evolutionary units. We would not expect to find significant differences in gene frequencies between any of the fly populations living in all the garbage cans throughout a large city. But we might expect to find significant differences in gene frequencies if we compared New York City's flies with those collected in, say, San Francisco. If so, the two cities would have different *Drosophila melanogaster* populations, and each of these evolutionary units would be composed of hundreds of local populations. Since by our definition a population is an evolutionary unit, many of its properties may be significantly different from other nearby populations of the same species. It is essential that we understand populations in the context of their genetic properties and evolutionary status when we try to define their functional roles in communities.

Figure 7–3 A species' range, in this case that of the mountain lion, includes all those regions regularly occupied by the species (dark areas). Can you think of a species with a very limited range? How would you describe the range of codfish?

Population structure

All of those things that play a part in controlling the patterns of gamete union in a population contribute to the population's structure. This includes the distribution of the population, its dispersion, dispersal, density, mating systems, social systems, and age structure. Population structure is often defined only in the context of age structure, but this is far too restrictive a definition. While an understanding of population structure provides us with a picture of populations in space, the study of the rates of genetic change in populations and the rates of growth or decline in population size provide us with a picture of a population in time. Both facets—how populations vary in time and in space—should be examined simultaneously but seldom are.

DISTRIBUTION: When we speak of the **range** of a species we are describing where the species occurs on a wide geographic scale (Fig. 7–3). The range of the Bay Area checkerspot butterfly, *Euphydryas editha,* is the western United States from Colorado westward and from Oregon south to Baja, California. The butterfly is not distributed uniformly throughout this rather large region, however, but is found only in certain areas. In California, for example, it is found in the San Francisco Bay region, San Benito and San Luis Obispo counties, the San Bernardina Mountains, and a few other local areas. An examination of its distribution around San Francisco Bay, for example, would reveal that it is found in only a few restricted localities there also—on Mount Diablo, San Bruno Mountain, Woodside, and Jasper Ridge near Palo Alto. And research has shown that the colony on Jasper Ridge consists of three local populations.

DISPERSION: We can get an even finer resolution on population distribution by finding out about the dispersion of organisms. Dispersion is the spacial distribution of organisms within a local population. When the location of one organism in a population does not influence the location of another organism, we say that the population is **randomly** dispersed. Random dispersions are rare in nature, however. More often, organisms occur in aggregations, at which times the dispersion pattern is said to be **clumped**. When organisms are more evenly spaced than random—for example, in territorial organisms such as most song birds and some mammals—we say that the dispersion of the population is regular.

The dispersion patterns of mammals often consist of a **home range** and a **territory** (Fig. 7–4). The home range includes the entire area over which the animal conducts its activities. A territory is a smaller area within the home range, an area that the animal defends against other individuals of the same species. In some cases, the boundaries of a home range and a territory are the same. In others, home ranges overlap with the home ranges of neighbors.

DISPERSAL: The movement of individuals from one place to another is called dispersal, so dispersal and dispersion are quite different. Certain features of the landscape may act as a barrier preventing organisms with poor dispersal powers to occupy other suitable areas of the habitat. For example, there are

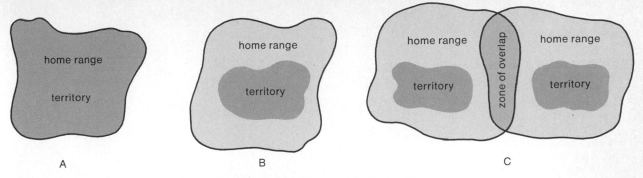

Figure 7–4 In some cases (A) an animal's entire home range may be its territory, and the animal will defend it against other individuals of the same species. In other cases (B) an animal may defend a territory occupying only a small part of its home range. In such cases it is common for home ranges to overlap (C), but not for territories to overlap.

many limestone outcroppings scattered through the southwestern United States. Each one has its own distinctive land snail species. The fact that we do not find one or two widely distributed species is good evidence that weak dispersal powers limit the distribution of these snails.

Another common limitation to dispersal and colonization is climate. Tropical butterfly species cannot establish populations in the American Midwest because of the winter cold. However, from time to time in late summer a few individuals of some tropical species are taken by collectors, which indicates that the dispersal powers of these species are adequate but that other influences must prevent their successful colonization. In this case an extrinsic influence, or some factor of the external environment, has set limits for the distribution of these species.

Once in a while we come across a population of organisms that does not occupy all of the apparently favorable habitat within its range, even though the individuals seem to have adequate powers of dispersal to colonize these areas. The reasons for such limited distributions are challenging questions for the ecologist. Occasionally, we discover that a seemingly suitable area is unsuitable for reasons that were not immediately apparent. In other cases the influence limiting dispersal seems to be intrinsic, or found within the organism and not in the external environment. Intrinsic barriers, then, are behavioral limitations to dispersal.

The Bay Area checkerspot butterfly mentioned earlier provides an interesting example of this type of behavior. One of the three local populations that has been studied on the Jasper Ridge experimental area of Stanford University is found on an extensive "island" of grassland surrounded by shrubby chaparral. The chaparral is an unsuitable habitat, but much of the grassland area is suitable. However, this population never occupies all of the suitable habitat available to it at any one time, although over several years all of the acceptable habitat probably is occupied at one time or another. Even though these butterflies provide an example of intrinsic barriers to dispersal, the mechanisms influencing such behavior are poorly understood.

Figure 7–5 J. B. Calhoun, a scientist at the National Institute of Mental Health, stands amid the "mouse universe" he designed for the study of overpopulation and crowding. The universe, with a capacity to feed and water nearly 4,000 mice, has runways along the floor of the 10-foot-square open space. Surrounding walls have wire-enclosed columns for access to "high-rise apartments." Between each set of four columns is a food supply, and water is available from large bottles. Ample nesting materials are provided. Starting with eight healthy white mice—four male and four female—the universe soon reached an "ideal" population of 600 animals, but continued to grow. When the number reached 2,200, behavior patterns had become so erratic that all rearing of young ceased. The population grew older and passed the age of conception without raising additional young. The remaining animals eventually died of old age.

Population density

The number of individuals occupying a given area in a given time is what we mean by population **density**. Each local population has a theoretical optimum density, which is defined as that density at which the probability of persisting for another generation is maximized. Laboratory demonstrations with cultures of *Drosophila,* for example, show that there is an optimum density at which adult flies live longest. Under conditions of either greater or lesser crowding, life expectancy decreases. Under proper conditions, the population will come into reproductive equilibrium near this optimum level. Later, when we take up population regulation, we will have something to say about natural populations maintaining themselves at such optimum density levels. Here, all we want to do is consider some of the disadvantages of very high or very low densities.

There are many obvious disadvantages to overcrowding: lack of food, lack of space, and lack of several less tangible resources (Fig. 7–5). At high densities, territorial birds may spend so much time defending their territories that they cannot devote enough time to incubating their eggs or feeding their young. Under these circumstances reproduction is almost sure to fail.

The locust plagues that overrun parts of Africa and Asia from time to time are the result of a response to overcrowded conditions. As local populations of *Schistocerca gregaria* become more dense, both morphological and behavioral changes occur in the individual members of these populations. When the density is low the insects are solitary, but as density increases, a gregarious phase begins to appear. The switch from a solitary to a gregarious phase takes longer than one generation, and the transformation seems to be helped along by increases in the frequency of contacts occurring between the nymphs. A positive feedback loop (Fig. 7–6) is established: As population density increases, frequency of contact increases, which in turn hastens the gregarious phase shift. Eventually, enormous flights of these insects occur as

Figure 7–6

peak density is reached. Such flights usually cause widespread damage to crop plants and natural vegetation. This is followed by a massive die-off and the density of the few survivors generally remains at a low level for several years.

At times, high population densities may be advantageous. The average survival time of goldfish poisoned with colloidal silver was found to be much longer when the fish were in groups than when they were alone. Evidently the slime secreted by the fish precipitated the silver before it could poison them. A single fish could not secrete enough slime to precipitate the silver at a rate fast enough for survival, but ten or so individuals secreted enough slime to remove most of the silver.

Individual chances of survival from predation may be greater at high densities than at lower ones. The immature stages of periodical cicadas remain underground for a number of years, thirteen for one species, seventeen for another. At the end of this time the adults emerge in enormous numbers. This delayed emergence protects the cicada population from high densities of predators. A yearly emergence of these insects could support a population of predators able to locate most of the insects on emergence. Massive emergences many years apart, however, do not provide a food resource sufficient to sustain a predator population. Also, it is highly unlikely that the few predators that could subsist on other prey during non-emergence years would consume enough of the breeding stock to endanger the population.

The schooling of fishes is advantageous for similar reasons. It is fairly easy for predators to capture solitary fish. However, the presence of a large number of watchful fish reduces a predator's chances of remaining undetected. Even if a predator captures one or two fish from the school, the rest of the school can escape. The phenomenon of **social facilitation** is another advantage of high population density. In some animal species individuals kept in groups learn faster than those leading a solitary life.

There are also definite disadvantages to low population densities, or undercrowding. The probability of finding mates may be very low in rare species. The Asian rhinoceros, *Dicerorhinus sumatrensis,* ranges widely throughout Southeast Asia. The population has been so reduced in recent years that there may not be more than fifty or so of the animals left. (In many Oriental cultures, when prepared in a certain way the "horn" of this animal is reputed to have aphrodisiac powers.) Both sexes of the species defend territories, except during the breeding season. Then, they leave their territories and wander about in search of mates. Because individuals are now so widely scattered, due to over-hunting and their territorial habits, the chance of a male and a female finding each other during the very brief breeding season is quite remote. Needless to say, the prognosis for survival of this species is grim.

A similar problem faces most of the few remaining species of great whales. Populations are now so low and the distances over which whales range so large, that the chances of a male and female whale of the same species, both in breeding condition, meeting each other are greatly reduced. The lack of genetic variability in these small remnant populations is also a threat to species survival. This is because reduced populations contain only a small part of the genetic variability once present in the species, and it is this variability that allows species to survive when inevitable environmental changes occur.

Mating systems and social systems

The dispersion patterns of populations may be in response to an environmental stimulus, such as patches of favorable habitat, or they may be a result of the response of one organism to another. In most cases, the distribution of plants is a response to environmental stimuli, but animals, with their sensory capacities and powers of locomotion, usually respond to both.

Animal aggregations resulting from the response of one animal to another are called **social systems**, which are given detailed attention in Chapter 10. Social systems introduce a second order of complexity to population studies because they may form sub-units of varying permanence and importance within a population. One of the simplest systems is that of the **pair bond** or mateship. Animals that form pair bonds often defend territories, at least during the breeding season. This behavior may temporarily alter the dispersion pattern of a population from clumped to regular.

The family units of howler monkeys or the coteries of prairie dogs, usually consisting of several adults and the young of previous years, are examples of a second level of complexity in social systems. If the family unit defends a territory, the dispersion pattern is a combination of clumped (the group) and regular (the territories). Still higher orders of complexity, such as herds, packs, or flocks make the definition of a local population even more difficult. In many cases, the local population may simply be the entire social unit. In other cases, exchange between the flocks may be frequent enough so that a local population may contain several social units.

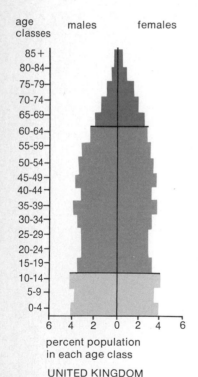

UNITED KINGDOM

Figure 7–7 In 1959, the age profile for the United Kingdom was as shown here, typical of a country with low birth rates and low death rates whose population is fairly evenly distributed by age. Note the inequality in sex ratio among those age 60 and above.

Age structure

Like the very young, the very old individuals in a population usually are not capable of reproduction. If we want to predict the patterns of gamete union in a population, we must know the percentage of organisms in each age class, which is the **age structure** of the population. If we want to predict rates of change in a population's size, we must have information about age structure, the age at which reproduction first occurs, and the age of peak reproductive activity.

Data on age structure may be expressed as an **age profile** (Fig. 7–7), which is constructed by plotting age classes on the y-axis of a graph against the percentage of the population in each age class on the x-axis. Usually, males are shown on the left and females on the right of a center line parallel to the x-axis. This arrangement of data may reveal inequalities in sex ratios, which are also important in determining patterns of gamete union. Figure 7–8 shows that an age profile for a young expanding population with high birth rates and low death rates has a broad base and a "pinched" apex. A stable population that is more evenly distributed over its age range will not have the pinched profile, but will be more triangular (Fig. 7–9). A profile for a stable population with high birth rates and high death rates will be shaped roughly like an equilateral triangle (Fig. 7–10), while one with lower birth rates and lower death rates will appear as a narrow triangle (Fig. 6–9). A declining population that has a low percentage of young produces an urn-shaped profile (Fig. 7–11).

Figure 7–8 An age profile typical of a young expanding population with high birth rates and low death rates.

Figure 7–9 A stable population with fairly even distribution of ages and with low birth and death rates.

Figure 7–10 The age profile for a stable population with high birth and death rates.

Figure 7–11 The age profile for a declining population with a low percentage of young.

Information about age structure in a population may also be used to construct what is called a **survivorship curve** (Figs. 7–12 through 7–15). The percentage of survivors in each age class is plotted against time. The curve produced shows the probability of survival for an individual at any age. The point where the curve crosses the *x*-axis (where percent survival is zero) is sometimes called the **physiological limit** for that population. Although all natural populations would be expected to show slightly different curves, it is possible to recognize four general and basic types.

The first, a semi-rectangular curve with a negative skew, is produced when mortality is concentrated among old organisms. The human female population of the United States in 1960 provides an example of such a curve (Fig. 7–12). Second, if the death rate is constant with time (and is, therefore, independent of age) an exponential curve is produced (Fig. 7–13). This shape curve is rare in nature, although *adult* vertebrates of many species show such survival patterns. A third type curve is produced when the death rate is constant with age (Fig. 7–14). This implies that the life expectancy of an organism is constant at any age, also an uncommon situation. Certain planktonic organisms may show this type of survivorship curve. The fourth general curve shape that we will consider is a rectangular one with a positive skew (Fig. 7–15). When heavy mortality is concentrated in the very early stages in the life history of an organism, but then tapers off after a certain age, this type of curve is produced. It is the most common situation in nature, and examples of it abound. One will make the point. An oyster produces staggering numbers of offspring, 99% of which die within the first year. Once an oyster spat has settled, however, its chances of living to old age are excellent (Fig. 7–16).

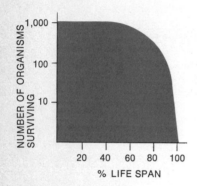

Figure 7–12 Convex survivorship curve. Most of the mortality is concentrated among old individuals.

Population structure in relation to habitat

As we have discussed at some length, the mosaic nature of the environment tends to subdivide species into populations and some populations into inter-

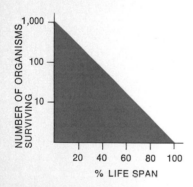

Figure 7–13 Straight-line survivorship curve. A constant number of individuals die per unit of time, regardless of age.

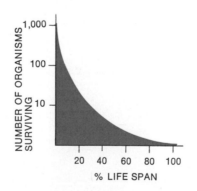

Figure 7–14 Concave survivorship curve. A constant fraction of individuals dies at each age.

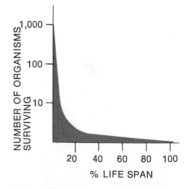

Figure 7–15 Concave survivorship curve. Mortality is very high among young individuals and then remains relatively constant throughout adult life.

spersed local populations. Although methods for describing such patterns of plant distributions are fairly well established, the fact that animals move around so much has tended to discourage development of techniques to characterize the nature of their distributions. What few studies have been done suggest that the distribution of most animal populations does not correspond with the distribution of plant species. The height of vegetation, its structure (including number of foliage layers, for example), and foliage density are more important, at least to vertebrates, than is the species composition of the vegetation. Evidently, the *ways* in which vegetation occurs determine the availability of many animal niches. Classifying communities solely on the basis of their plant species composition may be more misleading than helpful.

It seems clear that the proper study of any animal population must be done in all the plant communities or associations where local populations of the animal are found. For example, the descendants of the dozen or so rabbits released in Australia in 1859 have spread over the entire southern half of the continent, an area of more than 1,500,000 square miles. They inhabit all sorts of environments, from arid stony deserts and sub-tropical grasslands to sub-alpine valleys and wet coastal plains. Furthermore, within each major vegetation zone local populations are distributed discontinuously in relation to soils, vegetation, and topography. Some of these habitats remain favorable for many years, while others remain unsuitable until an exceptionally good year occurs. During the favorable years the local populations of rabbits expand into all habitats. But when average conditions return again, only small remnants of the local populations manage to persist in the most favorable sites. There is some evidence that the rabbit populations are becoming evolutionarily differentiated according to different major vegetation zones. However, local expansions into temporarily favorable regions occur on such a short time scale that they cannot become evolutionary units.

Another Australian mammal, the native red kangaroo *Megaleia rufa,* ranges over a large and heterogeneous area in the central part of that continent. To study the ecology of this animal, investigators had to establish a study area of nearly 6,400 square kilometers, divided into blocks of 10 habitat types based on differences in vegetation. They were able to get very accurate estimates of population size by flying over each block in a light plane and counting the animals. They found pronounced interactions between certain local populations and discovered that all populations moved freely into and out of vegetation zones, depending on the availability of water in each.

The point of these examples is to show that animal populations may react to habitat patchiness in two major ways. First, they may show a numerical response, as the Australian rabbits do. During those years when climate and other conditions are usually favorable, local populations expand into habitats that are usually unfavorable. Second, animal populations may react to habitat patchiness by showing a behavioral response similar to that of the red kangaroo, which moves into and out of different habitats as conditions change.

Other animal populations may show a remarkable fidelity to a certain

Figure 7–16 Plants, like oysters and most fishes, typically produce large numbers of offspring (seeds), which suffer a high mortality rate early. Milkweed seeds are shown here.

habitat type. Simple organisms with exacting habitat requirements sometimes find a suitable site quite by chance. Enormous numbers of individuals may disperse, but only a very few arrive at a suitable location. Animals with more highly developed nervous systems are often equipped with sophisticated sensory and locomotory equipment which enable them to "select" the proper habitat. For instance, many herbivorous insects respond to certain chemicals found only in their food plants and are able to detect these chemicals over large distances.

Learning experiences and genetic determination both influence habitat selection in deer mice (*Peromyscus maniculatus*). This ubiquitous mammal is found in nearly every conceivable ecological situation throughout North America. As a result, taxonomists recognize at least 66 subspecies.

In the Midwest, the subspecies *P. m. bairdi* is a short-eared, short-tailed, small form that inhabits fields. By comparison, *P. m. gracilis* is longer-tailed, longer-eared, and inhabits woods. A series of experiments involving the release of mice into a large enclosure that was half woods and half open field revealed that the choice of "proper" habitat in *P. m. bairdi* is genetically determined. Exposure to a field habitat at an early age reinforces this mouse's innate preference for fields, but animals deprived of early field experience still select field habitats.

Similarly, early experience in the "wrong" habitat does not override the genetically determined preference for the field habitat. Although several generations of laboratory confinement seem to reduce the innate preference, lines of animals raised under these conditions could not be induced to prefer a woods habitat when offered a choice between woods and field. Evidently, the behavioral repertoire of *P. m. bairdi* allows it to respond positively only to cues associated with field habitats.

Despite the many and varied responses that different organisms make to the environmental mosaic, we need only two models to describe population structures from an evolutionary and genetic view. One is the **island model,** which describes the situation in which two or more populations are spatially separated. The extent to which two such populations differ from each other depends on environmental differences, which provide different local selection pressures. Differences between the populations will also depend on the extent of migration taking place between the populations. The checkerspot butterfly mentioned earlier provides an excellent example of such population structure.

The other model is called the **neighborhood model**. This one describes a large population distributed more or less uniformly over a wide area, but in which mating individuals are restricted to a neighborhood of limited distance, with the result that widely separated individuals have no chance to mate. If the neighborhoods making up such a population are large ones, random mating will be the rule throughout the entire population. The butterfly *Erebia epipsodea* and the rusty lizard *Sceloporus* are among the few organisms that seem to fit this model. However, this sort of population structure may be much more common than we now think. The fact is that most population studies have been done on organisms that fit the island model, simply because they are easier to study than are those described by the neighborhood model.

CHANGES IN POPULATIONS THROUGH TIME

The study of the rates of growth or decline in population size is called **population dynamics** and is intimately connected with population structure. If it were possible to hover in a helicopter over an area that contained a particular population in which we were interested, a still photograph might reveal such things as the distribution, dispersion, and density of the population, and if the photograph had sufficiently fine resolution, it might even reveal some details of age structure. A motion picture, however, would provide this information along with data on the increases or decreases in numbers of individuals in the population through time. Such a record should enable us to get a fairly clear picture of the dynamics of our population, in terms of changes in both structure and numbers. Unfortunately, since it is impossible to use such a neat device to record changes in most populations, we must piece the information together from many laboriously gathered samples, tedious statistical procedures, and careful interpretation of the results of these labors. And because simultaneous changes in both space and time must be considered for a proper understanding of population dynamics, few if any natural populations have been studied properly.

Rates of growth

To make a meaningful study of a population, an ecologist must have a means of calculating the population's rate of growth. We can begin simply by counting the number of individuals alive at a given moment in time. Next we can observe the number of individuals that die over a given period of time and that are born over a given period of time. Doing so enables us to say that the birth (or death) rate of a given population is so many per individual or per thousand individuals.

Now in a closed population, that is, one in which there is no migration either in or out, the birth rate (or death rate) per individual times the number of individuals in the population will be our only measure of population increase (or decrease). We can express all of this mathematically by the equation

$$N_t = N_0 e^{rt}$$

where N_t equals the number N present in the population at time t; N_0 equals the number at time 0; e is a constant (the base of Naperian, or natural, logarithms, which = 2.71828); r is the instantaneous rate of increase, and t is the time elapsed between 0 and t. For ease of calculation, the logarithmic form of the above equation is often used. It is

$$\log_e N_t = \log_e N_0 + rt$$

If we know the size of a population at any two times (N_t and N_0) we can calculate r; then once we know r, we can estimate the size of a growing population at any time in the future, so long as nothing impedes its growth.

For this reason, r is a measure of the so-called **biotic potential** of an

Figure 7–17 The California tortoise-shell butterfly *(Nymphalis californica),* like the migrating monarch butterflies shown here, stages mass migrations numbering in the tens of millions. So abundant are they that they defoliate their food plant all along the way. There is no apparent pattern to dispersal routes and no patterned regularity in outbreak years. The flights cross rivers, 12,000-foot peaks, and highways, making driving hazardous because of reduced visibility and slippery conditions caused by the thousands of squashed bodies.

organism, and, in the absence of any limiting factors, a population of organisms will grow geometrically at the rate r until some condition becomes limiting. Situations in which a population is able to increase essentially unchecked are not as unusual as they might first appear. Insect pests feeding on agricultural crops often provide an excellent example of geometric growth; "plagues" of small rodents provide another. For example, it has been calculated that the field vole *Microtus agrestis* has an r of 0.0147 per day. With this value of $r,$ a population founded by a single pair of voles would contain eight individuals after three months, 428 after a year, 91,505 after the second year, 19,572,717 after the third, and so on. Common sense and the observation that the entire planet is not carpeted knee-deep with field voles tell us that vole populations do not grow at an exponential rate forever (Fig. 7–17). The human population of the world presently is growing at an exponential rate. It is equally obvious that its growth, too, must stop. We will return to this important problem in Chapter 8.

LIMITATIONS TO POPULATION GROWTH

Suitable habitats within the range of a species are likely to be widely dispersed, and the mosaic nature of the environment tends to divide species into separate populations, each of which may have to cope with somewhat different conditions. If conditions are sufficiently different over a long period of time, the gene pools of these populations will diverge from each other as each population undergoes different evolutionary experiences. Under these conditions we should not be surprised to find significant differences in behavior, density, survival, and reproduction between relatively isolated natural populations, even though differences in physical appearance may be difficult or impossible to detect.

In addition, the habitats occupied by each population may be very heterogeneous. Habitats also consist of mosaics on a smaller scale and may differ in many environmental variables. Even when habitats appear to be homogeneously structured, certain subtle differences may be important to the population. In many cases, habitat heterogeneity leads to the formation of local populations of varying permanence. Since the chances for survival and successful reproduction may be quite different for individuals living in each local population, the dynamics of local units are likely to be different from each other.

Thus, in many species local populations are continually being founded, grow, persist for a while, then eventually go extinct. For the population as a whole, however, the effect of local extinctions in one place may be damped to some extent by the effects of favorable conditions leading to expanding populations in other places. In other words, from generation to generation the risk of wide fluctuations in numbers is spread unequally over many local populations and may result in a relative reduction in the amplitude of fluctuations of numbers for the population as a whole. Intra-population movement generally contributes to the stabilizing tendency of spatial hetero-

geneity, and localities that suddenly become favorable are soon colonized by emigrants from established local populations.

Figure 7–18 A large African mammal known as the wildebeest, or gnu, migrates in herds numbering many thousands in response to the dry season, a time of radical food shortage.

Unresponsive requisites

In order for a given population to exist in an area, there are certain minimum requisites that must be met. Some can be classified as **unresponsive requisites**, or those not affected by the presence or abundance of the population. Such requisites include climate, physical space, hiding places, and various other characteristics of the habitat. Although unresponsive requisites are not affected by the size of the population using them, they are subject to change through time as the environment itself changes. Also, because of the patchiness or heterogeneity of the environment, unresponsive requisites are likely to differ from one place to another. For example, saw-whet owls nest in hollow trees, the cavities of which must be of a certain size to be acceptable to the owls. A young growing forest may have few older trees with the right types of nesting holes. Even though other resources may be abundant, this type of forest could support only a few saw-whet owls because of the limited number of nesting sites. A mature forest that included many old trees with abundant cavities could support many more.

A hospitable climate is a very important unresponsive requisite for any population, since a certain amount of moisture and a minimum number of days with above-freezing temperatures are necessary requirements for all life. Outside of the wet tropics, yearly weather cycles not only limit the amount of these resources available for organisms, they may also create conditions detrimental to a population's survival. However, because these weather cycles, or seasons, are predictable, it has been possible for organisms to evolve a number of responses and so cope with the seasonal changes.

Migration is one of these adaptations (Fig. 7–18). The long and dramatic trips of migratory birds at the end of the breeding season enable them to avoid the rigors of unfavorable weather on their breeding grounds. Remarkably, even after trips covering thousands of miles, many birds find their way back to the precise locality they left the year before. Other species also migrate. Caribou have well established migratory routes across the Arctic tundra, and many species of bats travel toward the tropics for the winter. Monarch butterflies also move south for the winter, but the adults seem not to return to their place of origin the following year. Rather, the adults that reach favorable wintering areas form a nuclear population for waves of northward expansion the following spring. As reproduction and survival become possible at higher latitudes, those areas are gradually colonized by northward migrants.

Photoperiodism, another adaptation to seasonality, is a physiological response in an organism brought on by changes in day length. Day length is a much more reliable predictor of the onset of favorable seasonal conditions than are other environmental variables such as temperature and rainfall. The response to increasing day length usually includes coming into breeding condition and involves changes in sexual behavior, temperament, the gonads, and the accessory sex organs. Flowering in plants is commonly a response to photoperiod. Why don't such organisms retain the capacity to reproduce all year? By not expending energy on reproductive activity during unfavorable periods—that is, during periods when offspring might not survive—organisms increase their chances of survival during these periods.

Dormancy is a third response to seasonality. At the least, dormancy involves a reduction of normal activities; for example, bears remain in their dens during periods of especially cold weather, but actively forage during warm days. Dormancy may also involve physiological changes and a significant reduction in metabolic rates. When this occurs during summer, enabling the animal to avoid heat or drought, it is called **aestivation;** the winter equivalent for avoiding extreme cold is **hibernation** (Fig. 7–19). The life

Figure 7–19 Chipmunks, like certain other small mammals, are true hibernators. During hibernation, the heartbeat is extremely slow, respiration may be only five breaths per minute, and body temperature drops to near freezing. Chipmunks may awaken once or twice during unseasonably warm spells, hence the stored nuts seen here.

histories of many insects also involve a dormant period during which time development is arrested. It is called **diapause** and can occur in the egg, larval, or pupal stages.

Many temperate plants undergo **vernalization**, exposure to low temperatures which reduces the time required for flowering. The cold period must be long enough to trigger seasonally related physiological processes such as leafing out or flowering. Thus premature development during unseasonably warm winter weather is averted. Similar exposure to low temperature is necessary to break diapause in many insects.

Seeds of annual plants adapted to desert conditions may remain dormant for a decade or more; eventually, sufficient rainfall breaks the dormancy and the desert is briefly carpeted with a profusion of wildflowers. Occasionally, a desert rain temporarily fills a dry lake bed. Within a few days the water is alive with populations of one or more species of small crustaceans numbering in the hundreds of millions. They have hatched from eggs that have lain dormant in the lake bed for perhaps twenty years. The water soon evaporates, or seeps into the ground, and the populations go extinct, but not before they have left more resistant eggs that eventually will hatch into the next generation when favorable conditions return again. A number of plant and animal species have been able to adapt to such long periods of unfavorable conditions followed by brief periods of favorable ones. Most populations of these organisms generally are doomed to extinction at the end of each favorable period. In some cases survival depends on very effective dormancy adaptations.

Survival of other species adapted to brief periods of favorable conditions depends on patchy distributions and good dispersal capabilities. The persistence of populations at low levels in a few localities during sub-optimum periods acts as a nucleus for expansion on the return of favorable conditions. The eventual size these populations reach depends on the value of r for the particular species and the length of time that favorable conditions persist. The story of the fluctuations of rabbit populations in Australia provides a good example of this type of response.

Another example is an Australian species of thrips studied by the biologists H. A. Andrewartha and Charles Birch. Thrips are minute winged insects that feed on a great variety of plant material. The species mentioned requires pollen in its diet and must live inside flowers. Flowers, of course, are an ephemeral habitat, and when one flower dries up its resident thrips must disperse to another. During the wet spring, flowers are abundant, and a census revealed that an average of 190 thrips inhabited each rose in a certain garden. This number fell to only five per rose during the dry, hot summer. The drop in population density was not caused by a shortage of food, since each rose contained plenty of pollen for the thrips, but rather because the flowers were fewer and harder to find. The small thrips population that could find these few flowers provided reservoirs for dispersal and expansion on return of favorable conditions. Thus, dispersal activity in thrips provides an example of one species' adaptation for dealing with the unresponsive requisite of climate.

Responsive requisites

The second class of requisites are called **responsive requisites**—those that can be changed by the presence and relative abundance of a population. Food supply is the most important requisite in this category. Food may be limiting in an absolute sense; for instance, an owl population may be limited by the number of mice that a certain type of forest can support. Also, there may be an insufficient supply of the proper kind of food. Saw-whet owls prey in Nevada primarily on deer mice. If the deer-mouse population in a forest is low, the owl population may be limited even if other species of mice are available in large numbers. The difference between responsive and unresponsive requisites becomes clear when we realize that deer-mouse populations depend to a certain extent on the activity of owls. If there are two hundred mice in the forest and if half are killed by the owls, the future food supply for the owl population will have been directly affected by the population's own activities.

The upper limit beyond which a population cannot grow in a particular area is set by the abundance and availability of both responsive and unresponsive requisites. Some biologists call this limit the **carrying capacity** of the environment, and it is represented by the symbol K. K, then, represents a saturation level, or the maximum size resources alone permit a population to reach. The carrying capacity for any population is liable to change through time for any given environment, not only because of gradual changes of the unresponsive requisites, but also because of the effects the activities of the population itself have on the responsive requisites of the environment. For example, soon after the prickly-pear cactus (*Opuntia*) was introduced into Australia, it spread over thousands of square kilometers in Queensland, forming impenetrable thickets in many areas. In an attempt to control the cactus, Australian scientists introduced a Central American moth, *Cactoblastis,* the caterpillar of which feeds on the cactus. When the moth was first introduced, Queensland's carrying capacity for it was large, and the moth population reached a very high level; however, the feeding of the caterpillar soon destroyed most of the cactus. Today the plant is relatively rare and the carrying capacity of Queensland for the moth has been greatly reduced.

COMPETITION AND POPULATION CHANGE

A population grows very quickly until the supply of one or more requisites is exceeded. When this happens, an important interaction occurs and depresses population size. This interaction is called **competition**, defined as the active demand by more than one organism for a resource that is limited in supply.

Intra-specific competition

Competitive interactions between members of the same species are called **intra-specific competition** (Fig. 7–20). Such competition operates as a simple

Figure 7–20 Intra-specific competition among these tulips is kept to a minimum by man's intervention and care, which provisions the plants with the proper kinds and amounts of nutrients.

negative feedback loop (Fig. 7–21). When the population density is sufficiently low, the supplies of resources necessary for a population's survival and growth are greater than the demand for them, and all members of the population get a sufficient share. So long as these conditions exist, the population continues to grow. Eventually, however, the density of the population increases to the point where the supply of available resources is insufficient for all members of the population. This shortage causes the population to decrease until the supply of resources is once again greater than the demand for them.

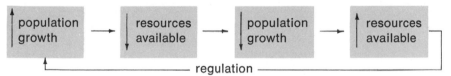

Figure 7–21

Often the availability of only one resource, such as food or nesting sites, acts as the critical limiting factor necessary for competition to occur. In other cases, the interactive nature of many environmental variables may make a single "key factor" hard to define. For example, usually we assume that territoriality in birds is advantageous in assuring an adequate food supply for adults and young. Under high densities, however, territories may become so compressed that the areas are not large enough to provide adequate food for successful reproduction. Food, then, would be considered the chief limiting factor. However, territoriality may also be an adaptation that prevents predation; the chances of a predator finding a nest are much reduced when the nests are widely spaced. Thus, another effect of compressed territories might be increased predation, and reproduction may fail for that reason also.

Generally, we recognize two categories of intra-specific competition. The first, called **contest competition,** occurs when successful individuals in a population obtain an adequate supply of some limiting resource and prevent less successful individuals from obtaining any of the resource. Frequently, territoriality is cited as an example of this type of competition. Successful members of bird populations obtain territories and are able to survive and breed; those individuals that fail to obtain territories may survive but are excluded from breeding.

The second type of intra-specific competition is called **scramble competition**. In this case, all members of a population have equal access to a limited resource. Two possible outcomes may result from such a situation. Sometimes, no member of the population gets enough of the limiting resource and none survives or reproduces. Experiments with blowflies have shown that at high densities with limited food none of the larvae gets enough food to grow to the proper size for metamorphosis to occur. Such a situation obviously results in a precipitous crash in population size.

The second outcome of scramble competition occurs when only certain individuals are able to get enough of the limited resource, and that part of the population most capable of gathering or using the resource survives and reproduces. "Self-thinning" in plants is a kind of density-dependent mortality that works this way. Only some of the seeds of one species that germinate in a certain area manage to survive, presumably because of competition for water, sunlight, or nutrients when any of those factors becomes limiting. Obviously, the concept of intra-specific competition is closely related to natural selection, and in this case selection is operating at the seedling stage. Plants may also escape competition by developmental plasticity. When essential resources are in short supply, some plants may respond by putting more energy into reproduction than into growth, or by varying the quantity or quality of their needs. Selection here operates at still a different stage in the plant's life history.

V. C. Wynne-Edwards has suggested that, in addition to competition over a limiting resource, there is another type of competition. He contends that the sizes of most animal populations are kept far below the level at which food resources become limiting by competition for "status," such as high places in a pecking order, or desirable territories. At high densities this competition limits reproduction; conversely, reproductive activities increase when densities are low. For the system to work, some sort of a censusing device is necessary, and various types of group behavior, such as the swarming of gnats or the flocking of birds, are said to fulfill the need. Although this hypothesis has attracted considerable attention and apparently has much popular appeal, it is difficult to explain how the hypothesis works in the context of natural selection, which operates in favor of those organisms producing the greatest number of surviving offspring. The genes of individuals who exercise reproductive restraint, even during times of diminishing abundance, would soon be eliminated from a population.

The idea of group selection, in which differential reproduction of populations replaces differential reproduction of individuals, has been proposed to support the Wynne-Edwards hypothesis. Proponents claim that any population that does not overtax its resources by overpopulation will be favored by selection over less provident populations that continually exhaust their resources and suffer precipitous declines. This is theoretically possible if "regulating" populations replace "non-regulating" ones faster that the genes for reproductive restraint are eliminated from the "regulating" populations by natural selection. Such ideas, however, remain as hypotheses and have no convincing supporting evidence.

Inter-specific competition

In addition to the competition that occurs between members of the same population when some requisite becomes limiting, competition can also occur between populations of two different species. Such interactions are called **inter-specific competition** (Fig. 7–22). Most of our data on inter-specific competition comes from experimental laboratory populations. Kept under controlled conditions, a single species culture grows until it either runs out of food or poisons itself with its own metabolites. Such growth often results in the S-shaped curve called the **sigmoid growth curve** (Fig. 7–23). Let's consider what happens when two populations of different species, each growing in its own culture, are combined in one culture vessel. As soon as some resource becomes limiting, competition will occur. What is the outcome of such competition? One possibility is that the population of one species increases while the other decreases. The population that increases has a **competitive advantage** over the other, and the disadvantaged population will be eliminated. Sometimes the outcome of competition depends on the initial densities of the two populations, since competitive advantage may change with abundance or rarity. In other cases, one species will always eliminate the other.

What if one population does not eliminate the other and both continue to

Figure 7–22 The strangler fig, the light-colored "tree" wrapped around the darker tree barely visible, provides an example of inter-species competition. The tree grows up the stem of its host plant and eventually kills it, by which time the strangler fig is totally independent.

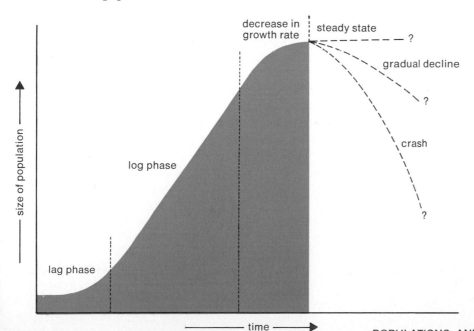

Figure 7–23 No known population has remained for long on the log phase of the sigmoid growth curve. Such a rapidly growing population plateaus and maintains a steady state, or it declines gradually, or it crashes.

coexist? Many competition experiments have been performed, and in every case where there have been really homogeneous and uniform conditions throughout the culture vessel, one species is always eliminated. In cases where coexistence seemingly occurs, non-uniform conditions allow one species to make use of the environment in a slightly different way from the other. This has led to the competitive exclusion principle, which simply states that complete competitors cannot coexist.

THE COMPETITIVE EXCLUSION PRINCIPLE: In order to understand why this is true, it will be necessary for us to re-examine the concept of "niche." A niche is the total of environmental parameters that establish the conditions in which a population can exist and reproduce. Let's consider some of the parameters that might affect the existence of a population of a small aquatic organism, such as the protozoan *Paramecium*. Temperature is one variable that we can easily measure, and we will find that there is a temperature range in which a *Paramecium* population can exist. We can represent that range by one axis on a graph. Another important parameter is the *p*H of the water, its tendency to be acidic or basic. We can represent the acceptable range of *p*H values by the second axis on our graph. Salinity, oxygen concentration, toxic substances, turbidity, food items all occupy other axes, and the more we understand about the requirements of our *Paramecium* population, the more dimensions we will be able to add to the graph. Eventually the axes will define an *n*-dimensional shape that will represent an abstraction of our species' niche.

If we were to go through the same process for a second species of *Paramecium*, we would find that the dimensions of its niche shape overlapped the first considerably. In general, if we constructed these "niche hyperspaces" for a large number of species, we would find that the more closely two species are related, the more parameters will overlap (Fig. 7–24). If two such species are confined together in the same culture vessel, one or more of the overlapping parameters will include some resource that is in short supply, and the two species will be forced to compete for it. One, however, will be slightly better at making use of the limited resource since the niche hyperspaces of two species never *exactly* coincide. One species will have a competitive advantage over the other under these particular conditions. The disadvantaged species will not get enough of the limiting resource and eventually will be eliminated. Thus, we can restate the competitive exclusion principle: If two non-interbreeding populations that occur together occupy the same niche, eventually one will eliminate the other.

The principle has been tested extensively in the laboratory with such diverse organisms as yeasts, *Paramecium*, beetles, and water fleas, and it seems to hold true. Several lines of evidence from nature also support competitive exclusion. First, when there is a large number of closely related species in a given region, the niches for each tend to be narrower or more compacted than when only a few such species are found together. This is most clearly seen when species occur in both island and mainland populations. Because islands are relatively inaccessible and isolated, they almost always have fewer

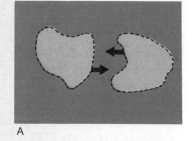

A

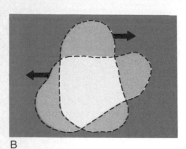

B

Figure 7–24 The niche hypervolume concept as applied to a population of two species whose ranges do not overlap is shown in A. The color density within the range areas represents the total resources available. If the ranges of the two populations overlap as shown in B, competition becomes intense.

species than adjacent mainland areas. Because of this, most island populations have fewer competitors than their mainland counterparts. When we compare the sizes of the niches occupied by island and mainland populations, invariably we find that island niches are larger. In contrast, selection tends to reduce competition between closely related species on the mainland by reducing niche sizes.

Avoiding competition

A second line of evidence comes from the observation that closely related organisms living in the same place often make use of different features of the environment to avoid competition. Plants may use different pollinators, or they may flower at different times; animals may use slightly different habitats or food types. For example, the 14 species of Darwin's finches (Fig. 4–16) on the Galapagos Islands constitute a unique and separate subfamily. On islands where several of these species occur together, selection has favored the evolution of different feeding habits (Fig. 7–25). Some feed on large seeds, some on small seeds; others eat insects and similarly divide this food into size classes. Still others feed primarily on cactus flowers. In other parts of the world, however, far fewer species of finches are found in such close proximity, and all species outside the Galapagos tend to be seed eaters.

Finally, closely related species often replace each other along environmental gradients. Even though similar species generally have similar tolerances to environmental variables, competition forces these species to occupy different parts of their tolerance ranges. Barnacles, for example, although free-swimming as larvae, are sedentary as adults and fix themselves permanently to rocks or other substrates on which they settle. Along the Scottish coast, Joseph Connell observed that barnacles of the genus *Balanus* occupy rocks in the lower part of the intertidal zone, while a related genus, *Chthamalus,* lives in the upper part. However, experiments showed that *Chthamalus* will settle and grow in the upper part of the zone occupied by *Balanus* as long as *Balanus* is not there. In this intermediate area where both can survive, *Balanus* eliminates *Chthamalus* by competition.

Figure 7–25 Differences in beak structure among Darwin's finches enabled each species to avoid competition with other species by virtue of occupying a unique niche. From top to bottom are a large cactus finch whose beak can crack tough nuts and crush smaller seeds; a tree finch that is an insect eater; a small cactus finch that is a seed eater; and a small tree finch ("warbler") that has a beak specialized for probing bark recesses for insects.

Density-depressing factors

In many cases, there may be an excess supply of responsive and unresponsive requisites for a population because of the operation of other limiting factors that prevent the population from ever reaching K, the carrying capacity. These we will call **density-depressing factors.** The intensity of operation of some of these factors may depend on the density of the population, while other density-depressing factors operate independently of the population's size. Examples of the former include genetic, physiological, and behavioral changes that occur in populations as their densities increase and certain interactions with other kinds of organisms such as predators, parasites, and other symbionts. Sudden changes in the physical environment, especially the weather,

Figure 7–26 The population cycle of phytoplankton is affected by a number of density-depressing factors. In spring, surface temperature, daily illumination, and other abiotic factors cause a diatom "bloom" in the temperate ocean. Within a week or two, exponential (log-phase) growth rate turns the water green with diatoms. Decreased transparency of the water, a depletion of nutrients, and an increase of predators (zooplankton) bring about a population crash. Although the diatom population recovers slightly in September, it does not bloom again until the next spring, thus cycling annually.

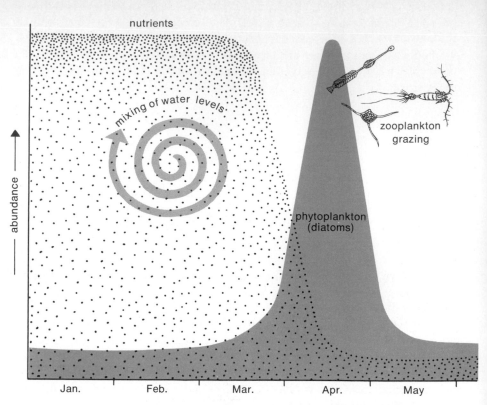

are the most important density-depressing factors that operate independently of population size (Fig. 7–26).

EFFECTS OF WEATHER: Weather as a density-depressing factor is especially important to populations that live in marginal or rigorous environments. For example, several butterfly species living in high, mountainous Colorado have been studied by Paul Ehrlich and Peter Brussard for several years. These insects are faced with a very short flight season between the last spring frost and the onset of freezing weather in late summer, and the populations must complete their development, pupate, emerge, mate, and lay eggs, and the next generation must reach the proper stage of development for diapause, all within about two and a half months. In the summer of 1969, an unseasonal blizzard brought freezing temperatures and up to half a meter of snow to the study areas. The following year, many local populations of butterflies had become either extinct or very nearly so in the subalpine zones, but the populations in the alpine zones apparently did not suffer. Midsummer snow and freezing temperatures are a predictable part of the alpine environment in Colorado, and the butterfly populations living there evidently have developed adaptations to this rigorous climate. Weather typical of alpine areas only rarely occurs at lower elevations during summer, however, and selection cannot produce cold-resistant populations when extreme conditions are such an irregular event.

EFFECTS OF PREDATION: One of the most important density-depressing factors that increases in its effects as the size of the population itself increases is predation. Predation, the situation in which one population (the predator) uses a second population (the prey) as food, occurs between all trophic levels. (It is even legitimate to say that herbivores are predators on plants.) The intensity of predation as a density-depressing factor varies. In some cases a predator may severely limit its prey and depress prey numbers to a very low level. Oliver Pearson has documented such a case. Feral house cats preying on voles and harvest mice in a California grassland depressed the numbers of the mice so severely that the local populations became extinct. This can occur only if the predators are so good at catching their prey that they can increase even when the prey are scarce. These situations arise most often when predators are a newly introduced species and the prey have not had time to evolve methods of avoiding predation by that particular predator. This is one reason why Pearson's house cats (a newly introduced species with regard to evolutionary time) are so good at catching native mice.

A second case, perhaps the most common one, involves a more or less dynamic balance between the predator and the prey populations. Some of these relationships oscillate. When the prey population increases, a higher percentage can be taken by predators. This results in an increase in predator density (Fig. 2–12). As more and more prey are taken, however, their density falls and fewer and fewer are available for the predators. This results in a decline of predators, slightly out of phase with the decline in the prey. A mathematical model with such oscillatory properties can be easily developed, but it is not possible to create a simple predator-prey system that displays such oscillations in the laboratory unless spatial heterogeneity is provided in the environment. If heterogeneity is not provided, the predators eat all of the prey and then they themselves starve. Spatial heterogeneity adds stability to the system by providing temporary refuges where prey species can increase before they are found by the predator.

Just such situations are found in nature. Some predatory species wander extensively, and local build-ups of prey populations eventually are found by the wandering predators. After they have lowered the prey population to the point where prey become sufficiently difficult to catch, the predators wander to other places. For example, the short-eared owl is a common species found throughout most of North America. It preys primarily on voles, whose populations generally show large build-ups and sudden declines. When a local population of voles is at a high level, wandering owls may take up residence in the area and remain there until the vole population declines. Whether the decline of the vole population is caused by owl predation or by certain other factors is currently being debated; however, it is clear that vole populations are fully capable of crashing, even in the absence of a predator.

Generally we assume that two selective forces are at work in predator-prey interactions. Selection would favor those predators with the most efficient mechanisms for capturing prey, while simultaneously increasing the ability of the prey to avoid being eaten. Hence, predation is beneficial to a prey species (although not to the individuals being eaten) since it acts as a potent selective force. Many prey species characteristics that we find appealing, such as alertness and agility in deer, are the result of such selective pressures.

If prey are sufficiently able to avoid predation so that the predator can increase only when the prey are so common that their own resources are becoming short, the oscillations inherent in predator–prey systems tend to be damped. In such cases, prey and predator populations may exist at relatively constant levels for many years.

The account of the deer herd on Arizona's Kaibab Plateau on the North Rim of the Grand Canyon often serves as a classic example of such a situation. For many years the herd remained at about 4,000 to 5,000 head. However, a vigorous and successful predator control program directed against wolves and mountain lions was begun in the early 1900s. The effectiveness of this program was amply demonstrated when the deer herd increased to 20 times its original level within two decades. Over-browsing by the deer threatened the entire Kaibab Forest, and starvation soon reduced the deer population to approximately its original size. Obviously, predation was a very important factor in limiting the Kaibab deer herd, and since the demise of its original predators, active management procedures are now required to maintain it at a size that is not detrimental to the forest.

Another important stabilizing influence in predator–prey systems is the presence of alternate prey. Stable predator–prey systems are usually found where a relatively large number of prey species are available to a predator. Thus, when one prey species begins to get scarce, the predator switches to another. It is quite possible that such predators play only a minor role in the limitation of their prey populations, a circumstance also true when the predator is extremely rare. Since many of the large predatory birds and mammals in the United States now fall into the latter category, it is doubtful that they exert any significant influence whatever on any prey species. Yet many states still have bounties on these predators under the pretext of "conservation."

EFFECTS OF PARASITISM: Several other types of interactions between populations may act as density-depressing factors on one or both. Parasitism is much like predation in that one population uses another as a resource. The parasite population derives its nourishment from the host population, and is located either in or on the latter. For this reason, the life histories of the two are intimately related. Parasites rarely kill their hosts. Selection favors those that do not, since they live longer and leave more progeny than those whose hosts are so debilitated by the parasites that the hosts die. Nevertheless, parasites limit their host populations by using energy that the hosts would otherwise put into reproduction. Besides parasitism, various other symbiotic associations such as commensalism and mutualism may act as controlling agents in certain populations.

OTHER DENSITY-DEPRESSING FACTORS: Finally, populations may be limited by genetic and behavioral changes that occur in individuals as density increases. For example, Charles Krebs has studied vole populations in southern Indiana grasslands. He found that there were significant changes in aggressive behavior as the populations increased and declined; males in peak density populations were typically most aggressive. This increase in aggressive behavior may increase dispersal activity and directly interfere with mating. Krebs also has followed gene frequencies at two different loci and found that the fitnesses of different alleles are not constant but vary with population density.

It certainly is not true that any of these density-depressing factors operating alone or in combination always prevents a population from ever reaching K; indeed, populations may repeatedly reach K even in the presence of several of the factors. In such cases, however, the density-depressing factors influence, at least to some extent, the rate of growth and nature of the fluctuations that occur in the populations between their founding and eventual extinction.

Behavioral adaptations and social units

By now it should be clear that the behavior of animals in natural situations is intimately related to the structure and dynamics of their populations. For example, the dispersion of a population results not only from the distribution in space and time of resources needed for survival by its individual members, but also from the ways in which individuals in the population react to one another.

The **primary social unit** is the smallest group in which individuals of a certain population normally can interact, survive, and reproduce. In some cases, the primary social unit will be an individual animal, while in other cases the unit may be a pair bond, a family group, or a colony. Since the presence of other individuals of the same species alters the quality of the environment for better or worse, behavioral adaptations leading to different types of social units are selected for during evolution.

Feeding behavior is a good example. Feeding strategies that yield the maximum net energy per feeding time are selected for. The optimization of feeding strategies results from a combination of four different things. The first is the selection of an optimal diet. For example, **food generalists**, those species that use a large range of food and have varied feeding habits, are favored in some situations; on the other hand, **food specialists**, which concentrate on a narrow range of food and have limited feeding behaviors, may be favored in some situations but not in others (Fig. 7–27). Reasons for this vary. If, for example, a diet becomes more varied than before, search time for food decreases; but at the same time the efficiency of searching for any particular kind of food also decreases. Furthermore, pursuit time increases as harder-to-catch food is added. The caloric values of the food involved must also be considered. Hard-to-catch but highly nutritious food ultimately may be more desirable to a predator than more easily caught but less nutritious food.

The second consideration in feeding strategies is the size of the optimal foraging area. It is reflected in both home range size and the degree of exclusiveness of the feeding area, and is thus closely related to the dispersion

Figure 7–27 Caterpillars of the silkworm, which feed on mulberry, are examples of food specialists. While odor as a stimulus attracts the caterpillars to mulberry (and to certain other leaves), taste causes them to reject all leaves but mulberry. When deprived of their taste sensors, however, the caterpillars will readily eat cherry and certain other leaves with the right odor. Japanese biologists recently developed a synthetic food, shown here, on which these food "specialists" apparently thrive.

pattern of the population. A third consideration is the amount of time individuals spend feeding to get the optimal yield of energy. In general, time spent feeding increases when food is scarce and when energy requirements are higher. For example, R. K. Murton found that wood pigeons spend 10% of their day feeding during the summer, but 95% during winter.

Finally, there is an optimal size of the foraging group. In some cases the presence of more than one individual may hinder foraging effectiveness. This can happen when the presence of more than one predator hastens the retreat of prey into inaccessible areas. Grouping may increase efficiency, however, increasing the effective prey availability by "flushing" food sources that normally would be overlooked. Groups also increase the area that can be searched for food and may increase the ability to defend the foraging area. In any event, the favored strategy will be determined by the availability, abundance, and dispersion of acceptable food supplies. These topics will be developed further in Chapter 9.

WHAT "REGULATES" POPULATIONS?

Dynamic equilibrium in energy relationships

At any one time, the animals in a community consist of a certain array of species, each occurring with a certain degree of commonness or rarity depending on their exploitation abilities. The proportion of rare to common species depends in part on the stability of the environment. The stability of climax communities, however, does not come from a balance of births and deaths in all its populations. Even though there may be a balance in natality and mortality in many plant populations in a climax community, annual plants and most animals continually change population sizes. Their contribution to the stability of the community comes from a dynamic equilibrium in energy relationships. As one population declines, another, perhaps a competitor, may increase. When a local population of one species goes extinct, it may be replaced by a population of another species that has a niche similar to the former one.

We recognize three different patterns in the changing levels of abundance of populations. **Fluctuations** are any type of numerical variation without respect to a trend or consistency; most natural populations show this sort of variation. **Cycles** are created by some regularity of the fluctuations; a few populations display cyclic trends. For instance, voles often have peak abundances followed by sharp declines every three or four years. **Oscillations** are changes with a tendency to return to a mean value. The interpretation of certain fluctuations as oscillations has led to the belief that population sizes tend to vary about a mean level of abundance and that they are maintained at such levels by the efficacy of feedback controls. However, there is no convincing evidence that animal population numbers are in this sense "regulated."

After it is founded, a population begins to grow exponentially, and unless some density-depressing factor intervenes, it keeps growing until it reaches a point where the shortage of some resource prevents further growth. Usually, as the carrying capacity of the environment is approached, competitive relationships slow the growth before it eventually stops. In other cases, growth stops abruptly as saturation level is reached. In theory, a population may remain for some time at saturation level, but more often a downward trend occurs. A downward trend is inevitable when the saturation level is exceeded.

Downward pressures are continuously exerted on the population both by resource shortages leading to competition, and by various density-depressing factors. Eventually, the combined influence of several downward pressures decreases a population's size so much that subsequent increase is impossible. This is the floor level for the population—the minimum size below which extinction is inevitable. Through time, then, a population fluctuates between its saturation level and its floor, with a downward fluctuation guaranteed every time the saturation level is exceeded.

Social insect populations

A discussion of population "regulation" would not be complete without at least a passing reference to the social insects—the ants, some bees and wasps, and termites. Each local population consists of several colonies that act as a unit of selection, much as individuals do in other populations. Each colony consists of genetically identical individuals belonging to two or more "castes," which are either reproductive or non-reproductive. The reproductive castes include females, or queens, and males. Usually, there is one queen for each colony; several males may belong to a colony initially, but they die soon after mating. The non-reproductive castes consist of sterile females who provide for the young, defend the colony, forage for food, and tend the queen. Morphological differentiation of these individuals often occurs, and the non-reproductive castes are often classified as "soldiers" or "workers."

Colonies may be founded in one of two ways, by swarming or by nuptial flights. When swarming, representatives of all castes leave the nest and move to a new locality; this is most often caused by overcrowded conditions resulting from an environmental change. Nuptial flights occur with more regularity and consist only of newly emerged queens and males. Nuptial flights from all the colonies in an area belonging to the same species usually occur at the same time; thus, in addition to serving as a dispersal mechanism, these flights allow cross-fertilization between colonies. An enormous number of these emergent reproductives soon die, but a few new colonies may be founded by newly mated queens.

The queens produce large numbers of eggs that hatch into members of the non-reproductive castes. Since large colonies have greater survival rates than small ones, it is important that a colony expand as quickly as possible. Eventually, however, a colony may meet with a resource shortage of some sort, most likely a shortage of food. When this happens, a queen is capable of regulating the size of her colony either by cutting down on her egg production or by eating eggs already produced. The stimulus usually is the quantity or quality of the food brought to her by the workers. The workers themselves are also capable of some regulatory activities, at least in termite colonies. Termite workers may speed up or slow down the development of immatures according to the needs of the colony, or by killing supernumerary members of various castes, preserving desirable proportions.

These self-regulatory devices work because of the genetic identity of all members of the colony. Because a population of social insects consists of a number of colonies, and each colony is a unit of selection, the colony that contributes more genes to a subsequent generation of colonies has a selective advantage over other colonies. It can, therefore, be selectively advantageous to limit the size of the colony during times of shortage, much as it is advantageous for individuals to conserve energy during unfavorable periods. For this reason it is more fitting to compare a colony of social insects to an individual or "super organism" rather than to claim that it provides a clear example of population "regulation."

As you can see, a number of factors operating together limit the numbers of any species within a natural system. When one or several limiting factors are removed, populations quickly respond and grow until some other factor stops the growth. The house sparrow, introduced into New York City from England and Germany in 1852, spread rapidly throughout North America. Primarily feeding on grains associated with horses and their barns, house sparrows occupied a niche quite different from that of any native American bird. Thus, lack of competition and density-depressing factors allowed house sparrow populations to become tremendously abundant. The coming of the automobile and the resultant demise of the horse lowered the carrying capacity of the environment for this bird, and the sparrow populations have declined. Even though the presence of this bird is still considered an annoyance by many, it is at least in the process of becoming an integral part of the ecosystems in which it is found.

Another species that has been freed, momentarily at least, from most of its limiting factors is our own, *Homo sapiens*. Understanding the implications of the rapidly increasing human population is our next subject.

1 Explain the notion of a population being an "evolutionary unit." In what way do such evolutionary units influence the future of a species as a whole?

2 Giving examples, cite three or four advantages of high population density to individual members of the species. Also cite three or four disadvantages of low population densities to individual members of a species and to the species as a whole. Give examples.

3 Construct an age profile for your home state. Do immigration and/or emigration play significant roles in shaping your state's age profile? What shape age profile do you think Florida has?

4 Name half a dozen or so factors that determine the carrying capacity (K) of a home aquarium. Are they unresponsive or responsive requisites?

5 Describe three ways in which intra-specific competition can affect population size. How does intra-specific competition tend to keep a species "healthy"?

6 Why is it not possible for any population to remain for long on the log phase of the sigmoid growth curve? Categorize your answers as responsive or unresponsive requisites.

SELECTED READINGS

Hazen, William E., ed. *Readings in Population and Community Ecology*. 2nd ed. Philadelphia: W. B. Saunders, 1970. A collection of readings that introduce you to the original literature of ecology. Articles especially relevant to this chapter appear on pages 40, 47, 156, 170, 191, and 382.

MacArthur, Robert H., and Connell, Joseph H. *The Biology of Populations*. New York: John Wiley & Sons, 1966. A not-too-technical book on this subject with a number of interesting examples.

Wilson, Edward O., and Bossert, Willima H. *A Primer of Population Biology*. Stamford, Conn.: Sinauer Associates, 1971. The mathematics of population biology are explained better in this little book than anywhere else. A rudimentary knowledge of calculus is required.

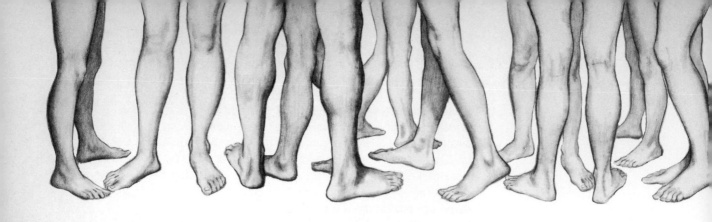

Figure 8–2 This sigmoid growth curve shows human population growth from pre-Neolithic times to the present, and it projects population increase to the year 2000. We are now at the log phase of the curve. No known population of organisms has ever remained for long at the log phase before experiencing a major change.

8

THE HUMAN POPULATION

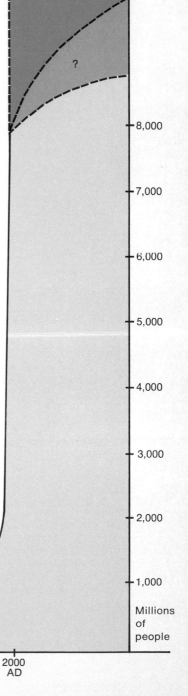

HAVE WE REACHED CRISIS PROPORTIONS?

As you found in the previous chapter, populations grow at an exponential rate until something begins to limit them. In some cases, the limiting factors become most intense when a population nears the carrying capacity, as competition for one or more resources slows and eventually stops population growth. In other cases, random fluctuations in the environment or the activities of predators, parasites, or disease organisms retard population growth before the carrying capacity is reached.

Although man has achieved a certain degree of control over his environment, his human population depends on the same planet-wide life support systems that sustain all other populations. The ecological principles that govern and limit the size of all populations apply to man as well as to mice and whales and sheep. What, then, are the causes of the human "population explosion," and has the world's human population reached crisis proportion?

History of human population growth

Very early man lived in small, wandering bands and pursued a simple food-gathering and hunting existence. Life was short and harsh, and a high birth rate was necessary to balance the high death rate. Because of the use of simple tools and a command of language, early *Homo sapiens* were efficient hunters, so efficient that they may have brought about the extinction of many of the large mammal species of the Pleistocene period. Yet, even though stone-age man had some limited capacity to alter his own environment, he was very much a part of the biological community and his numbers were probably limited in much the same way that the numbers of any other large predator are. Evidence from societies today with similar economies indicates that the human density during the pre-Neolithic period approximated 0.3 to 0.5 persons per square mile, and the total population was no more than 5 to 10 million individuals (Fig. 8–2).

8,000

7,000

6,000

5,000

4,000

3,000

2,000

1,000

Millions of people

Year 3000 BC 2000 BC 1000 BC 1 AD 1000 AD 2000 AD

During the Neolithic "revolution" ("transition" probably is a better word since the time span involved was several thousand years) man's ability to increase the carrying capacity of his environment enlarged considerably. The domestication of animals was a first step in this direction, and along with it the appearance of agriculture about 10,000 or more years ago led to the settlement of villages and many improvements in material culture (Fig. 8–3). While these advances led to an increase in the human population, they also contributed to the destruction of the natural environment as trees were cleared, pastures overgrazed, and drainage patterns changed. Nevertheless, by the time of Christ the human population had reached about 200 to 300 million.

During the next millennium and a half the population continued to grow, though fairly slowly. Wars, famines, and diseases made life short and uncertain, and local increases were often counterbalanced by subsequent disasters. For example, it has been estimated that bubonic plague (the "Black Death") killed between 25% and 50% of the population of Europe at various times during the 14th century.

Around 1600 the commercial and urban revolutions began. These and the Industrial Revolution, which followed a century or so later, caused a population boom in Europe. This rapid increase in human numbers was paralleled in Asia, although reasons for the increase there are not very clear. In Europe these were times of relative peace; more land was brought under cultivation and improved agricultural practices brought an increase in food production. Trading activities and increased national prosperity brought about by mercantilism improved living standards. Meanwhile, improvement in sanitation reduced the risk of epidemic diseases. As a result, the world population may have increased as much as 50% in the century between 1650 and 1750. Much of this increase was absorbed by emigration to the New World.

After the population boom of the late 17th and early 18th centuries, the

Figure 8–3 When man became urbanized, specialization of labor and a surplus food supply became possible, both contributing to an increase in the carrying capacity of his environment. Specialization of labor enabled him to take the first steps toward civilization, here represented by a Mayan temple dated around A.D. 800.

population in Western Europe began to level off. The cause was a decline in birth rates, a phenomenon that is called the "demographic transition" and is characteristic of a country that has undergone successful industrialization. Even after demographic transition, however, the populations in these countries continue to grow at a rate of 0.5% to 1% per year. There is no satisfactory explanation for the causes of the demographic transition, but it has been suggested that children are less of an advantage in industrial societies than they are in agrarian ones. In an industrial society children reduce potential for accumulation of capital, but in an agrarian society they serve as extra hands on the farm and are a form of old-age insurance.

Thus in industrialized countries two demographic trends occur. At first there is an initial decline of death rates with the onset of industrialization. This causes population growth to increase at first; but birth rates then decline and the rate of growth slows down once again. Most Western European nations have followed this pattern and have grown at a slow but steady rate since the 19th century.

Patterns in non-industrialized or underdeveloped countries are somewhat different. Before World War II, most such nations were characterized by high birth rates and high death rates, resulting in fairly slow growth overall. After the end of World War II, however, an important new trend occurred. At that time, the developed countries began to export modern drugs, sanitation techniques, and medical aid to underdeveloped countries. This resulted in a significant decline in death rates in these countries, especially among children and young adults. More people were living to reach their peak reproductive years. Also, people continued to have large numbers of children and birth rates remained high. With high birth rates and low death rates, populations in underdeveloped countries began to rise rapidly. This trend was reflected in the change in the world growth rate: In the decade between 1940 and 1950 the world population was growing at a rate of 0.8%, or with a doubling time of about 90 years; however, the doubling time for the next decade was half that. The trend continues, and world population doubling time is even faster now—35 years.

We have defined populations as aggregations of similarly adapted individuals. Even though many local groups of people differ from other groups in minor ways, there is only one human population, the world population, and all of the world's people share a common gene pool. Because of cultural differences and minor differences in skin pigmentation or hair color, the fact that there is only one human population is often obscured or ignored. However, it is quite clear that any significant environmental change capable of altering the world's capacity to support human beings will affect *all* the world's population in a similar way. When an ecologist speaks of the human population, he does not exclude any local subset.

When we divide the human population into various units along political or geographical lines, we can speak of the population of the United States, or of Nassau County, or of Asia. Because man is not distributed evenly over the face of the planet, these can be useful sampling units; also, conditions that influence the size of the human population may be quite different from

one of these areas to another. We must never forget that the population explosion is a crisis for all the world's people. As Paul Ehrlich has pointed out, it is of little use for the passengers in the forward part of a boat to say to those aft, "Your end of the boat is sinking."

THE STRUCTURE OF THE HUMAN POPULATION

As we have discussed previously, all the factors that control or determine the patterns of gamete union within a population constitute the population's structure. The structure of the human population differs from place to place, often because of cultural reasons (Fig. 8–4). While the causes of these differences are best left to the social sciences, the biologist wants to know how the differences affect rates of population growth.

There are very few environments on Earth that are not at least temporarily suitable for human habitation. Even high mountain tops and the polar ice caps have supported human settlements for short periods of time. Permanent habitation is confined to more benign parts of our planet, and the density of humans within these areas varies widely. On the average, there are about 65 people for every square mile of land area on Earth at the present time, although such figures are misleading because of the dispersion pattern. While the United States as a whole has a density of about 55 persons per square mile, there are 75,000 people per square mile on Manhattan Island and fewer than one per square mile in rural Nevada. Average density figures for a nation as large and geographically diverse as the United States cannot be compared directly with more uniform areas such as Holland.

Effects of urbanization

An increasing concentration of the population in cities is one of the oldest demographic trends and is an important factor in human dispersion patterns. In primitive societies population densities were probably in the neighborhood of 0.3 to 0.5 persons per square mile. When agriculture and the domestication of animals enabled more food to be produced in less area, it was possible for groups of people to become more concentrated. Once permanent villages were established, increasing urbanization became a characteristic trend in human civilization. This is strikingly illustrated in the United States: In 1800, only 6% of the population lived in urban areas compared with more than 70% today. Urbanization is also an important trend in less developed countries, especially in Africa and South America.

The age structure or percentage of individuals in each age class, as discussed in Chapter 7, is extremely important to know when we try to predict the rate at which a segment of the human population will grow. The age profile for the population of the island of Mauritius in 1959 provides an example of the shape of a young, expanding population (Fig. 8–5). The relatively

Figure 8–4 Urbanization brought about drastic changes in population dispersion. While the population density for the United States as a whole is 55 persons per square mile, in New York's Manhattan it is 75,000 per square mile.

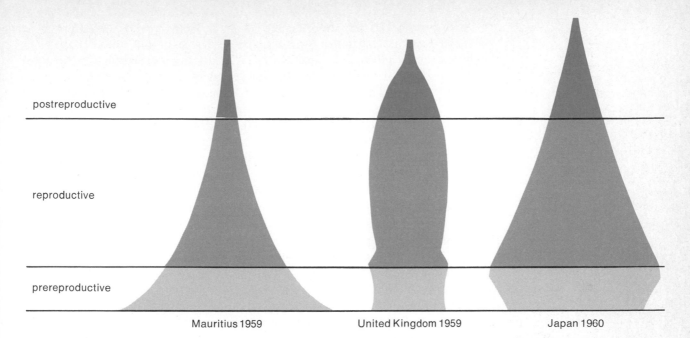

postreproductive

reproductive

prereproductive

Mauritius 1959   United Kingdom 1959   Japan 1960

Figure 8–5 The age profiles here show typical shapes of a young expanding population (Mauritius), a stable population (U.K.), a population with a sharp decrease in birth rates (Japan), one with high birth rates and high death rates (India), and one bell-shaped due to an expanded proportion of young people caused by a significant rise in birth rate.

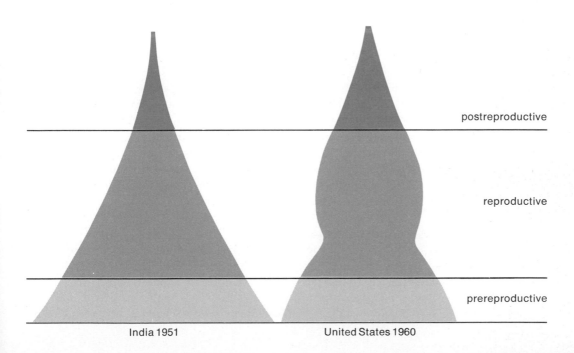

postreproductive

reproductive

prereproductive

India 1951   United States 1960

narrow profile of the United Kingdom in that same year is indicative of a stable population with low birth and death rates. A profile with a constricted base such as shown for Japan in 1960 results from a decreased birth rate and a corresponding reduction in the fraction of the population in the lower age categories. The triangular profile of India in 1951 is typical of countries with both high birth rates and high death rates, and the bell-shaped profile of the United States in 1960 shows an expanded proportion of young people caused by a significant rise in the birth rate.

Any population with a high proportion of young people can be expected to show explosive growth as soon as these people reach their reproductive years. Even if the average number of children born per female is reduced somewhat, the large numbers of females bearing children will still result in a growing population. Unless the number of births per female is cut drastically, these people will have moved into their post-reproductive years —a 20 to 30 year process—before the growth of the population can be slowed. Age structure may also be displayed by survivorship curves, an example of which is shown in Fig. 7–12.

Capacity for population increase is also affected by the age of first reproduction and the age of peak reproductive activity. By delaying the age of first reproduction from age 15 to 23, for example, it is possible to more than halve the rate of increase of a population. Relationships such as these must be well understood by all who attempt to predict the size of the human population at some future time.

Rate of growth

Like all other populations, the human population is growing at a geometric rate, and it will continue to do so until checked by some factor or combination of factors. The intrinsic rate of increase is equal to the birth rate (B) minus the death rate (D), or $r = (B - D)$. Human birth rates are usually expressed as the number of live babies born per thousand people per year; likewise, the death rates are expressed as the number of people per thousand who die each year. If, for example, there were 200 million people alive in some segment of the population at the midpoint of a given year and there were 3.5 million live births, there would be an average of .0175 births per person for that year. Multiplied by 1,000, the birth date would equal 17.5 per thousand. If 2 million people died during the same period, the death rate would equal 10/1,000. Since the growth rate equals the birth rate minus the death rate, or

$$17.5 - 10.0 = 7.5,$$

this corresponds to an annual increase of 0.75%.

Sometimes it is more impressive to express annual rates of increase as doubling times. The doubling time is simply the length of time it will take for a population to double in size; for example, an annual increase of 0.75% means that a population growing at that rate will double in just under 100 years. The population of the United States was growing at just such a rate in 1968. The world population is now growing at an annual rate of about 2%, which equals a doubling time of 35 years. The implications of such growth are staggering.

A look to the future

Predicting the size of the world population for some future time is a difficult task, since projections must be based on simultaneous considerations of all the socio-political-economic factors that influence birth and death rates. The impacts of rapid cultural changes are especially hard to assess. Estimates of demographers tend to be on the low side, although their short-term predictions seem to be more reliable than their long-term ones. If present trends continue in the United States, median demographic projections call for 240 million people in 1980; 275 million in 1990; 320 million in 2000; and 650 million by 2040.

The story is much the same in the other developed countries. Europe, for example, should have 560 million people by 2000, a fairly modest increase (compared with worldwide growth) from 430 million in 1961. Some of the other developed countries, such as Canada, Australia, and New Zealand, are growing at even faster rates than the United States. Japan has had a reasonably stable population during the last two decades, but recently there has been pressure to increase birth rates to meet a growing labor shortage. Patterns in the Soviet Union closely resemble those in the United States; the population for the year 2000 is projected to be around 316 million, an increase of more than 50% from the 1959 level of 209 million.

The developed nations account for less than one-third of the world's present population of 3.5 to 4.0 billion people. Projections for the remaining two-thirds of the population are even more difficult to make for several reasons, but it is clear that population growth in the rest of the world will be even more explosive than it is in the developed countries. The ecology of human reproduction is different in the underdeveloped nations. Generally, large numbers of children are considered to be prestigious for the parents. The reduction of juvenile mortality is far too new to have overcome the social pressures of having many children to assure that at least a few will survive. As one example typical of underdeveloped nations, the median projection for the population of India in the year 2000 is 980 million; for India and Pakistan combined it is 1.2 billion people. At the present time mainland China has about 750 million people, with a doubling time of about 50 years. There is some evidence, however, that the mainland Chinese government is making efforts to limit population growth. The expected total world population for the year 2000 is between 6.5 and 7.5 billion people, based on the 1968 annual rate of increase of slightly more than 2%. Growth of this sort means that there is an annual increase in the world's population of 70 million. This means that 192,000 people are added to our planet *every day*—enough to fill a new Pittsburg every 2.5 days, or a new Los Angeles every 2 weeks.

IMPACT OF POPULATION GROWTH ON THE PLANET

No population can keep growing forever. At some point one or several important factors must become critically limiting, and the population will either go into a precipitous decline or level off. The idea that the human population also has a carrying capacity was first advanced by an Englishman, Thomas R. Malthus, in 1798. In *An Essay on the Principle of Populations,* Malthus explored two axioms which helped shape Darwin's views on selection. The first was that food is necessary to man's existence; the second was that passion between the sexes is also necessary and will continue to be so. He also pointed out that populations increase at a geometric rate, while food production increases only arithmetically. Malthus concluded that the power of population expansion is infinitely greater than the capacity of Earth to produce man's subsistence, and that population growth must somehow be checked. The checks to population growth in Malthus' eyes were misery and vice, brought on by disasters such as widespread disease and war. The so-called Malthusian doctrine fell into disrepute as England's population increased beyond all predictions with decreased misery (but perhaps not decreased vice). He had not counted on the Industrial Revolution making available non-human energy sources to increase production and distribution of food, nor had he expected that much of the expansion of Europe's population would be absorbed by emigration to the New World (Fig. 8–6).

Although about 25 years ago a few scientists began to realize that the human horde was expanding much too quickly, the Malthusian doctrine was

Figure 8–6 Emigration to the New World in the 1800s helped reduce Europe's growing population significantly. Such shifts in population become less likely for political reasons and because the more habitable regions of the planet have already been populated.

essentially forgotten until the early 1960s. At this time several neo-Malthusians began to write books pointing out that world food production *may* be able to keep up with population growth for a time, but not for long. The message of these prophets was largely ignored until a few biologists began to publicize it widely in print, on radio, and on television. Soon, being a spokesman for the world population crisis became fashionable, and various biologists began to write on the subject.

We seem to be faced with a double crisis: a runaway population and a runaway technology. Both are creating a critical situation from which man may not be able to extricate himself. The capacity of planet Earth to feed its burgeoning millions is nearly exhausted. Attempts to increase food production will further perturb the life-support systems of the ecosphere. Many conventional sources of raw materials and energy are nearing depletion; present levels of industrial production far exceed the capacity of Earth to absorb its effluents. The long-term consequences of using novel sources of energy and materials are very poorly understood. It is clear that population growth must be replaced with population stability; it is also clear that man must stop fouling the environment. Let's examine these two propositions in more detail.

The food crisis

At the present writing, some authorities estimate that of the 60 million deaths each year, 10 to 20 million result from starvation or causes aggravated by severe malnutrition. To feed the present population, food production must be increased and systems of food distribution improved. And of course in order for food production to keep up with a population that is growing at the rate of 70 million people per year, it must be increased even more. Are such increases possible, and if so, where will they come from?

We often hear that there are millions of untapped tons of food in the sea. This is simply not true. Most of the ocean is a biological desert; nutrients critical for phytoplankton (one-celled drifting plant life often called the "grass" of the ocean) are abundant only in places where the nutrients periodically well up to the surface through the action of currents. Food production in the open ocean is exceedingly small. For the most part, it is restricted to those relatively shallow regions along the continental shelves. John Ryther has predicted that even these regions will be essentially depleted of marketable fish within 10 years if the present rates of exploitation continue. But as supplies dwindle and demand increases, exploitation is likely to increase, so 10 years can be viewed as an optimistic upper limit. Various schemes for "farming" the sea are not, at least at the present time, economically feasible. Thus the short-range potential of the sea as an important source of additional food is regarded by most informed biologists as essentially zero.

None of the other "fantasy" solutions to the food problem, such as hydroponics, direct synthesis of food from petroleum or coal, and algae cakes that "taste just like prime beef," are presently possible on any significant scale, nor are they economically feasible. These potential food sources also have one other important drawback. The people who need additional food the most usually have very conservative eating habits and generally are unwilling to eat novel foods, even if they are available. Incaparina, a vitamin-rich and protein-rich food supplement has been available and heavily promoted in South America for more than 10 years, but it is not widely accepted, even among severely malnourished people.

At least in the next 20 to 30 years, most of the increase in food production will come from increasing the yield of lands already under cultivation. Most of the land that is not farmed today is not farmed for very good reasons: poor soil, lack of water, or unsuitable climate. Even though it is possible to grow crops almost anywhere with a sufficient input of capital and technology, it seems unlikely that sufficient national wealth will be diverted toward bringing marginal lands under cultivation until a worldwide food shortage has reached crisis proportions.

There is a popular fiction that it is possible to farm the tropics, but we do not presently have the expertise to do so. The tropics are a biologically diverse area, and the problems of tropical agriculture are very difficult to solve. Crops and farming practices developed for temperate areas are inappropriate, and far too little funds have been appropriated to study agricultural problems in non-temperate regions. Not the least of these problems has to do with tropical soils. Many of them, called laterites, harden like concrete a few years after the native vegetation has been cleared, which makes both agriculture and the re-establishment of native vegetation impossible.

Other land regions not presently farmed present similar problems. For example, the cost of supplying water to desert regions is usually prohibitive, and the water for such schemes is becoming less and less available. Desalinization of sea water is often proposed as a cure for these ills, and the possibilities of using desalinated water for irrigation have been demonstrated by scientists from the Environmental Research Laboratory of the University of Arizona. They have established a small station on the Gulf of California that uses diesel power for desalinization. The water is then circulated through a series of greenhouses in which various vegetable crops are grown. However, the costs of this agriculture still exceed the costs of conventional farming, and it is very definitely a small-scale operation. The construction of sufficient similar facilities to feed even a small fraction of the world's burgeoning population would require enormous capital and technological expertise. Those nations that need additional food the most are usually those who are most lacking in both.

Certain recent gains in the productivity of "Third World" agriculture have been referred to as the **green revolution**. New high-yield varieties of wheat and rice combined with updated farming practices and the use of synthetic fertilizers have caused significant increases in cereal production in India, Pakistan, the Philippines, and Ceylon. Although the excellent harvest in 1968 was partially due to very favorable weather, it is certainly possible that the green revolution may have the potential for significant short-term increases in food production in many underdeveloped countries. However, the new strains require high inputs of fertilizers, which are not always available to farmers in those nations, and in order to get the most out of the "miracle varieties," pesticides and mechanical planting and harvesting machines are required. Underdeveloped nations cannot afford such mechanization. Furthermore, it is not always easy, for cultural reasons, for people to change over to a new diet (Fig. 8–7). There are also potential biological problems associated with a rapid increase in acreage planted with these new cereals. For instance, resistant varieties of pests will almost certainly appear ("miracle rats" to go with the "miracle rice" have already been noticed) and the genetic variability of crop plants needed for resistance to the pests will be lost if only these high-yield varieties are planted. As we have seen, there is always a higher risk of widespread catastrophe associated with any enlarged monoculture. Most important, however, even the most enthusiastic proponents of the green revolution concede that it cannot keep up with the growth of the world population for more than about 20 years.

Even if it were possible to increase worldwide production of food significantly, socio-economic influences usually restrict the availability and distribution of food after it is grown. Time and time again there has been widespread famine while abundant food is available on the other side of a political boundary.

Thus, it seems inescapable that famines will become more and more common in underdeveloped countries in the next two decades. Even in the developed countries the food shortage will become apparent; food prices will continue to rise and the quality of food will continue to decline. Such items as fresh ocean fish and sirloin steak will become unavailable or too expensive.

Figure 8–7 So-called "miracle" foods can be somewhat less than the label suggests. One variety of miracle rice known as IR8 (left) was too gluey and unappetizing for most Southeast Asians and sold at a 20% discount, or was left to spoil. Intensive agricultural practices of the Japanese, who for centuries have used natural fertilizers, have given yields of appetizing rice high enough for export.

Figure 8–8 A nuclear power plant—and one symbol of our runaway technology. According to Senator Mike Gravel: "The possibility of a major accident at one of our nuclear power plants is undeniable. One really serious accident could release as much long-lived radioactivity over the countryside as 100 Hiroshima bombs . . . and bring this country to its knees." According to physicist Ralph E. Lapp: "Before the year 2000 we will probably have 500 nuclear reactors . . . and it would appear a certainty we will have a serious accident."

Environmental deterioration

A large human population armed with modern technology has had an almost infinite capacity for altering Earth's environment. Much of the alteration has been done in the name of "progress" without regard for the long-term consequences of our acts (Fig. 8–8).

Any attempts to increase food production also accelerate environmental deterioration. The unstable nature of monocultures and their liability to catastrophe were demonstrated in the United States during the summer of 1970 when a blight destroyed 10% of the midwestern corn crop. Increased fertilization of crop lands also increases the eutrophication of our waters, and the repeated application of pesticides has not only caused the near-extinction of many species of wildlife, but has also made fish caught in many of our lakes and streams unfit for human consumption. In many areas, continued irrigation eventually makes the soil so saline that crops can no longer be grown at all. Stable, natural ecosystems have disappeared under the axe to make farm land; often after a few years most of the soil has eroded away and farming is no longer profitable. The abandoned land is taken over by rank vegetation or thorn thickets and is no longer productive, attractive, or useful.

At the same time, much highly productive farm land is being taken out of production by housing developments, shopping centers, freeways, and other monuments to "progress." Green space, considered by many psychologists to be essential to mental health, gives way to billboards and used car lots; even our national parks have become so crowded that vacationers there are subjected to the same indignities of crowding as in urban or suburban areas.

Sources of water and power are already becoming critically limiting. Brownouts are familiar every summer in the East when masses of air conditioners go into operation. The fossil fuels that furnish energy for power generating stations are finite in supply and will not last forever, yet the demand for power increases even faster than population growth. Nuclear power is still experimental, expensive, inefficient, and an additional source of pollution. Air pollution from automobiles and industry has made many of our cities all but uninhabitable (Fig. 8–9), and the effects of water pollution

Figure 8–9 In St. Louis, Missouri, air pollution obscures the downtown area on what would otherwise have been a bright, cloudless day.

Figure 8–10 Water pollution by three paper companies helps make Maine's once-beautiful Androscoggin River one of the most highly polluted rivers in the country. Like Vermont and New Hampshire, Maine is awakening to the realization that "growth" necessarily is accompanied by by-products that reduce quality of living.

(Fig. 8–10) are evident almost everywhere, Lake Erie being a grim reminder. Solid wastes of all descriptions litter the countryside. Make a beer-can-count per mile the next time you drive along a "scenic" country road. The mineral resources necessary to manufacture civilization's comforts also are in finite supply. Some authorities predict that the world will run out of tin, lead, zinc, silver, uranium, natural gas, and crude oil by the year 2000 if the present rates of consumption continue. Obviously, as the population increases, rates of consumption must increase.

For purposes of illustration, imagine that fixed levels of per-capita consumption of non-renewable resources such as minerals and fossil fuels and of renewable resources such as water, forest and agricultural products, and fisheries are to be set for the future. With a growing population, however, rates of consumption of these resources must increase to meet these fixed levels of per-capita demand. As the richest and most conveniently located supplies are depleted, lower grade (less productive) sources must be tapped. Successful use of these lower grade sources requires larger expenditures of energy and increases environmental degradation; therefore, the per-capita demand for energy will continue to increase, along with per-capita impact on the environment. Even this one example of diminishing returns clearly shows that the human population has reached, or perhaps even exceeded, the carrying capacity of this small planet. Population growth must stop. There are two ways this can happen: Birth rates can be lowered, or death rates can be increased.

POPULATION CONTROL

Many prefer to think that the global population crisis is a problem only in the underdeveloped nations and that the crisis in the United States, if indeed there is a crisis at all, is generated by the poor and underprivileged. Nothing could be further from the truth. The United States, with about 3% of the world's population, consumes an estimated 40% to 50% of its resources. Thus this country, along with the other industrialized nations, is using up a very disproportionate share of Earth's carrying capacity. The same is true within the structure of our own society: The purchasing power of the upper and middle classes is mainly responsible for the polluting by-products of a consumer-oriented society. Their demands for more and more goods, freeways, shopping centers, airports, and housing developments put a far greater strain on the environment than do the demands for bare subsistence made by the poor. On the other hand, it is the poor who bear the disproportionate share of human misery and suffering, and as their numbers increase, the chances of breaking the cycles of poverty, poor health, and ignorance decrease proportionately. Thus, population control is relevant to all social and economic classes and must not proceed at the expense of any one of them. Likewise, any reduction in the world's population must be shared equally by all countries, developed and underdeveloped alike.

Many are of the opinion that, because of its power and influence, the United States should feel a moral obligation to be a leader in the battle against overpopulation and its attendant effects. Only when we have stabilized our own numbers and achieved a significant level of control over environmental destruction can we morally be in a position to influence other nations to follow suit. To attain such stability, it would be necessary to bring our birth rate down from 17.5 per thousand to 14 per thousand. Essentially, this would mean limiting families to two children. At present, however, there are both social and economic penalties imposed on those who want a small family.

Economic and psychological penalties alike are in part a result of our national heritage of expansion. When our nation was young, an expanding population was considered desirable and people were encouraged to have many children. These sentiments, unfortunately, are still deeply rooted in our society and are extremely hard to dislodge; furthermore, they are sentiments that cannot always be dealt with on a rational level. Judith Blake has found that most Americans still want more than three children and are planning to have families at least that large. Most of those people interviewed in her survey were well aware of birth control and were using various artificial methods to space the arrival of their children. Her findings tend to discredit the popular idea that control over population growth will automatically come about when birth control devices and information are made available to everyone. Clearly, there must be real motivation to have two or fewer children per family.

The problem is how to achieve such motivation. Promoting advantages of small families might be one way—the idea that one or two well educated, well fed, and well brought up children are infinitely preferable to three or more who lack those advantages. Other steps could also be taken, such as making it easier for women who choose not to have children to enter a satisfying career without being accused of "avoiding their maternal responsibilities." Careers could also be made increasingly available to those women who want some combination of home life and career. Sex education would have to be made a required course in every high school. Birth control devices and information could be made available to everyone who wanted them, and at minimal cost. Legal abortion could be made available and easily accessible to all women who want an abortion. As Paul Ehrlich has said, "Denial of abortion subjects . . . [women] to compulsory pregnancy and the burden of unwanted children—a burden that mothers share with siblings who may already be receiving insufficient care and attention, with unwanted children who may be abused or abandoned, and with the society that ultimately must cope with the maladjusted product."

Economic adjustments could also provide motivation. Tax deductions would not be allowed for any children beyond the second (except for children living prior to enactment). Some have proposed a tax liability. Those parents who insist on large families would then have to share the burden of the psychological and material costs to society.

Finally, motivation for reducing family size would come when the general public were made to realize that the population and environment crises are two sides of the same coin, and that all of society's present ills—pollution, poverty, racism, social injustice, and war—are further aggravated by an expanding population. All must realize that as the population continues to grow, the standard of living will inevitably go down for all of us. Goods will become increasingly scarce and costs will rise. Pollution will increase, interference and regimentation in our daily lives will increase, and individual privacy and freedom will decrease. Do we want to support many people marginally or a fewer people comfortably?

If we can effectively cope with the population–environment crisis in America, what are the chances for similar successes in the underdeveloped countries? Unfortunately the desire for large families is even more deeply rooted in most of these cultures, and it is also actively reinforced by most of their governments.

Many of the leaders of emergent nations believe that a standard of living equivalent to that of Western nations can be achieved only by increasing the size of their own countries' populations. Even in underdeveloped countries where birth control is encouraged, it is usually introduced after the fact. In Punjab, India, for example, of 5,196 women who sought birth control assistance, more than half already had six or more children.

Unhappily, every year that the world population continues to increase, the risk of nuclear war, widespread famine, pandemic disease, and irreversible ecological catastrophe increases. We can only hope that a rational population policy will become a worldwide reality before any such event occurs.

Man alone as a species has the capability to be aware of his behavior as a species, and thus he can design possible courses for his future. It is ironic that he is one of the leading entries on a list that he himself has drawn up, the endangered species list. One question we must ask ourselves: Is our rationality a powerful enough force to enable us to remove ourselves from that list? But before we can answer that one, we must pose an even more difficult question: Is the problem—a runaway world population—one that *can* be solved rationally?

QUESTIONS FOR REVIEW

1 What were some of the factors that limited human population growth among stone-age cultures? What are some of the ways in which man increased the carrying capacity of his environment when his mode of living altered from that of a nomad–hunter to an agrarian economy? In what ways is 20th-century industrial man increasing, and in what ways is he decreasing, the carrying capacity of his environment? Does one balance the other, or is there a net loss or net gain?

2 Compare demographic trends in a typical industrialized country with demographic trends in a typical non-industrialized country.

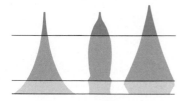

3 Which of the populations represented by the age profiles at the left is expanding most rapidly? Which tends to be most stable? Explain why in each case.

4 What justification is there for making the following statement? "It seems inescapable that famines will become more and more common in underdeveloped countries in the next two decades."

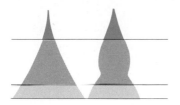

5 The problems associated with controlling human populations are charged with emotional snares. It is extremely difficult to approach the problem purely on rational grounds. To demonstrate this, determine the attitude of your state, and those of a half dozen or so of your classmates, on the following:

   a legal abortion made available to all who want it for any reasons whatever.

   b sex education being a compulsory course in all public high schools.

   c tax penalties imposed on families who have more than two children.

   d birth control counseling and free or low-cost birth control devices made available by the state to all.

SELECTED READINGS

Ehrlich, Paul R. and Ehrlich, Anne H. *Population, Resources, Environment.* 2nd ed. San Francisco: W. H. Freeman, 1972. The population and environment crisis as seen by two of the outstanding authorities on the subject. The book is exhaustively researched and has up-to-date information on almost every facet of the crisis. It should be required reading for every college student. Well written, profusely illustrated, key concepts well explained.

Meadows, D. H., Meadows, D. L., Randers, J., and Behrens, W. W., III. *The Limits to Growth.* New York: Universe Books, 1971. The sobering report of the Club of Rome's computer model of the future of the world.

Murdock, William W., ed. *Environment, Resources, Pollution, and Society.* Stamford, Conn.: Sinauer Associates, 1971. The most thoughtfully assembled collection of articles presently available on this broad subject.

Wallace, Bruce. *Essays in Social Biology*: Vol. I, *People, Their Needs, Environment, Ecology*; Vol. II, *Genetics, Evolution, Race, Radiation Biology*; Vol. III, *Disease, Sex, Communication, Behavior.* Englewood Cliffs, N. J.: Prentice-Hall, Inc., 1972. A collection of interesting and well-written essays on many aspects of the population and environment crisis. Non-technical and good recommended reading for your parents.

9
SOCIAL BEHAVIOR
AND COMMUNICATION

WHAT IS SOCIAL BEHAVIOR?

Of all the areas of biology, the one that draws us closest to other animals is the study of their social behavior (Fig. 9–1). No matter how bizarre an animal's shape, how exotic its habitat, or how unattractive we may find its visage, when we see a female nuzzling her newborn young, or cubs at play, we immediately feel a close kinship to the animals.

The study of social behavior in animals is rather like looking in a set of fun-house mirrors. In almost all the mirrors we can see recognizable features and behaviors of our own. While some are exaggerated out of proportion and others seem to shrink to ridiculous rudiments, some of the mirrors reflect undistorted images when we compare them with images of ourselves. It is easy to identify with a pair of cichlid fish, sparrows, or foxes as they fret over the care of their demanding young. It is harder, on the other hand, to identify with a member of a bee colony, in which the behavior of each member is regulated by a complex series of odors secreted by the queen. While some economists have tried to fit humans into such fun-house mirror images, we shall see that the whole behavioral repertoire that enables a bee society to survive is radically different from our own.

The function of signals

Most of the time, we have little difficulty in agreeing that two animals have interacted socially: a dog fight, mutual preening by two birds, an exchange of smiles between human beings. All are clear-cut behavioral exchanges that we call **signals** and that can be described and recognized again in subsequent situations (Fig. 9–2). If we examine a list of such interactions in any species,

Figure 9–1 How dangerously inviting it is to interpret certain of the behaviors of animals by ascribing to them human, or human-like, emotions and feelings. The tendency to do so is one of the major obstacles in the study of animal behavior. How much can we say, with confidence, about the emotions of the baboon mother shown here with her offspring?

Figure 9–2 Each posture in a sequence of courtship behaviors is stereotyped and can be predicted. Here is one stage in the courtship display of the albatross.

we cannot help but be struck by how many of the behaviors are devoted to the transmission of information. Dogs rarely fight. Usually they growl, raise the hair on their necks, move their tails, sniff each other, and bare their teeth. Most of these actions are signals. In the majority of animals, aggressive encounters are resolved by such signals much more often than they are by actual combat.

Sexual behaviors in most animals also involve elaborate signaling behavior, both before and after copulation. In relation to time spent, insemination is often only a minor part of the courtship and mating process. Even in the care of young, most species of animals have evolved signals that bring about the transfer of food between parents and progeny and that enable the parents to recognize their own young in social contexts. So we find that to a large degree social behavior involves a highly formalized exchange of signals between individuals. The series of illustrations on pages 206 through 209 shows a wide variety of social signals involving sight—including color, shape, and patterns—sound, smell, touch, and "taste."

Of course, not all behavior is social. All animals must find and capture food, avoid predators, sleep, and keep themselves clean, for example. Many species are able to accomplish these daily needs without social interactions. In some cases, frequent social interactions would hinder the meeting of daily needs. The simple problem of finding food is so demanding for many vertebrates that social interactions, whether by signals or by direct confrontations, take up only a trivial fraction of the time and energy budget.

However, appearances can often be deceiving. A solitary shrew running through grassy tunnels in the daily search for its own weight in food may well be marking its runways with secretions from glands on its back. These secretions do not require any special movements for application; the shrew needs only to rub gently against the vegetation. Such secretions are not yet clearly understood, but they may well be signals that maintain individual spacing (Fig. 9–3). Similarly, the deposition of feces and urine is often used by dogs, cheetahs, hippopotamuses, and antelopes to mark territories or hunting

Figure 9–3 Rarely are animals distributed at random. Instead, as shown by these royal terns, they form aggregates in which the evenness of distribution is more than could be expected by chance alone. (OMIKRON)

routes. These animals need spend little if any extra energy using these waste products as signals (although some dogs are quite industrious about it), and the signals have the advantage that they can be "read" long after the depositor has moved on.

When animals do interact in characteristic or predictable ways with each other, we say that they have a social system, mentioned earlier in Chapter 7. The ordering of their behaviors may range from the very simple to the highly complex. Social ordering often takes the form of temporal synchronization. For example, the timing of behaviors in most bird flocks is not random. Instead, at any given time a large percentage of the flock will be engaged in exactly the same activity, whether feeding, preening, sleeping, or flying. Even non-social animals, such as shrews, may synchronize their behaviors, particularly reproduction, through various kinds of signals. Social ordering may also be spatial. We have already seen that animals are rarely distributed at random. Instead, we usually find them either in clumps or evenly spaced out.

Whether we are considering the temporal orderings or the spatial orderings of social systems, we must be careful when we discuss the causes of the patterns. As we have seen, animals may be dispersed in a particular way because that is the adaptive dispersion for a particular food resource. In this case, we can cite an ecological cause for the pattern. But usually, if we examine the same animals closely, we find that the pattern is set up as a result of behavioral patterns of the animals themselves. Perhaps they are territorial and emit calls or odors that mark their territories. We can then say that territoriality is a behavioral cause for this particular dispersion pattern.

As in so many areas of biology, it is important here to distinguish between function and mechanism. The basic course for pattern—spatial or temporal —being adaptive is the function of the pattern. The function of a dispersion pattern may be that this particular pattern is the most adaptive means of exploiting a given food source. The mechanisms are the means by which the animals have managed to set up this temporal or spatial ordering. In so very many cases, we find that the functions of a pattern are quite different from the

ADAPTATIONS FOR "KEEPING IN TOUCH"

A

The rooster's comb (A), the lion's mane (B), and the elaborate plumage of many birds say male or female. Courtship often involves the use of these visual cues in complex behavior patterns—head bobbing, posturing, crowing or singing, pawing the ground, and the like.

The world is not always what it seems to be, and what it *seems* to be depends on our abilities to perceive it through our senses and interpret what we perceive. Since the perceptual apparatus of different species of animals differ widely— bees can detect polarized light for navigation; rattlesnakes have special infrared (heat) receptors for detecting prey at night—the world seems quite a different kind of place depending on what species you happen to be. What may be perceived as a significant stimulus by an animal of one species may be undetectable by another. But because individuals of a given species all have the same perceptual apparatus, they tend to respond to environmental stimuli, and to each other's behaviors, in similar and predictable ways.

The variety of signals animals use to communicate a behavioral state, such as aggressiveness or an intention to take flight or attack, includes postures, colors, odors, sounds, shapes, and motions. These are as meaningful to friend or foe of the same species as are raised eyebrows denoting surprise among humans. The illustrations on these four pages show a wide variety of ways in which animals "keep in touch" with each other by displaying, recognizing, and responding to certain morphological features and behaviors that serve as signals. The accurate transmission and reception of social signals can mean life or death to an individual or its offspring.

B

C

D

E

Signals used in locating and courting a mate may be acoustical, as with toads (C), frogs, and crickets, or principally visual, as with frigate birds (male's inflated gular pouch shown in D) and male fiddler crabs, which wave an enlarged claw (E) to attract a mate.

Social bonds among many groups of animals are maintained through touch, as among the lion cubs (F) and prairie dogs (H) illustrated. Ants identify nest-mates through a combination of odor-taste perceived with their antennae. They also maintain a social bond during brief encounters when they exchange food (G).

F

G H

OMIKRON

I

Aggression among animals is signaled in ways involving visual, olfactory, and auditory cues. These Canada geese (I) hold necks low in typical threat display accompanied by a hissing sound. The crest of the blue jay (J) is raised over a range denoting degree of aggression, hence it acts as a "graded" signal.

J

Social bonds between mother and young of many species depend on frequent tactile association, as demonstrated by the young kangaroo (L) just about old enough to leave the pouch and the opossum with young (K).

L

K

Defense, among mammals and insects alike, often is achieved through gregarious behavior (M). Singly, (as on right branch) the cotton backed aphids shown here are easy targets for bird predators. But when they are clustered (at left) and all waving their cotton tails up and down, bird predators usually are frightened away.

M

N

O

Olfactory marks are used by many animals to establish territorial boundaries, urine and dung being commonly used among mammals. At N a male dik-dik marks its territory by depositing secretions from an eye gland onto twig ends. When a territory is challenged by competition for a mate, as between these male fallow deer (O), the defender nearly always wins.

Much of man's nonverbal behavior underlies his culturally acquired behavior and includes visual and acoustical signals, among them a wide range of facial expressions (P) that often transcend cultural barriers. The French actor Fernandel is a master at using facial expressions as word substitutes.

P

Figure 9–4 In many species of songbirds, the male establishes a territory and nest site. He then defends his territory by singing (A). His song plays a double role, also attracting a mate (B). The female approaches warily, but if she has already interacted several times with the male, he is unlikely to attack her and she is unlikely to flee if he approaches. The male next leads the female to the nest site and executes certain displays (C). If the female is receptive, courtship may lead to a solicitation posture (D), and then to copulation (E).

effective mechanisms, and unless we make this distinction we can waste many hours in disputing the causes for the pattern.

In social behavior, the mechanisms for social ordering are usually signals. So we will devote the balance of this chapter to signals. The functions of social orderings, which fall largely within the area of ecology, will be discussed in Chapter 10.

PATTERNS OF BEHAVIOR

The variety of signals

When we study the behavioral repertoire of any species of animal in detail, immediately we notice that periods of activity alternate with periods of relative inactivity. The active periods are called **bouts**. Within bouts of activity, we will find some actions that are repeated and easily recognized (Fig. 9–2). These are **stereotyped behavior** patterns. As a rule, sequencing of such recognizable patterns is fairly consistent from bout to bout for a particular kind of activity. Sometimes, however, activity may vary so much in form that it is difficult to identify it in successive bouts. In these cases, we tend to rely on the stability of the bout sequencing and presume that the variable actions are in some way related to the more recognizable stereotyped patterns that precede and follow them. For example, in successive bouts the way an animal searches for food may be highly variable. However, if the bout ends in the stereotyped pattern of eating, we would generally assume that the variable behavior was in fact a search for food. If the bout lacks such stereotyped patterns, it is often difficult to know whether the animal was searching for food, chasing a mate, or just keeping warm.

As you will see, much of our study of social behavior is built around the identification, classification, and sequencing of the more stereotyped patterns of behavior. This does not mean that stereotyped patterns are more "important" from the animal's point of view (they may constitute only a minor part of its time and energy budget), but rather that they often provide the only means of classifying and understanding the variable patterns. Even when patterns are highly stereotyped, they are sometimes difficult to observe and recognize. Pat-

A

B

C   D   E

terns of activity that involve major body movement and that are "voluntary" often are called **motor patterns**. Motor patterns usually are the easiest behavioral patterns to identify. On the other hand, animals often exhibit other patterns such as sweating, blushing, or hair erection, which are controlled by the autonomic nervous system and are usually involuntary. These **autonomic patterns** often occur in stereotyped ways but are much more difficult to observe than motor patterns. Both motor patterns and autonomic patterns can be used as signals.

When we find that behavior is sequentially ordered in a predictable way, we can ask what cues or signals might be important in establishing this order. Take for example the observations illustrated and described in Fig. 9–4 on a bout of sexual behavior by a hypothetical songbird. In any study of behavior, the first task is one of description. Let us suppose that we have observed this same sequence several times in several bouts and that we find the same basic sequence each time. While there might be differences in the amount of time spent singing, the number of times the male performs each courtship display, or the place where copulation is performed, we still see the same basic progression from song to courtship to copulation.

Once the sequence is clear, we can study the means by which it is achieved (Fig. 9–5). For example, what triggers song in the males? By injecting nonsinging males with hormones and by altering the environment in which they sing, we find that sexual hormone levels and the appearance of the surrounding vegetation both play a role in eliciting singing behavior. What makes the female approach? By making artificial playbacks of tape-recorded songs, we find that hearing the songs triggers a response in the females. What cues are necessary to trigger the performance of courtship displays by the male? By using stuffed or model females, we can determine by experiment how close a female must be to the nest site to release display behavior in the male, and what features of the female's posture or plumage identify her as a receptive female. In turn, we find that the female's hormonal state and the male's displays trigger in her the soliciting posture, and that this leads both to copulation.

An interesting generalization about behavior-eliciting cues emerges when we study bouts of different behaviors in different animals. Most of the cues are simple and few in number. In the songbird example just mentioned, one might suspect that a large number of environmental and behavioral conditions have to be met before females approach males. Instead, we often find that certain significant fragments of the male song are enough to attract females. The complete song is rarely necessary. The recognition of "femaleness" by the male also depends on very simple cues. A special term is used to describe this widespread use of few and simple cues to synchronize and elicit behavior. It is **sign stimuli**.

Social behavior and sign stimuli

Sign stimuli are used by animals to trigger both social and other behavior patterns. For instance, a single simple cue may be all a predator needs for quick

Figure 9–5 To find out what attributes of a robin stimulate aggressive behavior in a male defending its territory, investigators eliminated all features except featheredness and redness. As the diagram shows, a male territory defender will often attack a clump of reddish feathers crudely attached to a limb by a wire.

A   FREQUENCY OF RESPONSE

B   FREQUENCY OF RESPONSE

Figure 9–6 At A we see a stereotyped response with "variable intensity"; that is, the more often responses in a sequence are repeated, the more intense the responses become. At B we see a response pattern of "typical intensity"; that is, only at low and high frequencies do the responses increase in intensity. At most frequencies the response does not change in intensity. What kind of response pattern does the term "fixed intensity" suggest?

identification of its prey. Many herbivorous insects locate their food plants by homing in on highly specific chemicals present in those plants.

The more familiar examples of sign stimuli are related to social behaviors. The male stickleback exhibits a bright red belly during the breeding season. Tinbergen's classic studies of these fish showed that a red patch on the ventral side of a model is enough to cause males to attack the model. Herring gulls feed their chicks by regurgitating fish that they have caught and partially digested. During the breeding season, adults of both sexes develop a red spot on the lower bill. This red spot is a target that stimulates pecking by the chicks when the adults visit the nest. The pecking in turn stimulates regurgitation in the adults. Again, experiments with models have shown that the red spot *and* the shape of the bill are important in releasing the pecking behavior of the young. Many other parameters, such as shape of the head, do not affect the response.

Sign stimuli need not always involve specific morphological structures whose only function is signaling. In many cases, existing organs such as wings, legs, lips, and eyes may be used in special secondary ways. Male fruit flies court females by touching them with their feet and by performing a stereotyped scissoring of their wings. When motor patterns such as these are used as sign stimuli, it is important that the patterns remain stereotyped. One might expect such a motor pattern to vary considerably with the motivation of the performer, but it doesn't. If we examine the sexual displays of a wide variety of animals, we find that the motor patterns tend to be highly stereotyped, even when the animal has a very much higher or lower motivation than usual. What does change is the frequency, or rate, at which the animal repeats the motor patterns. Such motor patterns are said to have a **typical intensity** (Fig. 9–6), which does not vary with fluctuating motivation levels. The fact that typical intensities and sign stimuli exist in so many social signals argues that stereotypy must have some advantages in communication.

The elaboration of sign stimuli and typical intensities would be of little value if the receiver of such signals could not separate them from other stimuli. In some species, we find that the animals' receptor organs are highly specialized. The gypsy moth female, for example, produces a chemical that is attractive to males. The males respond to the chemical by means of highly selective chemoreceptors in their antennae. These receptors are so sensitive that only a few molecules of the chemical are enough to elicit a response. A similar phenomenon occurs in the auditory systems of frogs. Male frogs produce species-specific calls that attract females for mating. The peripheral auditory system of the bullfrog is "tuned" to those frequencies present in the normal calls of males, and it is inhibited by, or not tuned to, certain other frequencies usually not present in the calls of adults.

Not all species that use sign stimuli for social signals have developed "peripheral filters" as the gypsy moth and bullfrog have. While such filters insure that only the correct stimuli send nerve impulses to the brain, the filters make these sense organs useless for other functions, such as finding food or avoiding predators. It would seem to be much more advantageous to an animal to have a broader sensitivity receptor and do the filtering in the brain. This is, of course, what birds and mammals generally do because they have the necessary neurological equipment. Rarely are birds limited to hearing only those frequencies present in their own songs. Owls, for example, would be unable to hear their prey if that were the case.

Graded signals

BEHAVIORAL INFORMATION: As a rule, most signals between adults and young and between sexually motivated animals tend to be highly stereotyped, but signals that resolve aggressive encounters between individuals often are not. Only a few cues are used, and instead of having stereotyped positions or uses, these **graded signals**, as they are called, vary continuously over some range of behavior. In addition to the behaviors shown in Fig. 9–7, the blue jay's crest is a good example of a graded signal. It can be positioned over a continuous range from straight up to flat against the nape, depending on the aggressiveness of the bird. It is a single-sign cue, but its position varies widely. The lip position and hair position of a dog, the angle at which certain birds hold their body relative to the horizontal, and the degree of black patterning on a cichlid fish are other examples. All these behaviors vary over wide ranges during aggressive encounters.

Often the information transmitted by such signals is hard to evaluate. The extremes, we may presume, are clearly distinguishable to members of the same species, but it is not obvious whether fine discriminations are or not. The fact that graded signals usually are limited to situations of aggression, where an accurate evaluation of the enemy's confidence and motivation may mean avoiding serious injury, suggests that some graded information is transmitted in such signals. We need further study of these signal systems.

ENVIRONMENTAL INFORMATION: Graded signals also are used to transmit environmental information. However, it is interesting that very little of the signal repertoires of most species deals with environmental communication. The largest fraction of these signals is concerned with communicating species identity, sex, age, status, motivational state, and so on. In those cases where environmental signals are used, such as alarm calls and food calls, the signals tend to be less sophisticated both in form and in the information conveyed than comparable social signals in the same species. Two exceptions to this generalization are the danced language of bees and the spoken or written languages of man.

Figure 9–7 In his book, *The Expression of the Emotions in Man and Animals* (1872), Darwin illustrated various aspects (graded signals) of aggression in dogs. Aggressive attitudes include lip position, erectness of hair on neck, a stiff-legged walk, and erectness of tail. Submissiveness includes a slowly waving tail and an arched back.

The graded nature of the bee dance is, in a sense, the secret of its success. A returning worker from the field enters the dark hive. She then begins to perform a rapid figure-eight dance, which is closely attended by her fellow workers (Fig. 9–8). Because the angle and vigor of waggling can be varied over a large range and used to represent direction and distance respectively, the bee is able to provide a highly accurate and detailed account of the location of the food. In contrast to most other species, the environmental information transferred by this dance is much more sophisticated than the sign stimuli used by bees to identify each other or to effect mating. While not without its own limitations, the language of human beings is also capable of conveying enormously complicated environmental information.

Though the ability of bees and humans to communicate complex environmental information has presumably contributed to their great ecological success, this behavior is not always possible or adaptive. Animals can devote only so much of their neural and somatic machinery to signaling. The kinds of information that must be conveyed in social and sexual contexts are so predictable that a few standard signals often are enough. Environmental information, on the other hand, is much less predictable. If an animal roams over wide distances and feeds on a variety of foods, it requires an elaborate number of signals. Only man seems to have evolved such ability. In honeybees, the type of food is relatively restricted and the location generally is near the ground. The dance of the bees has taken advantage of this predictability, which means that only two pieces of information—distance and horizontal angle—are needed to find the food. If a food source is placed on a tower and bees are fed at this location, workers who are directed to the site by the dances of the discoverers mill about at the base of the tower. The bee dance, it seems, does not give any information about the height of the food source. Another factor that affects the signaling of environmental information is time. Bees can afford to dance several minutes to convey the location of a new food source. A bird that emits an alarm call does not have the time to signal the identity of a predator, its location, or speed of approach. Even if he took this time, the long-winded vocalizations necessary might reveal his location to the predator. Thus time, the economics of neural programming, and the unpredictability of the environment all contribute to the rarity with which environmental signaling has evolved.

Figure 9–8 The waggle dance of the honey bee, performed on the wall or sometimes the floor of the hive, informs hivemates of the direction and richness of a food source. The angle of the mid-section of the dance relative to gravity conveys to other workers the angle between the Sun and the food source that the dancing worker has just visited. The number of times the dancer waggles her abdomen per circuit indicates the distance between the hive and the food. Having followed the dance with their antennae (and perhaps through vibration receptors in their feet or legs), other workers leave the hive and fly directly to the new food source.

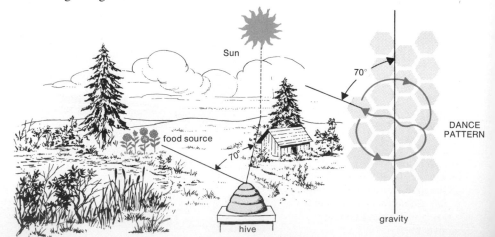

Advantages of sign stimuli

No adaptation, whether morphological or behavioral, is perfect. Specialization, which usually means increased success in some respect, invariably means certain sacrifices in some other respects. For example, an eye that has evolved for diurnal vision rarely can see adequately at night. Animals that live in personal territories may benefit from monopolization of food and shelter in those territories, but they may have to evolve special behaviors to attract mates. Few structures or behaviors are universally advantageous. Diurnal eyes would be useless to an owl. Solitary territories are a disadvantage for many small oceanic fish. In the following section, we will discuss the potential advantages and limitations of the use of sign stimuli for social communication. As with all adaptations, we expect natural selection to preserve or eliminate this method of signaling depending on the relative benefits and sacrifices.

We have already mentioned one advantage of using sign stimuli. Associated with all communication systems in animals is the problem of distinguishing between signals and noise. Suppose, for example, that two animals communicate by using sound signals. If their signals consist of sound frequencies that occur only rarely as noise in the environment, the probability of erroneous triggering of behavioral responses is reduced. However, there is still the problem of sorting out a weak signal from loud noise. We all know how difficult it is to talk near a waterfall or beside operating machinery. If the signal is a sign stimulus and consists of only a very narrow band of frequencies, it is possible to evolve a receptor that responds only to those frequencies and not to most of the noise. Receptors tuned in this way are called **stimulus filters**. Because they receive only the specific signals relevant to the animal's needs, that animal is unlikely to confuse signals and noise.

Another way an animal can cope with noise is to produce signals that are redundant. For example, consider a bird that uses songs containing five elements to transmit messages. Suppose further that for each element the bird can use any of five separate sounds. One message might consist of the same sound repeated five times. Another message could consist of one sound followed by a different sound repeated twice followed by a third sound repeated twice. The bird would have the potential ability to transmit 5^5 (or a total of 3,125) different messages. Such a system would be highly sophisticated, especially for a bird, the potential for information transfer being enormous. But no bird has such a system. Why not? The most probable answer is that while signal complexity is necessary to increase information content, at the same time it increases the probability of misinterpretation. What if a bird receiving one of the five-element messages misses one element due to noise interference. It will have only a 20% chance of guessing the intended message. Furthermore, if two elements are obscured, the probability drops to 4%. While these might be acceptable odds for confirmed human gamblers, who bet regardless of the odds, they are terrible odds from an evolutionary point of view. No animal in its right mind would risk its survival or reproduction on such a proposition. It would be better to devote the same energy to building redundancy into the message and so decrease the probability of certain elements being obscured by noise.

That is just what we find in communication systems based on sign stimuli. Motor patterns are simplified and the elements of displays are often repetitive. In most bird songs, we do not find five different sounds that are reassembled into different messages. Instead, we find one or two typical themes that include many repetitions of elements and are themselves repeated frequently in successive song bouts. An increase of information content results in an increase in the chances of misinterpretation. Or to put it another way, if we want assurance that a given message will get through, we may have to modify our communication system in such a way that it handles a smaller total number of messages.

One interesting difference between most courtship and aggression signals is that the former tend to be stereotyped and the latter graded. Since reproduction is an activity that usually involves tremendous outlay of energy and exposure to predators, one can see why courtship signals should employ cues that are unambiguous and redundant.

The use of graded signals for aggression seems at first glance to be maladaptive. Since graded signals are potentially more liable to misinterpretation and a fight can end in death, shouldn't aggressive signals be stereotyped also? There are two reasons why graded signals are used in aggressive contexts. First, graded signals increase an animal's ability to evaluate subtle motivational changes in an opponent. If you can read another's likelihood of attack, you can keep provoking him just up to the point of actual attack in the hope that you can win the encounter by bluff. If you misjudge and actually provoke an attack (and you are any typical animal expect man), you will have final recourse to a stereotyped signal known as an **appeasement gesture**, which, when performed, is an admission of defeat and will inhibit attack by the other animal. Two dogs will growl and circle around each other in a graded threat sequence. When fighting breaks out and one dog knows it is losing, it will roll on its back with its belly exposed and the other dog will halt the attack. Man seems to use the graded threat technique frequently, but somewhere along the way his responsiveness to appeasement gestures seems to have been lost.

At this stage it is important to consider one more reason for the wide use of sign stimuli. If one man wants to discuss cows with another man, he has two basic options. Visually, he can either draw a sketch of a cow or write the word for cow in his language. If he chooses vocal communication, he can either try to imitate the *moo* of a cow or say the word "cow." The first option in each case requires from the *receiver* only that he know what a cow looks like and sounds like. The two men could be from quite different cultures and yet communicate with each other. However, the sender's skill in producing an effective sketch or imitation of a *moo* is critical. The second method, using symbols, depends less on the artistic skills of the sender, but it does require that both men know the meaning of the symbols used (Fig. 9-9).

We find these two options in most forms of animal communication. Animals of some species signal threat by performing the initial motions of attack, as men do when they clench a fist. Often such signals do not require previous experience for interpretation and are even interpretable by members of other

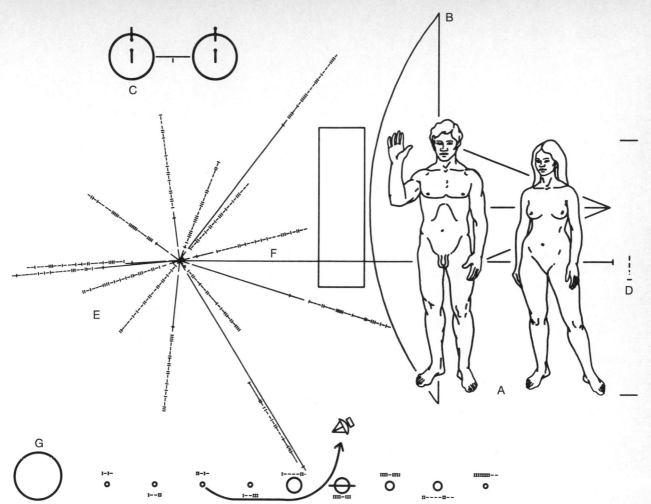

Figure 9–9 In 1972 the U.S. launched the space probe Pioneer 10, destined to leave the Solar System and hopefully to be intercepted by intelligent beings elsewhere in the Galaxy. The complex message consisting of pictograms and symbols etched on the six-by-nine-inch aluminum, gold-anodized plaque is designed to be understood by any physicist anywhere in space or time. At A are representative Earthlings, their height compared with a schematic of Pioneer with its dish antenna, B. The symbol at C indicates a hydrogen atom changing energy states, during which it emits radiation of 21-cm wavelength. At D is the binary symbol for eight, confirming the woman's height of 163 cm (21 × 8). E locates the Solar System in space and time by representing the directions of 14 pulsars, their relative distances (solid lines), and current rate of pulsation (dashed lines marked with binary cross-hatches). Solid line F shows the direction to the center of our galaxy, while G shows the Sun and its nine planets and the fact that Pioneer was launched from the third planet, then gravitationally whipped out of the Solar System by the fifth planet (Jupiter). Assuming that there are extraterrestrials with a technology advanced enough to retrieve Pioneer 10 from space, would you have any doubts that their scientists would be able to translate this message? Some linguists do, maintaining that the pictorial aspects of the art are symbolic, culturally oriented, and, therefore, probably incomprehensible to intelligent beings radically different from us in morphology and physiology.

species. However, the use of a symbolic signal has distinct advantages. In the first place, the form of the signal can be selected so that it is optimally transmitted. The growl of a dog, for example, has no value in a fight; it is a symbol, a ritualized signal. Because dogs often stand head-to-tail before a fight, visual threats such as baring the teeth may not be seen. A growl, on the other hand, can be perceived by the dogs regardless of position. Thus, using a symbolic form of threat allows the dogs to evolve a signal that is most easily communicated. The other advantage of using a symbolic signal is the possibility that the same sound or posture may be used to communicate a wide variety of information. A clenched fist essentially means one thing; the red belly of a stickleback, however, symbolizes species identity, sex, motivation and territorial ownership all at once. Thus, symbolic signals can be advantageous in optimizing signal transmission (as with the dog growl) or in economizing on signal performance (as in the stickleback). Just as in the example given of the two humans discussing cows, symbolic signals *do* require that somehow both sender and receiver be familiar with the conventions used. While this requirement does not seem to be difficult from an evolutionary point of view when simple sign stimuli are used, very few species have evolved complex symbolic systems. As we have noted, bees and human beings are notable exceptions.

Limitations of sign stimuli

In spite of all the advantages of sign stimuli, there are a number of risks in using them. Since only a single cue is used to trigger a whole behavior pattern, there is the possibility, even with the most unique signal, that the behavior will be triggered by an erroneous stimulus. In most cases, strong selective pressures evolve sign stimuli that rarely, if ever, are present in other objects in the environment. The red belly of the stickleback is such a stimulus: The usual colors of its environment are green, blues, and browns.

Sometimes we find stimuli that are *more* likely to evoke a given response than is the usual sign stimulus. Such cues are called **super-normal stimuli**. Often, super-normal stimuli are simply exaggerated sign stimuli: for a stickleback a large red object, for a butterfly a much more rapid than normal fluttering of wings, and so on. So in some cases, sign stimuli with less than maximum conspicuousness seem to have evolved. Perhaps these stimuli are a compromise between high conspicuousness to a potential mate and inconspicuousness to a predator. In the absence of predators, it is possible that signal cues more conspicuous than the standard signals would evolve. In one zoo, female peacocks respond to displays of albino males to a greater extent than they respond to the displays of normal males, in spite of the fact that albino males are rare in nature and are short-lived.

Another limitation of sign stimuli is that individuals of the same species may be unable to distinguish each other. For some birds, a mate is not another individual recognizable on all occasions, but at one time simply a member of the opposite sex signaling intention to copulate, at another time a random member of the flock signaling intention to fly, and so on. Because many of these behavioral exchanges are stimulated by a few simple cues, such birds never really learn to recognize each other as individuals. In species such as swans or parrots, which pair for life, mates seem to recognize each other. But for most species, the ability to distinguish individuals would not be useful and would only use up neurophysiological machinery that might be better put to other uses.

One other limitation of sign stimuli is the relative lack of plasticity in the signaling system. Because many messages are often carried by the same cue, it is not possible to reassemble sub-units of displays into new messages or combinations of messages. Human language and bee dances do have this potential, and so a wide variety of information can be generated.

No signaling system is "best" for all species at all times. Signaling has evolved and become adaptive in the same ways that morphological features must be adaptive. Having fins makes for good swimming, but not for efficient locomotion on land. In the same way, signals may be stereotyped or variable, may employ a few or many cues, or may rely more on visual than on auditory or chemical or tactile reception, all depending on the content of the message, the possibilities of misinterpretation, and ecological contexts. One major reason for the enormous diversity of animal signals is the diversity of needs of an animal and the diversity of contexts in which the animal operates. Another influence stems from the mechanisms through which signals evolve.

HOW DO SIGNALS ORIGINATE?

In the previous section of this chapter, you found that bouts of behavior are often composed of predictable sequences of behavior patterns, and that each pattern is triggered by a specific sign cue. If we study this triggering of behavior more carefully, we find that a sign stimulus does not evoke the expected behavior every time. Sometimes there will not be any response at all, particularly when the subject has just been exposed to the stimulus and has just responded to it. Other times, it is necessary to present a stimulus several times over short intervals to trigger a response. In this case the stimulus has some sort of cumulative effect. One person nagging another person is a good example. Finally, sometimes the animal produces the response spontaneously without exposure to the stimulus. This is common when long periods of time pass between exposures to the stimulus.

So we can say that the tendency to respond to a sign stimulus varies according to past experience. We also find that the tendency to respond depends on such things as the hormonal state of the animal, the location of the animal when exposed to the cue, and the strength of the stimulus. Given this variability in response, we can ask whether there are any common patterns in the ways that animals behave when either the tendency to respond is very low or when several tendencies are likely at the same time. What happens, for example, when we present only a weak version of a sign stimulus or present two contradictory sign stimuli simultaneously? A study of the resulting behavior gives us insights into the nature and evolution of signals.

Figure 9–10 Rapid head bobbing of mallard ducks is an intention movement signaling that the head bobber is about to fly.

Special types of behavior

INTENTION MOVEMENTS: Presumably, when we present a familiar sign stimulus in a familiar way to an animal we can expect the normal motor or autonomic response. However, often when we present only a weak version of the stimulus, or two normal versions of the same stimulus one right after the other, the probability of a normal response is very low. Sometimes in such cases, only parts of the appropriate response are given. We call such responses **intention movements** (Fig. 9–10). If a hostess is about to present one of her guests with a second portion of dessert after a seven-course dinner, he might pick up his fork and begin to raise the last bite of his first portion in preparation for a second serving but then put the fork down because he simply cannot manage another bite although he wants more. Assuming the normal response would have been to eat, we call the activity with the fork an intention movement.

AMBIVALENT BEHAVIOR: Suppose we expose an animal to two familiar sign stimuli at once, but they are weak and, therefore, not normal versions of the stimuli; or say that we present the animal with two different but familiar stimuli soon after the animal had given normal responses to those stimuli. In view of what was just said above, we would expect that the tendency to respond would be low. What would the animal do? Usually, the subject responds by performing some mixture of the two appropriate responses, either

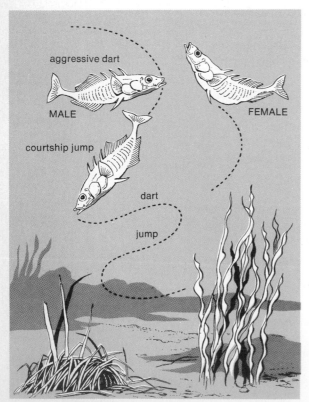

Figure 9–11 One part of the courtship display of the stickleback includes the zig-zag dance, which is an example of ambivalent behavior. The dance is perfomed by a territorial male when a female enters his territory. The zig-zag consists of alternating darts toward the female and sideways jumps away from her toward the nest. The darts toward the female often result in nips by the male similar to nips administered to trespassing males. Hence, the darts are associated with aggressive tendencies in the male. The jumps toward the nest are associated with the subsequent phase of courtship, in which the male leads the female to the nest. Thus, the zig-zag dance of the male stickleback is a courtship sign that appears to have arisen from both aggressive and sexual motor patterns.

in concert or alternatively. This is called **ambivalent behavior** (Fig. 9–11). Using our previous example, suppose our guest is a cowardly glutton and decides he had better leave before his hostess actually offers the second portion of dessert. He is about to excuse himself and say his good-bys, but just then he realizes that the brandy is yet to come. Torn, he oscillates between leaving (and avoiding the need to eat more) and staying (to await the brandy and cigars). Since leaving and returning are rather difficult to manage at the same time, he may end up just standing still by his chair. This is ambivalent behavior.

Figure 9–12 Redirected behavior, in this case aggression, is expressed by a little girl spanking her doll when in reality she wants to spank her mother for having scolded her.

REDIRECTED BEHAVIOR: Now suppose we have this situation: Say that we expose an animal to one strong stimulus and one weak one, both being familiar stimuli; or alternately, we expose the animal to one sign cue soon after the last exposure and to the other cue long after the last exposure. In these cases, the animal often tends to execute the motor pattern appropriate to the stronger tendency but "redirects" it toward another object. Our cowardly, gluttonous, frustrated guest returns to his chair wanting to throttle his hostess because she expects him to eat more, but he redirects his tendency by starting an argument with the guest to his right who had the courage to decline dessert. **Redirection** is the name we give to this kind of behavior (Fig. 9–12).

DISPLACEMENT BEHAVIOR: In a final example, we expose the animal to two sign-cue stimuli simultaneously. Both are familiar and strong cues and the animal has not been exposed to either for some time. Quite commonly, an animal responds in such a situation by doing something quite irrelevant. This frustrated type of response is known as **displacement behavior** (Fig. 9–13). Returning to our cowardly, gluttonous, now thoroughly frustrated guest, suppose he catches sight of the brandy bottle across the room and the neighbor he has just been arguing with dares him to go help himself. But to get to the brandy he must pass his hostess who is still eagerly serving second portions of dessert. Thoroughly frustrated now, our guest performs the most typical of human displacement behaviors: He scratches the back of his head and looks down at the floor.

This gives us a list of five possible outcomes when an animal is presented with one or more sign cues: the normal motor pattern, an intention movement, ambivalent behavior, redirected behavior, and displacement behavior. In general, we can classify almost all observed behavioral patterns into one of those categories. The point of the classification is that any one of the categories can provide a pattern which, through evolution, can develop into a signal. Since both sexual and aggressive behaviors often involve several tendencies—for example, the simultaneous urges to attack and flee or to attack and court (Fig. 9–11)—it is natural for these behaviors to include intention movements, ambivalence, redirection, and displacement behaviors. However, **conflict behavior**, as the simultaneous occurrence of two tendencies is called, is not the only basis of either sexual or aggressive displays, in spite of the fact that studies in animal behavior have concentrated on them in great detail. On the contrary, any motor or autonomic pattern, and practically any part of the

Figure 9–13 Will Rogers, comedian of former decades, was well known for his head-scratching (displacement) behavior during his monologues when moments of frustration occurred. Students often show this same behavior during examinations. (THE BETTMANN ARCHIVE)

external anatomy, can be incorporated as signals through evolution. Consider the following examples.

How behavior patterns acquire signal value

A number of normal voluntary body movements, or motor patterns, have acquired signal value in many species. For example, many bird flocks are highly synchronized in feeding, preening, sleeping, and carrying out other activities. Often this synchronization is performed not by special signals, but by a tendency among flock members to observe each other's behavior and be stimulated to perform identical patterns. Such behavior, as mentioned earlier in this book, is known as social facilitation. An example of the survival value of social facilitation among schooling fish was given in Chapter 7.

A group of ducks suddenly startled usually takes flight immediately. If, however, you sneak up gradually on a group of semi-tame ducks, the birds will not immediately fly. Instead, as you approach they become nervous and move about eyeing one another and you. At some point, one or more will begin an upward flipping of their heads. As you approach more closely, soon all the ducks are flipping their heads and eventually, with a large upward flip, all of the animals launch into flight. This head-flipping is an intention movement for flight, as we have defined it, and clearly has signal value—and, in the context of evolution, survival value—to conspecifics by coordinating the group take-off. You can also observe this same behavior when a flock of ducks finishes feeding for the day and commences to leave for night ponds. The whole flock will not leave until a large number of birds have signaled their intent to fly by head-flipping.

The zig-zag courtship dance of the stickleback (Fig. 9–11) includes a motor pattern display that apparently arose from ambivalence behavior. Redirection is often used in signaling during aggressive encounters. Many dominant male animals in groups will destroy nearby objects when threatened by other males or intruders. This behavior is seen in mandrills and bulls, for example. Finally, displacement activities often are used for signals. Ducks, for example, use a wide variety of preening movements for displays. While the activities are clearly out of context and usually are ineffective as preening behavior, the basic motor patterns are similar and recognizable. For many ducks, the preening activities expose or call attention to specialized colored feathers, thereby accentuating the display.

Many autonomic (involuntary) responses have been modified for signal functions. The fluffing or sleeking of feathers, the blush of an embarrassed person, the secretion of specific chemical signals by skin glands, and the modifications of breathing for vocalizations fall in this category.

Ritualization

Certain basic changes appear to be made on existing motor or autonomic patterns and so produce signals, an example of such an event being the loss of certain individual behaviors in an original bout or sequence of behaviors.

Certain remaining behaviors in the sequence may then be accentuated, often by the addition of morphological features, but just as often by an increased energy of performance. Finally, the temporal programming is changed either by repetition of remaining behaviors, or by considerable slowing down or speeding up of one behavior relative to another. The final result usually is performed in the same manner over a wide range of tendencies and contexts, hence giving rise to a "typical intensity," illustrated in Fig. 9-6. All of these changes are ones we would expect to be necessary to transform complex behavior patterns into sign stimuli. Almost all of them are simplifications of behaviors that already exist.

The more ritualized a motor pattern becomes, the more difficult it is to recognize the probable source of a display. Usually, as with many duck displays, the retained elements show varying degrees of modification in related species. By comparing a series of such species, we can find displays with very little ritualization and, at the other extreme, highly modified patterns and structures. Often the original pattern (preening, say) and the modified display (a courtship display) are both exhibited by the same animal. This is taken to mean that ritualization basically involved the *adding* of new controls, both through neurophysiological and hormonal means, to existing motor patterns, rather than the irreversible re-coordination of the original behavior. This process has been called **emancipation** of the behavior.

CONSTRAINTS ON SIGNAL EVOLUTION

While most signal evolution seems to tend toward simplification of the original motor patterns and accentuation of remaining elements, the selection for one element over another and the form of the accentuation are never random. Instead, the evolution of signals is subject to many physiological, ecological, and social constraints. At all times, strong selective pressures are operating and favoring those signals that most effectively elicit a response. The information content and stereotypy of each signal evolved depend on the social contexts in which a signal is used, and the total number of signals required by a species will be greatly affected by this "information packaging."

Physiological constraints

There are many physiological constraints on signal evolution. Since most birds have no olfactory sense, we would not expect them to include chemical secretions in their signal repertoires. Eyes specialized for night vision tend to have poorer temporal and spatial resolution than diurnal eyes. Hence, we would expect any visual displays of nocturnal animals to be slower and involve larger morphological features. Sensory organs that are of major importance for food capture or predator avoidance are unlikely to undergo changes in sensitivity similar to the stimulus filters of moth antennae or frog ears. Animals without color vision cannot use a wide variety of color cues; they tend to use more complicated patternings of light and dark.

Ecological constraints

Ecological constraints also pervade the selective forces producing ritualized signals. Consider the courtship of fruit flies. Fruit flies aggregate at food sources, mate, and lay their eggs there. There is no reason for long-distance mating signals to have evolved. Courtship among fruit flies includes stereo-typed wing movements, which in completely diurnal forms constitute visual displays.

Katydids and other forest grasshoppers, on the other hand, do not congre-gate at food sites. Instead, they are widely dispersed in the forest where they escape predation by being cryptic by day. Males attract females over moderate distances by moving their wings in certain ways, but wing movements for visual displays would be of little value to katydids. Many species are active only at night, and in dense forest visual signals cannot be seen at great distances anyway. Thus, katydids have evolved special rasping structures on their wings, structures that produce chirping stridulations as the wings are moved.

These two examples point up the fact that similar motor patterns can be modified in radically different ways and produce different signals in different ecological contexts. Visual signals are of little value in long-range communica-tion in either dense forest or water. Hence, sound usually is used for long-range signaling in such situations. The source of sound is harder to locate than the source of a visual signal. Sometimes this is a disadvantage, such as in the localization of a hidden mate; sometimes it is an advantage, such as in the production of alarm calls, which alert conspecifics without betraying the location of the caller to a predator. Neither visual nor acoustic signals have long signal times: Each time the signaler wishes to communicate infor-mation, it must repeat the signal motor pattern. Olfactory cues have long signal times: A single deposition of feces, urine, or secretions can be read by conspecifics long after the signaler has moved on. In all these cases, the choice of modality (vision, audition, olfaction, or tactile cues) and of the actual physical properties of the signal (long duration, frequency composition, color, and so on) will be made so as to optimize signal transmission in a particular environment.

By comparing related species of animals, we can see how similar basic patterns have been dropped or modified, and new patterns enlisted in signal-ing when environmental contexts are different (Fig. 9–14). For example, most species of gulls breed in open areas where large colonies of nesting pairs are formed. Kittiwakes, on the other hand, nest on slim ledges of steep cliffs. Pairs are formed in gulls not at the nesting grounds but at special sites prior to nesting. Courtship first involves the use of a special call, and when the birds arrive at the nesting grounds there is a stereotyped movement of the head called **choking**. Kittiwake males do not look for mates at communal sites, but immediately set up nesting territories on the cliffs. Instead of advertising with a special call, they perform the display typically used at nests in most gull species, choking. Thus, in the kittiwake, choking is one of the major displays in pair formation, in marked contrast to ground-nesting gulls. If we examine the basic signal repertoire of the kittiwake and compare it to that

of ground-nesting gulls, we see that some patterns have been lost (the upright threat and long mating call); some kept (choking); and some added (the appeasement behavior). In all cases, these differences can be associated with the different breeding habitat of the kittiwake which has made some signals out-of-place and required the accentuation or invention of others.

Social constraints

The structure of the social system in which one animal signals to another greatly affects both the form of the signals and the number of signals in the available repertoire. One item of information that is frequently of major importance in sexual signals is species identity. Many species suffer large losses to their own reproductive success by mis-mating with members of another species. As a defense against such loss, most mating and courtship signals include special features that make them easily discriminable from the sexual signals of related and adjacent species. We say that these signals must have **species distinctiveness**. The need for species distinctiveness is often another major force producing stereotyped sign stimuli. Any such signal must be easily and quickly identified by members of the species that has evolved it; otherwise reproductive errors are likely. Often, however, there is a contrary tendency in sexual signals. Within any breeding population, we usually find competition between males for females and *vice versa*. There are times when a signal that permits some individual recognition of the signaler confers an advantage on that animal. Also, sometimes signals must convey motivational information and graded signals evolve. In reproductive behavior, there is frequently a conflict between the forces promoting sign stimuli and species distinctiveness on the one hand, and signal variability for individual or motivational information on the other. One compromise is the evolution of a signal in which a few conspicuous components identify the species in sexual contexts and others facilitate individual recognition and motivational state. In some bird songs, this is precisely what seems to have occurred.

The size of signal repertoires also depends very much on the nature of the social systems in which animals live. Animals that are widely dispersed and have infrequent occasions for interaction usually have simpler signaling repertoires than more gregarious species. Similarly, groups that are permanent

Figure 9-14 In most gulls, aggressive gestures take the form of upward stretching of the neck and downward pointing of the bill. After combat, the defeated gull usually runs away. Kittiwakes, a ledge-nesting gull (left), do not attack from above, but clinging tightly to their ledges they grab at each others' beaks and wrestle. Kittiwakes do not have the threat posture typical of gulls that nest on beaches (below), nor does a defeated kittiwake run away, for usually there is no place to run to. Since that is so, these birds have evolved a special "appeasement" posture that shows defeat and prevents further attack. It entails hiding their weapon, the bill, in their feathers. This difference in aggressive behavior between the two species of gulls is an example of an ecological constraint on signal evolution.

and have internal cohesiveness generally require more elaborate signaling to maintain group structure and facilitate coordination of movements and behaviors than less permanent groups. Asymmetries in access to mates or commodities invariably result in elaboration of signal repertoires. These signals are both the means and the results of such competition. Finally, whenever groups have elaborate sub-structure, such as recognition of kinship, dominance hierarchies, or divisions of labor, one would expect more elaborate signaling to maintain this structure. As a rule, we can say that greater temporal or social structuring will require greater signal complexity. If signals tend to be stereotyped, it will mean a greater number of signals.

One further factor may affect the form of signals. We will see in Chapter 10 that signaling behavior can develop in young animals by several routes. In some cases, the signals are built into the young animal and only need an appropriate sign cue and hormonal level to stimulate performance. In others, as we shall see, various kinds and levels of learning are necessary. The songs of some male song birds are learned from the male parent. This produces in many such species local dialects that often reproductively isolate one population of the birds from neighboring populations. With birds that form life-long pair bonds, such as parrots and bush-shrikes, each pair builds up over a time a set of individual vocalizations peculiar to them alone and which may be sung in a duet: that is, one member sings the first part, and the partner another. Duetting often occurs with such rapidity and precision that it is difficult to tell that two birds are singing. In the vocalizations of birds, as in most signals, we find a spectrum of ways by which the form of signals are developed during life. While the mechanisms of development are the subject of Chapter 23, their effects are relevant here. Where learning and experience play a large role in signal development, we generally find more intra-specific variation in the performance of signals; where experience is less important, signal performance tends to be fairly uniform throughout the species.

The signals animals use are their basic means of interacting socially. The evolution of specific signals is often a highly complex process involving the physiology, environment, heritage, and social systems of the animals using the signals. Most species use simple sign stimuli to communicate sexual information, and graded signals for aggressive interactions. A few animals have evolved systems for communicating environmental information. The majority of species use signals that, in form, bear no relation to the information transmitted; thus they are symbolic. Such signals can be evolved from any existing motor pattern or structure by the process of ritualization, a simplifying and accentuating of specific cues to produce sign stimuli. The sensory system used, the cues accentuated, and the variability of the signals depend on the ecology in which the species lives and the proximity of related species. The methods by which the signal conventions are built into the animal—that is, learning, genetic programming, or both—also affect the form of the signals. Since all these factors vary widely, we can see that the signal systems of animals are bound to be highly diverse. This richness and diversity are reflected in the social organizations of animals, the topic taken up in our next chapter.

QUESTIONS
FOR REVIEW

1 In what ways can anthropomorphic interpretation of a non-human animal's behavior prevent us from ever understanding the essence of the particular behavior we might be observing?

2 Cite two examples each of motor patterns and autonomic patterns functioning as signals in humans.

3 Cite several examples of sign stimuli used in social behavior by three or four different species, including man.

4 In what class of situations do graded signals function more effectively than sign stimuli? Give specific examples in at least two species. In what class of situations do sign stimuli function more effectively than graded signals? Give examples.

5 When we speak of communication among animals other than man, why is a communication system with a small repertoire potential and high redundancy preferable to a communication system that can be given a large repertoire potential but low redundancy?

6 Cite examples (other than those given in the text) in humans and in one other species whose behavior you may be more than routinely familiar with, of the following classes of behavior: normal motor patterns, intention movements, ambivalent behavior, redirected behavior, and displacement behavior. Over the next several days, analyze some of your own behaviors and see if they seem to fit any of these five categories.

7 Cite several ways in which physiological factors might constrain or facilitate the evolution of signals in a given species.

8 Cite several ways in which ecological factors might constrain or facilitate the evolution of signals in a given species.

9 Cite several ways in which social factors might constrain or facilitate the evolution of signals in a given species.

SELECTED READINGS

Bastock, M. *Courtship: An Ethological Study*. Chicago: Aldine-Atherton, Inc., 1967. This excellent little book discusses the evolution of courtship in animals. It covers typical courtship sequences in insects, fish, and birds, discusses the evolutionary mechanisms by which signals evolve, and explores the genetic and physiological constraints placed on signals during evolution.

Marler, Peter, and Hamilton, W. J. *Mechanisms of Animal Behavior*. New York: John Wiley & Sons, 1966. This is now one of the classic texts in animal behavior. Its major value to a beginning student in biology is as a readable reference for topics on which the student wants more detailed information.

Sebeok, T. A., ed. *Animal Communication*. Bloomington, Ind.: Indiana University Press. This book is a collection of chapters written by numerous authors and based on an earlier symposium. It treats animal communication in the earlier chapters from more general points of view and then works through various kinds of animals taxonomically, discussing the types of signals they use. A student interested in more specific problems in animal communication will find several chapters of interest here.

Figure 10–1 Social units in birds and mammals vary widely and may change seasonally. During the breeding season, as shown by these pelicans, animals may organize themselves in colonies, rookeries, harems, or simply in pairs, but they may live in mixed groups during the non-breeding season. (OMIKRON)

10

SOCIAL ORGANIZATION

TYPES OF SOCIAL ORGANIZATION

Signals constitute one of the major exchanges between individuals in any society. In the previous chapter we discussed some of the basic characteristics of animal signals, how they have evolved, and why they may have evolved as they did. We will now turn to the broader contexts in which social behaviors occur, that is societies, and see what basic patterns are present, how they have evolved, and hopefully why (Fig. 10–1).

Temporal stability of social structure

Not all societies are equally stable. If we examine the social structure of some animal group for an extended period, immediately we can identify two basic types of variation. In some cases, we can identify periodic changes in the *structure* of the social group. For example, a flock of birds of both sexes in the non-breeding season may in spring change into a widely dispersed assemblage of mated pairs. This change constitutes an alteration of the structure of the social group. Alternately, we may not observe any change in structure, but only in composition. Continued observation at the same site may always show the presence of a flock of 100 birds. However, if we band the birds and keep watch over which ones are present, we may see drastic changes in the composition of the flock even though the structure and size of the flock are constant. These two kinds of changes must be kept in mind as we compare the societies of different animals over time.

When we compare the social structures of various species, we find that some are structurally invariant during the year and others go through cyclic changes. Among those that are structurally stable, or during the periods when a variable species has a given structure in its cycle, we find varying degrees of compositional stability. Sometimes, either the structural or the compositional changes can be correlated with seasonal changes. Often, the breeding of a species occurs during a very short period of the year and social changes accompany this important activity. For most vertebrates in temperate parts of the world, seasonal changes, reproductive periods, and variations in social structure all go together. Spring is the typical period for giving birth to young, and much of the rest of the social cycle is built around raising the young and preparing for the next breeding period. In tropical animals, we find almost all possible patterns of structural and compositional variability. Some species breed at specific times of year and yet maintain annually permanent social structures. Others breed all year. The more constant conditions of the tropics result in highly complicated patterns of reproductive activity and social cycling.

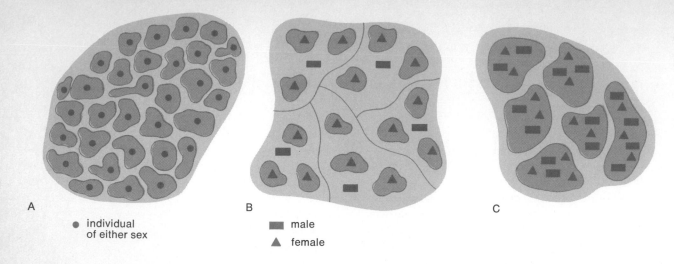

A   ● individual
       of either sex

B   ■ male
       ▲ female

C

Figure 10–2 Social systems may consist of widely dispersed individuals, each in its own territory (A), which is defended against all intruders. This arrangement is typical of many small mammals such as field mice and shrews. A more complex system (B) has females in individual territories from which other females are barred, and males in larger territories that include several female territories. This pattern is typical of some rodents and forest deer. Certain birds and monkeys live in groups and share and defend a group territory (C).

Non-breeding social systems

During the times of year when animals are not raising young, they often form social structures that are different from those seen at breeding. Many species form territories in which they live, build nests, store food, or in other ways monopolize the use of certain commodities in a delimited region (Fig. 10–2). During the non-breeding season social groups can take several forms. At one extreme we find loose aggregates of individuals with little internal structure or compositional stability. At the other extreme we find more stable and structured schools of fish, flocks of birds, or herds of mammals. These groups differ from loose aggregates in that they are cohesive. Usually, they display social facilitation and group synchronization in their activities. They have evolved specific signals and sensitivities that maintain contact and spacing. Many have also developed additional communications mechanisms for identifying specific role or status rankings within the groups and for mediating changes in these rankings.

Structured non-breeding groups can take several forms. In fish and some mammals, we find groups divided according to age and sexual maturity. In many plains ungulates, we find unisexual herds. In certain rodents, such as beavers, we find permanent families with a pair of adults and their recent young. Annually permanent harems of a single male and many females exist in certain baboons and in vicuñas. Large assemblages of both sexes are typical of rabbits.

In all these cases, there may be stable sub-structures in the social units. A typical pattern is the existence of a **dominance hierarchy**. In chickens, this is known as a pecking order because the chicken lowest in the hierarchy gets pecked the most and the highest least. Dominance hierarchies may be simple and linear: By watching competition for food or space, we can easily identify each individual's ranking relative to his fellows. One animal may get to eat first, then a second, and so on. If these orders are stable and predictable, we say a dominance hierarchy exists. If it is possible to rank them all in a single sequence, the system is linear. Sometimes, as in rabbits, there are two linear hierarchies, one for males and one for females. In other cases, for example in certain monkeys, the hierarchy for food may be different from that for access to reproductive females. Finally, not all hierarchies are linear. Sometimes one finds that individual *A* is dominant to *B,* who is dominant to *C,* who strangely enough is dominant to *A.* These non-linear dominance systems are frequent in complex monkey troops. Not all social groups have dominance hierarchies. This is only one way to stabilize overt competition within social aggregates which for other, often ecological, reasons must stick together.

A final type of non-breeding group is the mixed-species flock or school. These groups are extremely interesting because whatever signals are used to integrate and synchronize movements, they must be recognized by individuals from different species. Sometimes, simple social facilitation is sufficient to explain the movements of such groups; however, in many cases it can be seen that members of these groups actually respond to the contact and social calls of individuals of other species. Mixed flocks of insectivorous birds commonly form in eastern woods in winter. Typical members include chickadees, nuthatches, woodpeckers, and creepers. In the tropics, one often finds either fruit-eating or insectivorous birds moving in single large flocks. In the rest of the forest, it is often difficult to find any birds at all. Mixed schools of fish are quite common, particularly in reef species (Fig. 10–3). We also know that certain species of monkeys move in troops of several species and have common signals that promote synchronized activities.

Social systems during breeding

Mating in most vertebrates is basically an affair between two individuals. In fish such as herring, where several males may discharge gametes simultaneously, this is not so, but as a general rule sexual behavior involves transactions between a single male and female. In spite of this basic similarity, there is enormous diversity in the way mating occurs. There are several reasons for this diversity. First of all, mating is rarely random in vertebrates. In most

Figure 10–3 Reef fish of the tropics often occur in schools of mixed species during the non-breeding season. This social grouping is particularly interesting since synchronous movements of a school must involve communication signals commonly understood by each species in the school. (OMIKRON)

Figure 10–4 Spectacular differences in secondary sex characteristics, called sexual dimorphism, operate as social signals with important functions in courtship. Nearly always the male is more spectacular in appearance. The male of this pair of Hercules beetles is below, the female above. (THE GRANGER COLLECTION)

cases there is competition, either between females for nest sites and food, or between males for opportunities to fertilize the greatest number of females. This competition has led to courtship displays and sequences with elaborate eye-catching, stimulating, or intimidating signals (Fig. 10–4).

Secondly, to prevent mis-mating with members of other species, courtship behaviors must be species-specific. This has also led to considerable diversity in displays, especially when related species share the same habitat. In birds and frogs, we find that allopatric species (species that normally do not overlap in their distributions) often have similar vocalizations and that sympatric species (with overlapping distributions) invariably have very different vocalizations. In some species, one finds that vocalizations of populations that overlap with a related species differ from the vocalizations of non-overlapping populations. The changes in the vocalizations of overlapping populations make the song of individuals distinguishable from that of individuals of the related species. This phenomenon is known as **character displacement**, and is a reflection of the importance of species distinctiveness in signaling.

A third cause for diversity in courtship behaviors is due to variations in the types of tendencies involved in mating. For example, a species in which males are highly territorial is more likely to exhibit conflict behaviors stemming from both aggressive and sexual tendencies than is a mobile herd or school where territories are not established. Since many displays have evolved from and reflect these motivational conflicts, we expect such differences to be reflected in courtship behavior.

Finally, the need for temporal synchronization in mating varies widely in different animals. In some fish, mutual simultaneous discharge of gametes is required to fertilize the eggs. This requires a relatively elaborate prelude to discharge in which several display sequences by both male and female are performed to bring both into the same motivational state at the same time. Similarly, doves exchange a complex sequence of signals that coordinate the equally complex sequences of mating behavior necessary to raise their young. Repeated signals by one mate eventually trigger special behaviors in the other, which in turn elicit the next sequence in the first mate. By this means, doves go through a courting, copulation, nest-building, egg-laying, and young-feeding cycle with each mate participating at the right time. Other birds do not require this synchronization and their courtship behavior differs accordingly. If we take all these different factors into consideration, we can categorize most mating systems into one of the following categories.

MONOGAMY: The simplest system is that of **monogamy**. Single breeding pairs that form at least a temporary pair bond are considered to be monogamous. However there is a wide variation, even in related animals, in the strength and duration of this pair bonding. For example, pintail ducks breed in pothole areas of prairies where there is not much water. Large numbers of both sexes aggregate in these potholes and temporary bonds are formed between pairs. Males do not associate with their females much beyond copulation, and the latter soon leave the ponds to make nests and lay eggs. During the pairing period, males frequently chase and rape females, and even apparently "pair bonded" males will leave their mates to rape another. Male pintails are not aggressive to each other and many of them congregate for raping in the small potholes while the females perform most of the nesting and incubation. Mallards, on the other hand, breed in areas with greater amounts of water. Males are more aggressive to each other than are pintail males and frequently help the female select a nest site. Males leave the females after nest building and then aggregate in areas where some raping may occur. Shoveller ducks tend to form more stable pair bonds. Each male sets up an individual territory from which other males are aggressively excluded. Males leave females after the young hatch and even then remain aggressive toward other males although they rarely rape females. Finally, at the opposite extreme from pintails are geese and swans, which pair for life and generally share most of the reproductive duties. All these waterfowl are monogamous, but they differ radically in the details of their mating systems, particularly in the strength and duration of pair bonds and in the sharing of duties.

POLYGAMY: Many animals form pair bonds with more than one mate, either simultaneously or sequentially. Such animals are said to be **polygamous**. The type of polygamy in which one male mates with several females is called **polygyny**. The stickleback, for example, courts up to five females in sequence, each of which is stimulated to lay her eggs in his single nest for fertilization. Male red-winged blackbirds behave similarly, attracting one female at a time to their territories, contributing to nest-building, and then soliciting another female. Other animals, such as some baboons and seals, form harems in which a single male has reproductive access to all the females in his group. In the case of the Hamadryas baboon of Ethiopia, each group consists of one male and many females. Other males are actively excluded and form all-male groups. In the olive baboon, other males are members of the groups, but a reproductive dominance hierarchy effectively reserves copulation for the males of highest status. All these examples demonstrate polygyny. A second form of polygamy, very rare in vertebrates, is the mating of one female with several males. This is known as **polyandry**. Polyandry has been described only in some schooling fish, a few birds, and man.

In some species, pair bonds are not formed for mating. Such animals are said to be **promiscuous**. However, this should not be taken to mean that mating is necessarily *random*. In very rare cases is mating ever random and without some choice by one sex or both. Probably the most interesting promiscuous mating system is the **lek**. "Lek" comes from the Swedish word *leka* ("to play"). A lek is a display ground, generally in a very limited area, where many males gather, set up tiny territories, and spend most of their time performing elaborate displays. Females are apparently attracted to these communal mating sites, select particular males, and copulate. In most lek species the males have nothing to do with the young; instead, they spend their time trying to inseminate as many females as possible. Competition for mates at leks is generally very intense, and in those species where it has been studied, usually only a few males out of the whole lek do most of the mating. This competition is associated with elaborate sexual dimorphism in colors, size, and adornments and invariably with the evolution of complicated displays. Most temperate species of grouse form leks during the breeding season (Fig. 10–5). In the tropics, small perching birds known as manakins and some hummingbirds spend almost all year on leks. Lek behavior has also been recorded in some island species of fruit flies and in some savannah antelopes of Africa. While leks can occur in almost any group of sexually reproducing animals, they constitute a rare, though interesting, phenomenon.

Some animals exhibit more than one mating system and are therefore hard to classify. Two related types of reef fish, wrasses and parrotfish, apparently can have three basic types of color and size phases in their populations. The smallest sized fish are immatures. Both male and female immatures share a single common color pattern and often swim about in schools. Mature males and females also swim in schools and constitute another color phase. They frequently mate in large aggregations where a number of males may discharge

Figure 10–5 Prairie chickens (grouse) are typical lek species, the males of which engage in intense competition for females during the mating season; displaying male, left.

simultaneously with a given female. The third color phase is invariably of larger size and male in sex. These large males apparently are old females that have turned into males with age. They defend individual territories into which they try to lure females of the second phase for mating. Thus these fish have two kinds of mating systems: multiple spawning in schools and individual pairing by large females turned male.

An equally curious system occurs in the shore bird known as the ruff. Ruffs breed seasonally and form leks in traditional sites. Most males on the lek behave typically by setting up individual territories and displaying to females. However, there is a second color phase of the male which does not set up territories on the leks, but instead wanders from place to place. For reasons that are not yet understood, these secondary males can enter the territory of most males on a lek, and even mate with the females attracted to the territory site. Apparently the secondary males have evolved special behaviors that inhibit attack by a territory holder, and are thereby able to march about the lek relatively safely. This unusual system is at present a unique case and one that deserves much further study.

THE DIVERSITY OF SOCIAL ORGANIZATIONS

So far we have described typical *kinds* of animal social organizations, both breeding and non-breeding. Our task now is to examine the distributions of social orderings in several groups of animals and try to see how basic physiological, genetic, and ecological constraints have shaped social evolution.

Social systems in bees

Honeybees live in colonies of hundreds of bees. Each colony has a queen who is somewhat larger than the worker bees (Fig. 10–6). The queen lays the eggs, which develop into new workers, drones, and queens, and she emits a complex

Figure 10–6 Worker bees groom their queen (center), during which process a "queen substance" is passed from one worker to others in the colony. The quality of the queen substance seems to communicate to hive members the state of the queen's health. (OMIKRON)

series of chemical secretions that regulate much of the behavior of the workers. Chemical signals that alter the behavior or physiology of another member of the same species are called pheromones. Genetically both queens and workers are diploid (Chapter 3), and both are females. Queens, however, are fed a special rich larval food that is necessary for normal queen size and sexual development. Workers can in fact develop into sexually reproducing females, but their reproductive organs are kept undeveloped through the influence of the queen's pheromones. Drones are males that are produced by the laying of unfertilized eggs. They are haploid genetically.

When a hive of honeybees prepares to swarm, or when an old queen becomes feeble, the regulating pheromones of the queen grow weak. This serves as a signal for workers to begin raising new queen larvae. In the case of swarming, the old queen leaves with a group of workers and forms a new colony. In the case of an aging queen, a new queen displaces the old one. When a new queen hatches out, she kills any other newly-hatched rivals and flies off to mate. By this time, drones have left the hive and have aggregated in traditional sites in large flying clouds. The drones from several neighboring hives may all combine in such a cloud. When newly-hatched queens approach such a drone cloud, the drones rush at the queens avidly and several may mate with a queen in succession. The new queen then returns to her hive, lays her eggs, and regulates the behavior of workers.

A beehive is a marvelous society. Just as a mammalian body has elaborate homeostatic mechanisms that maintain a constant temperature, water balance, and nutrient level, so a beehive has elaborate mechanisms that maintain hive homeostasis. When the hive is hot, bees fan air throughout it and cool it off. When the nurse workers attending the larvae are short of water, they turn to the nearest workers and signal a need for water. The latter give what water they have and then turn to their neighbors; thus, the shortage of water moves from bee to bee until it reaches a worker who leaves the hive and returns with more water. When a predator or parasite enters the hive, workers rush forward and defend the colony, with the result that many die. It is almost as if the hive itself, and not the individual bees, were the organism. A bee colony's efficiency as a social system is unmatched among social animals, and we may well ask why it is not a more commonly occurring system.

One feature that sets bees, ants, and wasps apart from most other insects is the fact that males are haploid. That, plus the fact that in a colony most of the workers are daughters of the same queen, results in the workers' being more closely related to each other genetically than they would be to their own progeny if they left the hive and mated. The peculiar behavior of social bees, ants, and wasps in behaving for the good of the colony can be partly explained as an outcome of a peculiar genetic situation. But if these genetic factors were all that were necessary to evolve complex societies, we would expect all bees, ants, and wasps to be social. The fact is that colonial species are the exception. Among the bees, for example, more than 90% of the species are solitary. Each female associates with a male only long enough to mate; then she wanders off and lays her eggs in a hole, provides the eggs with food, and moves on. Few such females ever see their offspring hatch.

Haploid males are only part of the story. Presumably other adaptations of the social species, particularly ecological ones, were necessary before elaborate colonies could evolve. Some investigators have suggested that the longevity of females was a major step toward sociality. Others point out that the solitary bees don't put all their eggs in one basket, so to speak, while the colonial queen does just that. If a beehive is raided, the queen may lose all her offspring and hence all her fitness. A hive is often a large and conspicuous affair, even in hollow trees, and any clever lover of honey and larvae can spot it by watching for areas where bees are flying in and out repeatedly. A solitary bee female, however, may make several small nests that are scattered over a large area. If a predator finds one nest, he is not likely to find the others. While the fitness of such a female is reduced, it is not reduced all the way to zero as it is in the case of the hive queen. So beehives have both advantages and disadvantages. If predators are few or not clever, hives may be successful; if there are many predators, either the colonial bees must achieve extra ability for defense or solitary bees will be better adapted to that environment.

Because the members of a beehive are all so closely related, genetic variation within a colony tends to be low. A certain amount of genetic variation is often necessary if a species is to survive amid environmental change. How do bees cope with fluctuating environments if they are relatively homogeneous genetically? The answer seems to lie in that very homogeneity. In general, we find that genetic programming of behavior (behavior that is "innate" and need not be learned to any great degree) is often difficult if signals and responses are very complex. There is always some individual in any natural population who is just different enough not to understand the signals or not to respond to them in the right way. But in a beehive this genetic variability is reduced, with increased likelihood that all members will produce the appropriate signals correctly and respond to them correctly. This increased accuracy permits the programming of very complicated signal sequences in bees. The dance (Fig. 9–8) is one example. The accurate exchange of these signals results in the amazing homeostasis of a bee hive. Thus, the genetic homogeneity of the hive permits a complex signal repertoire that is accurate enough to keep the hive stable whatever the external conditions. The signals in some ways compensate for the lack of genetic adaptability. Again, there are limits to this compensation. Once outside the hive, a worker must depend on her own attributes and cannot count on the group-induced homeostasis. Here genetic variability may play a major limiting role.

Social systems in fish

Many species of fish are pelagic. In such a habitat, where there is no substrate or vegetation in which to hide, the best defense against predation seems to be in numbers. Many pelagic fish form large and highly coordinated schools that move as single units over wide stretches of open ocean. The carefully maintained spacing and group synchronization of such schools are remarkable and rely heavily on sensitive visual and water displacement receptors. Partly because of the need to act in unison, often rapidly and suddenly, both sexes

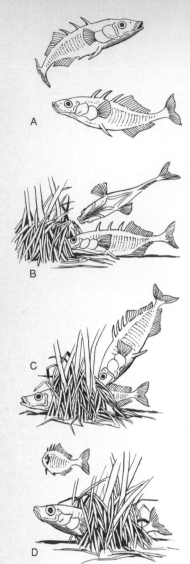

Figure 10–7 A number of sign stimuli and appropriate responses are involved in the successful mating of sticklebacks. The red belly of the male warns other males to stay away, but also attracts females (A). After performing his zig-zag dance (see Fig. 9–11), the male leads the female to the nest (B) and then taps her near the tail (C). That is a signal for her to lay her eggs, after which the male forces her from the nest, enters it himself, and deposits sperm over them (D).

in such schools tend to have identical body shapes and markings. In a sense, the advantages of these similar shapes and colors are the usual ones typical of sign stimuli: Speed and accuracy of signaling are achieved with a minimum of cues. If the school consisted of two kinds of fish, the double set of cues might sometimes lead to ambiguity or delays.

There is another and perhaps more important advantage in having common body patterns in the two sexes. Pelagic species discharge their gametes into the ocean currents, and since there is no opportunity to cache the eggs or defend the young, mating behavior is limited to fertilization and dissemination of eggs. In open oceans, this requires accurate timing of discharges by both males and females. If timing is off, even by a small amount, the eggs may be carried away unfertilized and there is no chance of recovering them. Courtship in almost all pelagic species consists of a sequence of mutual displays by both male and female. By the time the sequence terminates, the behaviors of male and female are identical and motivations are similar, so the chances of mutual discharge are maximized. The simplest way to achieve this result appears to be the sharing of courtship patterns by both sexes. One mate will display a step in the sequence until the other performs the identical display. This triggers the next step in the first fish and so on until the behavior of both mates is identical. Since displays are identical for male and female, we expect little sexual dimorphism in these fish, and we find little.

Competition for mates is limited to the males' ability to isolate females from other males. In turn, this activity is limited by the ecological advantages of remaining in the school. In some species, several males may discharge with a single female, and a given female may discharge several times, each time with different males. So mating may be promiscuous or polygamous. Pelagic fish, therefore, live in schools all year, have little if any sexual dimorphism or competition for mates, show mutual and simple courtship behavior, are generally polygamous or promiscuous, and do not care for eggs or young.

A second pattern is that of the stickleback (Fig. 10–7). These fish live in schools during the non-breeding season. During the breeding season, the schools migrate to shallow water (if they are not already there) and break up. Males assume breeding colors and stake out individual territories into which they attract females. Breeding in a shallow water site facilitates the building of nests in which eggs can be hidden and so reduces predation. Males care for the eggs and young in such species. Because the eggs can be deposited in a given site, mutual discharge is not necessary. In contrast to pelagic species, the courtship behaviors of the two sexes in the stickleback and similar species are often very different. Being freed from the constraints of mutual discharge, males can devote their energy to attracting several females to their nests, can evolve highly specialized displays and patterns to do so, and can fertilize the eggs at their leisure. Typically, such fish are sexually dimorphic and polygynous.

A third pattern, also found in shallow water species, is typical of cichlid fish. Many are tropical and breed at all times of the year. Cichlids differ from both of the previous types by forming long-term monogamous pair bonds. In some species, both sexes establish territories before mating, but reproductive activities are usually limited to the territories of males. Courtship for these fish is long and involved, and most of the behavior is identical in both sexes. As in pelagic fish, there is usually little sexual dimorphism. Once pairs have formed, both parents defend the territory aggressively and share duties in caring for eggs and young. After the eggs have hatched, at least one parent stands guard over them at all times, and the two adults have elaborate signals for "changing the guard."

A fourth pattern is found in the guppy and its relatives. These fish are unusual in that fertilization is internal and the young are born alive. Guppies live in schools of varying sizes all year, although they often live in relatively shallow waters. There seems to be considerable competition among male guppies to inseminate females and they are quite sexually dimorphic. Courting occurs in the schools but includes attempts by males to lead females away for copulation. Neither adult cares for the young.

This survey of fish social systems is not exhaustive, and many species have social behaviors that lie between our examples. However, several basic trends are apparent. First of all, most fish are polygynous. This is not surprising because it is easier, both energetically and physiologically, to make sperm than eggs. Generally females have fewer eggs to spread among several males than males have sperm to spread among females. We have seen that pelagic species rely on group cohesiveness for protection, and this results in pressures for similar form in the two sexes. This similarity in form is reinforced by the need for simultaneous discharge at mating. However, shallow water forms are freed from this constraint. Where fixed nest sites are available, males can defend territories and fertilize the eggs of several females. Females benefit from this system by being able to expend all energies on making eggs and not on defending them. Males benefit by having reproductive access to several females and hence spreading their genes more effectively. Internal fertilization is similar in its effects on social behavior. In both cases, we find sexual dimorphism, elaborate displays by males, and polygyny. Finally, in some fish, we find both males and females caring for the young and the existence of long-term monogamy. It is not obvious why these fish have evolved monogamous bonds when the majority of species are polygamous. Does higher predation necessitate the care of both parents in the habitats where cichlids live? Whatever the reason, we see some convergence in these fish with the social behavior of pelagic species: the presence of mutual display patterns by both male and female, and a lack of sexual dimorphism.

Social systems in birds

When they are not breeding, most non-carnivorous species of birds form flocks. The flocks may consist of highly coordinated monospecific groups, as in finches, or looser aggregates of several species, as in the mixed-species flocks of tropical forests. Most carnivorous birds, such as hawks and owls, never form large groups or cohesive flocks. However, they are the exception when we consider all birds.

Most species of birds form monogamous pairs for breeding. Usually males set up territories that they actively defend by song or displays. Courtship is prolonged and involves attraction of the female, pair formation with reduction of aggression in the male, nest construction, and joint care of the young. This pattern is found in both temperate and tropical birds, the major difference being a tendency for year-round breeding in the tropics.

Some birds do not breed in dispersed fashion but form dense colonies. Each pair then establishes its own territory within the colony and subsequent behavior is similar to that of dispersed species. This is common among sea birds such as gulls and penguins. Not all colonial nesters are monogamous. Some species are polygynous, a single male mating with numerous females, each occupying her own nest. The tropical relative of our red-winged blackbird, known as the cacique, has just such a social system. A single nesting tree may contain up to a dozen long pendular nests. The nests are woven by the females while the male spends his time copulating, calling, and chasing away rival males. Females do all the caring for the young.

Polyandry does not occur commonly in any vertebrate group. Tinamous, a group of primitive ground birds in the neotropics, do have such a system. Male tinamous have individual territories in which they build rough nests. They call during the early morning and evening with a long warbling sound that carries far in the forests. Females visit males, are fertilized, and lay eggs in the nests. One female may leave eggs in the nests of several males. In some species, males may also be polygynous and incubate the eggs of several females. Polyandry usually occurs only in those few species in which the sexual roles of males and females are reversed, at least from the point of view of behavior. In these species females usually are more brightly colored than males, defend territories, and perform displays. The males incubate the eggs and care for the young.

Leks have already been mentioned as typical of several bird species, such as grouse, manakins, ruffs, and hummingbirds. Leks are also found in many of the birds of paradise. These species are remarkable for the beautiful and elaborate plumage of the male members of the species. Clearly the patterns are related to the evolution of elaborate and striking displays that males perform on the leks in competition for females. In general, all lek species show extreme dimorphism between the sexes, at least during the breeding season. In lek species the male does not help with nest building or caring for the young. Since most lek species females rely on cryptic nests to escape predation, the presence of gaudily colored males at nest sites might be highly unadaptive.

There are several unusual bird social systems (Fig. 10–8). Tropical America has several species of cuckoos, known as anis, that live in small groups of both sexes in the open country. Each group actively defends the territory in which it feeds and reproduces. During breeding, the group con-

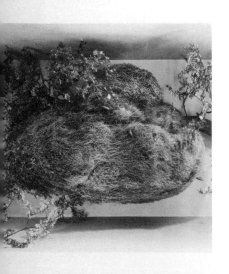

Figure 10–8 The communal nest of birds known as social weavers consists of a large roof-like structure carefully woven by many birds working in cooperation. Mated pairs of the birds—up to 100 or so pairs—then occupy individual nests within the "apartment house" complex. In what ways are such communal nests advantageous to the birds?

structs a single communal nest into which all the females place their eggs. Incubation and care of the young are also a communal affair, with males, females, and juveniles all vying to take a turn on the eggs or to feed the young. Smooth-billed anis have the curious habit of carrying a green leaf to the nest. The leaf is dropped or tucked into the nest and serves as the signal (or "ticket") causing the currently incubating bird to yield its position to the leaf carrier. Cooperative breeding of this kind is rare in birds but is also known in certain species of jays.

Some close relatives of the anis, the true cuckoos, have even more divergent breeding habits. They are nest parasites, laying their eggs in the nests of other species of birds. Cowbirds and the Argentinean black-headed duck have similar habits. In most nest parasites, males display or sing, and pair bonds are formed just as if the eggs were to be laid in the nest of the parents.

If we tally the occurrences of these different social systems in birds, we find that most species are monogamous, sexually monomorphic, and inclined to nest in individual territories. A much smaller proportion of species are polygynous and sexually dimorphic, and even smaller fractions are promiscuous or polyandrous. When not breeding, most birds are fairly gregarious, and highly coordinated flocks are common social units. For the most part, birds are diurnal animals and few if any have the sense of smell. Accordingly, most rely heavily on visual and acoustical signals in their displays.

In the previous chapter, we found that animals with more complex or more competitive social systems tend to have more complicated signal repertoires. Birds, with their elaborate mating behaviors, flocking behaviors, and meticulous care of the young, are excellent examples of this trend. The repertoires of mockingbirds or the colorful birds of paradise include some of the most spectacular and complicated sexual signals known. While we recognize that this signal complexity is associated with concomitant social complexity, we do not yet understand why it should be so in any species. Only further study can clarify the problem.

Social systems in mammals

Most mammals are small, secretive, and nocturnal in their habits. Typically, they are widely dispersed in individual territories that they delineate by vocalizations or by leaving olfactory marks on the boundaries. Most such species do not form pair bonds during breeding. Instead, males leave their own territories at certain times of the year and enter the territories of females. Copulation is usually fairly quick, after which the female may drive the male away. Because of the special attributes of female mammals for developing and feeding their young, most male mammals play little if any role in caring for their progeny. Instead, they occupy themselves in mating with as many females as possible. Even in dispersed and relatively solitary mammals such as mice, shrews, and small carnivores, there is a tendency toward polygyny or promiscuity. Most of these species do not have elaborate signal repertoires. Instead, most signaling is devoted to the delineation of territories and to short-range sexual or aggressive exchanges.

Figure 10–9 Caribou, elk, and other ungulates usually form unisexual herds most of the time (male caribou here). During the mating season they aggregate into temporary harems.

More gregarious mammals form a wide variety of social units. In some species, unisexual groups are formed during the non-breeding season. They may consist of groups of females and solitary males, as in coati mundis, or separate herds of each sex, as in ungulates (Fig. 10–9). Usually, such species form temporary harems for copulation and then break up again into unisexual groups. Other seasonally variant systems include mixed groups of both sexes during the non-breeding season and harems during breeding. This is typical of seals and their relatives.

A number of mammals form permanent social units all year. Several species of tropical bats, camels, vicuñas, and Gelada and Hamadryas baboons have harems and all-male groups throughout the year. Permanent harems are also found in species that have highly seasonal breeding periods. Beavers and gibbons live in permanent monogamous pairs with their young. However, permanent families are rare in mammals. Wolves, rabbits, and several primates form permanent groups with several males and several females. Usually, these species also have reproductive hierarchies, with one or a few males doing most of the mating.

The basic trends in mammalian social organization can now be seen. Most mammals are solitary in habit and have relatively simple social interactions. Those that are gregarious tend to form polygynous mating groups and various kinds of non-mating aggregations. Female mammals seem more likely to aggregate than males. Because of special adaptations of female mammals, males usually have very little to do with the young. The tendencies of many mammals to be solitary and polygamous is in direct contrast to the trends in birds toward gregariousness and monogamy. Mammals also differ from birds in their heavy reliance on olfactory signal cues, which are long-lasting and can be read at much later times by conspecifics. This is a useful means of communication for dispersed mammals that rarely encounter members of their own species. Mammals also use acoustical cues to maintain spacing over wide distances. Tree hyraxes, whales, monkeys, and bats all have evolved special calls that carry for long distances and facilitate communication between widely dispersed individuals or groups. Unlike birds, most mammals rely less on the use of visual signals. To a large degree this is a result of their greater nocturnality.

Comparison of fish, birds, and mammals

Why do we find such differences in the basic social behaviors of social bees, fish, birds, and mammals? Bees are a special case because they have haploid males. While it is not the exclusive cause for colonial organization in bees, this characteristic is a contributing influence, along with female longevity and lowered predation pressures. Most fish are polygynous, most birds are monogamous, and most mammals are polygynous. For the majority of fish, fertilization is external. Although the fertilized eggs of pelagic species are exposed to predators, most pelagic fish have compensated by producing enormous numbers of gametes. In sites where nests can be made, some protection by one parent can help ameliorate egg loss. Since gametes are shed by both sexes, there is no *a priori* reason why one sex or the other should be singled out to perform this task, yet invariably we find the male caring for the young. Producing sperm is less taxing than producing eggs. In addition, the eggs carry the nutrients for the embryo, and the number of eggs produced sets the upper limit on the number of young possible. A male always has enough sperm to fertilize surplus eggs. So, if the female is free to devote all her energies to egg production, and the male to caring for the young, more young are likely to be produced than if the male let the female perform the task. Once the male assumes this task, often it is as easy for him to care for several sets of eggs as one set. Hence, he tends to try to attract as many females to his nest as possible and so increases his own reproductive output. We could argue that external fertilization, the availability of sites where young can be protected, and the energetics of egg and sperm production all combine and encourage polygyny in shallow-water fish. Monogamous species, like cichlids, are exceptions to these tendencies but do not constitute a large fraction of all fish species. The reasons for their deviance from the basic patterns are presumably ecological and probably of considerable interest.

In contrast to fish, birds usually are monogamous. Unlike fish, fertilization in all birds is internal, but like most fish, birds lay eggs. Birds share with fish the problems of protecting the young from predators. However, they have a different problem, one associated with their land habitat. Most fish need only aerate and protect their young from predators; they do not need to provide their young with food. Fish live in a medium that contains large numbers of small prey. Schools of fry can usually feed within the territories of the male without making major excursions. Because air is less amicable to small organisms, a young bird cannot sit on the edge of its nest feeding on small prey that pass by. As a result, almost all adult birds must provide for their young. In a majority of species, this means considerable work by two parents simultaneously, so monogamy is the rule. In a few species, where the female alone feeds the young, or where predation is so high that having only a single adult come and go reduces the nest's conspicuousness, we find polygyny.

In some ways, mammals tend to be more like fish than birds. Like birds, mammals have internal fertilization. Unlike birds, only female mammals can provide for the young directly. However, males are useful in warding off predators, and in a few cases in helping provide for the females. Since the males' family role is relatively limited, they can afford to spend their time mating with several females, so we find a strong tendency toward polygyny in mammals.

One other factor is worth comparing in the three groups. During non-breeding periods, most fish and birds are highly gregarious, but most mammals are solitary. Earlier we found that schools, flocks, and herds can be of some value in reducing predation. Certainly the advantage of a communal set of senses makes an aggregate of animals more likely to spot approaching predators than are solitary individuals. In some instances, large numbers of individual prey distract attacking predators, making it hard for the predator to concentrate on any one individual. An alternate strategy for prey would be to live dispersed, in which condition the probability of being located as an individual is very small. Why have mammals tended to adopt the latter strategy, but birds and fish the former? There is no easy answer, but some possibilities emerge.

Consider any small animal. To survive, it must be able to find sufficient sources of energy, by eating, to at least balance the energy spent on locomotion. If we scale up this animal by a factor of two, it will be able to walk twice as far, but it will also need twice as much food. While the accessible range for this twice-larger animal has doubled, the total increase in *accessible area* for foraging will have increased by a factor of four. As a rule, the energy requirements for increasing size are not linear, but actually decrease per unit body weight for larger animals. So increasing the body size simultaneously decreases the relative energy needs and increases the accessible foraging area. For a given diet, we should be able to find a size at which the accessible area can support more than one animal. This critical size will, of course, depend on the density of the food source. We expect it to be larger for a carnivore than for an herbivore. Most small mammals have limited mobility. This means that their accessible foraging areas rarely can support more than one individual. That is why these mammals tend to lead solitary lives and disperse more than is necessary for a low rate of predation. Their habits, accordingly, are secretive and often nocturnal. Larger mammals, as a rule, are gregarious, although even in dense tropical forests many deer are solitary.

We could argue that birds, being small, also should be solitary. However, all birds have the benefit of a mobility much beyond that of small mammals of equivalent size. Flight in birds is a remarkable boon because it means that a fairly large group of small birds can migrate considerable distances in search of new food sources. While flight usually consumes more energy than, say, running, the increases in accessible area due to increased mobility generally outweigh the added energy demands of flight. If we compare small birds to small mammals, we find that few small mammals move great distances except, as in mice, during overpopulation or some other major ecological catastrophe. The only known examples of highly social small mammals that make such migrations are species that feed on very densely stocked foods (such as prairie dogs on grass), or those that are uniquely mobile (such as bats). In both groups we find highly gregarious species with complicated social groups.

THE EVOLUTION OF SOCIAL SYSTEMS

With at least some understanding of the types of social organizations found in bees, fish, birds, and mammals, and of some of the selective forces that might have affected social evolution of these animals, we are now in a position to discuss the interactions of signal evolution and social structure.

Reproductive success and ecological adaptedness

There are two ways a particular gene increases in frequency in a population. One is to give its carrier and his descendants some superior advantage in coping with environmental problems, such as acquisition of food or avoidance of predation. The other is to provide some advantage in reproductive competition. Reproductive success does not often entail producing the most young, but being the parent of the greatest fraction of total young produced. These two alternatives constitute the major driving forces for selection. On the one hand, individuals better able to cope with the environment will leave more offspring in the long run, and their genes will dominate subsequent generations. On the other hand, males more likely to attract and arouse females, or females who nest in the best territories, are more likely to spread their genes than are their competitors. The first force leads to ecological adaptedness and is called natural selection; the second force leads to elaborate reproductive systems and was called by Darwin "sexual selection."

We are already familiar with most of the results of sexual selection: sexual dimorphism, unequal sex ratios (usually caused by differential mortality due to the dimorphism), polygamy in its various forms, and even different uses of the environment by the two sexes. It is very difficult to know which of these various effects came first. Is polygyny the cause or the result of there being more adult female birds than males in many species? Given that competition for mates existed, then we would expect selection pressure to favor sexual dimorphism for the advantages it would provide in successful courtship and mating. Elaborate and colorful males might acquire several females and so initiate polygyny. However, these more colorful males might simultaneously be more conspicuous and liable to predation. This would shift the sex ratio in the population in favor of females. In this case, the sex ratio differences would arise because of polygyny. Alternately, since some monogamous birds are sexually dimorphic, we might find that increasingly severe differential mortality might shift an initially equal sex ratio toward females. In this situation, monogamy would no longer be practical and polygyny would arise.

Without further information, we cannot decide whether polygamy gave rise to sexual dimorphism or whether it happened the other way around. The examples given raise a fundamental issue. The evolutionary forces promoting ecological adaptedness and those promoting reproductive success usually work in opposition to each other. The peacock's elaborate tail is of great value in the competition for mates; without it a male would be unable to attract and mate with females. On the other hand, the elaborate tail is clearly an ecological detriment to a male. No male peacock can escape predators or fly to new food sites as easily as females do. We can conclude only that the ecological disadvantages are balanced by the reproductive ones.

If we examine social evolution with these examples in mind, we find that much of the diversity of social behaviors is the result of a different balance between ecological and reproductive factors. A bird living in an extremely harsh environment is more likely to be constrained in the amount of energy or exposure that he can devote to sexual competition. We would expect such a species to be monogamous and that males would help with the young.

The balance struck by any one species will also depend to a large degree on the differences in constraints on males and females. As a rule, all animals are selfish; this is a natural outcome of the selective forces that have shaped them as individuals. There is no reason, genetically, why any individual should not pursue the social system that optimizes his own reproduction. In many cases, the optimal systems may be different for males and females. The compromise reached in this battle of the sexes will depend on the differences in ecological requirements of males and females and in their individual behavior patterns. Highly aggressive males may succeed in dominating a social system to the detriment of females; in some arid country weaver birds, this results in a high mortality of females during periods of food shortage. Thus, the social system of any species depends not only on the overall problems of ecological and reproductive needs, but also on the outcomes of inter-sexual competition. This fact is often hard for us to accept in viewing the social behavior of other animals.

Signals play an enormous role in the evolution of social systems. They are the major form of social transactions and usually are highly formalized and specific. We know that many signals have evolved in specific ways to attract and arouse the receiver (Fig. 5–9). We also know that in many cases, it is possible to enlarge a stimulus object and produce a supernormal stimulus, one that is preferred to a normal one. Much of the course of sexual selection is presumed to have gone along lines of increasing stimulus effect. One way to increase stimulus effect, say of displaying males, is to put all the males in a common site. This would be possible only if ecological conditions permitted such aggregations. Is it possible that an aggregate of displaying males is more stimulating than the same number of males dispersed? One study on colonial weaver birds suggests that this is so. In the study, the number of females attracted to the colony per male increased with the size of the colony. Since adjacent colonies shared the same food and predator pressures, one concludes that the increased signal stimulation brought the greater number of females. If the reliance on a few simple sign cues that are more effective when aggregated than when dispersed is common to other species, it might account for the evolution of many colonial breeders, and perhaps for the evolution of the phenomenon of leks as well.

The adaptedness of social systems

Throughout this chapter, we have argued that ecological factors are major determinants of the social systems of animals and of the behavior typical within those systems. If that is so, do similar social systems turn up in similar environments? One outstanding study, again on the weaver birds of Africa and Asia, suggests this conclusion. John Crook compared the social structure and courtship behaviors of a large number of these birds in a variety of environments. In all species, males select nest sites and weave elaborate nests. Then they display and advertise their nests to females. Crook found a remarkable convergence of social behaviors in similar habitats. Forest species of weavers are nearly all monogamous and sexually monomorphic, and courtship consists of chases and leading females to the males' hidden nests. Nearly all forest species are insectivorous in diet. Species living in grassy savannahs generally are granivores, hide nests in the grass, perform aerial displays over the nests, and are sexually dimorphic and polygynous. Arid country weavers are also granivorous, build nests in large colonies in trees, display on the nests, and are sexually dimorphic and polygynous. These correlations between habitat and social organization are quite remarkable. There are many examples of anatomically closely related species that live in different environments and have totally different social systems, and of quite unrelated species that live in the same environment and have identical social systems. At least in the weavers, one is led to conclude that ecology is a much more important determinant of social behavior than is phylogeny. If this is so in other animals, it should be possible through comparative studies to derive some general predictions about the kinds of social systems a given type of animal can be expected to manifest.

The weaver study and others like it raise the question of *how* ecological factors affect social evolution. In some species of birds, such as the marsh wren, there is evidence that the quality of the territory defended by males is important to females. A female exposed to an already mated male holding a good territory, and to a single male with a poor territory, will usually select the former. This leads to polygyny in these birds. Not all species of birds resolve mate "choice" by responding to the quality of a male's territory, since not all species build their nests in the territories of males or even feed their young there. Lek species are classic examples. The choice of mates, as evidenced by sexual selection, does not always hinge on ecological criteria. Instead, we find again that ecological factors and reproductive competition combine in complicated ways, so shaping social structure.

A subject of great relevance to the effects of environment on social structure is the occurrence of intra-specific variation in social units. In many rodents, low density populations show a classical formation of individual territories from which other individuals are actively excluded. At high densities, territorial behavior breaks down and dominance hierarchies are set up. Since population levels can be affected by external factors such as food and predation, we have here evidence of direct social responses to environmental conditions. On their wintering ground in Israel, European wagtails either live in migrant flocks or set up individual feeding territories, depending on the density of food supplies. In a number of monkey species, such as langurs, social organization also seems to differ, depending on the food and population levels, within the same species. This kind of variation implies that not only does ecology largely determine the kinds of social organization a group of animals has, but it does so in short time periods. Clearly, it is not necessary to wait tens of thousands of years for new species with new morphological differences to evolve and generate the social system appropriate to a particular environment. Instead, social changes occur in different populations of the same species, and in rodents and wagtails even in the same population at different times.

The special case of primates

In different species of primates, early experience plays different roles in determining adult behavior. It does not take much early experience for a chick to learn vocalization patterns. Duetting birds, on the other hand, build up elaborate repertoires over periods of years as part of pair bonding. To some degree primates are an extreme case of the latter trend. Much primate signaling is both complex and variable. As a rule, the form of primate signals is fairly species-specific and does not depend much on early experience. However, the contexts and uses of those signals are highly dependent on early experience, and without this "education" most primates behave extremely abnormally.

Most primates have long juvenile periods during which they learn both social and environmental behaviors (Fig. 10-10). Few primates, if any, know what to eat, where to drink, or how to avoid predators until they are taught. They acquire this "culture" by observation of other members of their troops. Not all troop members are equally likely to be teachers. When certain new habits, such as food washing, appeared in one study group of Japanese monkeys, the new trait was passed along kinship lines and between peers. Social behaviors, then, as well as environmental behaviors, are acquired by learning in monkeys. Olive baboons live in mixed male-female troops in which a few dominant males rule the group. Hamadryas baboons live in permanent harems with a single male per group. The mechanisms of group cohesion and the tendency of females to follow particular males and mate with them differ radically in the two species. If one moves females from groups of one species to groups of the other, the transplanted females quickly abandon nearly all their former behavior patterns and adopt those of the group in which they have been placed. These and similar studies clearly show that social behavior in primates is highly dependent on learning experience.

The fact that both ecological adaptedness and reproductive success in monkeys depend, at least in part, on learning changes the selective forces on their social evolution. By building up cultures over time, a population of monkeys can become locally "adapted" to a particular environment without

Figure 10–10 Because of their relatively long juvenile periods, some of the behavior of most primates is acquired through learning from adult members of the community, just as this very attentive juvenile baboon watches the activity of an adult male.

needing extensive genetic changes in their morphology or physiology. This accounts for the ecological success of many tropical primates, such as the savannah baboons that live in many different kinds of habitats with apparent success. The reliance on learning for local ecological adaptations clearly promotes an evolutionary plasticity that has made these species populous and widespread. This same reliance does, however, necessitate a long juvenile period during which transmission of the "culture" is accomplished gradually. Uneducated monkeys usually end up dead monkeys. An animal's use of environmental culture clearly frees its ecological success of many of the genetic constraints that apply to other animals. Similarly, success in reproductive competition also may not depend as much on genetic constitution as on early experience.

In many species of monkeys, dominance status is associated with kinship, and hereditary monarchies can be formed. However, early associations also affect subsequent dominance status. A male born to low status may rise to peak dominance through peer affiliations and superior learning. In many monkeys, it may well be that the male best able to spread his genes and survive is not a relative of the previous males in that position. Social evolution with reduced genetic constraints can take very unusual and complicated paths; perhaps man is an extreme case of this trend.

Man has evolved a unique ability to modify and ameliorate ecological restraints through technology. Given that social evolution in man is also limited by ecological necessities, one expects human societies to undergo continual evolution as, one after another, the environmental limits are rolled back. If we add to this freedom from environmental constraints the enormous social plasticity afforded by a major reliance on learning, we can see that human social evolution can take off on many varied and complicated tacks that make little sense from either genetic or ecological points of view. Social systems in humans, especially in the more advanced cultures, may be totally unadaptive in the sense we have argued that bee or fish or bird or other mammal societies are. This makes man particularly interesting and unique among animals. Free of many restraints, he is in a position to be master of his own social evolution.

QUESTIONS FOR REVIEW

1 Cite some examples of ecology being a more important determinant of behavior than phylogeny.
2 Select five species and explain how their seasonal breeding behavior affects their social organization.
3 How do the following classes of mating behavior differ: monogamy, polygyny, polyandry, and promiscuous behavior?
4 In the context of natural selection, how can we account for the biological success of two such vastly different social systems as colony bees and solitary bees?
5 Do human beings have any recognizable patterns of courtship behavior? If so, is this behavior genetically or culturally derived? Explain.
6 What is meant when we say that a social system *evolves*? Cite an example.
7 Do you think it possible for man "to be master of his own social evolution"?

SELECTED READINGS

Wilson, E. O. *The Insect Societies*. Cambridge, Mass.: The Belknap Press of Harvard University Press, 1971. This large and beautifully illustrated volume on social insects is superbly written and covers many areas in social biology. Many basic issues, such as the adaptive value of social systems from genetic and ecological viewpoints, are treated clearly and generally enough to be of wide applicability.

Crook, J. H. *Social Systems and Evolutionary Ecology*. Edinburgh: Oliver and Boyd, forthcoming. This book is one of the only comprehensive reviews of social organization in higher vertebrates. It also discusses many of the ecological factors which appear to shape and determine social evolution.

Kummer, Hans. *Primate Societies*. Chicago: Aldine-Atherton Inc., 1971. This small book gives an excellent review and introduction to the complex structure of primate social groups. As in the two foregoing titles, the emphasis is on the effects of ecology and on careful field study and experimentation.

Part 3
INTEGRATION

In Parts 1 and 2 of this book
we concentrated on behavior in terms
of what animals, and in many instances
plants, *do*. In Part 3 we narrow our focus
and search inside the organism
to find the physiological mechanisms
that enable the organism to detect and
respond to stimuli of its own internal
environment and to stimuli of the
external environment.

Figure 11–1 A common sight in many parts of the world—the V-shaped pattern of migrating geese. Why do these birds, twice yearly, abandon one region and fly hundreds or thousands of miles to a new region? What signals the beginning of this migration? How do they remain on course despite constantly changing terrain and climatic conditions? How is migrating behavior related to the nerve and sensory mechanisms? Do other organisms respond similarly to environmental cues?

11

BEHAVIOR AND THE NERVOUS SYSTEM

In the preceding chapters we were concerned with the social relationships of animals. Each member of a family or colony was considered as an interacting unit in an organization, and the behavioral factors giving the organization survival value for the species were the center of our interest. The problems that we encountered are among the most complex in the study of the behavior of organisms.

In the chapters that follow we will be concerned with matters that in some ways parallel those problems, but we will be thinking at a very different level of organization. Nerve cells will be substituted for whole organisms as the units of our concern, and we will examine the specialized roles they play as part of the mechanism for generating the behavior of an individual animal.

The methods used for studying nerve cell organizations are very different from those needed to study animal organizations. We must probe not only inside the nervous system but also inside individual nerve cells in order to find out how they interact with one another. Nevertheless, the intent of many of the questions we will be asking will be the same. As always, we will be concerned with the adaptedness, or survival value, of this or that arrangement of nerve cells and will want to know how it got that way.

The present chapter makes the transition from thinking about social animals to thinking about social nerve cells. We will begin by examining some relatively stereotyped behavior patterns in single animals (Fig. 11–1) and then consider how the nervous system has evolved in the animal kingdom, how it is constituted in different groups, and the form of nerve cells.

PRE-PROGRAMMED BEHAVIOR

The most elementary behavior patterns are those that protect animals from being eaten by predators. Evasive behavior is simple for several reasons. Its mechanism must work rapidly and must, therefore, be uncomplicated and as direct as possible. Also the behavior must work the first time it is needed. It is pre-programmed and not learned in most cases. These are points that favor attempts to analyze its mechanisms.

In addition to evasive behavior, many quite complex behavior patterns are pre-programmed or built into the nervous systems of animals. Built-in behavior is a necessity for organisms that live solitary lives and that do not have parental care, thereby lacking any opportunity to learn by imitation how to carry out certain actions. Even then, of course, they could learn by experience,

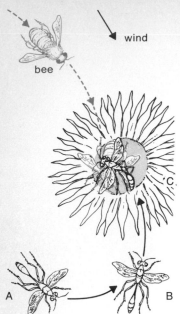

Philanthus

Figure 11–2 The hunting behavior of the digger wasp *Philanthus triangulum* is shown. At A, odor of the prey (a bee) is irrelevant; instead, a visual stimulus is required to elicit the first in a series of three responses in the wasp. On sighting a bee, the wasp turns and faces prey (B). Only at this stage in the behavior chain does the odor of the bee trigger a response—a dash to grasp her prey (C). A tactile cue then seems to trigger the third and final response in the series, stinging the bee.

but many animals such as spiders and insects have short adult lives and little time for such learning, particularly when the behavior is complex and must work right away if the animal is to survive. Let us examine two examples.

A bee hunter

A solitary digger wasp, *Philanthus triangulum* (Fig. 11–2), provisions its developing larvae with honeybees, which it captures and paralyzes with its sting. Tinbergen describes its hunting behavior:

> A hunting female of this species flies from flower to flower in search of a bee. In this phase she is entirely indifferent to the scent of bees; a concealed bee, or even a score of them put out of sight into an open tube so that the odor escaping from them is clearly discernible even for the human nose, fails to attract her attention. Any visual stimulus supplied by a moving object of approximately the right size, whether it be a small fly, a large bumble bee, or a honeybee, releases the first reaction. The wasp at once turns her head to the quarry and takes a position at about 10–15 cm to leeward of it, hovering in the air like a syrphid fly. Experiments with dummies show that from now on the wasp is very susceptible to bee-scent. Dummies that do not have bee-odor are at once abandoned, but those dummies that have the right scent release the second reaction of the chain. This second reaction is a flash-like leap to seize the bee. The third reaction, the actual delivery of the sting, cannot be released by these simple dummies and is probably dependent on new stimuli, probably of a tactile nature.

The wasp's feeding behavior is a chain of reactions, each link distinct in itself. These reactions depend on "bee-look," "bee-smell," and "bee-feel." If the first test is satisfied it leads to the second, the second to the third, and so on. If any one test is not satisfied, the chain breaks off. These various tests of "beeness" seem to comprise a most efficient way of hunting, yet if one tries to bypass one or two links in the chain, the wasp will be unable to carry on.

A caterpillar hunter

A related wasp, *Ammophila campestris*, shows an even more complex hunting and provisioning sequence that involves a delayed response or memory. In spite of this, the wasp is imprisoned in its pre-programmed behavior sequence and is unable to change it to suit unusual circumstances.

The female wasp (Fig. 11–3) provides a number of her larvae—each of a different age and living in a separate hole in the ground—with caterpillars. The mother wasp digs a hole, seeks and paralyzes a caterpillar with her sting, and then deposits the prey at the bottom of the hole after laying an egg on it. This done, she digs a new hole and repeats the process. Later she prepares still a third hole in the same way. Thus, the mother wasp may have as many as three holes containing different-sized larvae (with appetites to match) that she has

Figure 11–3 The digger wasp *Ammophila campestris* with caterpillar prey.

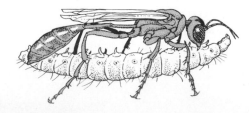

to feed in the course of each day. Gerard Baerends found that the wasp visits and inspects each hole and its larva first thing each morning. She then hunts for caterpillars and brings to each hole a number apparently determined on this inspection visit. Baerends changed the number of caterpillars still un-eaten in each burrow before the wasp's inspection visit, adding an extra supply to some and reducing the supply in others. He found that during the day the wasp brought extra caterpillars to the burrows that had been robbed and fewer to those burrows that had a surplus on her first visit. He could force her to regulate the provisions according to need if the changes were made *before* her first inspection visit. But any change made *after* the early inspection had not the slightest effect on her subsequent behavior, even though the wasp entered each burrow several times in the course of the day and had ample op-portunity to reassess the stock in each. She would overstock a burrow to which caterpillars had been added after the inspection visit and under-supply one from which food had been removed.

Only during the first morning visit was the wasp in a *stock-taking* behavior mode; on later visits she was only in a *delivery* behavior mode that had been set by the early morning visit. Her behavioral repertory lacked instructions for coping with mysterious deposits and withdrawals of caterpillars from the bur-rows. Thus, she was unable to extemporize in these unusual situations; yet at the same time she could learn and remember the "marketing needs" of each of three burrows over a working day of 12 to 15 hours. Her behavior is pain-fully reminiscent of some operations of the human bureaucracy: once having determined upon a course of action, she must proceed immutably along it, oblivious to variables not programmed into her behavioral repertory.

ORIENTATION

Another class of behavior patterns that involves single animals and invites attempts to analyze their neural mechanisms is that of orientation. Most ani-mals are distinct from plants in that they are able to move at some stage of their lives from one place to another and so encounter optimal food con-ditions, avoid crowding and predation, and find mates.

Random movement may have certain advantages in survival and in offsetting crowding, but most animals on the move are going somewhere, or orienting. Even a seemingly random search pattern may lead to an oriented one when a certain physical or chemical cue is encountered. The simplest movements to study are those in which the animal's track is obviously related to some physical or chemical polarization of the environment, such as a source of light or chemicals or the force of gravity. Whereas growth in a certain direction is called a "tropism," movements of this type are called **taxes** (singular, **taxis**).

Taxes as behavior

A specific taxis is defined by a prefix denoting the particular aspect of the en-vironment that directs it. The term positive or negative is used as a modifier to indicate whether the animal moves toward or away from the source. Taxes were once called forced movements, a misleading term since they are as variable as the rest of behavior. A given taxis may depend on nutritional or sexual state, time of day, or stage of development and may change in type or sign at short notice.

PHOTOTAXIS: The mechanisms of **phototaxis**—movement in relation to a light source—have been studied extensively, mainly because most animals readily react to light and because light is so easily controlled in quality, direction, and intensity. Many animals tend to become minimally active at certain light intensities. Hence, in a medium having different levels of light intensity their random movement tends to aggregate them at the optimal level. This behavior requires only the simplest of eyes—a single photoreceptor.

A slightly more direct light response becomes possible if the photoreceptor is placed asymmetrically in the body so that it is more shaded when the animal is at certain angles to the light. Often it lies in front of a dark pigment spot. Such a situation is found in many protozoa and in the maggots or larvae of flies. Protozoa rotate as they swim and maggots bend from side to side as they crawl. This behavior is called **klinokinesis** (*klinein* meaning "to lean"). The rotation or bending enables the animal to make a *sequence* of comparisons of light intensity as it progresses (Fig. 11–4). If increased light causes more vigorous bending as well as increased activity, then these actions of the animal will carry it more directly away from the lighted region and into darker parts of its environment. This type of orientation is called **klinotaxis**.

Organisms having a pair of shaded eye spots pointed in slightly different directions can make *simultaneous* comparisons of the light intensity falling on the two sides of the body. An example is the negative phototaxis shown by planarian worms, which instead of bending from side to side take a fairly direct course away from the light. Again, higher light intensities cause greater locomotor activity so that the planaria tend to come to rest in the darker part of their environment. If such an animal uses two eyes in light orientation, and if removal of one eye causes it to move in circles in the light but not in the dark, then the behavior is called **tropotaxis**.

Figure 11–4 Klinotaxis in a blowfly maggot causes the animal to move away from the light source (1) as shown. Its first movement (A) is elongation followed by contraction, which moves it to position B, and so on. When the light source is repositioned (2), the maggot makes a large lateral swing away from the light.

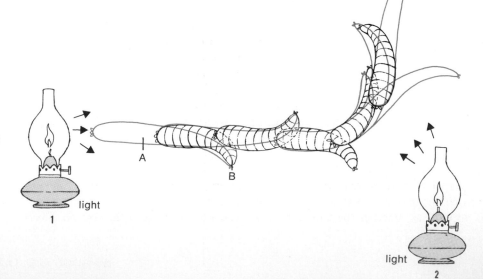

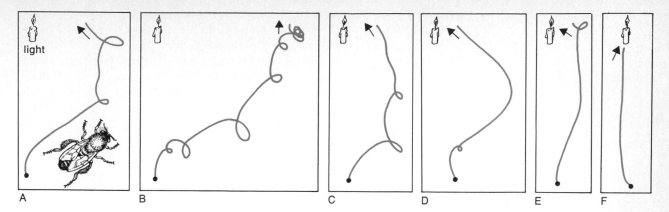

A   B   C   D   E   F

A further advance is when each of the two eyes contains several light-sensitive elements or photoreceptors covered by a lens. This means that some crude degree of form vision is possible, light coming from certain directions falling only on certain photoreceptors in each eye. In theory such an animal should be able to orient in a straight line after one of its eyes has been removed. Orientation with form vision is known as **telotaxis**. In the compound eyes of insects the photoreceptor cells vary in number from half a dozen to many thousands. When one eye of an insect is blinded, its reactions to light vary with the complexity of the remaining eye. Most insects show a combination of movements, turning toward the side with the intact eye if they are positively phototaxic, and at the same time moving toward the light source (Fig. 11–5). The result is a track consisting of a series of loops. In insects with more complex eyes the looping path may be insignificant and temporary, occurring only immediately after unilateral blinding. The insect is able to adjust to the apparent imbalance of illumination on its two sides and use its remaining image-forming eye to move directly toward or away from the light source, often with a somewhat crab-like gait.

The advantage of having two eyes each containing an array of photoreceptors and some means, such as a lens, for stimulating different parts of this array is that the animal can steer any course in relation to a light source, in addition to moving directly toward or away from it. All that is needed is that a direction be taken so that light from the source continues to fall only on certain receptors in the array in each eye. The path can be at any angle in the horizontal or vertical plane so long as the source remains within the purview of the eyes. This type of orientation is known as **pharotaxis** (*pharos* meaning "lighthouse"), a descriptive term since it is in just this manner that a ship navigates at night by the flashes from a distant lighthouse.

Pharotaxis is a sophisticated form of orientation, but it can lead an animal (including naive mariners) badly astray. If a sailor kept a constant angle between his ship's course and a distant lighthouse he would travel in a closing spiral and end up on the rocks at its base. This seems to be what happens to moths and other animals when they are attracted to a candle flame or other point source at night (Fig. 11–6). They tend to approach the light source slightly from one side and then spiral in on a collision course. The usual explanation of this maladaptive behavior is that the insects are indeed naive

Figure 11–5 When one eye of a honeybee is blocked, in this case the left eye, the animal walks in looped paths, or "circus movements," (A and B) toward the light source. Notice that turns are toward the intact eye. After several trials (C through E), the animal learns to compensate and eventually (F) walks directly toward the light.

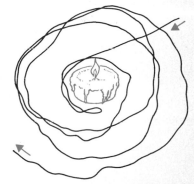

Figure 11–6 *Elysia*, a small slug-like mollusk, circles a candle at an angle of about 90°, first on its left and then on its right. If the animal maintained this angle with respect to a distant light source, such as the Sun, it would move in a straight line at a right angle to the light rays.

navigators with respect to Earth-bound light sources, their pharotaxis having evolved to operate with respect to very distant (astronomical) light sources whose rays are practically parallel. This enables them to hold to a substantially straight course during a journey of short length and duration. However, pharotaxis by astronomical light sources is also misleading on a trip of longer duration because of the 24-hour cycle of Earth's rotation. If one followed a course having a fixed angle to the Sun's position from sunrise to sunset, one would end up traveling in the opposite earthly direction by evening. Long-term orientation by astronomical bodies requires in addition a measure of the passage of time, that is, an internal "clock" that is regularly consulted as the stars, Moon, and Sun change their apparent positions owing to Earth's rotation. We shall return to this important matter later.

GEOTAXIS: Much less is known about the mechanisms of other kinds of taxis. **Geotaxis**, orientation with respect to gravity, is practically universal in animals. Some, including the vertebrates, have special gravity-sensing organs in the form of sacs lined with displacement-sensitive and innervated hair cells and filled with fluid containing a small dense granule of some mineral. The granule falls to one side under gravity and stimulates some of the hair cells. When the animal changes its position, another group of hair cells is stimulated. Insects depend on sense cells that detect the direction of gravity on long appendages such as the antennae as these are held outspread from the head. Most animals can detect up from down with great precision, and may show positive geotaxis (downward movement) under one set of circumstances and negative geotaxis under others. Caterpillars move down the stems of their food plant when about to pupate in the ground; moths emerging from the pupae show a marked negative geotaxis as they climb to the top of the nearest stem, where they spread and dry their wings.

PHONOTAXIS: Orientation in relation to a sound source, called **phonotaxis**, may be almost as precise as phototaxis in animals having two directionally sensitive ears. Some moths hear the ultrasonic cries made by a hunting bat as it uses its sonar to find its way and its prey in the dark. Their two very simple ears enable them to take a flight path directly away from their potential predator. Bats in their turn can locate and orient themselves with very great precision toward or away from objects casting back echoes from their cries. The croaking of frogs in spring and the cacophony of chirps made by crickets and grasshoppers in summer are signals for phonotactic orientation. In general the males "sing" and this attracts and directs the females to where they are sitting (Fig. 11–7). In 1913 a German zoologist, J. Regen, showed that a female cricket would approach a telephone receiver from some distance when a male was steadily chirping into the transmitter located elsewhere. In addition to being an elegant demonstration of phonotaxis, this must be regarded as testimony to the effectiveness of the early telephone! The ears of crickets and grasshoppers are located on their front legs, which can be spread quite wide apart so as to give them added information about the direction of a sound source.

There is no need to provide examples of birds and mammals locating and

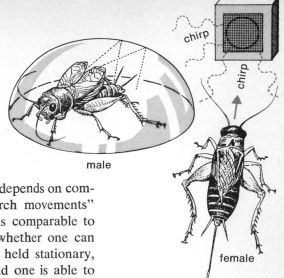

Figure 11–7 Laboratory studies show that a female cricket will home in on a loudspeaker broadcasting a male cricket call but that she will ignore a nearby male cricket "singing" under a glass enclosure in full view.

male

female

orienting themselves in relation to a sound source. Mostly this depends on comparing the signals reaching the two ears together with "search movements" such as turning the head back and forth. Thus, phonotaxis is comparable to tropotaxis or pharotaxis in vision. There is some question whether one can locate a sound source by using only one ear if the head is held stationary, although this is certainly possible if the sound is repeated and one is able to move one's head back and forth to compare a series of sound intensities coming from different directions. Animals such as the cat and horse with directional and highly mobile external ear flaps undoubtedly are better at acoustic localization than we are.

CHEMOTAXIS: Orientation with respect to the source of some chemical diffusing in air or water—called **chemotaxis**—is almost universal, although it is less precise than phototaxis or phonotaxis because of the way in which chemical stimuli become distributed through the medium. Nevertheless, chemotaxis makes possible some behavioral performances that seem amazing to "nonolfactory" creatures like ourselves. Protozoa such as *Paramecium* back-and-turn if they happen to swim into a region containing a noxious chemical (Fig. 11–8). Chemical stimuli may cause an animal to become active and then to engage in a trial-and-error search pattern, like a dog following the scent of game. Orientation to a chemical source is often accomplished by a combination of search activity and **anemotaxis**, that is, a tendency to move upwind if the signal is received on land, or **rheotaxis**, a tendency to swim upstream if water is the medium. The nose seems not to have an intrinsic directional capability as the eyes and ears do. Also, owing to rapid adaptation of the olfactory receptors, it is unlikely that animals can perceive gradual concentration differences in order to discover whether they are approaching or retreating from a source.

At the same time, olfactory organs are able to detect extremely minute traces of certain chemicals. Salmon larvae spend their early life in the shallow waters of a small tributary. On reaching a certain size they swim downstream, encountering successively larger branches and then entering the main channel of the river. After reaching its estuary and finally the open sea, salmon spend some years as marine fish feeding and growing. With the onset of sexual maturity the salmon return to the coast and enter the estuary of their home river. Here they travel upstream over rapids and falls and past numerous "choice points" as the river branches. There is reliable evidence that a significant number of adult fish finally reach the same small tributary stream where they hatched and spent their larval period years before. The only explanation

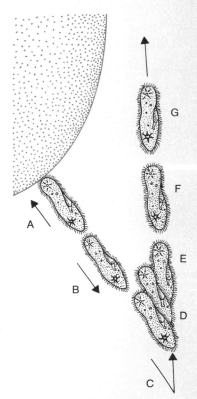

Figure 11–8 Paramecia exhibit an automatic response ("back-and-turn") when they come in contact with a noxious chemical, as shown in the sequence of movements here.

of such an astonishing feat of orientation is that the fish retain an impression of the smell (or taste) of the nursery tributary and are not only able to "remember" it for a long time but are also able to detect this chemical trace even after it has been diluted many thousand-fold by mixing of the water with that from innumerable other tributaries. The returning salmon must be able to determine, wherever the river divides, which branch has the trace of nursery odor.

Migration

The performance of the salmon is generally thought of as a migration rather than a taxis, although there is no clear distinction between the two kinds of behavior. Migrations are mass movements of animals covering considerable distances. Famous examples are the mass migrations of lemmings that occur at irregular intervals in northern Scandinavia and those of locusts in north Africa and central Asia. All the individuals of a resident population of animals appear to reach a state of *Zugunruhe* (meaning "restlessness"). Often the cause is obvious, such as a shortage of food brought on by overpopulation, but sometimes it is unknown. Herds of grazing mammals in Africa migrate during seasonal droughts. The adaptive value of this behavior seems to be that in spite of the additional stress it imposes on already hungry or thirsty animals, a few more individuals are likely to survive and find adequate pasture than if all remained in a region that had already been stripped bare. In most cases it is not known whether such migrations are oriented, that is, if they are steered by some cue from the environment.

The most closely studied migrations are the seasonal mass movements of many birds and some insects such as the milkweed butterfly. These take place southward in fall and northward in spring in north temperate regions. Although these seasonal migrations enable the migrants to avoid the northern winter and take advantage of the abundance of food during the northern spring and summer, they are not due to hunger and take place before the animals have begun to suffer any food deprivation. In fact, migrating birds feed voraciously before their southward treck and are usually loaded with stores of fat to fuel the long trip. The state of *Zugunruhe* appears to be set off by hormonal changes which are in their turn triggered by changes in the dark–light cycle, that is, in the proportion between the hours of daylight and darkness in each day. These hormonal changes are partly controlled by the pituitary gland at the base of the brain, whose secretory activity in birds changes in early spring and promotes the development of the gonads. It has been shown that this seasonal hormonal change may even take place in a duck that has been blinded, the increasing hours of daylight apparently being able to impress their effects directly on the brain through the bird's relatively thin and translucent skull. The migration of salmon to their home spawning grounds is also connected with the maturation of the ovaries and testes.

Navigation and homing

A variety of bird species, some as small as hummingbirds, fly southward from the northeastern part of the United States and Canada each fall. Some move in stages and may travel only a few tens or hundreds of miles in all. Others, including hummingbirds, fly partly or wholly over water as far as Florida and Central America. In spring they return to their northern breeding grounds and often to the very same locality they left in the fall.

This mysterious and wonderful performance raises many questions. How can an animal as small as a hummingbird store in its body—let alone carry aloft—sufficient metabolic fuel in the form of fat to sustain it during a flight of perhaps 2,000 miles? It is probable that flights of this length are not always made nonstop, but that the birds pause for feeding and rest on Atlantic islands or follow the eastern coast line part of the way. But there are authenticated cases of birds released at a known spot and timed on departure and arrival that seem to have flown thousands of miles without a chance to land. Migrants probably also get an assist from weather conditions. Departures from the eastern seaboard in the fall occur in great numbers at times when there is a southerly air flow, while arrivals from the south in springtime often coincide with storms in which the prevailing winds are from the south. Yet in spite of stopovers and favorable winds, these migrations must be extremely stressful on a species. One can only assume that almost no individuals would survive the northern winter or be able to compete for food or nesting sites in the densely populated south if such migrations did not take place.

An equally intriguing question is how the birds find their way on these migrations. The same question applies to the performance of carrier pigeons and many other birds that are able to find their way fairly directly to their home loft or nesting site after they have been displaced "blind" by car or plane several hundred miles into unfamiliar territory. The time in which they fly home often suggests that they have taken a fairly direct flight.

The answers to this question are now being sought intensively. Birds, like humans, seem to use a variety of available clues to find their way in strange territory. Some are quite mysterious. Since birds have the advantage of flying at an altitude, distant landmarks such as high trees, buildings, or mountain ranges are used. When the distance is too great for this they appear to navigate by means of a "Sun compass" and internal "clock." Nevertheless, it is hard to see how these could be of much help to a pigeon that has been displaced in a dark cage without clues as to the direction and distance of displacement. There is strong evidence that migrating birds, which often travel at night, are able to use star patterns in plotting their course just as day-flying birds use the Sun. Birds caught and caged at the time of the fall migration show their *Zugunruhe* by hopping persistently as though to escape from a particular corner of the cage. If the birds are exposed to an artificial sky in a planetarium, this restless hopping takes the south direction as indicated by the star patterns displayed to them and not according to their real geographic position. They even seem to compensate their direction of hopping if the artificial sky indicates to them that they have been displaced to the east or west of the geographic point where they were captured.

But birds also migrate under a heavy cloud cover at night, and pigeons find their way home by day under the same weather conditions. Night migrations under these circumstances have been followed in fall and spring by means of search and tracking radar. Migrating birds appear on the radar screen as thousands of tiny specks of light drifting slowly in one direction. Before these specks had been identified as birds, they were known as "angels" by radar operators. When the "angels" are moving under clouds and over the open sea, what possible markers could they use in plotting a steady course? Suggestions have included inertial navigation, or a physiological mechanism akin to a gyrocompass, or some means of orienting with respect to the prevailing wind. But there is no evidence of such means, nor have any biological mechanisms been suggested.

In the 12th century mariners began using magnetic compasses, which detect lines of force in Earth's magnetic field. Early attempts failed to demonstrate that animals have a magnetic sense, but in recent years Frank Brown, Jr. of Northwestern University has been gathering evidence that various invertebrates respond to weak magnetic fields. Still more recently, Martin Lindauer and his students in Germany have provided convincing proof that honeybees are affected by Earth's magnetic field when communicating the direction of feeding sites to their colony mates. They make certain consistent errors or misdirections when imparting this information. The misdirections disappear when the hive is surrounded by Helmholtz coils that counteract most of Earth's magnetic field.

These discoveries have prompted numerous experiments. Some investigators have attached small bar magnets or controls consisting of non-ferrous metal to the wings or heads of homing pigeons. Small coils driven by minute batteries and forming mini-Helmholtz coils have also been placed around the pigeons' heads. Birds are then displaced and tested for homing ability while bearing these devices, on the theory that the devices should either confuse the birds' magnetic sense by imposing relatively intense and nearby magnetic fields or partially counteract the effect of Earth's field. Although present evidence is incomplete, it suggests that Earth's magnetic field may provide the birds with a marginal directional cue, one to use when all others including familiarity with the area and orientation by Sun compass are unavailable. The physiological mechanisms that sense the direction of lines of magnetic force remain a complete mystery.

The language of honeybees

We will now look more closely into a subject introduced in Chapter 9 to see just how honeybees convey information about the distance and direction of rich sources of food. Unique in the animal kingdom, the bees' language was first discovered and "translated" by Karl von Frisch.

The economic facts of life about a bee colony show why a bee language is helpful. All working bees are sisters, and their communal labors are divided during their average adult working life of about one month in summertime. This does not allow much time to perfect newly learned tasks, so most of their behavior patterns are built-in and develop in sequence in the same way as their body functions. Young adult bees do most of the hivekeeping and feeding of larvae; older bees forage in the field for nectar and pollen, the colony's sole sources of carbohydrate and protein. These foods are gathered from blossoms that may be located as much as a mile or more in any direction from the colony. The food is transported back to the hive by air and stock-piled in cells of the comb for future use by the queen and developing larvae, and to sustain the colony in winter. It follows that distant sources of nectar and pollen must be both rich and copious if collecting them is to be economically worthwhile, since a longer round trip flight from the hive requires a greater metabolic energy expenditure and thus permits a smaller payload. Furthermore, many flowers produce nectar only during certain hours of the day and then only for a few days in succession. For these reasons the harvest will be more rewarding to the colony if as many bees as possible are rapidly mobilized to collect from a rich source in the short time available.

If one sets out in the field a saucer containing half-and-half scented honey and water on a distinctively marked background, many hours may pass before a lone bee discovers this rich source of food. After drinking her fill this scout bee departs, but in a very short time many bees begin visiting the dish, though it may be hundreds of yards from the nearest hive. It is clear that the good news has got around. Von Frisch discovered how the behavior of the scout bee informs prospective foragers of the honey's distance and direction from the hive.

This behavior can be watched in a glass-walled hive situated in a shed or other building so that the outside sky is not visible to the bees within. Normally, of course, the action takes place in complete darkness. When the scout bee enters the hive with her booty, she climbs onto the vertical surface of the comb and begins a series of excited circling movements. This is the bee dance. Other bees cluster around the dancer, touching her with their antennae and moving after her.

Von Frisch carried out a long series of experiments and observations by marking bees for individual identification with small drops of colored lacquer after they had discovered feeding stations placed at various distances and directions from the hive. These enabled him to interpret the dance of returning scouts. There are two main variations, the **round dance** and the **waggle dance** (Fig. 11–9). In the round dance the returning scout runs in a tight circle and then reverses and circles in the opposite direction with other bees following closely. This happens when the food source is less than about 100

Figure 11–9

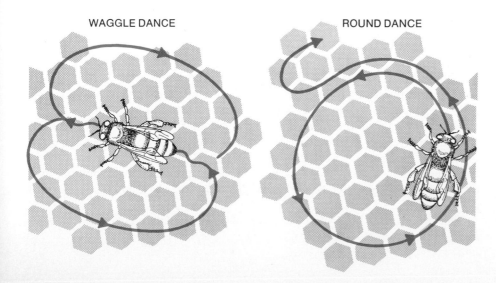

WAGGLE DANCE   ROUND DANCE

yards from the hive. The follower bees pick up the scent and then leave to hunt for the source within this radius. In the waggle dance the scout makes a tight half circle and then closes it with a straight run in the other direction at some fixed angle to the vertical on the comb. During the straight run she waggles or rocks her body from side to side. Following the straight waggle run the bee again makes a half circle back to the other side and closes it with a straight waggle run at the same angle. If the food source is rich, these half loops closed by straight waggle runs are repeated over and over again. These movements are closely followed by prospective foragers.

The follower bees obtain several pieces of information from the waggle performance. The scent of the particular blossoms is picked up from their contacts with the scout. The richness or profusion of the prospective harvest is indicated by the vigor and persistence of the dance. The straight waggle run indicates that it is at some distance, the actual distance being measured by the frequency of waggle movements during the straight run. Finally, the direction of the food source is shown by the angle of the waggle run with respect to the vertical on the surface of the darkened comb. If the dancer moves vertically upward this says, "Fly out from the hive in the direction of the Sun." A waggle run made 40 degrees left of the vertical says, "Fly out at an angle 40 degrees to the left of the Sun's position on leaving the hive." A waggle run made straight down the comb says, "Fly directly away from the Sun." Thus, if the flowers are at some distance the follower bees are informed of their scent, approximate distance, and direction. If the flowers are nearby, the round dance says merely, "Go out and use your eyes and antennae near the hive!"

Perhaps the most sophisticated aspect of this behavior is the translation or transposition of the Sun angle with respect to the line between the hive and the food source on the horizontal surface outside into an angle between the vertical and the direction of the waggle run on the vertical surface of the darkened comb. In effect, a pharotaxis with respect to the Sun is transformed into a geotaxis. If the comb is turned on its side so that the scout is forced to dance on a horizontal surface she is unable to indicate the direction of the food source outside and makes waggle runs in random directions. But if the horizontally dancing scout is able to see a patch of blue sky, the waggle run shows the true direction of the food source. Even if only the blue sky (but not the Sun) is visible, the pattern of polarized light in the sky gives the bee a clue as to its actual direction. The misdirections due to Earth's magnetic field mentioned earlier occur in the angle of the waggle run. The follower bees are exposed to the same magnetic conditions and presumably correct for them during their subsequent provisioning flights.

This transposition of Sun compass information into gravity makes one think of human reasoning: "Let Sun direction be equal to up, then. . . ." Yet except for being able to give, receive, and carry out these complex instructions, there is no evidence that bees are intelligent in our sense. They show no special ability to solve unfamiliar or novel problems or to learn tasks other than those for which their nervous systems have been programmed in evolution. No doubt a simple computer could be programmed to carry out an analogous performance.

The real wonder lies in the evolution of such a behavioral pattern, how it could have been perfected and built into the honeybee repertory through the selection of slight improvements and the elimination of countless defects in countless strains of bees over millions of years. This wonder can be compared with the wonder, perhaps limited to the young of an older generation, that filled one on seeing a bird or airplane in flight and prompted the question, "What makes it stay up there?" The answer is that it cannot help doing so. The bees cannot help dancing and following their behavioral instructions.

RHYTHMS AND BIOLOGICAL CLOCKS

Most living things are exposed to the rhythms of the Solar System. Possible exceptions are forms that spend their lives in the permanent darkness and constant temperature of deep caves or the oceanic abyss. The most obvious of these solar rhythms is the daily 24-hour cycle of alternating light and darkness due to Earth's rotation about its axis (Fig. 11–10). Then there is the annual rhythm of seasonal change due to Earth's tilted axis as it orbits the Sun.

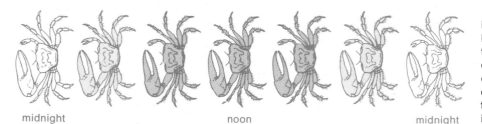

midnight   noon   midnight

Figure 11–10   Fiddler crabs have biological clocks causing them to respond to the solar day–night cycle. During a solar day of 24 hours their color changes from light at midnight to dark around noon, and then it lightens again at midnight.

Coupled with the annual rhythm in regions outside the tropics are seasonal changes in temperature and amount of light during the daily cycle. These changes become more marked as one approaches Earth's poles. A third extra-terrestrial rhythm is the lunar cycle of about 28 days. The lunar cycle exerts its influence in the form of moonlight at night and the height of the tides, which affects many marine forms.

Lunar cycles regulate the breeding behavior of at least two unrelated species of animals that breed once a year. The grunion (Fig. 11–11) is a species of fish that deposits its eggs in the sand along the beaches of southern California. The fish swim ashore during a period from March to August. Females burrow into the sand, tail-end first, and deposit their eggs a few inches below the surface. While a female is depositing her eggs, one or more males encircle her and release sperm, which flow down the wet sides of the female and fertilize the eggs. The fish return to the ocean on the next sweep of a high wave. Since the parent fish, in some way unknown to us, pick the highest tide that will occur for the next two weeks, their eggs have that much time to develop undisturbed. At the next unusually high tide the young fish larvae are washed into the sea. Grunion spawnings are so predictable that they are published in newspapers so that spawning fish may be collected for eating.

Natives of the Polynesian islands have long known that a certain marine worm has a regular cycle of activity. Once a year the natives find the surface

Figure 11–11   The mating activity of grunion is so precisely timed with high spring tides that their mass invasion of southern California beaches can be forecast unerringly.

of the sea covered with a wriggling mass of palolo worms, as they call this annelid organism. The palolo lives in tunnels in the coral reef. Invariably, during the months of November or December, all of the palolo break off their posterior portions, which then rise to the surface. This swarming phenomenon occurs seven to nine days after full moon. Once on the ocean surface, these reproductive segments of the palolo worm wriggle around in the water until the body wall breaks open and releases the egg or sperm. For miles around, the ocean appears to be covered with an oily scum. Fertilization occurs in the midst of this swarm of gametes, and the new individuals formed return to the coral reef below after a few days of development.

The lives of most plants and animals are keyed to some or all of the rhythmic cycles mentioned above—the lunar cycle, the day–night cycle, and annual or seasonal cycles. The 24-hour cycle is marked by alternating periods of photosynthesis and growth in plants and periods of waking and feeding during daylight and sleeping or resting at night in **diurnal** animals. This alternation is reversed in **nocturnal** animals. Seasonal changes in the number of hours of daylight during the daily cycle regulate the growth, flowering, and quiescence of plants as well as many activities in animals, including the reproductive cycle, hibernation, and migratory movements. It might be thought from this that living things would have no need of independent internal "clocks" and that their activities could be directly triggered and regulated by the Sun's apparent position and by the number of hours of daylight.

Such control indeed exists, but it is not the whole story. When discussing navigation and bird migration, we saw that the long journeys taken by some animals require an independent and portable measure of time or an **internal clock** if the paths of these journeys are to be in straight lines on the surface of a rotating planet. In recent years a great deal of evidence has been gathered that such internal clocks exist and that they are quite widespread in animals and plants even though their presence is not always obvious and their mechanism is unknown.

The behavior of an internal or biological clock is revealed by keeping an animal for some days or weeks under conditions of uniform light or darkness and isolated as much as possible from secondary daily changes such as temperature or humidity fluctuations. If the animal is diurnal in habit, being active in daylight and inactive at night, it persists in this rhythm in spite of being unable to receive any solar cues. But the rhythmic cycle of its activities tends to run slow, taking 24.5 or 25 hours to complete. These cycles may continue for many days or weeks, or the distinction between active and inactive periods may eventually become erratic.

The fact that the animal's clock tends to lose 30 or 60 minutes in each 24-hour period means that it has become uncoupled from the celestial timekeeper and is running independently of it. The situation is exactly parallel to that of the owner of a poorly regulated watch who forgets to reset it periodically. The daily errors add up and after a while the rhythm may become completely reversed according to the solar day. Since the cycle of this biological clock is not exactly one day or 24 hours, it is said to have a **circadian** (about one day) **rhythm**. Under the conditions we have just described, when no periodical cue is available to reset it, the circadian rhythm is said to be free-running.

More can be learned about the operation of this internal clock if one attempts to force it into other rhythms rather than allowing it to free-run. Imagine that an animal accustomed to a given cycle of 12 hours of darkness followed by 12 hours of light is phase-shifted—that is, is deprived abruptly of three or four hours of darkness toward the end of one of its accustomed dark periods and then placed on a new 12-hours-light, 12-hours-dark cycle. Its periods of activity and inactivity become confused for a time but then are reset to the newly imposed 24-hour rhythm. This is precisely what happens to transatlantic plane travelers. Flying east from America to Europe, you suddenly lose about five hours of darkness to which you are accustomed and must reset or phase-shift both your internal clock and your mechanical one. Many of us have experienced the difficulty and discomfort in first establishing proper waking–sleeping rhythms after making such a trip. In fact it is customary for diplomats planning delicate negotiations to take several days to adjust to the time difference before conferring.

Another experiment is to try to readjust the internal clock of an animal accustomed to a 24-hour rhythm to a cycle of different duration—say 20 or 30 hours in length. Its internal clock is now forced to run either faster or slower than normal. Adjustment to this sort of change is more difficult and incomplete. Although the existence of biological clocks in many animals has been established beyond doubt, their location within the body and their mechanism remain a complete mystery (Fig. 11–12).

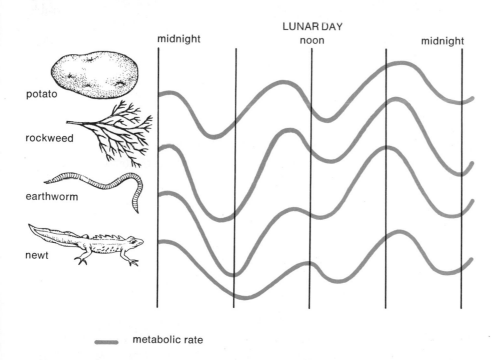

Figure 11–12 Although the four organisms shown are extremely diverse, there is a remarkable similarity in their metabolic rate, which fluctuates in rhythm with the lunar cycle. The mechanisms regulating such rhythmic responses have yet to be discovered. (AFTER F. A. BROWN, JR.)

NERVOUS SYSTEMS

There is no doubt that the kinds of behavior we have just discussed would become impossible if the nervous system of an animal were destroyed. The animal might be alive in a vegetative sense but it could no longer react or move. Specialized nerve cells, axons, ganglia, sense organs, and muscles have evolved and permit behavior in multicellular animals. Single-celled animals such as *Amoeba proteus* lack all these differentiated nervous tissues, yet ameba shows basic and adaptive behavioral patterns such as self-preservation, food seeking, and reproduction. Under optimal conditions this single cell extends its pseudopodia in all directions, searching for smaller organisms to engulf. If conditions become unfavorable it pulls in its pseudopodia and becomes a sphere, presenting a minimal surface to a hostile world. Even organisms such as bacteria and plants, which also lack nervous systems, show this capacity for self-regulation, that is, the ability to adjust to changing conditions. Self-regulation, or in a narrower sense self-preservation, is a basic quality that distinguishes the living from the non-living. In multicellular animals this quality is mediated mainly through the nervous system.

The simplest nervous systems

As we have seen, single-celled organisms and plants lack distinct nervous systems. Since early nervous systems have not been fossilized, we can only guess what they were like, making these guesses as educated as possible through comparative anatomy.

When plants and animals first evolved from single-celled ancestors their subsequent evolutionary paths differed in several respects. The difference that concerns us here relates to motility, the ability to move from one place to another. The cell colonies that evolved into plants remained sessile, or stationary, in the adult stage and solved the problem of distributing their kind by means of seeds or spores that were passively distributed by wind, water, or on the bodies of animals. The sessile habit means that an adult plant does not require a nervous system; integration of the activities of its cells is carried out by the diffusion or transport of chemical signals, or hormones, and of products of cell metabolism.

Animals followed the path of motility. Coordinated movement of a collection of cells required a rapid means of cellular interaction as well as slow chemical communication. In addition, it required a skeleton enabling the multicellular colony to support itself mechanically and to move as a unit, although this was not so important at first when water was its environment. This primitive organism was enabled to act as a whole when certain of its cells became specialized and detected external changes, when others distributed information rapidly throughout the colony, and still others propelled the colony as a unit. Chemical communication was retained and regulated long-term and so-called vegetative activities such as growth, readiness for reproduction, and nutrition. This system of chemical communication evolved into our endocrine system.

Before following the evolution of this primitive nervous system and the trend of animals toward greater motility, we should note that during the course of

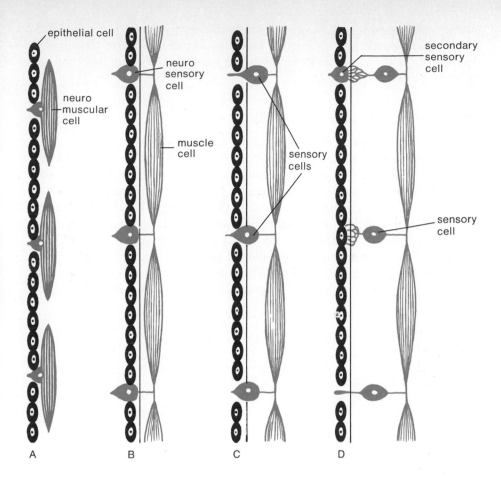

epithelial cell

neuro sensory cell

neuro muscular cell

muscle cell

sensory cells

secondary sensory cell

sensory cell

A   B   C   D

evolution animals have reverted to the sessile way of life a number of times. Sessile forms include the coelenterates, some worms and mollusks, many parasitic forms, as well as a few crustaceans and fish. Most of these organisms are sessile as adults but retain a motile immature or larval stage of development that has a fully developed nervous system, sense organs, and muscles. These organs degenerate when the sessile adult stage is reached. The active larval stage is an adaptation that distributes the species.

The earliest specialized excitable cells are found distributed in the skins of some coelenterates. These neuromuscular cells (Fig. 11–13) are isolated from one another, but each is able to respond to a noxious stimulus by contracting and pulling the surrounding skin away from the stimulated point. Local responses of this nature become more general in most coelenterates because the neuromuscular cells are coupled to a **nerve net** lying just below the skin. The nerve net is made up of elongated cells connected to one another and capable of conducting excitation over their membranes. This arrangement makes possible a spread of excitation over the whole organism. The next stage is typified by the free-swimming forms of coelenterates known as medusas or jellyfish. Here part of the nerve net is concentrated into a ring of interconnecting fibers encircling the mouth opening. This **nerve ring** is connected to special

Figure 11–13 Simple nervous systems may have evolved along lines suggested by the diagram here. At position A, simple neuromuscular cells make only local responses to stimuli possible. At B, differentiation into neurosensory and muscle cells has taken place, making more widespread responses possible. At C and D, specialized sense cells and nerve cells appear.

gravity-sensing organs, or **statocysts**, and to contractile cells that it coordinates into regular pulsations of the circular umbrella-shaped body. This arrangement enables the jellyfish to swim vertically in the water and to orient itself with respect to gravity (Fig. 11–14).

Ventral and dorsal nervous systems

A nerve ring encircling the oral opening was the forerunner of the central nervous systems of higher invertebrates. The primitive body form changed from the radial symmetry of the jellyfish to a bilateral symmetry with a tubular body shape that probably enabled greater mobility in swimming and in burrowing in the mud. The nerve ring around the esophagus became the brain of this proto-worm. Behind the head region with its ventral mouth, a string of muscular segments formed the bulk of its swimming and burrowing body (Fig. 11–14). Each segment had a pair of **ganglia**, collections of nerve cells that served as a local control center. The segmental ganglia lay along the mid-ventral region and were joined by connectives into a ladder-like string. This

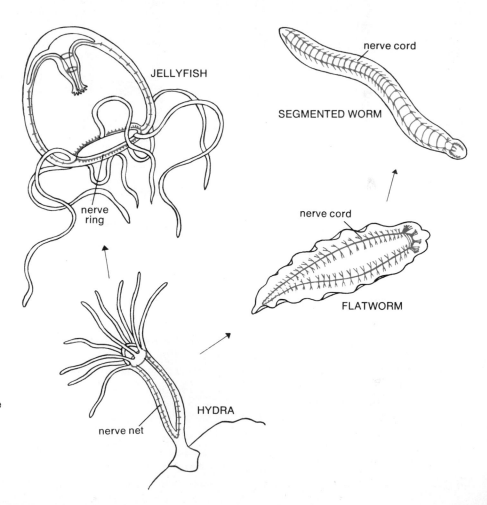

Figure 11–14 Hypothetical stages in the evolution of the nerve net of a simple Hydra-like animal into the nerve ring of an actively swimming jellyfish-like form on the one hand and on the other, into the nerve cords of flatworms and segmented worms, or annelids.

ventral nerve cord joined the nerve ring or **circum-esophageal nervous system**, which subserved sense organs on the organism's anterior end, that body region most likely to encounter novel conditions. This arrangement of a segmented nerve cord lying below the digestive tract and connected with a brain encircling its anterior end is characteristic of all the higher invertebrates (Fig. 11–15).

The central nervous system of vertebrates has quite a different basic plan, which suggests that these two major groups of animals diverged from an ancestral stock quite early in animal evolution, presumably when nerve nets first tended to concentrate into cords of conducting cells. The vertebrate brain and spinal cord come from a pair of parallel folds that develop on the future dorsal side of the very early embryo. These folds join above and form a hollow tube, the **neural tube**. The anterior part of the neural tube develops into the brain and its posterior part into the spinal cord (Fig. 11–15).

The dorsal central nervous system of vertebrates shows segmentation, but otherwise it seems to have no common origin with the ventral nerve cord and circum-esophageal ring of invertebrates. At the same time, both systems have undergone parallel changes in their evolution. The first was **centralization** in which nerve cells of the diffuse nerve net gathered into a compact and closely knit bundle or central nervous system. The second was **cephalization**, the concentration of important nerve centers into a brain at the head end of the animal. Undoubtedly this change was related to the need to concentrate major sense organs at the front end and to select and direct behavior patterns from a central point. The brain of man is the culmination of cephalization. A third similarity is that both systems depend on the properties of neurons for their operation.

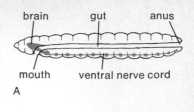

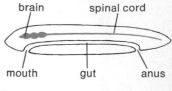

A

B

Figure 11–15 Two basic designs of central nervous systems are shown. At A are a ventral nerve cord of segmental ganglia and the circum-oral ring found in segmented worms, mollusks, crustaceans, insects, and spiders. At B are the dorsal spinal cord and brain found in all vertebrate animals.

Neurons

Nerve cells, or **neurons**, are the main functional units of the nervous system. Certain of their processes conduct nerve impulses from one point to another while others serve to transmit excitation from one neuron to another. Still other processes respond to changes outside the body by generating nerve impulses. Genesis, conduction, and interaction of nerve impulses at many points and in complex patterns constitute the mechanisms of behavior.

Each neuron is a single discrete cell with a cell body or **soma** containing a nucleus and is up to perhaps 0.05 mm in diameter. The soma may have one or many branching twig-like processes or **dendrites**. In addition to the dendrites there is another generally unbranched extension of the neuron that may be as much as a meter or more in length. This is the conducting portion of the neuron and is called the **axon** or **nerve fiber**. The axon is commonly surrounded by sheath cells of various types. It finally branches and becomes finer before it makes close contacts or **synapses** with the dendrites or soma of other neurons or with muscle fibers or gland cells. The soma, dendrites, and axon of a neuron are enclosed in a continuous and extremely thin **plasma membrane**. The plasma membrane has important selective properties and is the medium over which nerve impulses are transmitted. Normally, neurons are excited and caused to transmit impulses down their axons by the arrival of other impulses at synapses on their dendrites.

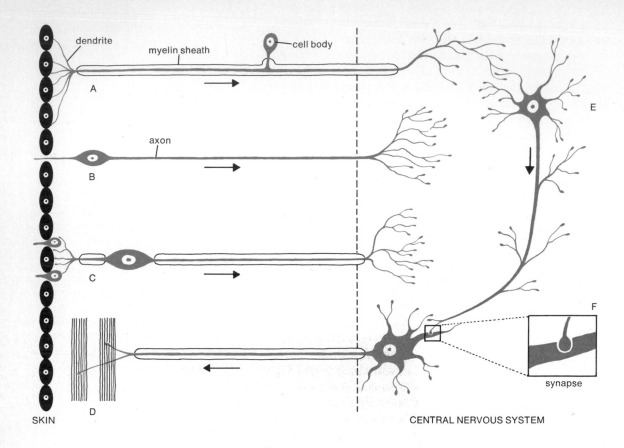

Figure 11–16 Schematic diagram of some vertebrate neurons. At left the body surface is represented by the line of "skin cells." The broken line at right represents the interior of the central nervous system. At A is a monopolar sensory neuron typical of pain receptors of the skin. At B is a bipolar sensory neuron typical of olfactory receptors. At C is a bipolar secondary sensory neuron with dendrites that make contact with short primary sense cells typical of visual and acoustic senses. At D is a multipolar neuron, its axon leading to two muscle fibers. At E is a multipolar interneuron with many dendritic and axonic terminations on other interneurons. At F we show a detail of one synapse. Neuron A synapses with E. (What other neuron does E synapse with?) Notice that neurons A, C, and D have myelin sheaths. Arrows indicate direction of conduction along nerves.

Neurons have a great variety of forms. The commonest are shown in Fig. 11–16. **Monopolar** neurons have a soma on the side branch of a T-shaped fiber with dendrites on the short arm of the straight portion and the axon forming the long arm. **Bipolar** neurons have a single process bearing the dendritic portion extending from one side of the soma and an axon arising from the other side. **Multipolar** neurons have large numbers of dendrites branching from the soma and receive synaptic input from a great many directions. D in the above figure shows two examples of multipolar neurons.

Neurons are also classified according to their function in the nervous system. **Sensory** or **afferent** neurons either have their dendritic ends on the surface of the body or in contact with specialized sense cells in this position. **Motor** or **efferent** neurons, also called **motoneurons**, lie within the central nervous system and extend their axons to muscles or glands. The bulk of the central nervous system—brain and spinal cord—is made up of **interneurons**. Interneurons serve as middle men between sensory neurons and motoneurons. They play a most important but little understood role in generating behavior since they **summate** (add up all separate impulses reaching a nerve cell), integrate, and transform signals arriving from sensory neurons into adaptively significant patterns in motoneurons for transmission to the muscles. The contraction patterns of the muscles are observed by us as behavior.

Much of our concern in the next three chapters is how these impulse patterns are generated and transmitted in the central nervous system. The size of this problem may be likened to that of trying to understand the foreign policy or national politics of a country when one's only experience is personal contact with a few of its inhabitants. The size of the problem is put in perspective when one realizes that the nervous system of man contains about 10^{11} neurons—several hundred times the population of the world. The nervous system of a cockroach or a moth has a million times fewer neurons—equivalent to the population of a small to medium-sized city.

The role of the brain

Earlier we saw that in spite of their different histories both invertebrate and vertebrate nervous systems have evolved in the direction of cephalization, the concentration of neurons into large ganglia at the front end of the animal. Originally, this concentration took place because important sense organs were most useful in the region that moved in front and was the first to encounter new conditions in the environment. The increased number of neurons served to process the incoming sensory information. Later in evolution this collection of neurons also became the major executive center for determining which behavior pattern in the animal's repertory had the greatest survival value under a given set of conditions. In the interests of unified action the states' rights, so to speak, of the various body segments became subordinated to control from a central governing source, the brain.

The concentration of behavioral control in the brain becomes evident when we do a simple comparative experiment. An earthworm has a brain, but the degree of cephalization is minor. If we cut an earthworm in half we find that both the front and the hind ends can carry out almost as many actions as an intact worm and that they are able to regenerate a new tail and a new head respectively. A cockroach or a wasp has a much greater degree of cephalization and a relatively larger brain. After decapitation both these insects are able to live for some time, but they are able only to make a few stepping movements and cannot run or fly.

The process of cephalization has gone a great deal further in vertebrates, and most cannot survive more than a few minutes after decapitation. Cephalization has reached its extreme in man, where coordination of all behavior beyond the very simplest reflexes is carried out by the brain. It is also the seat of those most human of attributes, speaking and understanding, learning and memory, and abstract thought.

With the consolidation of nervous control within the brain, the ability of organisms to modify their pre-programmed behaviors, to *learn*, increases. The capacity for modifying or changing behavior patterns adds a new dimension to our study, one which we explore fully in Chapter 24.

Our transition from social behavior to the structure of nerve cells is not an easy one. On one hand, we have observed several of the most fascinating behaviors in nature—the homing of salmon, the language of bees, the navigation of migrating birds. On the other, we have introduced the world "under the skin" in the form of nerve cells and brain. Between these two extremes lies a web of interacting stimuli, sense organs, muscles, glands and nerves. We will now proceed to examine this web, starting with the language of the nervous system.

1 Some of the behavior of animals is "pre-programmed." What aspects of your own behavior are pre-programmed? How is that behavior beneficial to you?
2 Explain what the behavioral term *taxis* means and cite several examples. In general, how does pharotaxis serve the animal? How might it lead the animal astray?
3 Discuss migration in the context of natural selection and the carrying capacity of the environment.
4 What is a "biological clock"? Give three examples of one that is cycled annually, of one that is cycled monthly, of one that is cycled daily.
5 How is bilateral symmetry more advantageous to a motile organism than radial symmetry?
6 Describe the various parts of a typical nerve cell and their functions.

SELECTED READINGS

Brown, F. A., Jr., Hastings, J. W., and Palmer, J. D. *The Biological Clocks. Two Views.* New York: Academic Press, 1970. A not-too-technical summary of current ideas about the nature of biological rhythms and the mechanisms which may control them.

Fraenkel, G. S. and Gunn, D. L. *The Orientation of Animals.* Oxford: The Clarendon Press, 1940. The classical description of animal taxes, written in general and non-technical terms.

von Frisch, K. *Bees, Their Vision, Chemical Senses, and Language.* Ithaca, N.Y.: Cornell University Press, 1950. The first description in English of Professor von Frisch's interpretation of the dance language of the honeybee. The book is written in a charming and informal style and is the modest description of some very famous experiments. Von Frisch's best-known student, Professor Martin Lindauer, has also written a popular account of this work (*Communication in Social Bees,* Cambridge, Mass.: Harvard University Press, 1961), while the most complete and recent account is K. von Frisch, *The Dance Language and Orientation of Bees,* Cambridge, Mass.: Harvard University Press, 1967.

Figure 12–1 The behavior of this spider, like that of other animals from sea anemones to surgeons, is controlled by signals traveling along the cells of its nervous system, which forms a vital network allowing communication between various parts of the body. Diverse animals use similar neural signals to transmit information. Try to imagine the minimum sensory and motor information a spider's nervous system must obtain and transmit to the appropriate muscles in order to produce a web such as this.

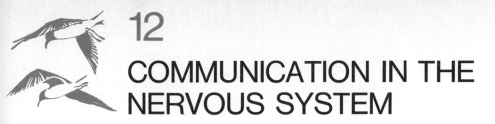

12
COMMUNICATION IN THE NERVOUS SYSTEM

Electricity in living cells

Philosophers and scientists have puzzled over the nature of the nervous system for many centuries, and numerous hypotheses have been advanced in an attempt to explain its function. Nerves were once thought to be hollow pipes through which a mysterious "nervous fluid" flowed; another hypothesis considered them to act as cords that conveyed messages to the brain by vibrating like the strings of a musical instrument. In 1791, the Italian anatomist Luigi Galvani demonstrated that the leg muscles of a freshly killed frog could be made to contract when electric current was applied to them. Half a century later, the German investigator du Bois-Reymond showed that small electrical currents could be detected during the normal activity of both nerve and muscle tissue.

Subsequent research has shown that these currents are associated with the signals by which the nervous system transmits and processes information and thus controls behavior (Fig. 12–1). The term **bioelectricity** has been coined to denote the electrical events that occur in living cells. Most of us have felt an electric shock at one time or another and know from experience that the body conducts electricity. This is possible because of certain salts, dissolved in our body fluids and said to be **ionized** because they carry an electric charge.

The membranes of living cells, although thin, are said to have high electrical **resistance** because they tend to resist a flow of ionized salts through them; also, their **electrical potentials**—that is, the energy needed to move charges across the membrane—may change very rapidly. This makes ordinary wires and slow-acting meters useless in measuring the electrical behavior of cell membranes. Present-day neurophysiology owes much to three important technical developments. The first was the development of sensitive electronic amplifiers used to enlarge the minute currents flowing across cell membranes. In principle, these are similar to public address amplifiers. The second was the development of the cathode ray oscilloscope, wherein an electron beam follows changes in potential with essentially no time lag and, therefore, more accurately represents rapid electrical changes taking place in the cell.

The third and most recent development was the use of tiny, fluid-filled micropipette electrodes. These are pulled from heated glass tubing. The tips remain open but are microscopically fine, being less than 1 micrometer. (The symbol for micrometer is μm and it is equal to 1×10^{-3} mm. Another term for it is micron.) The wide end of the micropipette is filled down to the fine tip with a highly conducting solution, commonly potassium chloride (KCl). The wide end contains a wire going to an amplifier, and the circuit is completed by

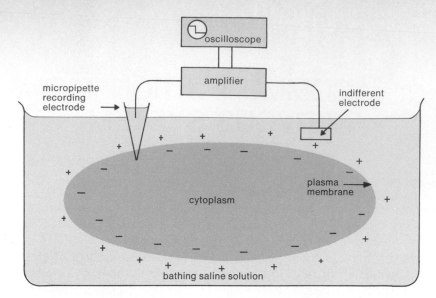

Figure 12–2 To measure the membrane potential of a cell, a micropipette electrode filled with KCl solution is maneuvered so that its tip pierces the plasma membrane and enters the cell. The potential difference between the interior and exterior of the cell is amplified and displayed on an oscilloscope. A step-like displacement of the oscilloscope trace occurs when the electrode enters the cell. This displacement indicates the size of the membrane potential.

another wire (indifferent electrode) connecting the fluid bathing the cell to the amplifier.

The micropipette is carefully maneuvered so that its tip barely penetrates the plasma membrane of the cell being studied. Hopefully this is done with minimum injury to the cell and minimum electrical leakage through the membrane on the outside of the micropipette. The membrane potential of the cell can now be observed and measured on an oscilloscope connected to the output of the amplifier (Fig. 12–2).

RESTING MEMBRANE POTENTIAL

Measurements obtained with micropipette electrodes suggest that all living cells, whether in nerve, muscle, or other tissue, maintain an electromotive force (voltage) across their plasma membrane. This electrical potential is present in the absence of any special activity by the cell (such as contraction of a muscle cell or the transmission of impulses along a nerve cell) and so is called the **resting membrane potential**. The value of the resting membrane potential varies considerably in different cells, but it is typically only a small fraction of one volt. Potentials this small usually are expressed in thousandths of volts, or millivolts (mV). The resting membrane potential of a neuron usually is between 50 and 100 mV, the inside of the cell being negative relative to the extracellular fluid (the bathing saline solution).

The signals by which neurons communicate consist of brief and transient changes in their resting membrane potential. Therefore, it is necessary to understand the basis for the existence of the resting potential in order to understand the way in which neural signals are produced.

An essential clue to the origin of the resting membrane potential is the way in which certain substances are distributed on either side of the plasma membrane. The outer surface of the plasma membrane is bathed in an aqueous solution—the **extracellular** or **interstitial fluid**—through which both the cell's nutrients and wastes pass. The cytoplasm inside the cell is made up of a protein gel 80% to 90% of which is water. This **intracellular fluid** also contains other chemicals needed for the cell's metabolism, chemicals that are not present in the extracellular fluid. The plasma membrane thus separates the intracellular and extracellular fluids and can be considered the gateway to the cell, since all the molecules needed to support the cell's metabolism must enter by crossing this membrane and metabolic wastes must leave by the same route. By controlling the passage of substances across it, the plasma membrane plays a vital role in maintaining a suitable environment within the cell. This is possible only because the membrane acts as a selective barrier to the movement of certain substances between the extracellular and intracellular fluids. Some molecules are able to pass through the plasma membrane passively, whereas others are not, and still others are actively extracted from the extracellular fluid. Hence the membrane is said to be **selectively permeable** and capable of active transport.

The substances that are most important in generating the resting membrane potential are charged atoms or molecules called **ions**. Certain compounds form ions when they dissolve in water. Ions are produced by the transfer of an electron from one atom in the original molecule to another atom. Since electrons are negative charges the atom gaining the electron takes on a net negative charge, while the atom losing the electron becomes positive. Sodium chloride provides a familiar example. Each molecule is composed of one sodium atom ionicly bonded to one chloride atom. When NaCl is placed in water the attraction of Na and Cl for each other is overcome by their attraction to oppositely charged parts of the water molecules, which break the ionic bond between the NaCl. In that way NaCl is dissolved in water, but chloride has a stronger affinity for electrons than does sodium and one of the outer electrons of the sodium atom is captured by the chloride atom. A sodium chloride solution thus consists of four distinct kinds of particles: water molecules (H_2O), positively charged sodium ions (Na^+), negatively charged chloride ions (Cl^-), and a few sodium chloride molecules (NaCl). (Negatively charged ions are called **anions** because they are attracted to the positive terminal, or **anode**, of a battery. Positively charged ions are called **cations** since they are attracted to the battery's negative terminal, or **cathode**.)

Diffusion and osmosis

The water molecules and ions of an aqueous solution of sodium chloride are in continuous random motion even though the solution appears to be motionless to the eye. Thermal energy acting on the invisible particles causes them to zigzag about, frequently colliding with each other and bouncing off in a new direction. Impacts on minute but visible particles suspended in the fluid cause them also to vibrate randomly. This vibration is called **Brownian movement** after the Scottish botanist Robert Brown, who first described it. The random nature of this thermal agitation ensures that each kind of particle becomes distributed evenly throughout the solution. If some salt crystals are allowed to dissolve in water without stirring, the sodium and chloride ions will at first be concentrated locally. The concentration of these ions (the "saltiness" of the

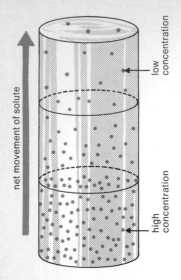

Figure 12–3 In diffusion there is a net movement of materials along a concentration gradient from the region of higher to the region of lower concentration.

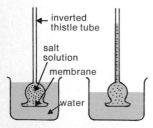

Figure 12–4 Water molecules in the beaker can pass through the selectively permeable membrane and enter the thistle tube, but the larger particles of the salt solution in the tube cannot pass out. Differential bombardment of water molecules on the membrane results in water entering the tube. It continues to enter until the hydrostatic pressure of the column of salt solution rising in the tube causes water molecules to move back through the membrane into the beaker as fast as they diffuse from the beaker into the tube. This hydrostatic pressure is equal to the osmotic pressure of the solution in the tube.

solution) will decrease as we move away from this spot. Therefore, there is a **concentration gradient**, and with the course of time thermal agitation carries the ions farther and farther away from the original spot. This net movement of ions or molecules down their concentration gradient is called **diffusion** (Fig. 12–3). Diffusion is a slow process but it is an effective means of transport over short distances. Diffusion depends only on random thermal agitation and it can take place only down a concentration gradient, eventually distributing **solute** particles (in our example sodium and chloride ions) throughout the solvent. When this happens there is no longer a concentration gradient and diffusion ceases. The ions will continue to zigzag through thermal agitation, but this is random, and there is no net displacement of ions from one part of the solution to another.

The ions in the solution can also be said to dilute the water molecules. If the ions are more concentrated in a certain region of the solution, that region has fewer water molecules than an equal volume of solution containing fewer ions. Prior to equilibrium the water molecules are thus distributed in a concentration gradient which has a direction opposite to that of the ions. Thermal agitation causes a net displacement or diffusion of water molecules toward the region where the ions are most concentrated. Water molecules diffuse into this region as ions diffuse out. Since the plasma membrane of a cell is permeable to water it is necessary that the total number of solute particles in the intracellular and extracellular fluids be similar. Otherwise there will be a different concentration of water molecules on each side of the membrane and water will diffuse down this gradient. This will result in swelling or shrinking of the cell as water enters or leaves it. The diffusion of water across a selectively permeable membrane is called **osmosis** (Fig. 12–4). The swelling that results when water enters a cell by osmosis is due to the increased hydrostatic pressure within. This, in turn, is due to the higher osmotic pressure (solute concentration) inside the cell. When the osmotic pressure of the intracellular and extracellular fluids is the same, the cell is said to be in osmotic equilibrium with its environment. There is no net movement of water across the membrane.

Electrochemical "tugs of war"

Although nerve and muscle cells are in osmotic balance with their environment, chemical analysis of intracellular and extracellular fluid shows that the concentration of certain ions may be quite different on opposite sides of the plasma membrane of a living cell. Osmotic balance depends on the total concentration or activity of *all* osmotically active particles on each side of the membrane. Figure 12–5 summarizes the concentration of several ions mainly responsible for the resting membrane potential. The exact concentration ratios vary for different cells, but notice that Na^+ is 9 to 13 times more concentrated outside the cell, where there is also more chloride, whereas the concentration of potassium is 40 to 56 times greater inside the cell. The interior of the cell also contains a group of organic anions not included in Fig. 12–5. Not all of these have been identified, but we will indicate them collectively by A^-.

Why hasn't each ion diffused down its concentration gradient and equalized its concentration across the plasma membrane? How is this unequal distribution of ions related to the resting membrane potential? The answers to these questions are most easily understood by considering first the large intracellular anions denoted by A^- in Fig. 12–5. Presumably due at least in part to their size, these ions are unable to pass through channels in the plasma membrane and enter the extracellular fluid. The plasma membrane is thus impermeable to them, making them prisoners of the cell.

This confinement of certain organic anions to the cell's interior has two important effects. First, a concentration gradient of A^- is steadily maintained across the plasma membrane. Second, an electrostatic force is generated between the interior and exterior of the cell due to the negative charge of each confined anion. The outward concentration gradient and the negative charge on its interior both represent forces tending to move A^- out of the cell, but such movement is prevented by the membrane's impermeability to these ions.

Although electrical neutrality cannot be restored by the outward movement of A^-, the electrical imbalance could be reduced by the *inward* movement from the extracellular fluid of smaller positively charged ions which can pass through the membrane, or the *outward* movement of small negative ions present inside the cell. If one positive charge entered (or a negative charge left) for each negative charge trapped in the cell, electrical neutrality would be restored.

The actual distribution of K^+ and Cl^- across the cell membrane can be understood in terms of such forces tending to restore electrical neutrality. Since the plasma membrane is somewhat permeable to both K^+ and Cl^-, the electrical imbalance due to A^- would be reduced by an inward movement of K^+ and outward movement of Cl^-. It is not surprising therefore to find K^+ most concentrated inside the cell and Cl^- concentrated in the extracellular fluid. It is important, however, to note that not enough K^+ has entered the cell—or Cl^- left it—to restore electrical neutrality completely. Although the voltage across the membrane is less than it would be if the concentration of these two ions were equal on each side, there is still a definite membrane potential. Why does the movement of K^+ and Cl^- across the membrane stop before electrical neutrality is restored and the membrane potential is reduced to zero?

Imagine for a moment a cell without any impermeable anions. If such a cell existed, we would expect an equilibrium to be established in which the concentrations of permeable K^+ and Cl^- were the same on each side of its membrane. Under these conditions there would not be any electrostatic force (voltage) or diffusion (concentration gradient) across the membrane (Fig. 12–6A). If we now add some impermeable organic anions to the intracellular fluid, their negative charges will create an electrostatic force across the plasma membrane. This force, as shown in the figure, will move potassium ions into the cell and chloride ions out (Fig. 12–6B). As soon as K^+ begins moving into the cell, however, it increases the intracellular concentration of K^+ and creates a concentration gradient that tends to move the K^+ in the opposite direction (out of the cell) from the electrostatic attraction of A^-. A tug of war begins between the outward-directed force of the chemical concentration gradient and the inward-directed electrostatic force. At first the electrostatic force is stronger and K^+ continues to move into the cell up its concentration

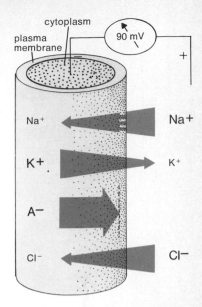

Figure 12–5 The distribution of major ions between the extracellular fluid and intracellular fluid of a vertebrate nerve or muscle cell. The size of the letters indicates the relative concentration of ions on each side of the plasma membrane. The arrows point in the direction in which diffusion should occur. Certain large intracellular anions (A^-) cannot pass through the membrane, and sodium ions are pumped out as fast as they diffuse in.

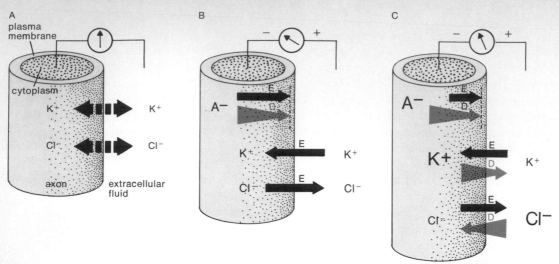

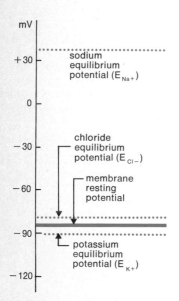

Figure 12-6 Diagram A represents a hypothetical axon lacking impermeable anions (A⁻). The plasma membrane is relatively permeable to K⁺ and to Cl⁻, both of which diffuse across it in both directions and equalize their concentrations on both sides, which means there is no electrostatic force across the membrane. However, when impermeable anions (B) are added to the cell, their passage out of it is blocked, so they make the inside of the cell negative. The resulting electrostatic force (E) across the membrane attracts K⁺ into the cell and causes Cl⁻ to move out. K⁺ and Cl⁻ continue moving in opposite directions across the membrane until the diffusion force (D) created by their increasing concentration gradients equals the opposing electrostatic force (C). There is then no further net movement of these ions across the membrane and they are said to be in electrochemical equilibrium. The membrane potential is less than in B, but the interior of the cell is still negative.

Figure 12-7 The membrane potential at which the electrostatic force on a permeable ion exactly counterbalances the diffusion force is the equilibrium potential of an ion. Here the resting membrane potential is close to the equilibrium potential of potassium (E_{K+}) and of chloride (E_{Cl-}) but of opposite polarity to sodium (E_{Na+}). Anything that increases the membrane's permeability to a particular ion causes the membrane potential to move closer to the ion's equilibrium potential.

gradient. By moving in, however, K⁺ decreases the electrical imbalance across the membrane and hence weakens the electrostatic force. At the same time the concentration gradient is becoming steeper and the diffusion force in the opposite direction becomes correspondingly stronger. K⁺ continues to move into the cell until the physical and electrical forces exactly counterbalance each other (Fig. 12–6C). At this point neither force is able to overpower the other so there is no further net movement of K⁺ across the membrane. Potassium ions are distributed according to an **electrochemical equilibrium.**

At electrochemical equilibrium the electrostatic force of the membrane potential balances the physical force of the concentration gradient of a specific ion. The physical force has thus prevented the achievement of electrical neutrality across the membrane. Knowing the concentration of K⁺ inside and outside the cell at equilibrium, we can calculate how large a membrane potential is needed to counterbalance the diffusion force. This membrane potential is called the **equilibrium potential** of the ion in question (in this case potassium) and is often written E_K (Fig. 12–7).

Exactly the same electrochemical tug of war will operate on Cl⁻, with the important difference that since chloride is a negative ion the electrostatic force (negative inside) will tend to move it out of the cell and the resulting concentration gradient will move it back in (Fig. 12–6). An electrochemical equilibrium will be achieved in which the electrical force exerted by the chloride equilibrium potential will just offset the force of the concentration gradient.

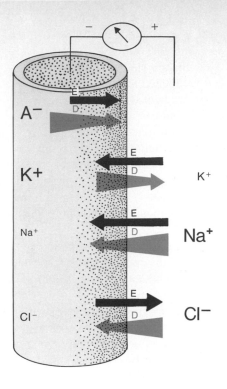

Figure 12-8 Unlike K^+ and Cl^-, Na^+ is not near its electrochemical equilibrium. Both electrostatic and diffusion forces (E and D) cause Na^+ to enter the axon. The inside of the cell would be positive at sodium's equilibrium potential, but Na^+ ions are prevented from accumulating in the cell by the sodium "pump," which actively transports Na^+ out as fast as it diffuses in.

The concept of an electrochemical equilibrium explains the relative concentration of K^+ and Cl^- on either side of a neuron's or muscle cell's membrane. This conclusion is supported by calculations showing that the equilibrium potentials of K^+ and Cl^- are both close to the resting potential measured across the membrane. To a first approximation the resting membrane potential can be thought of as a compound equilibrium potential of these two ions.

Metabolic pumps and the distribution of sodium ions

We must still consider the distribution of sodium ions, however. Unlike K^+ and Cl^-, Na^+ is not distributed in an electrochemical equilibrium. This positively charged ion is most abundant in the extracellular fluid so *both* the electrostatic and physical forces are acting in the same direction and tend to move it into the cell (Fig. 12–8). If Na^+ were to redistribute itself according to its electrochemical equilibrium, it would enter the cell and make the *inside* of the cell positive. The equilibrium potential of Na^+ is thus of opposite polarity to the resting membrane potential.

How can Na^+ defy electrostatic and chemical forces and remain primarily in the extracellular fluid? At one time the plasma membrane was thought to be impermeable to Na^+, just as it is to A^-. It is now known that this is not the case. Even though Na^+ enters less readily, it would certainly reach equilibrium if free to do so. How, then, is the sodium concentration gradient maintained? An important clue lies in the discovery that the intracellular Na^+ concentration rapidly increases if the cell's metabolism is stopped by a poison such as cyanide or by removing the cell's oxygen supply.

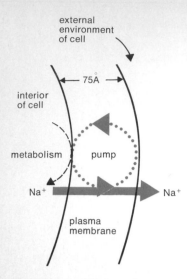

Figure 12–9 The term "metabolic pump" is used to designate the mechanism that moves sodium through the plasma membrane and out of the cell. The "pump" is located in the plasma membrane.

These and other experimental observations can be understood if we assume that although Na^+ is continuously diffusing into the cell, it is being actively pumped back out again at the same rate. Thus there is no net increase of intracellular Na^+ (Fig. 12–9). The situation can be likened to that of a leaky ship, which will float indefinitely if the bilge pumps are kept working to remove the water as fast as it enters. The metabolic pump that extrudes the Na^+ does so against both its concentration gradient, or diffusion tendency, *and* an electrostatic force. Therefore, the cell is doing work to maintain a membrane potential and in this respect can be likened to an electric battery or power station. Energy is supplied by the cell's metabolism. If prevented from respiring, the pump stops. Sodium and other ions then diffuse passively across the membrane and down their concentration gradients and the membrane potential drops to zero.

This "uphill" pumping of sodium is an example of that widespread biological process called **active transport**. The mechanism of the sodium pump is located in the plasma membrane. Its operation is not fully understood, but sodium ions that collide (through thermal agitation) with the membrane surface are thought to be in some way attracted or "captured" by special molecules within the membrane and then transported outward and released in the extracellular fluid. This selective outward transport of sodium maintains a low internal concentration of sodium, and since it goes on continuously it also allows for a continuous exchange of the few sodium ions inside with the excess outside. Should the sodium pump stop working, sodium ions with their positive charges would immediately accumulate in the cell and greatly reduce or even reverse the polarity of the membrane potential.

Bioelectricity and the electricity that travels in wires are really the same phenomenon. The carriers of electric charge in bioelectricity are ions rather than electrons. The current is due to their mass movement from one place to another. An electromotive force develops when ions of one electrical sign are actively separated from those of the other rather than being allowed to intermingle freely. By maintaining such separation, the sodium pump generates the membrane potential.

These matters seem far removed from animal behavior. However, brief and abrupt changes in the membrane potentials of nerve and muscle cells are known as **local potentials**, **action potentials**, or simply as impulses, and patterns of action potentials make up the communications code of the nervous system. Action potential patterns are transmitted inward from sense cells, along and between many millions of nerve cells of the central nervous system, and out along motor nerve fibers to the multitude of muscle fibers that directly define animal behavior.

Our thoughts and actions alike are all generated, coded, and transmitted in the form of fluctuations of membrane potential at myriad points in our brains and along a complex pattern of motor nerve fibers leading to our muscles. It is important to understand the nature of the membrane potential in a single cell if we are to understand how action potentials are transmitted along nerve axons, those elongated extensions of nerve cells. This is the subject we will now turn to, after which we will consider how excitable cells interact through action potentials transmitted from one to another.

PASSIVE AND ACTIVE MEMBRANE RESPONSES

We have seen that the resting membrane potential signifies a state of electro-chemical equilibrium sustained by the sodium pump. From this it follows that any change in the concentrations of ions near the membrane—particularly those of sodium and potassium—would alter the balance point of the equilibrium and hence change the membrane potential.

This can be done chemically, that is, by adding or subtracting sodium or potassium salts either within the cell or in the fluid that surrounds it. In practice, it is much easier to do this in a precise manner by passing electric currents from an external source through the membrane in such a way as to alter the local concentrations of ions. Special electronic stimulators are used to deliver rectangular (square) pulses of current variable in their sign (positive or negative), amplitude (voltage), and duration (length). These pulses are delivered by a micropipette (or sometimes a small wire) placed close to the membrane or inserted just inside it, and the circuit is completed by another (indifferent) electrode lying in the fluid surrounding the cell. The responses of the membrane potential to these electrical pulses imposed on the membrane are registered by another micropipette.

Passive changes in the membrane potential

Such experiments can be carried out only on very large excitable cells whose extensive membranes are damaged relatively little by the insertion of micropipettes. Favorite subjects have been giant nerve fibers from the squid and muscle fibers of frogs (Fig. 12–10). These are dozens or hundreds of times greater in diameter than the nerve fibers belonging to neurons of our own brains, but there is strong evidence that both behave in the same fashion.

Let us consider the effect on the membrane potential when current flowing in the stimulating circuit is such that the stimulating electrode just outside the membrane is made negative suddenly. We speak of this electrode as the cathode since it attracts and neutralizes the charge on cations such as Na+ and K+. Withdrawal of some of these positive charges just outside the plasma membrane reduces the membrane potential somewhat. The membrane is then said to have become partially depolarized. This membrane potential change is called an **electrotonic potential** (Fig 12–11). (The depolarization produced in this case is called a catelectrotonic potential.)

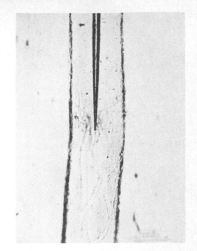

Figure 12–10 This photograph, taken through a microscope, shows the tip of a micropipette electrode inserted longitudinally into a giant fiber. The cut end of the giant fiber closes around the shaft of this intracellular electrode, so the fiber can be kept alive in a proper salt solution while the electrode is used to study its membrane potential.

Figure 12–11 Diagram A shows the set-up for recording an electrotonic membrane potential by using an intracellular electrode and external stimulus pulses. Diagram B shows that potentials are graded in amplitude according to the amplitude of the stimulus. A positive stimulus to the outside of the membrane increases the membrane potential; a negative stimulus reduces it.

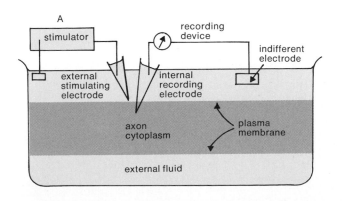

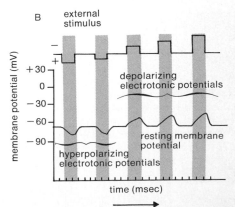

If the active electrode near the membrane is made positive, the reverse change occurs in the membrane potential. Its effect adds to the potential already existing and generated by the action of the sodium pump. The outside becomes more positive with respect to the inside, and the membrane is said to have become **hyperpolarized** (Fig. 12–11). (The hyperpolarization produced is spoken of as an anelectrotonic potential.)

These electrotonic potentials are passive responses, but they are important to understand in the light of what is to follow. When the membrane is partially depolarized its state moves in the direction of generating an action potential or nerve impulse. When it is hyperpolarized it becomes less likely, or less able, to sustain and transport a nerve impulse.

There are three important things about electrotonic potentials imposed on the membrane from an external source. First, they are entirely passive responses. So long as the imposed stimulus is small, the size of a catelectrotonic potential change is proportional to the size of the stimulus. Second, both types of electrotonic potential spread decrementally over neighboring membrane; that is, they are greatest in the membrane closest to the stimulating electrode and die out gradually a short distance away. The distance they spread before dying out depends on the electrical resistance or ion impermeability of the membrane, the size of the axon, the electrical resistances of the extracellular and intracellular fluids, and the volume of conducting fluid surrounding the

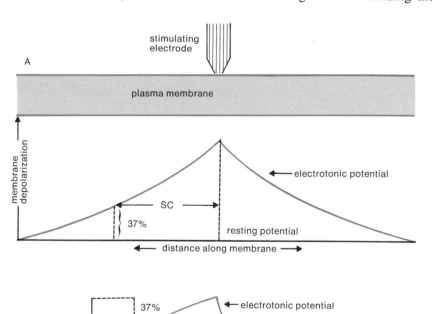

Figure 12–12 The space and time constants are important properties of membranes. Diagram A shows that the space constant (SC) is the distance from the stimulating electrode to the point at which the depolarization is only 37% of its value at the electrode. Diagram B shows that the time constant (tc) is the time it takes for an electrotonic potential to rise to within 37% of its maximum value.

axon or muscle fiber. The distance in millimeters at which the electrotonic potential has dropped to 0.37 of its value right under the stimulating electrode is referred to as the **space constant** of the fiber in question (Fig. 12–12A). Third, ions take a finite time to transfer in any number across the relatively resistant plasma membrane. Therefore, even though the rectangular stimulus pulse rises instantly when the current is turned on, the electrotonic potential rises to its peak more gradually a short distance from the stimulating electrode. The time in milliseconds, for the electrotonic potential to develop completely at a point along the membrane where it has dropped to 0.63 of its maximum value under the electrode is called the **time constant** of the membrane (Fig. 12–12B).

Time and space constants measure important characteristics of the membrane of a nerve fiber. These characteristics limit the speed at which it is able to conduct an impulse, the duration of individual impulses, and the number of impulses that it is able to conduct in a given time interval. All these factors in their turn limit the speed with which the nervous system can receive and process information in the form of nerve impulses, and ultimately, of course, the speed with which an animal can react. Since speed in evading predators and capturing prey often determines survival, these factors have been very important in evolution. Ultimately, they determine the speed with which we can think and calculate. The advantage of modern computers over our brains is that the time constants of their components are measured in nanoseconds (one million millionth of a second) while nerve fibers, the components of our nervous systems, have time constants measured in milliseconds (one thousandth of a second).

Active local potentials

As the stimulus voltage is gradually increased the electrotonic potential across the membrane gets progressively larger. Its size and spread depend on the electrical properties of the resting membrane. As the stimulus amplitude is further increased, a degree of depolarization is reached at the cathode where the shape of the voltage change across the membrane becomes different in form and greater than can be explained only by the properties of the passive membrane. This suggests an active change in the membrane, allowing certain ions to flow across it more readily. The sodium ion, in particular, begins to move inward and toward its equilibrium, tending to produce additional depolarization beyond that due to the passive electrotonic potential caused by the stimulus pulse. This effect is called a **local potential** (Fig. 12–13).

Beyond the fact that the local potential indicates an incipient response of the membrane, it is similar to the electrotonic potential in that it is limited to local and decremental spread over the neighboring membrane. Also, within limits the local potential is proportional to the amplitude of the applied stimulus. Local potentials, then, are graded potentials.

Local potentials have a duration determined in part by the time constant of the membrane. If a short stimulus pulse generates a local potential and then a second stimulus is given before the first local potential has died out and the membrane returned to its resting condition, the local potential produced by

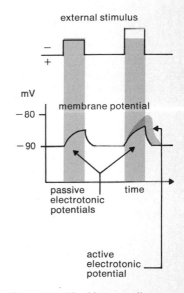

Figure 12–13 Very small negative stimuli delivered to the immediate environment of the nerve cell cause small passive electrotonic depolarizing potentials. As the amplitude of the stimulus is increased, an active potential of longer duration appears on top of the passive potential.

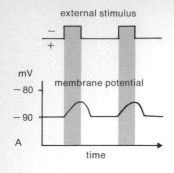

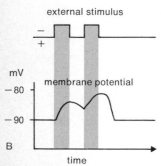

Figure 12–14 Summation of two local potentials. When the second of the pair of stimuli in A is delivered, before the local potential of the first has disappeared, its local potential adds to that of the first and depolarizes the membrane more than it would otherwise.

the second stimulus will add to that produced by the first. This ability of local potentials to interact is called **summation** (Fig. 12–14).

It is important to note that the membrane is in a state of great instability when it is depolarized by a local potential. If the influx of Na^+ is small, the excess of entering sodium can be removed by the sodium pump, which is actively transporting sodium out of the cell. However, as the amplitude of the stimulus is increased the local potential is also increased, allowing more Na^+ to enter. Now Na^+ entrance in itself promotes depolarization so that the effects of the local potential and increased Na^+ influx combine, promoting increased Na^+ permeability and further depolarization. This type of effect is said to be regenerative and belongs to the same class of phenomena as a spreading forest fire and an avalanche. A small amount of heat causes more material to catch fire; a slight movement of snow on the mountain side causes more snow to begin sliding. There is "a point of no return" beyond which these processes promote themselves and are out of external control. Another term applied to processes that promote themselves is **positive feedback**—some of the action is "fed back" to the event in such a way that it has a positive effect in speeding up the action (Fig. 12–15).

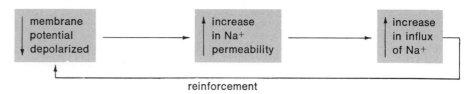

Figure 12–15 The "vicious cycle" of events leading to an action potential is an example of a feedback loop involving reinforcement. When the membrane is depolarized to the point that sodium ions enter faster than they can be pumped out, the membrane reaches its "firing threshold" and an action potential results.

The nature of the action potential

From this it will be seen that when the local potential reaches a critical value, known as the **firing threshold** of the membrane, an inward and self-sustaining "avalanche" of Na^+ is triggered. The result is a rapid depolarization of the membrane, which in fact momentarily reverses its electrical sign and becomes positive inside (Fig. 12–16). This is because Na^+ continues to enter the cell until its membrane voltage approaches the sodium equilibrium potential.

As this point is approached and the electrochemical forces driving positive charges in the form of Na^+ into the cell become less, the permeability of the plasma membrane to Na^+ decreases suddenly and the membrane becomes even less permeable to Na^+ than it was in the resting state. This abrupt drop in permeability to sodium ions is called **sodium inactivation**. The mechanism of sodium inactivation is unknown, but its effect is to end the dependence of the membrane potential on sodium permeability. At the same time there is an increasing permeability to K^+, which begins more gradually and reaches its peak about the time sodium inactivation occurs. Since K^+ is more

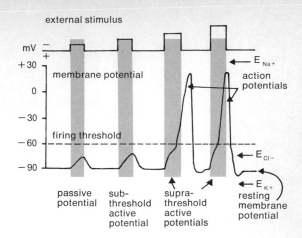

Figure 12–16 This diagram shows membrane responses to increasing amplitude stimuli. The first stimulus pulse is too small to affect the membrane, but the third and fourth produce active potentials that increase the membrane's sodium permeability enough to depolarize it to its firing threshold. Note that at the peak of the action potential the polarity of the membrane potential is reversed and the inside of the cell is momentarily positive. Also note that once the firing threshold is reached, larger stimuli do not produce larger action potentials. In each case the peak of the action potential approaches the equilibrium potential for sodium.

concentrated inside than outside, these potassium ions diffuse out, carrying positive charge out of the cell and restoring the membrane potential close to its resting value. In the course of this sequence of events the cell has gained some sodium ions and lost some potassium ions. When the cell is once more at rest the excess sodium is extruded by the sodium pump and the lost potassium re-enters the cell, restoring the original concentration gradients of these ions.

The sequence of electrical changes in the membrane potential—the rapid depolarization and overshoot during sodium influx followed by repolarization through potassium outflow after sodium inactivation—is called an **action potential**, **spike potential**, or **impulse** (Fig. 12–17).

The combination of the regenerative sodium influx that starts the action potential, the sodium inactivation near its peak and the heightened potassium permeability that follows have two important consequences. First, the cycle of changes indicated by the action potential is all-or-none. Once a critical local depolarization has been reached, the sequence of membrane potential changes must go through its cycle completely and irrespective of the stimulus. Its program is determined by changing membrane properties and not by external events. Second, since a second stimulus arriving during the sodium "avalanche" or during the subsequent sodium inactivation is obviously incapable of altering these events and is relatively impotent during the period of heightened potassium permeability, the cell is at first completely inexcitable. This interval is the **absolute refractory period.** It is, therefore, impossible for two action potentials to combine or summate, as can electrotonic and local

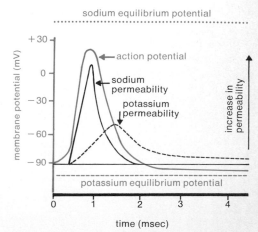

Figure 12–17 Sequential changes in membrane permeability to sodium and potassium are responsible for rise and fall of action potential.

potentials. In fact, if an action potential is started simultaneously from both ends of a nerve fiber, the two will meet and collide and die out in each other's refractory periods. The absolute refractory period is followed by a **relative refractory period** during which a second action potential may be generated, but only if the second stimulus is larger than the first.

It is worth noting that the all-or-none nature of the action potential and the absolute refractory period that accompanies it are characteristic of regenerative events. Earlier we compared the action potential to a forest fire and mountain avalanche. The forest fire cannot begin again until there is more combustible material; the avalanche cannot repeat itself until there is a fresh fall of snow. Both are all-or-none and refractory while they are occurring.

Propagation of the action potential

The units or "bits" of information dealt with by the nervous system are action potentials. To be useful this information must be transferred from one place to another. Action potentials propagate along, or are conducted by, nerve fibers from one point in the nervous system to another.

We have seen that electrotonic and local potentials die away as they spread from their point of origin. They die out within a few millimeters and are unable to transmit information over greater distances. An action potential is a much more intense and rapid depolarization of the membrane. At the action potential's peak the region just outside the membrane becomes suddenly more negative than neighboring regions because of the influx of positive ions. It acts like a local cathode, and since the region occupied by an action potential is electrically connected to regions of membrane on either side by the conducting extracellular and intracellular fluids, a local depolarization of critical size is induced in these neighboring regions. An action potential then flares up at these points also and propagates off in both directions (Fig. 12–18). An action potential cannot move backwards, that is, into the region that it just occupied, because of the residual refractoriness at this point. We must note that although action potentials can travel off in both directions along an axon when an electric shock is applied to a mid-point, this does not normally occur in the body. Here natural excitation occurs only at one end of a neuron so an action potential can travel only away from this point.

Figure 12–18 A single stimulus applied to the middle of a length of axon produces an action potential (A) that divides and becomes two action potentials traveling in opposite directions (B). Small curved arrows indicate direction of current flow causing the action potential to move along the axon. Heavily colored regions of the axon in Diagram B are refractory parts of the membrane immediately behind the action potentials.

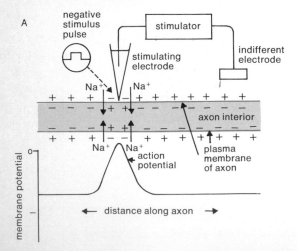

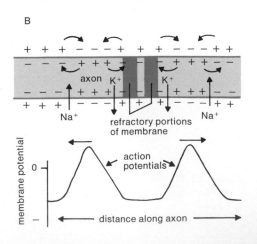

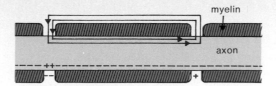

myelin

axon

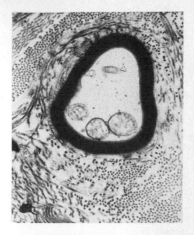

Figure 12–19 Action potentials travel rapidly along myelinated axons by saltatory conduction. The myelin sheath insulates the membrane so that the ionic currents of the action potential must flow from gap to gap along the axon, as indicated by the arrows. A photomicrograph of a myelinated axon is also shown. The dark ring is the myelin sheath, the light area inside it is the axon, and the circular bodies within are mitochondria.

The speed of impulse conduction varies from a few mm/sec in some sea anemones up to 120 m/sec in certain mammalian nerves. Speed of conduction is determined by a number of factors, including temperature and the time and space constants of the nerve fibers in question. Large diameter axons, for example, conduct more rapidly than those of small diameter. But large axons take up more space in the nervous system and cannot transmit so much information as an equal volume of many smaller axons. They can transmit only a small amount of information rapidly. Therefore, evolving nervous systems have had to compromise between speed and quantity. Vertebrates (and a few invertebrates) have avoided this difficulty by evolving a wrapping of an insulating material, myelin, around many of their large axons (Fig. 12–19). Myelin is laid down in a series of short segments along the axons. The plasma membrane is exposed between gaps in the insulating myelin. Current flow due to an action potential is thus funneled through these gaps, and impulses essentially jump from one gap to the next. This is known as **saltatory conduction** and greatly speeds impulse transmission without unduly increasing the size of the axon.

Speed of impulse transmission has been a premium factor in survival during animal evolution. The expression "the quick and the dead" has a special meaning when applied to prey and predators. The vertebrates probably could never have evolved to their present large body size (compared with invertebrates) without the development of myelin. Lacking myelination it would simply have taken too long for an animal many feet in length to be informed that it was in trouble when attacked in the rear by a small predator. Squid species, which are among the largest invertebrates, met the problem by evolving giant axons 20 to 50 times the diameter of ours. But, again, this takes up space in the nervous system and decreases the amount of information that can be processed.

COMMUNICATION BETWEEN EXCITABLE CELLS

We have seen how action potentials sweep in succession along a nerve fiber and that once initiated they are beyond the control of the stimulus. From this it follows that if the nervous system were merely a continuous network of nerve fibers a stimulus applied at any point would cause action potentials to invade the whole network and reach all muscles. All stimuli would produce only a total spasm of the animal.

But we know that behavior is highly patterned. A given stimulus causes only certain muscles to contract in a set order while others are prevented from contracting or made to relax. Every animal has a repertory of many different

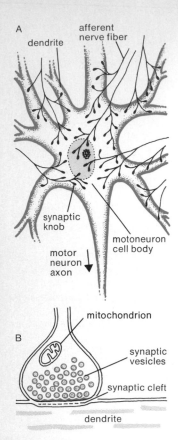

A
dendrite
afferent nerve fiber
synaptic knob
motor neuron axon
motoneuron cell body

B
mitochondrion
synaptic vesicles
synaptic cleft
dendrite

Figure 12–20 The cell body and dendrites of vertebrate motoneurons (A) are located in the spinal cord where they receive synaptic contacts from the axonal endings of many interneurons and sensory neurons. The structure of these synapses is shown in greater detail in B. Transmission across these synapses determines whether or not an action potential will be generated in the motoneuron and travel out its axon to cause a group of muscle fibers to contract.

contraction patterns, each called into play only by certain types of stimuli. Some stimuli stop action and cause the animal to become motionless. Thus, nerve impulses started by a given stimulus are prevented from taking some paths in the nervous system while their pattern is reformed and combined with other nerve impulse patterns as they travel along prescribed paths to certain muscles.

The need for a selective mechanism promoting transmission along some paths and prohibiting it along others is clear if we think of a telephone network. It would be easy to build a network in which each subscriber was connected to all the others, but hard to imagine the chaos that this would produce. The famous mathematician Norbert Wiener once pointed out that the importance of a telephone exchange is not that it connects you with the right number, but rather that it prevents you from becoming connected with all the wrong numbers.

The selective mechanism of the nervous system consists of measureless millions of synapses. When the axon of a nerve cell approaches another nerve or muscle cell the plasma membranes of the two do not fuse but remain separated by a submicroscopic gap called the **synaptic cleft**. The cell along which neural signals arrive at the synapse is called the **presynaptic cell**; the cell that receives excitation is called the **postsynaptic cell**. The process whereby signals are communicated across the synapse is called **synaptic transmission**. Synapses frequently occur between the axonal endings of the presynaptic cell and the dendrites or cell body of the postsynaptic cell (Fig 12–20). However, there are many kinds of synaptic contact.

Despite their varied appearances synapses are all discontinuities of one kind or another. The simplest kind are simply relays, transmitting a pattern of action potentials from one cell to the next with little or no change. Others modify, filter, or combine the signals from a number of presynaptic fibers as they converge on a single postsynaptic cell. This convergence may include inhibition as well as excitation. The first group of synapses we shall refer to as relay synapses; the second as integrative synapses.

Relay synapses

Basically, the movements made by higher animals are due to the minutely patterned contractions of an immense "orchestra" of muscle fibers. Each muscle fiber is controlled at the synapse formed by the axon termination of a motor neuron and the plasma membrane of the muscle fiber. As we shall see later, there are various patterns of motor innervation. Here we shall consider vertebrate skeletal or voluntary muscle. Each motor axon branches to supply from a few to a hundred or more muscle fibers. Each of its branches typically forms one synapse with each muscle fiber.

THE VERTEBRATE NEUROMUSCULAR JUNCTION: The synapse formed by a motor axon and a muscle membrane is also called a **neuromuscular junction** (Fig. 12–21). The myelin sheath of the axon ends as it reaches the muscle membrane. Here the axon branch terminates in a short naked twig embedded in a trough-like depression in the membrane of the muscle fiber. The plasma mem-

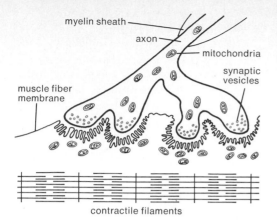

myelin sheath
axon
mitochondria
synaptic vesicles
muscle fiber membrane
contractile filaments

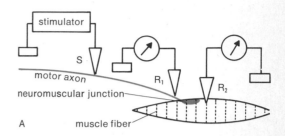

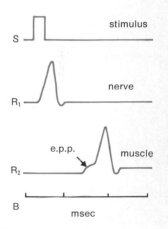

Figure 12–21 The synapse between a vertebrate motoneuron and striated muscle fiber is known as a neuromuscular junction, or motor endplate. Note the specialized folds of the muscle membrane at the synapse. (After C. Coens in *International Review of Cytology*, Vol. 22, 1967.)

stimulator
S
motor axon
neuromuscular junction
R_1
R_2
A
muscle fiber

S — stimulus
R_1 — nerve
R_2 — e.p.p. — muscle
B
msec

Figure 12–22 Diagram A shows the set-up for studying the transmission of excitation across the neuromuscular junction. Diagram B shows that a stimulus at S elicits an action potential that travels along the axon and reaches R_1 near the end of the axon. Nearly a millisecond elapses before R_2 registers a depolarization of the muscle fiber membrane. This synaptic delay is due to chemical transmission of the excitation across the synaptic cleft. Notice that R_2 shows the local potential in the post-synaptic membrane, which gives rise to the spike.

brane of the axon does not fuse with that of the muscle fiber, however, but the two membranes remain separated at all places by a minute gap or **synaptic cleft**. The electron microscope shows that the synaptic cleft is only 200 to 500 angstrom units wide and that there are many minute **synaptic vesicles** just inside the axon membrane but not inside the muscle membrane. The muscle membrane is elaborately folded. This kind of vertebrate neuromuscular junction is also called a **motor endplate**.

Many of the special properties of synapses have been discovered by studying transmission of excitation across the vertebrate neuromuscular junction. One electrode is placed on the motor axon as close to the endplate as possible, a second micropipette is inserted into the muscle membrane, also as close to the endplate as possible (Fig. 12–22). An electric stimulus is now given to the central end of the axon, causing an action potential to propagate toward the muscle. If the electrical responses of axon and muscle are recorded simultaneously, there is a time delay of as much as a millisecond between the two. In other words, there is a short period of electrical "silence" between the arrival of the nerve spike at the endplate and the genesis of an electrical change in the muscle.

This endplate or synaptic delay suggests a gap in the electrical sequence of ion movements that has carried the impulse along the nerve axon, namely that the action potential is not electrically transmitted across the neuromuscular junction. Ion flow due to the arriving impulse is unable to cross the synaptic cleft and directly affect the muscle membrane. Electrical transmission gives way at this point to chemical transmission.

The arrival of a nerve action potential causes the axon ending to release a chemical into the synaptic cleft. This chemical, called a **transmitter substance**, or chemical mediator, is thought to be stored in the minute synaptic vesicles that crowd just inside the axon membrane but are absent below the muscle membrane opposite and across the synaptic cleft. The transmitter substance at the neuromuscular junction of vertebrate skeletal muscle has been identified as the chemical acetylcholine (Ach). Diffusion of Ach across the cleft is thought to occupy the synaptic delay. On reaching the post-synaptic (muscle) membrane, Ach molecules combine with special receptor sites and cause a general increase in the muscle membrane's permeability to

Na$^+$ and K$^+$. Then the plasma membrane of the muscle fiber behaves much like that of an axon, and these ion movements cause it to depolarize locally (Fig 12–23). The local potential that develops is called an **endplate potential** (e.p.p.), or **junctional potential** (j.p.).

From here on matters proceed as in a nerve axon. If the e.p.p. is of critical size, as it always is in a normal rested muscle fiber, the muscle membrane is depolarized to its firing threshold and an action potential develops and propagates itself over the length of the muscle fiber.

The propagating muscle action potential is much larger than the endplate potential that started it. At our electrode in the muscle membrane, the e.p.p. will be overshadowed by the action potential, making it hard to study the e.p.p.

South American Indians were using a poison, curare, on their arrow heads long before these electrical events were discovered. Curare kills by causing flaccid paralysis of all the skeletal muscles, including the respiratory muscles. In the 19th century biologists discovered that curare does not hinder the transmission of nerve impulses, nor does it interfere with excitation and contraction of skeletal muscle, which can still be made to twitch if directly stimulated. More recently curare was found to paralyze by blocking neuromuscular transmission. It does this by making the muscle membrane less sensitive to the depolarizing action of Ach, thus reducing the e.p.p. to a point where it no longer reaches a critical size to generate a propagated muscle action potential.

Thus, although curare reduces the endplate potential, it also unmasks it by preventing the "avalanche" of an action potential. This enabled study of the endplate potential alone. Much of what we now know about the details of synaptic events was discovered by experiments on muscle fibers poisoned with curare. For instance, if just enough curare is applied to block genesis of the muscle action potential, an electric shock applied to the motor nerve results in a somewhat reduced endplate potential. A minute squirt of Ach injected at the endplate region was also found to produce an e.p.p. whose size is proportional to the amount of Ach injected. If Ach is momentarily injected at the endplate of a normal muscle fiber a propagated muscle action potential and twitch follow. If Ach is injected at other points on the muscle membrane no effect is produced. The muscle membrane at the endplate is 1,000 times more sensitive to Ach than elsewhere on the muscle fiber.

A muscle twitch is brief. The action of Ach molecules released into the synaptic cleft must not only be rapid but it must be brief in duration if each motor impulse is to produce only a single twitch. Some Ach molecules diffuse away out of the synaptic cleft without combining with receptor sites. Those that arrive at the sites are soon destroyed by an enzyme, called **acetylcholinesterase** (AchE), concentrated close to the muscle membrane.

AchE plays an important part in preserving the 1:1 ratio of motor nerve impulses to twitches. First it "cleans up" Ach molecules that might be lingering at the junction from a previous impulse and thus allows rapid repolarization of the muscle membrane in preparation for the next depolarization. Second, even when the system is at rest there is a series of minute transient depolarizations of the muscle membrane occurring in a random sequence.

These **miniature endplate potentials** are thought to be due to minute packages or quanta of Ach leaking out of the nerve fiber terminal in a spontaneous fashion. Individual miniature endplate potentials are not sufficient to produce a local potential of critical size, but they could add if the leaking Ach were not destroyed or hydrolyzed by AchE as fast as it leaked. The quanta of Ach are thought to come from the random bursting of vesicles clustered just inside the nerve membrane. The arrival of a nerve impulse causes many vesicles to discharge simultaneously into the synaptic cleft, resulting in a much larger e.p.p.

Although the vertebrate neuromuscular junction is merely a relay junction —that is, it only repeats in the muscle membrane the pattern of spikes transmitted down the motor fiber—it has important properties also found in integrating junctions (described in the next section). The first of these we have discussed—the synaptic delay or "hiatus" breaking the smooth process of electric spike transmission. The second is the fact that the neuromuscular junction is unidirectional. The nerve axon terminal acts as transmitter source and the muscle membrane as the transmitter receptor. Like the relation of a radio transmitter and receiver, the system cannot be made to work backwards. Direct electrical stimulation of the muscle membrane will cause propagation of a muscle action potential, but this will have no effect on the motor nerve

Figure 12–23 When an action potential arrives at a chemically transmitting presynaptic terminal, it causes many synaptic vesicles to release their transmitter molecules into the synaptic cleft. These molecules diffuse across the cleft and some reach receptor sites on the postsynaptic membrane. There they alter the membrane properties so that certain ions (such as sodium) can diffuse more easily across the postsynaptic membrane. Compare the membrane at A and B. C and D show a hypothetical, simplified diagram of a transmitter molecule opening a channel through which a particular kind of ion can move into the postsynaptic cell and depolarize it.

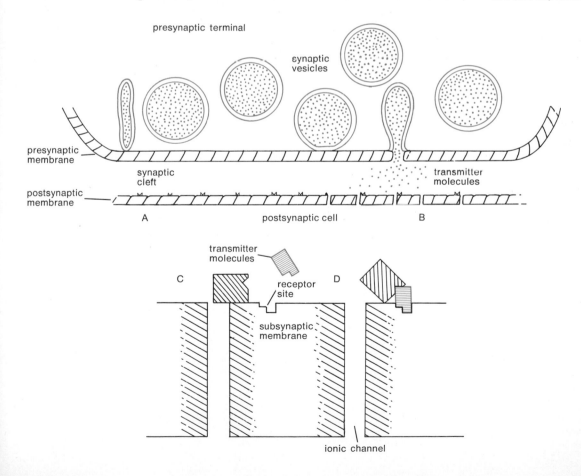

terminal when it reaches and depolarizes the endplate region. This one-way property of synapses limits the natural impulse traffic of the nervous system to one direction even though impulses are capable of traveling in either direction within the confines of individual axons or muscle fibers.

SEGMENTAL SEPTA OF EARTHWORM GIANT FIBERS: Most of us have watched a robin hopping across a spring lawn. Every now and then he stops, cocks his head to one side, and then suddenly plunges his beak into the ground. Sometimes he comes up with a worm, sometimes not. It is not clear how he detects the worm. Perhaps the tip of the worm's body is barely protruding from its burrow. This is a typical example of the many contests between predators and their prey. Can the robin get a firm hold before the worm can withdraw into its burrow? Obviously speed is a prime requisite for both parties, and the evolution of their species clearly has selected for speedy response mechanisms. It is again a matter of the quick and the dead.

Earthworms are sluggish animals when they crawl on the ground. But if you pinch either end of an earthworm it will almost instantaneously shorten its body to less than half its extended length while crawling. This action is made possible by a system of relatively enormous axons called **giant fibers**. Giant fibers lie within the worm's central nervous system and extend the length of its chain of ganglia. Giant fibers are common among invertebrates and seem to have evolved under the same survival pressure—speed of response.

Because of their size and attendant ease of manipulation giant fibers are also the favorites of electrophysiologists. Most of the information in the first part of this chapter is based on research with the giant fiber of the squid. The fiber is a giant motor axon that extends to the mantle muscle of the squid. The mantle muscle expels water by contracting forcefully, an action that jet-propels the squid away from the attack of a large fish or a whale. Many insects, including the common cockroach (Fig. 12–24), have central giant fiber systems similar to that of earthworms. In every case these systems quicken reaction time, both in attack and defense.

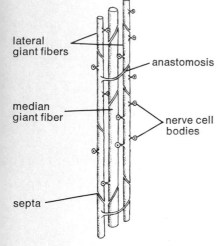

Figure 12–24 This photomicrograph shows a cross section through the abdominal ventral nerve cord connective in a cockroach. Several giant fibers and many smaller axons are visible. Earthworms have three giant fibers that run the length of their ventral nerve cord. A short section of these fibers is shown in the drawing above, which also illustrates the segmental septa. (See Fig. 11–15 for nervous systems in segmented worms.)

lateral giant fibers

anastomosis

median giant fiber

nerve cell bodies

septa

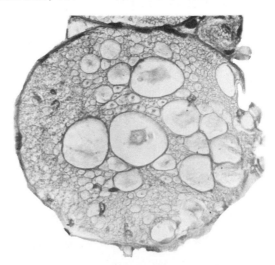

The main giant fiber of the squid is a single large motor axon. In development it is formed by the fusion of a number of embryonic nerve cells and its cell body region contains many nuclei. But the cell membranes separating them have disappeared in the giant axon, which is a continuous and unbroken tube of plasma membrane. In contrast, the giant fibers of earthworms belong to that group of nerve cells called interneurons. Interneurons make up the bulk of the central nervous system and mediate between sense cells and motor neurons. Most of an animal's behavior is patterned by the network of interneurons. An earthworm's body including its central nervous system is highly compartmentalized. Each of the 50 or more body segments contains its ganglion responsible for organizing local actions. Each segmental ganglion is joined by connectives to those before and behind to enable joint action by all the segments. One of the limitations of a high degree of segmentalization is that the processes of nerve cells tend to be confined to their own body segments. How does this arrangement affect the earthworm's giant fiber system that seems to extend throughout the length of the animal?

The common earthworm, *Lumbricus*, has three giant fibers, a median giant that normally conducts from head to tail and two lateral giants that normally conduct impulses initiated at the tail end toward the head. In each segment the giant fibers send out short branches to the body wall's longitudinal muscles, the contraction of which causes the body to shorten. The largest, the median giant, may be 50 to 75 micrometers in diameter. A microscope reveals each giant not as a continuous tube but divided into a series of compartments, or segments, arranged end-to-end. Each segment is really a short, fat axon that has developed from the fusion of several neurons and is sustained by a group of cell bodies within the ganglion belonging to the body segment. Thus, the whole giant fiber is regularly interrupted by oblique segmental septa formed by the closely apposed membranes of each segmental compartment with that before and behind. The two membranes forming each septum are closely apposed (about 65 angstrom units apart) but not fused (Fig. 12–24).

Each septum constitutes an electrical synapse. The gap between the two membranes is very small, only about a fifth of that found at the motor endplate, and the area of contact is very broad. Also, the electrical resistance of the membranes is low. This enables ionic currents due to an action potential in one segment to cause critical depolarization of the membrane of the next without the aid of a chemical transmitter substance. Functionally, the giant axon behaves almost as if it were a single axon, although structurally it is composed of many in series.

Transmission via this series of electrical synapses has several important consequences: (1) each synaptic delay is almost negligible, being less than 0.05 millisecond; (2) the action potential in each segment is not preceded by a separate local potential analogous to the endplate potential; (3) transmission across the septa can take place equally well in either direction. In the intact worm, however, the median giant receives sensory input only from the head, while the lateral giants are excited only at the posterior end.

Electrical synapses are now found to be more common than was originally thought to be the case, particularly in neural connections where speed is paramount. Some have complex and asymmetric membrane arrangements that permit ion flow more easily in one direction than the other, making transmission partially or completely unidirectional.

Finally, to return to the affair of the robin and the worm. If a worm of upwards of 100 segments had to depend on chemical mediation in its giant fibers, there would be a 1- to 2-millisecond delay at each segmental septum, and it would take a good fraction of a second merely to distribute the alarm over its body length. Furthermore the longitudinal muscles could not be excited almost simultaneously. The contest for survival would then be weighted heavily in favor of the robin, a situation which, in the long run, would be bad for both contestants.

Integrating synapses

Relay junctions are an effective means of intercellular communication when all that is required is that the signal in the presynaptic cell be transferred unchanged to the postsynaptic cell. But the genesis of a behavioral response to a given stimulus requires a great deal more signal transformation than this. Complex trains of nerve impulses from a number of sense organs are arriving simultaneously in the central nervous system. Some require attention and perhaps immediate action, others do not. Incoming information must be evaluated and combined, some being transformed and facilitated before being allowed to affect the orchestra of muscles. Other information may be blocked or diverted for later action. In any case, the ultimate behavior must be unified and smooth in spite of the diversity of incoming messages.

The term **integration** covers this process of combining, subtracting, sorting, and suppressing that reduces a multitude of input signals to a smooth and coherent output. Integration of behavior is carried out collectively by a multitude of synapses in higher animals. We have no adequate picture of how the overall integration of behavior is accomplished. However, a closer look at the operation of some of the individual integrating synapses concerned gives us some idea of the principles underlying the process.

LOCAL POTENTIALS: An understanding of the mechanisms and properties of local potentials helps in understanding how a sequence of spikes arriving in succession in one presynaptic fiber or simultaneously along several converging presynaptic fibers are integrated by the postsynaptic cell. We have already seen how an active local potential of critical size generates an action potential in an axon, also how an endplate potential at the neuromuscular junction serves as the source of a propagating action potential at the vertebrate neuromuscular junction. Each of these local potentials, though different in mechanism, served the same purpose. Under normal conditions they are of critical size and thus are *always* able to relay an impulse from one point on an axon to another or from a motor axon termination to a muscle fiber membrane.

Let us now suppose that a local potential just fails to produce a critical degree of local depolarization. The obvious answer in the case of the neuromuscular junction will be that it will fail to generate a propagating muscle action potential and the muscle fiber will fail to contract. But let us combine this idea with two other properties of local potentials—time and space constants. The time constant of the e.p.p. is largely determined by the rate of release of Ach by the motor axon terminal and its rate of destruction by AchE. The space constant is determined by the distance the depolarization of the membrane spreads on either side of the depolarization site. These temporal and spatial properties of a local potential that does not reach critical dimensions *by itself* allow for some very interesting possibilities.

NEUROMUSCULAR EXCITATION IN CRUSTACEA: The muscles of crayfish and lobsters are innervated quite differently from those of vertebrates. Let us take a close look at the muscle that opens the claw (the "pincers") of a crayfish.

All the muscle fibers of the opener muscle are supplied from a single motor axon. Each muscle fiber in turn is supplied with many motor endings of the axon, arranged closely together over its length. If neuromuscular transmission were as we have described it for vertebrate striated muscle, an impulse in the motor nerve could cause only a maximal twitch. The crayfish could either open its claw maximally or not at all—a very inconvenient arrangement that does not correspond with the gently graded opening of different degrees and speeds that the crayfish can actually accomplish.

How can this be? The answer is at hand if we stimulate the motor axon with electric shocks delivered at different frequencies, then record the electrical potential changes in the membrane of single muscle fibre, and register the mechanical performance of the muscle. A single shock to the motor axon will not produce a contraction in the opener muscle. Not until nerve action potentials arrive at the multiple neuromuscular junctions at the rate of about 12/sec does the muscle contract slightly. From this point the speed and strength of contraction increase in proportion to the frequency of arriving motor impulses, reaching a maximum at about 140/sec. Therefore, *frequency* of excitation determines contraction speed and muscle tension in this case.

Some hints about how this system of motor control works can be obtained from a microelectrode inserted into a muscle fiber. Local transient depolarizations or postsynaptic potentials are produced by each arriving motor impulse. These are also called junctional potentials, or **excitatory postsynaptic potentials** (e.p.s.p.). The opener muscle e.p.s.p. differs from the vertebrate muscle endplate potential in that each is not followed by a discrete muscle shortening. However, the effects produced on the muscle membrane by each successive impulse interact if the time between them is sufficiently short. These interactions between successive arriving impulses are of two kinds, which are most important in understanding integration.

One of these effects is **facilitation**. In the first e.p.s.p. of a series the depolarization of the muscle membrane is very slight. The second and succeeding e.p.s.p.'s show progressively greater degrees of membrane depolarization. It is as if the first action potential arriving at the nerve terminals had modified the junction so as to make it more sensitive to subsequent (but otherwise identical) nerve action potentials. The mechanism of facilitation is unknown; perhaps the second impulse releases more transmitter substance than the first impulse does.

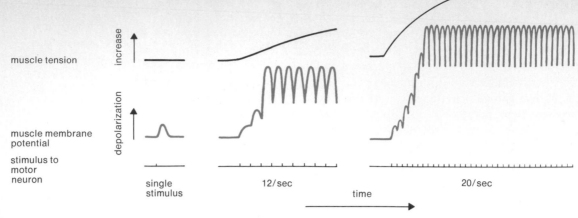

muscle tension

increase

muscle membrane potential

depolarization

stimulus to motor neuron

single stimulus | 12/sec | 20/sec

time

Figure 12–25 This diagram shows the effect of the firing frequency of the motoneuron on the rate and strength of contraction of a crayfish pincher-closer muscle. A single action potential elicits a small excitatory postsynaptic potential in the muscle fiber but does not cause contraction. Contraction requires repetitive neural stimulation at rates rapid enough for e.p.p.'s to summate and facilitate. The muscle fiber membrane is thus depolarized enough to produce contraction in proportion to the amount of depolarization.

The second effect is temporal summation, which we discussed earlier in connection with local potentials in nerves. If a second depolarization occurs before the negativity due to the first has died away, the effects of the two summate or add, the second riding on top of the remains of the first and producing a greater net depolarization of the membrane (Fig. 12–25).

Facilitation and temporal summation cause signal transformation at a synapse. The output is not identical but is some integral of its input. The integration is a function of the timing of arriving impulses, and is, therefore, determined by the time constants of the membrane depolarizations produced. Such effects are widespread between interneurons of the central nervous system and are important in generating behavior.

INHIBITION: Crustacean muscles are innervated (supplied with nerves) in a variety of ways. In most cases, a muscle has some or all of its fibers multiply innervated. As many as four or five separate motor axons may branch repeatedly, the branches and their terminal twigs lying alongside each other and making contact with each muscle fiber at a number of points over its length. Stimulation of one or more of these axons may produce gradual and graded shortening. This is called a "slow" system. In another, the "fast" motor axon, single stimuli may call forth fast twitches in all or most of the fibers through non-facilitating junctions similar in their action to the vertebrate motor endplate. Stimulation of a third type of motor axon may produce no observable contraction at any frequency. However, if this axon is stimulated repeatedly while the muscle is in slow partial contraction due to excitation of the slow system, the contraction may be partially or completely abolished. The muscle then relaxes in spite of continued excitation of the slow system. This in an inhibitory neuron (Fig. 12–26).

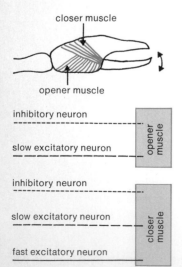

closer muscle

opener muscle

inhibitory neuron

slow excitatory neuron

opener muscle

inhibitory neuron

slow excitatory neuron

fast excitatory neuron

closer muscle

Figure 12–26 The muscle fibers of the **opener** muscle of a crayfish claw are innervated by a single slow excitatory neuron. Vollies of action potentials on this neuron cause gradual contraction. The effect of slow motoneuron stimulation can be canceled by impulses arriving at the same muscle fibers on the inhibitory neuron. The closer muscle also has a fast motoneuron. One or a few action potentials on this nerve cause the closer muscle to twitch. Closer muscle fibers also receive an inhibitory neuron that reduces or prevents their depolarization to motor stimuli and thus prevents contraction.

Figure 12–27 At right is an inhibitory and excitatory neuron synapsing with a crustacean muscle fiber. Excitatory stimulation alone produces an excitatory postsynaptic potential (e.p.s.p.), which depolarizes the membrane to the firing threshold and elicits a muscle action potential. Inhibitory stimulation alone causes a hyperpolarizing inhibitory postsynaptic potential (i.p.s.p.), which moves the membrane potential away from the firing threshold. When the inhibitory and excitatory nerves are stimulated simultaneously, the i.p.s.p. reduces the size of the e.p.s.p. and prevents it from reaching the firing threshold. There is no action potential and the muscle remains relaxed. The e.p.s.p. increases the muscle fiber membrane permeability to sodium so the membrane potential shifts toward E_{Na}. The i.p.s.p. increases membrane permeability to potassium and causes the membrane potential to shift toward the E_K.

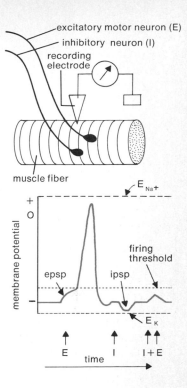

Inhibition works in several ways. In this case it is called **postsynaptic inhibition**. A terminal of the inhibitory axon lies close to each excitatory terminal at a number of points on each muscle fiber. A micropipette inserted below the muscle membrane shows that stimulation of the inhibitory axon of a relaxed muscle fiber causes no change in the resting potential of the fiber. However, if the slow excitatory fiber is being repeatedly stimulated and the muscle membrane is partially depolarized, stimulation of the inhibitory fiber then causes a repolarization, that is, a return of the membrane potential to the resting level. Thus, the effect of impulses in the inhibitory fiber is to cause a hyperpolarization that offsets the depolarization due to the excitatory impulses. This hyperpolarization is called an **inhibitory postsynaptic potential**, or i.p.s.p. (Fig. 12–27).

The i.p.s.p. in this case is thought to be due to an increased permeability of the membrane to K^+ and Cl^-. Increased outflow of K^+ and inflow of Cl^- tend to "clamp" the membrane potential close to its resting value, offsetting any increasing tendency of Na^+ to flow in through the membrane and depolarize it. This is supported by the observation that if the membrane is artificially hyperpolarized by passing current through it, inhibitory impulses will now have a depolarizing effect and so carry the membrane potential once more in the direction of its resting value.

Presynaptic inhibition is also known to occur. In this case the axon terminals of the inhibitory fiber lie on the postsynaptic membrane close to the presynaptic terminals of the excitatory fiber. Excitation of the inhibitory fiber is thought to reduce the amount of transmitter released by the excitatory endings (Fig. 12–28). In another form of inhibition both the e.p.s.p. and the level of membrane polarization are unaffected, and it is thought that inhibition takes effect at some later stage of excitation–contraction coupling.

Inhibition is a second, and indeed very important, form of integration. In temporal summation we have seen that a succession of e.p.s.p.'s can add their effects over short time intervals even though each was triggered by a separate and identical presynaptic spike. A similar sequence of spikes in an inhibitory axon can cause an effect subtracting from that due to the excitatory summation. Sequential inhibitory effects can also summate. The two fibers, one

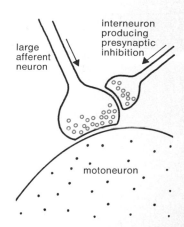

Figure 12–28 The large afferent neuron may be prevented—by an interneuron which bombards its synaptic knob with inhibitory impulses—from exciting the motoneuron. This is presynaptic inhibition of the motoneuron. (Adapted from D. J. Aidley in *The Physiology of Excitable Cells* (1971), Cambridge University Press.)

excitatory and the other inhibitory, converge on the same region of the post-synaptic membrane and their two effects are added in the algebraic sense according to their sign—excitatory or inhibitory.

CONTRACTION PATTERNS IN ARTHROPODS: Before returning to movement and its control in vertebrates we must note that in crustacea and other arthropods a considerable amount of integration is carried out peripherally, that is in the muscles and at their motor endings. Comparable integration is performed within the spinal cords of vertebrates.

Vertebrates may have hundreds of motor axons, each supplying its own group of muscle fibers in a large muscle. Crustacea may have from one to five motor axons in control of a comparable muscle, each branching to some or all of the muscle fibers. Yet, in spite of this economy, the crustacean can perform a wide variety of contraction patterns. These range from rapid and powerful twitches mediated by the fast non-facilitating motor axon through gradual and sustained shortening of any amount determined by the spike frequency in the slow and facilitating motor system. In addition, this tonic contraction can be suddenly turned off by the inhibitory system.

It seems likely that these different synaptic effects are mediated by different chemicals. The excitatory mediator at fast and slow synapses is unknown although it does not appear to be Ach. Gamma amino butyric acid (GABA) inhibits contraction of crayfish muscle in low concentrations and increases the membrane potential and Cl^- conductance. GABA, or a related substance, may be the inhibitory transmitter. It is interesting to speculate why arthropods and vertebrates have evolved such different methods of controlling their muscles. The arthropod system seems to be most economical of nerve cells, yet it permits a wide range of contraction patterns. Perhaps this economy was necessary because of the generally smaller body size of arthropods, their cold-bloodedness, and slow spike conduction velocities associated with the lack of myelin. To achieve speeds of response needed in survival, perhaps arthropods had to evolve axons of large diameter, and this forced them to economize in terms of numbers. We do not know the answer; at any rate, the arthropod system of motor innervation has a certain elegance when we compare it with our own massive arrangement. We shall consider the vertebrate system for controlling movement in the following chapter.

**QUESTIONS
FOR REVIEW**

1 What is an electrochemical equilibrium? Explain the role of the impermeable organic anions and sodium ions in the resting membrane potential of a nerve or muscle cell.

2 What is the difference between a passive and an active membrane response? In which category would you place each of the following: endplate potential, action potential, excitatory postsynaptic potential, inhibitory postsynaptic potential, electrotonic potential.

3 Describe as thoroughly as you can the sequence of events by which an action potential arriving at the motor endplate gives rise to another action potential in the membrane of the postsynaptic muscle cell.

4 How are the giant fibers of an earthworm adapted for rapid conduction and transmission of impulses? Why is this advantageous to the worm?

5 How do integrative synapses differ from relay synapses? What role do processes such as summation, facilitation, and inhibition play in integration? (Use the crustacean neuromuscular junction as an example in your answer.)

SELECTED READINGS

Hodgkin, A. L. *The Conduction of the Nervous Impulse*. Springfield, Ill.: Charles C. Thomas, 1964. A concise account based on a series of popular lectures.

Katz, B. *Nerve, Muscle, and Synapse*. New York: McGraw-Hill Book Co., 1966. This book provides an excellent discussion, in greater depth, of the topics included in this chapter.

13
MOVEMENT AND ITS CONTROL

Most behavior that we can detect takes the form of movement (Fig. 13–1). Even the songs of birds and insects are due to the contractions of muscles. Possible exceptions are the secretions of scent glands in many animals, the electric shocks generated by some kinds of fish, and the flashing of fireflies. Another exception might be mental activity, which must be classed as behavior. However, we can detect mental activity in others only through their actions.

Slow movements in plants are produced by differential osmotic changes—greater water uptake and turgor of cells on one side of a stem than on the other. In animals, movements are generated by changes in shape of the protoplasm within individual cells. These changes in shape may cause the pushing out of pseudopodia in ameba and the lashing of hair-like cilia and whip-like flagella in many swimming protozoa. Cilia also move a current of water bearing food particles over the gills of many mollusks and carry a slow but steady current of mucus out of our own lungs.

THE BEHAVIOR OF MUSCLES

Muscles are by far the most versatile and powerful sources of movement in multicellular animals. Most muscle contraction is initiated by nerve impulses, although some muscles such as the heart contract rhythmically in the absence of nerve connections. The activities of muscles that ring the walls of the digestive tract, blood vessels, the ducts of various glands, and as the heart are regulated by nerves belonging to the autonomic nervous system. So the **autonomic nervous system** controls the involuntary activities of the organism. Because we have little or no voluntary control over most autonomic activities, these muscles are called **involuntary muscles** (Fig. 13–2).

In the following pages we will be concerned primarily with **voluntary** or **skeletal muscle** since its contractions are responsible for most of the overt behavior we see in animals. Voluntary muscle makes up most of the "meat" of the body, and we are conscious of the fact that we can control its contractions at will. Skeletal muscles, such as those of the limbs, are composed of many very elongate cells, or **muscle fibers**, arranged in parallel and connected at either end to a common tendon. Each tendon is attached to a separate bone. The two bones form a joint, and when the muscle fibers shorten the muscle is said to contract, drawing the bone attachments closer together and decreasing the angle at the joint. Since a muscle can do work only when

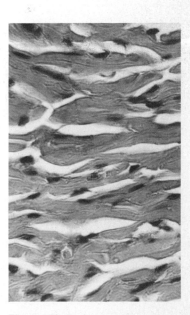

Figure 13–2 Involuntary or smooth muscle cells taken from the stomach wall of a cat.

A

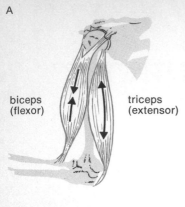

biceps
(flexor)

triceps
(extensor)

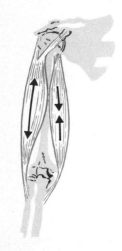

B

Figure 13–3 The biceps and triceps of the upper arm form an antagonistic pair of muscles; the contraction of the biceps raises the lower arm, and the contraction of the triceps lowers it.

it shortens, there is generally another muscle working across the joint on the opposite side. When this muscle contracts it increases the angle at the joint or extends the two bones. The muscles of such a pair are called **antagonists**, and in this case are the flexor and the extensor of the joint in question. These actions become clear if you examine your own biceps on the front of your upper arm, and triceps on the back of your upper arm (Fig. 13–3). They pull across the elbow joint. Which muscle becomes tense and hard when you lift a heavy object? Which hardens when you do a push-up?

The mechanics of these actions are relatively simple and obvious. Usually there are many muscles at each joint, some pulling in the same or a similar direction. In contrast to antagonists, these are known as **synergist muscles**. The forearm and wrist can be rotated in both directions as well as flexed and extended. These complex motions each have their synergistic and antagonistic sets of muscles. Remember that when one set of muscles contracts, its antagonistic group *must* relax. Otherwise movement of any limb would be impossible.

The dynamics of contraction

Even the most cursory consideration of animal behavior should impress upon us the great variety of activities of which muscles are capable. Certain muscles of sea anemones require up to four minutes to contract completely; midges and mosquitoes flap their wings up to 1,000 times a second, requiring their wing muscles to contract and relax within about a millisecond. Muscles moving the eyeball in mammals require only a few milliseconds in order to contract.

If the tendons on both ends of a muscle are clamped to fixed supports and the muscle is stimulated to contract, it cannot shorten appreciably and can only develop tension. Under such conditions the contraction is called **isometric**. When made to contract isometrically, muscles develop maximum tension when their ends are held apart at a distance normal for this muscle in the body (rest length). If a muscle is to do work by changing the angle at its joint and lifting a load, it must shorten. When the muscle shortens against a light and constant load, its contraction is called **isotonic**. In so doing it develops just enough tension to move the load. Since loads have inertia that resists the initial acceleration imposed by the contraction, when moving a heavy load a muscle develops more tension and shortens more slowly at first. This means that most body movements are produced by a combination of isometric and isotonic contraction.

Gravity acting on our body mass is the main force opposing the extensor muscles of our legs as we stand or crouch motionless. Therefore, these muscles are continually doing work against gravity by sustaining a steady level of partial shortening. This is called **tonic contraction**, during which hundreds of thousands of separate muscle fibers are twitching. Since they are twitching out of step with one another the contraction seems to be smooth. If you should jump from a crouching position, requiring a maximum but brief contraction of the extensors, the twitching of each individual fiber increases in frequency, more fibers become active, and all shorten more or less in step. This is called a **phasic contraction**.

Most vertebrate voluntary muscles cannot sustain continuous maximum tension for very long. They fatigue and require rest periods. This is not the case with certain involuntary muscles, such as the smooth muscle cells that regulate the diameter of small blood vessels and sustain the blood pressure. They maintain a degree of tonus throughout life. Another example is the muscle that holds shut the shells of clams, mussels, and oysters. It can close the shell in a second or so and then hold it shut against great tension for hours and days. The effect reminds one of the action of a vise and the muscle is known as **catch muscle**; its mechanism is only just beginning to be understood.

Contraction patterns in voluntary muscle

In the preceding chapter we saw how an action potential propagates down a motor axon and releases small packets of Ach at its terminal. The Ach diffuses across the synaptic cleft at the motor endplate and depolarizes the adjacent plasma membrane of the muscle fibers. The local potential (e.p.p.) that results triggers a muscle action potential that sweeps the length of the muscle plasma membrane and initiates a brief shortening, or twitch, of the fiber.

This is typical of the commonest pattern in vertebrate voluntary muscles. Each muscle may contain from hundreds to tens of thousands of fibers according to its size. Each motor axon branches and forms 10 to 100 muscle fibers and hence controls the contraction of this group as a unit. The motor neuron and the muscle fibers under its control, are called a **motor unit** (Fig. 13–4). Each motor unit of perhaps 100 or more making up the muscle can be independently thrown into a series of twitches. This produces various grades of smooth contraction in the muscle as a whole, since the individual motor units can be activated separately and are mostly out of step with one another. If the muscle fibers are all stimulated so that they twitch at maximal frequency and simultaneously the maximal contraction is called a **tetanus**.

There are many variations on this pattern. Some muscles require a succession of stimuli and consequent action potentials to initiate contraction. Contraction may be smoothly graded according to the frequency with which stimuli are given. In Chapter 11 you found how crustacean and insect muscle fibers may each be supplied by several separate motor axons, each axon forming synapses at many points along the surface of the fiber. Therefore, depolarization may be distributed over the fiber via a nerve impulse rather than through a propagated muscle action potential. Each of these separate axons may branch to all the fibers composing a muscle instead of to only a small group, as in the vertebrate motor unit. Contraction patterns can be very complicated. Stimulation of one type of motor axon can cause a twitch of the whole muscle, while others work only through summation of action potentials and cause graded contraction. Still other motor fibers have an inhibitory effect, their action potentials eliminating any contraction in progress.

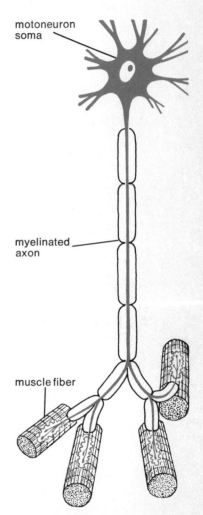

motoneuron soma

myelinated axon

muscle fiber

Figure 13–4 A motor unit of vertebrate skeletal muscle consists of a motoneuron and all the muscle fibers it innervates. When an action potential travels down the motoneuron, it causes all the muscle fibers in the motor unit to twitch.

How a muscle contracts

Before discussing how patterns of muscle contraction are controlled by the nervous system, we must consider how an action potential sweeping over the plasma membrane causes the fiber to shorten and do work. How is an electrical change transformed into a mechanical change? Hundreds of research workers are concerned with this question, and though it may seem far from the problems of animal behavior recent discoveries are both interesting and basic to biology. The search for answers has been largely directed at structural details of muscle as revealed by the light microscope, the electron microscope, and X-ray diffraction. The protein and other constituents of muscle fibers have been isolated and then recombined in the hope of simulating conditions in living muscle.

We have seen that the performance of muscle cells suggests that there are two classes—voluntary and involuntary. The microscopic appearance of muscle cells suggested two other classes—**smooth** and **striated**. However neither classification satisfactorily subdivides the wide range of muscle function and structure found among vertebrate and invertebrate animals.

Smooth muscle in vertebrates mainly surrounds hollow internal organs such as the digestive tract, blood vessels, and the ducts of excretory and reproductive organs and glands. It belongs, therefore, to the group of involuntary muscles. Smooth muscle is composed of long, spindle-shaped cells each containing a single nucleus and traversed by fine thread-like filaments running longitudinally through the cytoplasm (Fig. 13–2). Most vertebrate smooth muscle cells are only a few tenths of a millimeter in length, but certain invertebrate muscle cells may reach a length of several centimeters.

As we have seen, vertebrate voluntary or skeletal muscle, which is striated, is made of much larger and longer cylindrical cells called muscle fibers (Fig. 13–5). Each vertebrate muscle fiber contains many nuclei lying just under its plasma membrane. The main body of the fiber is packed with parallel filaments called **myofibrils**. Each myofibril in a muscle fiber 50 to 100 micrometers in diameter has a diameter of about 1 or 2 micrometers (Fig. 13–6). Under the light microscope each myofibril is made up of regularly repeating

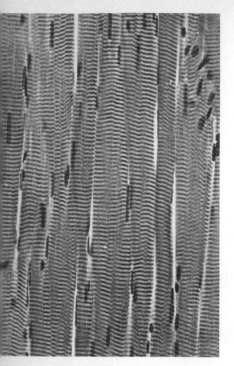

Figure 13–5 Striation and the general arrangement of fibers are revealed in this photomicrograph of striated muscle.

Figure 13–6. The organization of vertebrate skeletal muscle.

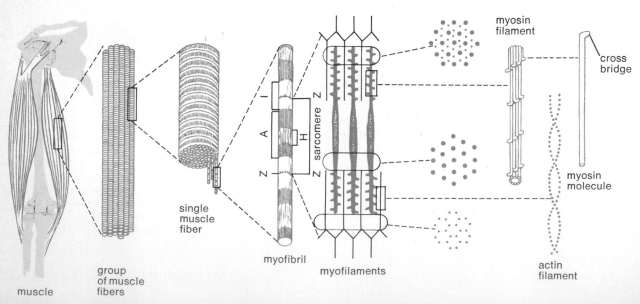

dark and light regions 3 to 4 micrometers apart. The dark and light regions repeat throughout the length of the myofibril and are accurately aligned with those in adjacent myofibrils of the muscle fiber. This gives the appearance of dark and light bands or stripes running across the fiber, and is the basis for the term striated muscle.

Let us consider a striated myofibril in a fiber of skeletal muscle. Its alternating dark and light bands suggest a high degree of fine organization, but this can be discerned only dimly through the light microscope. The introduction of the electron microscope made it possible to see a whole new level of fine detail and to understand how a muscle might contract.

Each myofibril contains a large number of parallel longitudinal **myofilaments**. These are intermixed and of two kinds—thick and thin (Fig. 13–6). The two kinds of filaments are separated longitudinally into groups by dark transverse bands called the **Z lines**. The distance between adjacent Z lines along the fibril is usually about 3 to 4 micrometers, and the repeating unit between two Z lines is called a **sarcomere**. Thus, a myofibril can be regarded as a string of sarcomeres connected end-to-end. The repeating sarcomeres are the ultimate units of contraction and correspond to the dark and light bands seen with the light microscope.

Within each sarcomere the thick and thin filaments are highly ordered. Figure 13–7 shows that the thin filaments appear to be attached to each Z line. Their other ends come to a stop before they touch the array of thin filaments attached to the next Z line. The thick filaments extend across the space between the free ends of the thin filaments which they overlap. The thick filaments do not, however, reach the Z line at either end of the sarcomere.

Biochemical analysis of myofibrils has shown that they contain mainly two proteins that are in the form of long chain molecules—**actin** and **myosin**, which can be extracted separately from myofibrils. If actin alone is extracted, we find that the fine filaments and sometimes the Z line disappear from the fibril; when myosin is extracted, the thick filaments are removed. These and other experiments suggest that the thin filaments are composed of actin and the thick filaments of myosin.

A glance at the diagram of Fig. 13–6 shows that a sarcomere is composed of three zones. The area of thin filaments alone and the Z line which it shares with the next sarcomere are known as the **I band**. In the relaxed state the thin filaments do not meet in the center of the sarcomere and there is a region bridged only by the thick filaments of myosin. This is the **H zone**. Between the I band and H zone there is a third region where actin and myosin filaments overlap. The electron micrographs of Figs. 13–7 and 13–8 show that in this region of overlap there is a hexagonal organization, each myosin filament being surrounded by six actin filaments. A closer look at the longitudinal section of Figure 13–7 shows that many minute projections or cross bridges extend from each myosin filament and contact the surrounding actin filaments.

Comparisons of electron micrographs made of muscle which is in contracted, resting length, and stretched states show, as might be expected, that each sarcomere varies from short and fat to long and thin. The distance between

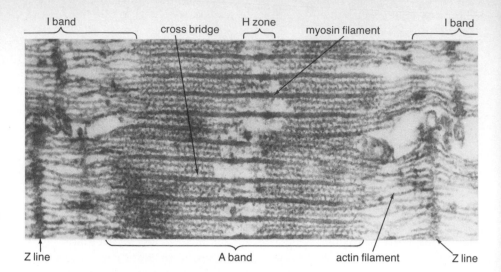

I band   cross bridge   H zone   myosin filament   I band

Z line   A band   actin filament   Z line

Figure 13–7 In this electron micrograph of muscle tissue, the cross bridges between the thick and thin filaments are clearly visible.

Figure 13–8 In this cross section of the A band region of skeletal muscle, the large, dark, circular areas are mitochondria. There are two sizes of small dots throughout. The larger of these are the thick filaments, and each is surrounded by about six smaller dots, the thin filaments.

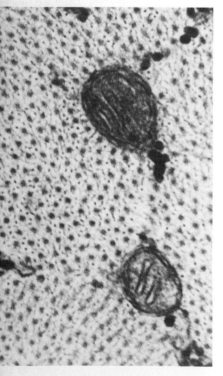

the Z lines increases but the length of the thick and thin filaments does not. Therefore, the thick and thin filaments must slide past each other during the length change, maximum overlap taking place during maximum shortening when the ends of the thin filaments meet and the H zone disappears. At this point, then, there will be a maximum number of cross bridges extending from the myosin to the surrounding actin filaments.

Energy and sliding filaments

The sliding filament concept of muscle contraction proposes that the force inducing a muscle to shorten is generated by the stepwise formation of **cross bridges** between myosin and actin filaments. This causes the two sets of filaments to slide past each other, pulling the actin filaments toward the center of the sarcomere and decreasing the distance between the Z lines (Fig. 13–9). Then the H zone becomes smaller and may disappear as the inner ends of the thin filaments approach each other. When the muscle is passively stretched, the H zone becomes wider as the thin filaments are pulled out from among the array of thin filaments. The distance moved by the Z lines of a single sarcomere is minute, but since thousands are connected in series over the length of each myofibril, these distances add up to a considerable overall change in length. Since thousands of myofibrils lie in parallel in a single muscle fiber, their combined exerted force is also considerable.

When pure actin and myosin are extracted from muscles and then recombined in a suitable medium they form a compound called **actomyosin**. If actomyosin is formed into fine strands, and a suitable chemical source of energy is added, the strands can be made to shorten. This concept may explain the mechanics of muscle contraction, but it poses several important questions. For example, during muscle shortening work is done. Work requires an energy source. How does expenditure of chemical energy cause the "stepping" of cross bridges from the myosin filaments along the actin filaments and the formation of new bridges so that the two slide past each other?

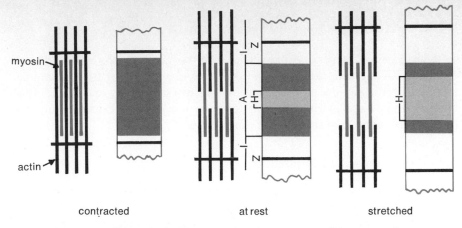

myosin

actin

contracted   at rest   stretched

Figure 13–9 The thick and thin filaments of each sarcomere slide past each other as shown here when muscle fibers contract and stretch. Compare this illustration with Figs. 13–7 and 13–8.

It is not yet entirely clear how chemical energy is mobilized from chemical bonds and transformed into active "stepping" at the cross bridges so as to pull the actin and myosin arrays toward and among one another. The ultimate and almost universal chemical source of energy for cells is **adenosine triphosphate (ATP)**. ATP readily splits off its terminal high-energy phosphate group (Fig. 18–13). This a reaction that releases energy and heat. If man-made threads of artificially extracted actin and myosin are extruded into a special solution and then ATP is added, the threads shorten and the terminal phosphate group of the ATP is split off. An enzyme on the myosin is thought to promote explosive but very local splitting of the phosphate bond and the transfer of some of the energy released to the cross bridges. Heat production indicative of such a reaction occurs very early in contraction and precedes any actual shortening of a muscle fiber. This is called the **active state.**

How the energy released from ATP causes "stepping" of the cross bridges is very unclear. The actin filaments are thought to have active sites at regular intervals along their length to which the myosin bridges can attach. ATP splitting is thought to cause the bridges to detach from one active site and reattach to the next. At the same time each bridge is thought to change its shape from a stretched-out form to a coiled form, thus pulling the active site on the actin toward its base on the myosin. The combined coiling of the cross bridges pulls the actin filament toward the center of the sarcomere. The ATP-splitting enzyme then releases more energy from ATP, causing the bridge to break, uncoil, and reattach to the next active site on the actin filament. These minute events are repeated a multitude of times on a multitude of actin–myosin sites in each sarcomere, drawing the Z lines closer together. The cross bridges have been compared to the hands of a group of men pulling on a rope. All hands are pulling simultaneously and exerting maximum tension. The faster the rope moves, however, the more frequently hands must change in position and the fewer the number actually pulling at any instant. A muscle exerts maximum tension when it contracts isometrically. The faster it shortens when contracting isotonically, the less tension it is able to exert.

THE NERVOUS CONTROL OF MOVEMENT

In the preceding chapter and the first part of this one, you were exposed to a few "bits" of the behavioral mechanism. Now our task is to try to assemble them and get some idea how the mechanism works. This is one of the most important questions in biology today; here we can hope to examine only one or two small corners of the gigantic jigsaw puzzle.

Spinal reflexes and body posture

We spend most of our waking lives compensating for the force of gravity. Were this not so we would sink in a heap to the ground. A partial exception occurs when we are swimming; a complete exception is an astronaut weightless in orbit. This means that the extensor muscles of our legs (all four legs in four-footed animals), and to a lesser extent our back and neck muscles, are in a state of partial contraction that exactly counteracts our body weight. Anything that tends to upset our balance is immediately compensated for. If we suddenly lift a heavy object, or if we are suddenly pushed to one side, or if we suddenly step on a sharp object and are forced to stand on one leg, we automatically and unconsciously adjust our muscles and retain our balance.

The neural mechanisms that regulate posture are many and complex. They were first outlined near the beginning of this century by the great British neurophysiologist Sir Charles Sherrington. The neuron systems that control posture reside mainly in the brain stem and spinal cord. These systems work automatically while we are awake, although they can be overridden by conscious control; that is, we are able to decide whether to use the same set of muscles to flop on the ground or to spring into the air. The automatic regulation of posture is an excellent example of negative feedback. Posture is maintained by varying the tension developed in anti-gravity muscles so as to keep their lengths constant under varying loads. This task of regulation is typical of dozens performed in the living body.

THE STRETCH REFLEX: In the knee-jerk reflex a sharp tap on the tendon just below the knee causes a person's free-hanging lower leg to kick out. The tendon involved, called the **patellar tendon**, is part of the quadriceps muscle group, the main extensor of the knee joint (Fig. 13–10). The tap briefly stretches the tendon and muscle, and the quadriceps responds after a short interval with a quick twitch. The quadriceps is a major postural muscle whose function in a standing person is to keep the knee extended against gravity in spite of perturbations such as changing loads. The quadriceps must contain sensors of length change so that any length increase is fed back to excite its motoneurons in the spinal cord and cause added contraction. The knee-jerk reflex is an example of a situation in which the correction of an "error" involves a delay in feedback. The brief stretch of the muscle caused by a tap

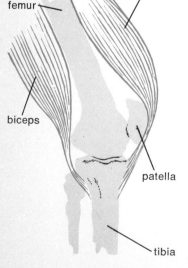

Figure 13–10 The quadriceps and biceps forming the antagonistic pair of muscles at the knee joint.

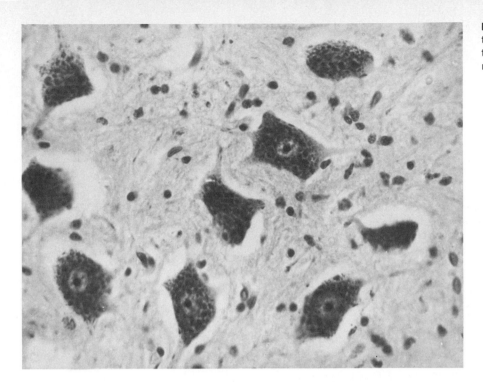

on the tendon is over before the muscle can compensate by added contraction. Therefore, the action tends to overshoot rather than exactly compensate for the momentary stretch.

What are the neural circuits forming this feedback loop? We shall see how they work by looking at one of the quadriceps' motoneurons and its motor unit.

The soma or cell body of the motoneuron lies together with hundreds like it in the **gray** (unmyelinated) **matter** of the **anterior** (or ventral) **horn** of the spinal cord in the lumbar region (Fig. 13–11). Its soma and dendrites are encrusted with hundreds of **synaptic knobs** formed by the axons belonging to sensory and interneurons. Its axon rises from a special elevation, the **axon hillock**. After leaving the axon hillock and entering the **white matter** of the spinal cord, the motor axon assumes a myelin sheath. In Chapter 11 we saw how myelin speeds spike conduction. The axon then passes out of the spinal cord by a **ventral** (or anterior) **spinal root** which joins others to form the **sciatic nerve**. The sciatic nerve runs down the leg and gives off branches to its muscles. The axon of our motoneuron joins one of these branches to the quadriceps muscles and finally distributes twigs to the muscle fibers composing its motor unit. The axon extends one to two feet from the soma, and is able to conduct impulses at a velocity of about 300 feet per second. This kind of motor neuron is called an **alpha efferent**.

Hundreds of alpha efferents and their attendant muscle fibers provide the main force in contraction and thus correspond to the energy source described above. Externally imposed loads that tend to change the length of the partially contracted muscle correspond to the source of perturbations. The sensors are

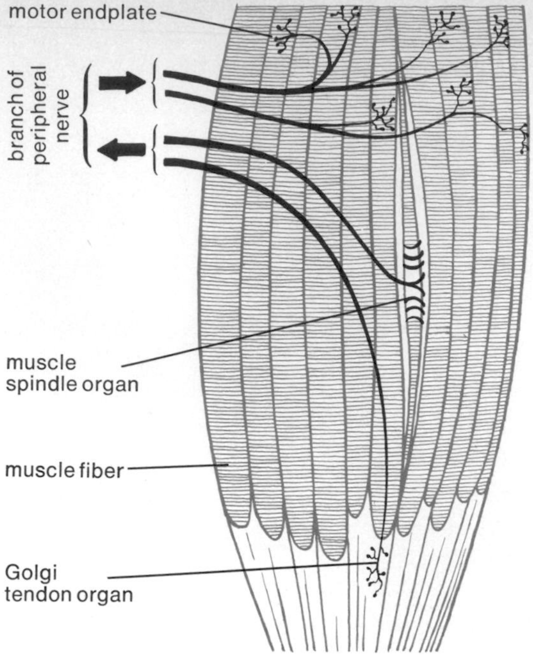

Figure 13–12 The diagram below shows a muscle spindle organ, which contains two intrafusal fibers inside a sheath of connective tissue. These stretch receptors are scattered through the body of the muscle between normal extrafusal muscle fibers. Parts of three extrafusal fibers are shown. The diagram at right shows striated muscle and part of its nerve supply, revealing the relationship of muscle spindle organ and Golgi tendon organ to the rest of the muscle. Notice that the spindle organ is in parallel with the rest of the fibers, but that the Golgi organ is in series with the muscle fibers.

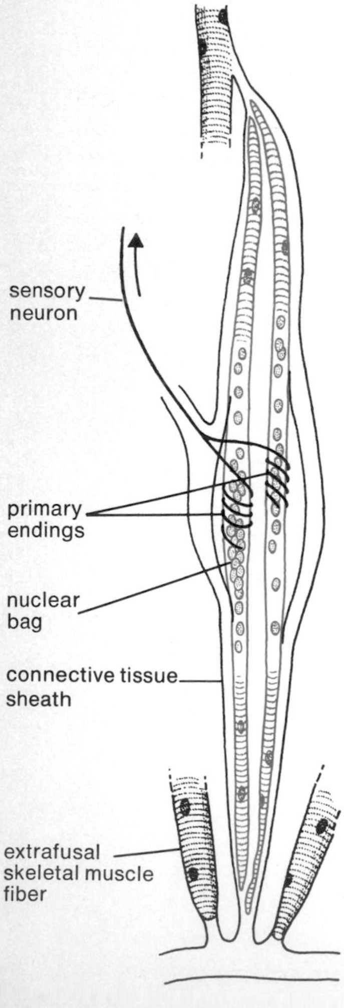

highly modified bundles of small-diameter muscle fibers called **muscle spindle organs** (Fig. 13–12).

Muscle spindle organs belong to the class of sense organs called **proprioceptors** (*proprius* means "one's own," literally "self detectors"). They detect changes in the length of the muscle. Each spindle organ is composed of up to a dozen modified muscle fibers called **intrafusal fibers** enclosed in a sheath of connective tissue. Spindle organs are scattered throughout the muscle and lie in parallel with the much larger and more numerous muscle fibers (called **extrafusal fibers**) that belong to the motor units of the alpha efferents and do most of the work of contraction. Each spindle is attached to a tendon at one end and either to one of the extrafusal fibers or to the tendon at the other end of the muscle.

The intrafusal fibers are peculiar in that their central or equatorial portions have lost their striations and are non-contractile. These non-contractile but elastic portions are enclosed in a swollen, spindle-shaped region called the **nuclear bag** and are surrounded by a network of sensory terminations. These sensory terminations belong to a sensory axon that rejoins the sciatic nerve and returns to the spinal cord via a dorsal spinal root.

The spindle organs act as sensors of muscle length in the following way. When the muscle is passively stretched by any force tending to flex the knee joint, the spindles tend to elongate together with the extrafusal fibers. This stretching of the intrafusal fibers tends to elongate the nuclear bag region and the enclosed sensory terminations, causing an increase in the frequency of action potentials that propagate inward over the sensory axon and into the spinal cord. This proprioceptor is non-adapting; that is, the frequency of spikes is sustained during a steady stretch and is proportional to the degree of stretch. On reaching the spinal cord one branch of the proprioceptive axon forms excitatory synapses with the alpha motoneurons that supply the extrafusal fibers of the extensor muscle. Another branch of the proprioceptor travels up the spinal cord to the brain (Fig. 13–13).

This synapse with the alpha motoneurons completes the feedback loop and explains the knee jerk. The tap on the patellar tendon briefly stretches the quadriceps and its spindle organs. This increases the firing rate of the contained sensory endings and there is greater temporal summation of their spikes at the excitatory synapses with alpha motoneurons. Hence there is greater contraction of the extrafusal fibers and shortening of the whole muscle.

The feedback delay, which causes the knee jerk, is minimized by rapid spike conduction both in the afferent or sensory fibers from the spindle organs and in the efferent or motor fibers from the alpha motoneurons. Furthermore this delay, which as we have seen is a source of error in a feedback system, is reduced by there being only one central synapse between the incoming sensory impulses and the outgoing motor impulses. The stretch reflex is therefore the simplest of all possible spinal reflexes, being a monosynaptic reflex.

THE CLASP-KNIFE REFLEX: This reflex protects a muscle from an overload, that is, against damage when the stretch reflex directs it to sustain constant length against an external load too heavy to bear without tearing the muscle or its ligament. The tendon attaching the muscle to the lower leg just below the knee contains proprioceptors called **Golgi tendon organs** (Fig. 13–14). Golgi tendon receptors discharge sensory impulses into the spinal cord with increasing frequency as the stretch on the tendon begins to approach its breaking point. These Golgi tendon impulses excite interneurons in the spinal cord, and the interneurons form inhibitory synapses on the alpha motoneurons (Fig. 13–14). An increase in the frequency of these inhibitory impulses may eventually override ongoing excitation generated at other synapses, causing the alpha motoneurons to stop generating motor spikes down their axons. Consequently, the muscle suddenly relaxes when the breaking point of its tendon is approached. This mechanism is called a **clasp-knife reflex** by analogy. When you open a clasp knife, the blade resists your efforts up to a point, but then suddenly it springs open.

We now have two classes of synapse converging on the alpha motoneurons —excitatory synapses from the spindle proprioceptors and inhibitory synapses from the Golgi tendon organs.

THE FLEXION REFLEX: When you step barefooted on a thumbtack your leg suddenly flexes before you have time to say "Ouch!" The action is an automatic spinal reflex in response to pain endings stimulated in the foot. The pain endings send trains of spikes along fast pain fibers to the spinal cord. On reaching the grey matter these pain fibers form several kinds of connections with interneurons. One set of interneurons excites the flexor motoneurons and causes the flexor muscles to contract. Another set of interneurons forms inhibitory synapses with the extensor motoneurons. Their effect is to override any ongoing excitatory activity and allow the powerful extensor muscles of the leg to relax. Another set of interneurons activated by the pain fibers forms tracts going to the brain, bringing a sense of pain into consciousness (Fig.

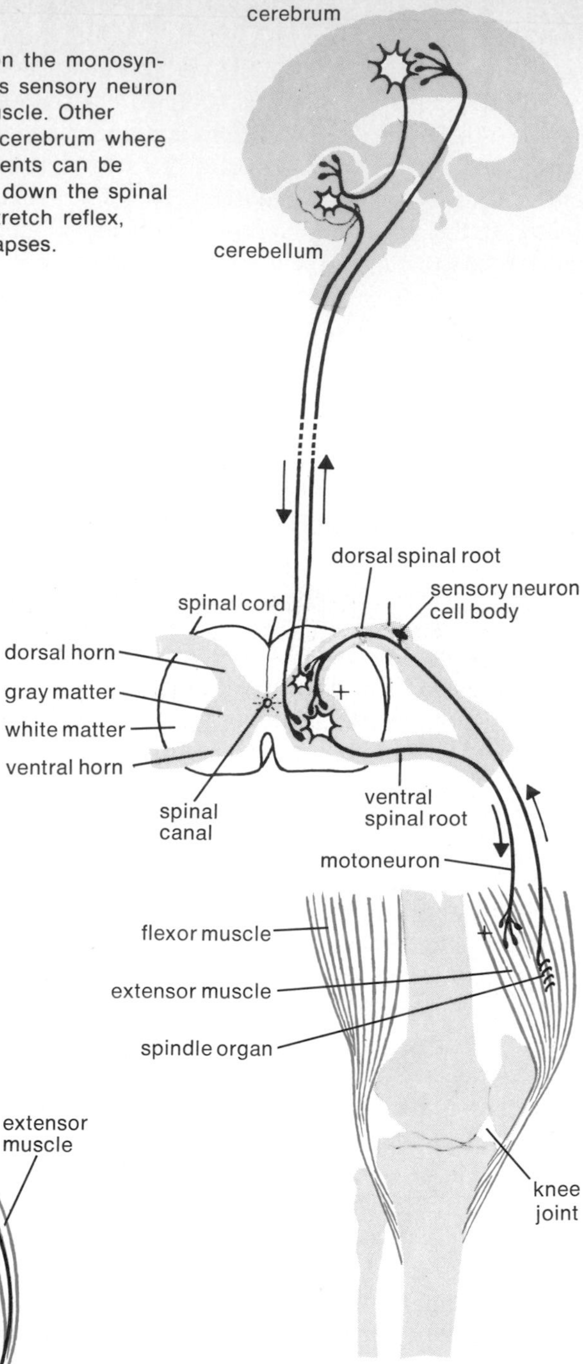

Figure 13–13 The stretch reflex depends on the monosynaptic pathway formed by the spindle organ's sensory neuron with motoneurons to the same extensor muscle. Other sensory impulses travel up the cord to the cerebrum where we become conscious of the reflex. Movements can be consciously controlled by impulses coming down the spinal cord. These pathways are not part of the stretch reflex, however. Plus signs indicate excitatory synapses.

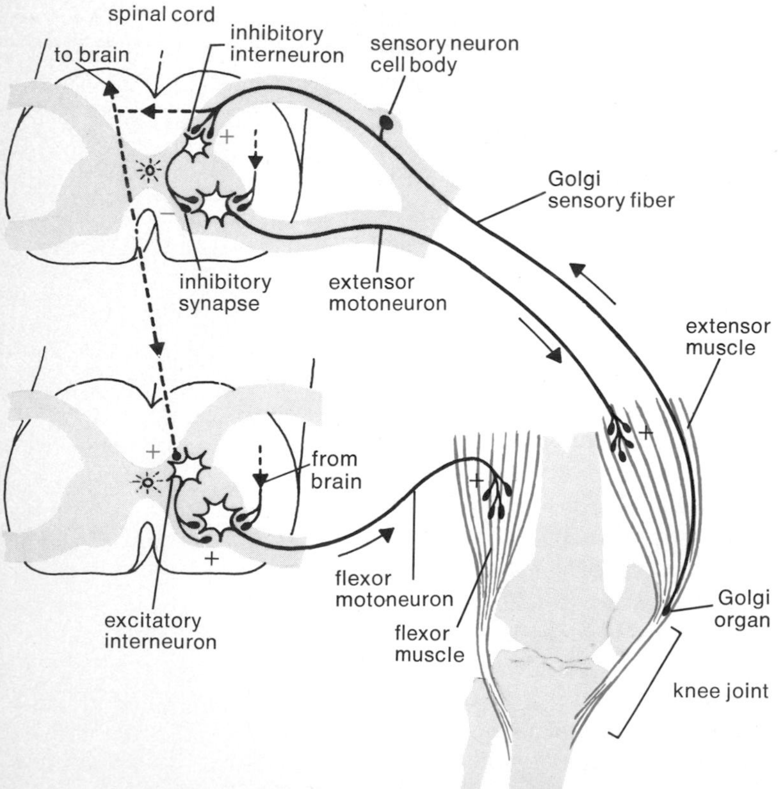

Figure 13–14 In the clasp-knife reflex, an inhibitory interneuron interposed between the sensory nerve and the extensor motoneuron causes the extensor to relax when the Golgi organ is stimulated. Impulses also travel via an excitatory interneuron to the flexor motoneuron of the same joint. These impulses cause the flexor to contract and bend the joint. Excitatory synapses are indicated by a +, inhibitory synapses by a −.

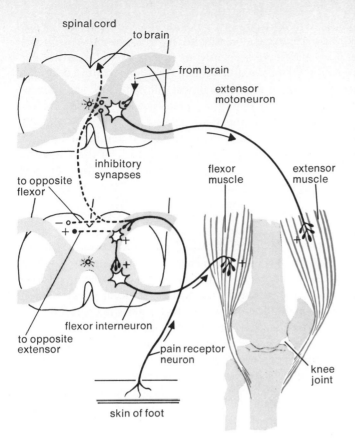

spinal cord
to brain
from brain
extensor motoneuron
inhibitory synapses
flexor muscle
extensor muscle
to opposite flexor
to opposite extensor
flexor interneuron
pain receptor neuron
knee joint
skin of foot

Figure 13–15 The flexion reflex is initiated by pain receptors in the skin and causes a rapid withdrawal of the foot from a painful stimulus. At the same time, extensor motoneurons in the opposite leg are excited by the crossed extensor reflex which prepares this leg to assume the full weight of the body. Excitatory synapses are indicated by a +, inhibitory synapses by a −.

13–15). If we return our attention to the motoneurons of the quadriceps, we see that the flexion reflex adds another class of inhibitory synapses to their input.

THE CROSSED EXTENSION REFLEX: If you can think calmly about what you do after stepping on a thumbtack, you realize that a fairly complicated action has been carried out. We have already mentioned simultaneous excitation of the flexor motoneurons of the injured foot by the pain fibers. Ordinarily, you do not fall down when you step on a tack, because all your weight suddenly is transferred to the other foot. This means that the extensor motoneurons of the uninjured foot must have suddenly received extra excitation in order to carry the additional load. Therefore, another set of interneurons excited by the pain fibers must cross to the opposite side of the spinal cord and form excitatory synapses with the opposite extensor motoneurons (Fig. 13–15). This is called the **crossed extension reflex** and adds another class of excitatory synapses on each extensor motoneuron in addition to the three—one excitatory and two inhibitory—already mentioned.

DESCENDING PATHWAYS: In addition to these local synaptic inputs, motoneurons in the spinal cord receive synapses from a number of tracts that descend the spinal cord from the brain. These tracts have both excitatory and inhibitory effects. For instance, we can command "at will" the extensor muscle to contract or relax. If we anticipate a painful stimulus to the foot we can partially or completely suppress the flexion reflex. Rhythmic contractions and relaxations can be commanded to alternate almost automatically, as when we walk or run. Descending pathways from the organs sensing gravity and displacement in the inner ear and from the visual system form synapses on the spinal motoneurons, so that the muscles balance each other in maintaining posture in relation to gravity and visible surroundings. Each of these assorted descending pathways terminates in excitatory or inhibitory synapses on each of the spinal motoneurons (Fig. 13–16).

The "final common path"

Sir Charles Sherrington chose this term to describe a motoneuron because it receives and integrates various synaptic influences impinging on its dendrites and soma and then expresses the result as a train of spikes transmitted down its axon to its attendant muscle fibers. Fifty years later, Sir John Eccles demonstrated the mechanism of this integration by inserting a glass micropipette into the spinal cord of an anesthetized cat and penetrating the soma of a single spinal motoneuron. It was then a matter of individually stimulating various axons of muscle spindle proprioceptors, Golgi tendon organs, or pain endings, and determining how they affected the membrane potential.

The soma of an inactive motoneuron has a membrane potential similar to that of its axon, commonly about 60 millivolts positive on the outside. Impulses arriving over a presynaptic pathway known to be excitatory cause transient local depolarizations called **excitatory postsynaptic potentials** (e.p.s.p.'s). The soma membrane is electrically inexcitable, so individual e.p.s.p.'s spread over neighboring membrane tissue decrementally with time constants and space constants characteristic of the membrane. This means that individual e.p.s.p.'s can summate in time if they follow one another closely. Also, they can summate in space; that is, an e.p.s.p. generated at a synapse at one point on the soma or dendrites can add its decrementally spreading depolarization to that generated at a neighboring synapse within the area of membrane where the spatial effects of the two e.p.s.p.'s overlap. Thus, there can be a temporal summation of e.p.s.p.'s occurring close together in time as well as spatial summation of e.p.s.p.'s occurring close together in space. Like the endplate potential in muscle, motoneuron e.p.s.p.'s appear to be mediated by Ach released from the presynaptic ending. The Ach causes a general increase in the ion permeability of the postsynaptic membrane. This permeability is then terminated by AchE. It is likely that synaptic endings at some points on the postsynaptic membrane are more influential in bringing about membrane depolarization than endings at other points.

Stimulation of a sensory pathway known to produce inhibition of the extensor motoneurons causes transient hyperpolarizations of the soma called **inhibitory postsynaptic potentials** (i.p.s.p.'s). The soma membrane potential then increases briefly by a few millivolts. This hyperpolarization seems to be brought about by an increase in the specific conductance of the membrane to

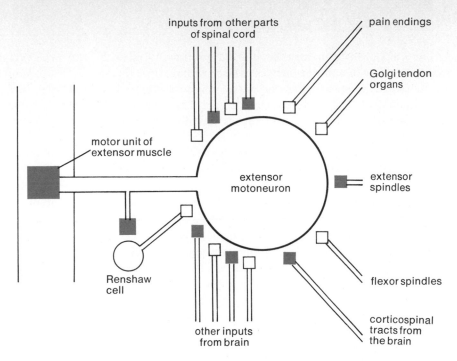

inputs from other parts
of spinal cord

pain endings

Golgi tendon
organs

motor unit of
extensor muscle

extensor
motoneuron

extensor
spindles

Renshaw
cell

flexor spindles

other inputs
from brain

corticospinal
tracts from
the brain

Figure 13–16 The "final common path": A selection of synaptic inputs to one motor unit of the extensor motor system of the legs is shown. Colored squares represent excitatory endings; open squares represent inhibitory endings. (AFTER K. ROEDER)

K^+ and Cl^- ions, bringing it closer to the equilibrium potential for these ions. I.p.s.p.'s can also sum, both spatially and temporally, with one another, and their effects are balanced against the combined effects of current e.p.s.p.'s. If the result adds up to a critical depolarization of the soma near a special elevation of the axon known as the axon hillock, one or more spikes propagate off down the electrically excitable axon. The hyperpolarization produced at inhibitory synapses is also thought to be chemically mediated.

We should now try to visualize a waxing and waning "shower" of impulses arriving at the hundreds of synaptic knobs encrusting the soma and dendrites of each motoneuron. Excitatory potentials are being weighed continuously against inhibitory potentials, and if the consensus at any instant causes critical depolarization at the root of the axon, then one or more spikes are sent on their way to the muscle fibers. Perhaps we can see now why Sherrington called the motoneuron the "final common path."

But if we are going to retain any perspective about behavior mechanisms, we must recall that each of the major postural muscles is represented by hundreds of motoneurons in the spinal cord, and that posture is regulated against external disturbances by dozens of muscles, each playing some slightly different mechanical role. All that these spinal mechanisms have explained is how an animal can remain standing upright in the presence of gravity and when its stance is disturbed by an injurious stimulus to one of its feet. It is time for us to examine other aspects of the behavioral mechanism.

SPONTANEOUS ACTIVITY

At one time it was generally thought that even complex behavioral acts were merely a series of reflexes such as those we have just discussed. They were considered to be stereotyped automatic responses to particular stimuli, and thus qualitatively little different from a knee jerk. This view is understandable in the light of the beautiful mechanisms revealed by the work of Sherrington and Eccles.

But then what makes an animal behave? Why does a bird start to sing and continue for long periods. One could argue from the reflex point of view that if an animal were deprived of all stimuli it would do nothing. We are unable to answer this question because we cannot produce a "no stimulus" situation, but we strongly suspect that this would not be the case. Many neurons, muscle cells, even whole organs show spontaneous activity, that is, rhythmic spikes or muscle contractions under conditions when, so far as we can tell, they are being deprived of all stimuli from the outside. They must be intrinsically unstable, expending their metabolic energy in rhythmic pulses of activity much as a watch continues to tick so long as energy is stored in its mainspring. Vertebrate heartbeat is perhaps the best known example; its rhythmic contractions continue throughout life and originate in the muscle fibers of the heart itself rather than depending on incoming nerve impulses. Let us consider some other examples in somewhat more detail.

Spontaneous nerve activity and behavior

Generally animals are doing something, and much of the time it is not obvious that they are reacting to stimuli. We suspect that some of this activity may be due to spontaneous discharges of neurons or neuron complexes somewhere in their nervous systems, but direct evidence of this is hard to obtain. There are, however, two experiments on insects that demonstrate fairly conclusively that the spontaneous activity of neurons in the central nervous system generates behavior patterns of some significance in survival.

The power of flight has played a major role in the evolution of insects. It distributes insect species over wide areas and enables them to find food and mates and to evade the attacks of predators. Flapping the wings up and down requires accurate coordination of two sets of antagonistic muscles in a fixed rhythm. This coordination is carried out in ganglia of the thorax through the interaction of two sets of motoneurons. Wing flapping can be started in most cases simply by lifting the insect so that its feet lose contact with the ground.

The late Donald Wilson recorded the activity of these motoneurons in locusts suspended from supports and in continuous stationary flight. He then proceeded to remove all proprioceptors that were suspected of reflexively exciting the flight motoneurons after the manner we have discussed in connection with the spinal reflexes of vertebrates. Finally he was left with the thoracic ganglia with all their nerves cut and thus completely isolated from any sensory input. The isolated motoneurons continued to generate a coordinated rhythm of spikes, though at a somewhat slower frequency.

The praying mantis, a carnivorous insect, is sometimes cannibalistic. When

A

B

C

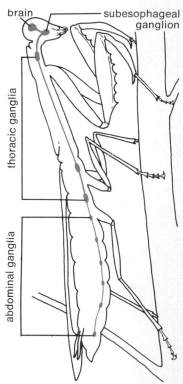

brain   subesophageal ganglion

thoracic ganglia

abdominal ganglia

Figure 13-17 A: A pair of mantises copulating, during which the male has not been attacked. B: A female mantis in the act of consuming the head of the male, demonstrating the cannibalism associated with the sexual behavior of these insects. Even though the male is being eaten, its abdomen performs the bending movements of copulation and will continue to do so. C: The decapitated male is in the act of copulation, a remarkable adaptation made possible by the fact that the motor center controlling copulation is located not in the brain but in the last abdominal ganglion (see diagram) and normally receives inhibition from neurons in the head. Thus a decapitated male mantis is able to fertilize a female in spite of her cannibalistic behavior. (K. ROEDER)

hungry, the large female sometimes grabs an approaching male and begins to eat him before he has an opportunity to mount her and mate. This behavior is clearly unlikely to promote the survival of the species, but the male's nervous system is organized so as to allow him to copulate even after his head has been eaten. The last ganglion of the abdominal nerve cord contains the motor center that generates the copulatory movements, which require quite complex muscle coordinations. This center is normally inhibited by nerve centers in the head. When the head is removed the male mantis makes continuous attempts to copulate, irrespective of whether he is in contact with a female (Fig. 13–17).

The nerve impulse patterns responsible for these copulatory movements appear to be generated spontaneously in the motor center. If the whole central nervous system of a male mantis is isolated, as in Wilson's experiment, few motor spikes can be recorded from the central stumps of the nerves that originally supplied the muscles of the copulatory apparatus. If the ventral nerve cord is then severed to isolate the last abdominal ganglion from the rest of the ventral nerve cord, there is a gradual but sustained increase in the motor spikes coming down these nerves. The spikes are arranged in rhythmic bursts, and we must conclude that they would have produced rhythmic movements of the copulatory muscles if the motor nerves had not been cut.

There is also behavioral evidence that some complex actions arise spontaneously in the course of development and depend upon neither sensory input nor experience for their perfection. For example, salamander embryos are able to make coordinated swimming movements at a stage when their sensory neural pathways have not yet been established.

TRIGGERED ACTION SEQUENCES

A large number of the actions of animals, some of great complexity and duration, merely need to be triggered by an environmental stimulus such as a particular visible pattern, a special sound, or a specific odor. Such "trigger stimuli," also called sign stimuli, were discussed in detail in Chapter 9. It is as if the sign stimulus has switched on a neuronal tape recorder, and the prerecorded tape has to run to completion. Whether or not the prerecorded sequence takes place depends on the internal state of the animal, such as the level of certain hormones in the blood, the nutritional state, the time of day, and various environmental circumstances. We have only the barest information about the neural mechanisms of such triggered actions and will discuss only some of the simplest for purposes of illustration.

The flexion reflex can serve as an elementary example with which you are already familiar and for which we have at least some idea of the neural mechanisms. When you step on a tack, the pain in your foot triggers a coordinated sequence involving excitation and inhibition of muscle contractions in the injured leg. At the same time, the crossed extension reflex in the opposite leg enables you to maintain balance. The same signals are relayed up the spinal cord and, after passing several synapses reach a specific area of the brain (cerebral cortex). At that point you become aware of the pain. Being a protective reflex, the flexion reflex takes precedence over whatever you were doing when you stepped on the tack.

The act of swallowing is slightly more complex. It can be voluntary—that is, initiated by a command from the brain—or it can be started involuntarily by tactile stimulation or fluid in the pharynx. Swallowing requires that almost 20 different muscles be excited by their motoneurons to contract and relax at the right moment and in the right sequence. Experiments have shown that the proper pattern and sequence of action potentials in these neurons is determined entirely within the central nervous system and depends only on the initial trigger for its performance.

Even though today we have no idea how the complex action patterns described in Chapter 9 are assembled in terms of the activities of neurons, it appears that some interneurons are able to control and coordinate groups of motoneurons. These interneurons are called **command fibers**.

Donald Kennedy and his colleagues at Stanford University have studied command fibers that control movements of the abdomen and tail of crayfish. The abdomen is capable both of powerful flexions, or flips, that carry the crayfish out of danger, and of subtle changes in position and attitude. Different muscles are involved in flexion and extension at each of the five intersegmental joints. Kennedy mapped the central connections of motoneurons involved in these and other movements of the abdomen and its appendages. He found in the ventral nerve cord command interneurons which, when stimulated several times a second, activate groups of other interneurons and motoneurons whose action potentials bring about a specific movement. Repetitive stimulation of the command fiber controlling flexion of the abdomen, for example, activates five slow flexor motoneurons in each half-segment, inhibits slow extensor motoneurons, excites the inhibitory neurons to the extensors, and inhibits the inhibitory neurons to the flexor muscles. Each command fiber may initiate the proper discharge pattern in more than 200 motoneurons.

At the same time, some or all of these motor neurons may be under the control of another command fiber, that controlling extension, for example. When the extensor command fiber is excited, the motoneurons are activated in a reciprocal pattern. Each discharge pattern is specific for a given movement, and it has been called the **motor score** since it orchestrates the contraction of a collection of muscles much as a musical score brings harmony to the instruments of an orchestra.

It is important to remember that a command fiber only initiates a given motor score and does not control or alter the discharge patterns of the motor neurons. It is as if each command fiber bears a label such as "flex abdomen slowly" or "extend joint between second and third segments." In crayfish, for example, a command fiber has been found that produces a series of complex rhythmic movements of the tail appendages. The rhythm of movement is unaffected by changes in the frequency with which the command fiber is stimulated, showing that the command fiber merely triggers but does not arrange a particular motor score.

The possibility of conflicting or antagonistic behavior patterns being called forth simultaneously appears to be guarded against by a process akin to stimulus filtering, which was mentioned in Chapter 9. The spatial and temporal pattern of synaptic excitation of a command neuron, as well as the space and time constants of its postsynaptic membrane, dictates that only a certain specific input pattern will cause it to discharge. It is as if each command neuron had a special "Open Sesame"—the "door" of excitation opening only in response to a particular pattern of knocks.

UNSOLVED PROBLEMS

Command neurons can be likened to executives in a large organization—each has a specific task and sphere of control within the whole. If we pursued this analogy, which indeed may *not* be valid, we would expect to find some ultimate decision-making mechanism that determines which action pattern out of an animal's repertory is selected at a given moment or under given circumstances. For one of the most universal and intriguing characteristics of behavior is that whatever action an animal takes, it performs as a whole. Whether an animal is eating or grooming or fighting or mating or hunting, it gives the impression of acting as a unified mechanism with all its muscles directed to the task at hand. Put another way, we say that the animal's attention is occupied with or directed to one set of stimuli at a time.

Attention is a universal attribute of behavior that we are fully aware of in our own actions. For this reason we are apt to accept it as commonplace and not to be questioned. Yet it is really rather an extraordinary phenomenon. Of all the multitude of streams of sensory nerve impulses continuously impinging on the central nervous system from the various sense organs, only one type of input pattern is "in charge" of behavior at a given moment. The other streams of input impulses are still being generated by their sense organs, yet they seem to be blocked or shunted aside while one alone has precedence. A moment later another sensory pattern may have precedence and direct our actions. Only in sleep or unconsciousness are all the input streams partially or completely blocked from our attention.

We have no clue to the neurophysiological mechanism of attention. We do not know whether it is directed by an oligarchy of neurons or by some democratic consensus. Its mechanism is certainly one of the most intriguing questions in biology.

Other characteristics that are found throughout the animal kingdom and reach perfection in ourselves are learning and its correlate, memory. Very active attempts are being made to discover the neuronal mechanisms of information storage and retrieval, but no firm information is yet available. Learning and forgetting have time constants, and it is very tempting to compare them with the time constants we have met with in connection with local potentials such as the e.p.s.p. But the time constant of the e.p.s.p. is measured in milliseconds and that of learning and forgetting ranges from minutes to years. One can only suppose that certain neural circuits are facilitated through being used, but the nature of the facilitation remains a mystery.

These are only two of the unsolved problems in understanding the mechanisms of behavior. Others will present themselves as we consider how the outer world impinges on our central nervous system through the sense organs.

1 Compare the motor unit organization of vertebrate voluntary muscle with the way in which crustacean muscles (discussed in the previous chapter) are innervated.

2 Describe the sliding filament hypothesis of muscle contraction. What is the role of the cross bridges? Of ATP? What is meant by "active state"?

3 How is the stretch reflex a good example of a negative feedback system? Can you sketch its neural circuit?

4 In what sense does a motor neuron represent a final common path of nerve impulses?

5 Distinguish between reflexes, spontaneous activities, and triggered action sequences. Can you give an example of each?

6 What is a command neuron? How is its role similar to that of an executive in a corporation?

SELECTED READINGS

Aidley, D. J. *The Physiology of Excitable Cells*. Cambridge, England: Cambridge University Press, 1971. This textbook provides a more rigorous introduction to neurophysiology and includes a particularly good discussion of muscle physiology.

Ochs, Sidney. *Elements of Neurophysiology*. New York: John Wiley & Sons, 1965. Several chapters on reflexes in this book are especially interesting and relevant to our discussions in this chapter.

Kennedy, Donald. "Nerve Cells and Behavior," *American Scientist*, vol. 59, no. 1 (1971), pp. 36–42. A highly readable article describing how a knowledge of simple nervous systems may help us understand some of the ways nerve cells can be organized to control behavior.

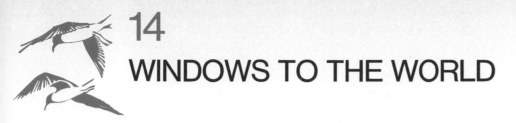

14
WINDOWS TO THE WORLD

A multitude of realities

Each animal lives in a world that exists for it only through its sense organs. The limits of this "real" world are set by the various response modes of the animal's sense receptors, by the richness and range of information these receptors can transform into trains of nerve impulses for delivery to the central nervous system, and by the capacity of the animal's central nervous system to integrate the separate spike trains into meaningful patterns. Sense organs have been likened to "windows" because like a window, each sense organ permits only a circumscribed view of the world outside.

Natural selection has placed these windows where they are most useful to each species for survival and reproduction in its particular ecological niche. A given aspect of the environment may be critically important to one species' survival but largely irrelevant to another species. Try to imagine, for example, how different must be the perceptual worlds of yourself, your dog, and a honey bee. You live largely in a world of color, form, and sound. A sense of smell, though useful and pleasant at mealtimes, determines only a small part of your behavior. A dog's visual world is without color and is a minor window when compared with its sense of smell. Walking through a field you take in the view, but for a dog the expedition is a rich panorama of odors far beyond our comprehension. The honeybee lives in two worlds; it is active in the darkness of the hive, and it forages in the sunlight. In the hive, a bee relies on an elaborate system of chemical and tactile signals informing her, among other things, of whether the queen is present, what types of food are in short supply, and where they are likely to be found outside the hive. While foraging in the field, a bee's color vision and olfactory sense guide her to certain blossoms; their shapes, hues, and scent all serve as cues. Her eyes are sensitive to ultraviolet light, so for her the centers of many flowers glow with colors we cannot see (Fig. 14–1).

The German zoologist Jacob Uexküll called this "self-world," defined for each animal by its sense organs, its *Umwelt*. Modern technology has equipped man with microscopes, telescopes, and telecommunication equipment enabling him to probe beyond his personal *Umwelt* and into that of other organisms and the far reaches of the universe.

General properties of sense organs

Each sense organ consists of an array of sense cells ranging in number from one to many millions. Such arrays have evolved with the result that their

Figure 14–1 The way the world appears depends on the kinds of perceptual apparatus an organism is equipped with. Honeybees can detect ultraviolet light, which is reflected by marsh marigolds, and must see the flowers somewhat as shown at top, observed through a television camera sensitive to ultraviolet. Below are the same flowers as we see them.

constituent receptor cells are capable of transforming particular kinds of energy into nerve impulses. The energy form that normally excites a sense organ is called its **adequate stimulus**. Light is the adequate stimulus for the eye, sound for the ear, and so on. Sense organs may be excited under abnormal conditions by forms of energy other than their adequate stimulus, particularly if the energy happens to be very intense.

Action potentials are the universal means of transmitting information rapidly from one place to another in the nervous system. Therefore, action potentials traveling in the fibers of the optic nerve or auditory nerve have no special quality that identifies them with light or with sound. Instead, each sensory nerve is a bundle of **labeled lines**; it is as if each sensory axon traveling into the central nervous system had a label identifying the location of the sense cell on the outside. Action potentials arriving from optic nerve fibers are interpreted as signaling "light," and those in the auditory nerve signal "sound." The label of an axon from a particular temperature receptor, for example, may say "heat" and "end of right index finger." If electric shocks are given directly to a sensory nerve, the sensation is one of light or sound or touch, depending on which sensory nerve is stimulated.

SENSORY THRESHOLDS: We have used the term *threshold* when discussing electrical stimulation of a single axon (Chapter 11). This is the minimum stimulus voltage that will precipitate a self-propagating action potential in the axon. Sense organs are commonly spoken of as having a threshold, defined as the minimum intensity of stimulus to which an animal will react or that will cause a minimum detectable change in the frequency of spikes coming from a sense receptor. But the term *threshold* is less meaningful here because it implies a definite "step"—a response or no response. When an animal shows no reaction it does not necessarily mean that it cannot detect the stimulus. Also, the axons coming from a sense organ often show spontaneous activity (Chapter 12), that is, a low frequency of spike discharge which merely increases slightly in response to a stimulus of low intensity. Thus we have to choose and then define an arbitrary criterion of responsiveness if we are going to talk about thresholds in the behavior of whole animals or of sense organs.

This means that there is no clear-cut way to measure the maximum sensitivity of most receptors, although a change in spike frequency of less than about one spike per second is unlikely to have much behavioral significance.

At the other end of the scale of stimulus intensity there is an upper limit to the frequency with which spikes can follow one another along an axon. This upper limit is determined by the time constants of the axon membrane and by its refractory period. After discharging a spike the membrane must recover its excitability before it is able to sustain a second spike. The refractory period lasts approximately for the duration of a spike and places an upper limit on spike frequency of about 1,000 or fewer spikes per second. This corresponds to an interspike interval of about 1 millisecond or longer. Since the receptor cannot generate spikes at a higher frequency when exposed to stimuli of still greater intensity, the receptor is said to be **overloaded** or **saturated**. This means that quantitative information about higher stimulus intensities cannot be transmitted by this cell to the central nervous system.

ADAPTATION: The exteroceptors, that is, those sense organs that serve as windows to the outside world, actually distort the world as it really exists in the physical sense. This is because their sensory receptor cells **adapt** in the presence of a constant and continued level of the adequate stimulus. Adaptation shows itself in the pattern of spikes delivered by the axon of a single receptor cell when it is exposed to a constant and continuing stimulus such as a steady light or a sustained sound. The spike frequency is highest at the beginning of the stimulus and then steadily declines to a lower level or may cease altogether as the stimulus continues. If the stimulus is suddenly increased to a new steady level there is a fresh burst of spikes that again declines to a low level. When the stimulus is removed altogether the receptor is "silent" and steadily regains its original sensitivity, or **disadapts**, with a time course similar to that required for the adaptation that took place when the stimulus was present.

In our daily life we take adaption of our receptors for granted. We accept the distortion of the physical world that it introduces into our nervous systems. In fact if adaptation did not occur, life would be very different and for the most part pretty unbearable. Imagine, if you can, what the following situations would be like if adaptation did not take place. When we enter a brightly lighted room at night the illumination is intolerable for a moment, but we soon adapt to it; when we leave the room the darkness outside at first seems absolute until our eyes disadapt, or dark adapt as it is more commonly called. Without acoustic adaptation rock bands would be utterly unbearable. A pleasant or a foul odor becomes almost unnoticeable after a few minutes' exposure; even when we put on a hat we are aware of its presence for only a few seconds.

In each of these situations we are primarily aware of a *change* in the situation and tend to disregard its steady state. All animals are subject to the same kind of distortion of reality, a fact well known to the hunter or observer of animal behavior who tries to remain as motionless as possible when in the presence of the animals of interest. In exchange for this distortion we receive an extension of the dynamic range of our sense organs and a heightened awareness of novelty in the scene before us.

There is another and equally important situation wherein adaptation would be not only disadvantageous but catastrophic. This concerns the proprioceptive mechanisms controlling posture (Chapter 13). In fact, the stretch receptors in muscle spindles do not adapt, but maintain a steady discharge of spikes so long as they are under a constant degree of stretch (Fig. 14–2). If we review once more the operation of this mechanism it is easy to see that adaptation of these proprioceptors would cause utter confusion. It would be impossible to maintain a steady posture for any length of time and all of our slow movements would have to be a series of quick jerks.

ENERGY TO ACTION POTENTIALS: At present there is no full explanation of how energy finally reaching the membrane of a sense cell becomes converted or **transduced** into a membrane potential change and eventually into a train of impulses in its axon. Presumably the energy brings about a change in the chemical configuration of the membrane causing a change in ion conductance

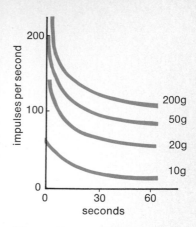

Figure 14–2 Frequency of impulses in an afferent nerve of the muscle spindle organ of a frog, plotted against various degrees of stretch caused by hanging weights from the end of the muscle.
(AFTER P. M. MILNER)

and also a local membrane depolarization (or sometimes a hyperpolarization). This in turn alters the firing rate of its axon. However, the actual steps for a given type of sense cell remain largely unknown, and the mechanism of sensory transduction is an unanswered question of sensory physiology.

Sensory transduction involves not only a transformation of the energy contained in the stimulus into an electrical change in the receptor cell, for this process is accompanied by a considerable degree of amplification. It has been estimated that a rod in the retina can be excited by a single photon of light, a chemoreceptor cell on a moth's antenna by a single molecule of odorous substance, and a hair cell in the ear by a displacement of less than 0.01 nanometer, or 10^{-11} meter. (The abbreviation of nanometer is nm, and another term for it is millimicron). Yet the effective generator potential produced in each of these receptor cells probably involves the movement of several thousand ions across its membrane.

The receptive processes of some sense cells appear to be no more than fine branchings from the cell body or from one end of the axon. These are called **primary sense cells**. In some cases these branchings are surrounded by capsules. In more specialized sense organs such as the eye, ear, and organs of smell and taste the actual receptor cells lack axons and appear to be concerned with transduction only. These are called **secondary sense cells**. Dendrites of sensory axons form synaptic contacts with the secondary sense cells and are the source of spikes generated by the receptor cell depolarization. In a few cases the stimulus causes hyperpolarization of the sense cell and a decrease in the firing frequency in the sensory axon.

CHEMICAL DETECTION

The ability of animals to detect and to distinguish between the chemical characters of substances is called **chemoreception**. Chemoreception is the most universal sense in animals—from protozoa to man—and it probably is the most ancient, yet we know least about its physiological mechanisms. What particular property of a given chemical makes it in one case highly flavored or scented while in another it is without taste or odor? What makes certain substances repellant and others attractive? Even man, who has a poor sense of smell compared with most animals, can learn to distinguish up to 10,000 odors. What are the neural mechanisms of such fine chemical discrimination? How does contact between a single molecule of an odorous substance and the membrane of a chemoreceptor cell alter the activity in its sensory axon?

While chemoreception is only a minor and much occluded window in our own world, it is a strikingly meaningful one in the worlds of a great many animals. The biology of chemical signals can give us an insight into *Umwelten* far different from our own.

The mechanisms of chemoreception

Usually we distinguish between the senses of taste (**gustation**) and smell (**olfaction**). Gustatory receptors require that the stimulating molecules be dis-

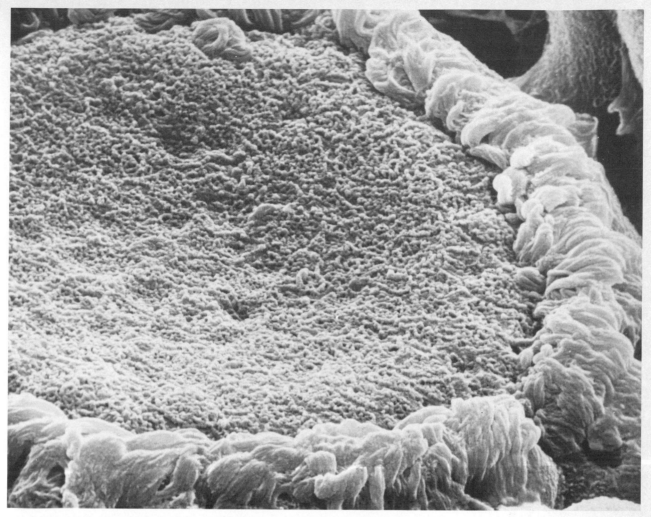

Figure 14–3 Photomicrograph showing the cilia-rimmed sensory papillae of a frog's tongue.

solved in aqueous solution (in the mouth in the case of vertebrates), whereas olfactory receptors are stimulated by molecules reaching the sense cells from a distance, which means through the air in the case of terrestrial animals. This requires that stimulating substances have some degree of volatility—they must give off a smell in order to be smelled. The distinction between smell and taste becomes somewhat hazy in the case of aquatic creatures.

Man is said to distinguish four principal qualities of taste: bitter, salty, sour, and sweet. The nuances of what we call flavor in our food depend on a combination of these taste qualities with odor and (to a lesser extent) vision. Much also depends on what we anticipate we are going to taste. You can test this yourself by comparing the flavors of familiar foods when you are blindfolded and have your nose plugged.

Taste receptors are secondary sense cells arranged in groups of 50 to 60 on **taste buds** (Fig. 14–3) scattered over the surface of the tongue. The tip of

Figure 14–4 Olfactory receptor cells are located in the olfactory epithelium in the upper part of the nasal passages. Molecules in the air we breathe are thought to excite the receptor cell if, after being dissolved in mucus, they contact an appropriate receptor site on the receptor's cilia.

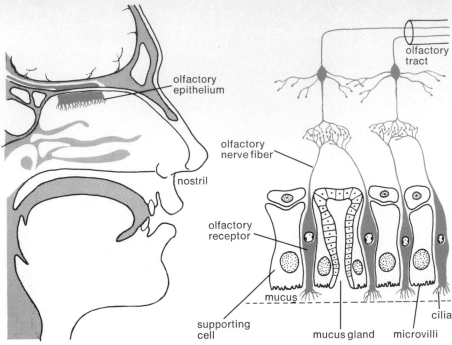

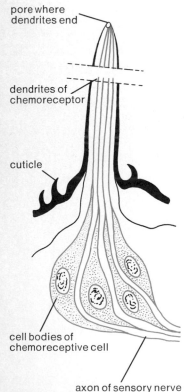

Figure 14–5 A chemoreceptive hair on a mouthpart of a blowfly.

each receptor cell is provided with fine processes and its base makes synaptic contact with a sensory axon. Vertebrate taste cells are continually dying and being replaced, those of a rat having an average life of 10 days. This short life may be a clue to their mechanism.

The **olfactory epithelium** in man occupies about one square inch of the nasal mucosa. Great numbers of bipolar primary sense cells each extend a short process into the mucus covering the epithelium and an axon inward to contribute to the olfactory nerve (Fig. 14–4). The first-order sensory fibers of the olfactory nerve enter the **olfactory bulb** where they form complex synaptic connections before the **olfactory tract** enters the brain proper. Sniffing increases your olfactory sensitivity because it wafts increasing numbers of stimulating molecules over and into the mucous covering of the olfactory receptor cells.

Not all animals have their chemoreceptors confined to these conventional locations. Protozoa show positive and negative chemotaxis—movement toward some substances diffusing in the water and away from others. Chemoreception must be a general property of their plasma membranes. There is evidence that some invertebrates have a general chemical sense in their skin. Many insects have taste endings on their feet as well as on their mouthparts. This is a useful adaptation since their feet are likely to encounter a source of food first.

V. G. Dethier and his colleagues at Princeton University have made an extensive study of taste in blowflies. Their chemoreceptive cells open at the tips of fine hairs and are thus readily available for experiments. Four dendrites end at a minute pore on the tip of each hair. Their bipolar cell bodies are within the cuticle at the base of the hair (Fig. 14–5). Microelectrode studies show that one dendrite in each hair responds to water, another to sugar, and two others to salts. Behavioral studies show that the fly extends its proboscis to feed when either a water or sugar solution is applied to the tip of a single hair, while this feeding response is prevented if small quantities of salts or acids are present in the sugar solution.

The caterpillars of many moth and butterfly species are **oligophagous**, meaning that they will eat only one or a few species of food plant among the many available to them. Dethier has discovered a small set of chemoreceptors on the mouthparts of certain oligophagous caterpillars that is not much more complicated than those found in blowflies but that codes the odor of acceptable food plants in terms of relative spike discharges of the various receptors. This built-in combination "unlocks," or releases, chewing behavior.

The amazing variety of odors that can be discriminated by an animal presents the main problem in understanding the physiology of olfaction. How is an odor discriminated in nerve impulses? When little is known about a given subject, there are usually many theories. One of the most promising dealing with olfaction is the **stereochemical theory** of John Amoore. Amoore studied the odors and chemical configurations of many kinds of molecules and concluded that they could be classified into seven groups according to the quality of their odor. He called these groups **primary odors** (Fig. 14–6). The substances in each of five of these groups have in common a similar molecular

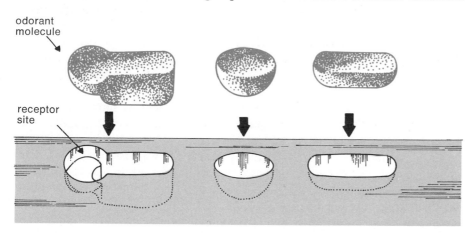

odorant molecule

receptor site

Figure 14–6 According to the stereochemical theory of olfaction, the shape of a molecule determines the class of receptor site with which it can combine. The classes of odors represented by the shapes of odorant molecules and receptor sites shown here are, from left to right, floral, camphoraceous, and ethereal.

shape. Molecules in the other two groups vary in shape but have either a positive or a negative charge. The theory suggests that there are seven kinds of receptor sites distributed over the membranes of the olfactory receptors composing the sensory array of the olfactory organ. The shapes of these sites correspond approximately to the shape of molecules which smell like one of the seven primary odors, much as the shape of locks corresponds to the keys that open them. The more snugly an odorant molecule fits into a receptor site the more effective it will be as a stimulant to the cell. Intermediate odors may be due to molecules that do not exactly fit a single receptor site but parts of which can stimulate two or more receptor sites.

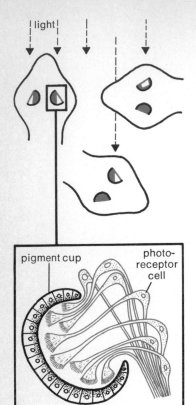

light

Figure 14–7 Photoreceptor cells in the eye of *Planaria* are enclosed in a darkly pigmented cup that opens to one side. Thus only light from certain directions can reach the light-sensitive pigment at the distal end of the receptor cell. This enables the animal to determine the direction from which the light is coming. (After Lorus Milne and J. Margery Milne, *Radiation Biology*, ed. A. Hollaender (New York: McGraw-Hill Book Co., 1956), Vol. 3, p. 622.)

PHOTORECEPTION

Electromagnetic radiation having quantal energies important to life is limited in wavelength to the narrow sensory window of about 400 to 700 micrometers for vision and slightly longer wavelengths for heat (see Fig. 6–10). It is probable that the ancestral forms of life were sensitive to light in one way or another, and today many simple forms react as if they had a general light sense even though they lack anatomically distinct eyes. A variety of organisms have adapted to life in the eternal dark of deep caves or in the lightless oceanic abyss. Usually, the eyes of these animals have become reduced or lost entirely in the course of evolution, since vision would have no survival value in such environments.

Eyes as light-gathering devices

Much of the structure that is superficially apparent in an eye is associated with its optical mechanisms, those structures that gather and focus light rays, regulate their intensity, and prevent light from entering from unwanted directions. The simplest of eyes consists of only one or a few photoreceptor cells, possibly with different but overlapping dynamic ranges. Lacking a lens, such an eye can measure only differences in light intensity. If backed by a screen of opaque pigment it may provide some directional sense by being more responsive to light coming from certain directions relative to the animal's body axis, but such an eye would be unable to detect differences in the forms of objects.

Planarian worms have eyes of this kind (Fig. 14–7). You can speculate about the sort of information such eyes might supply by trying to get around your house in the daytime with your eyes closed. Such eyes are obviously a long way from the complex image-forming eyes that have evolved at least three separate times to their present stage: in cephalopod mollusks such as the octopus, in the arthropods, and in vertebrates. We will consider the optical arrangement of the vertebrate eye first.

The vertebrate eye (Fig. 14–8) forms images the way a camera does. The eyeball consists of three layers of tissue: a tough outer **sclera**, an intermediate **choroid** that contains nutrient blood vessels and is pigmented (thus preventing light from entering from anywhere but the lens), and an inner **retina** containing an array of more than 150 million photoreceptor cells known as **rods** and **cones**. Inside the photoreceptor layer is a complex layer of interneurons that integrate potentials set up in the rods and cones.

Light enters the eye through the transparent skin of the **cornea;** passes through the **iris**, which by its changes in diameter can regulate the amount of light admitted like a camera diaphragm; and travels through the **lens**, which together with the cornea focuses the light on the retina. This means that light rays diverging from any discrete point in the surroundings are made to converge once more on a discrete point of the retina. Thus, a small image of the outside world is projected onto the array of closely packed rods and cones much as on the sensitive film in a camera. When at rest, the distance of the lens from the retina in a normal eye is such that distant objects are in focus.

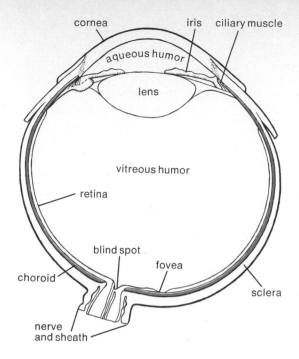

cornea   iris   ciliary muscle
aqueous humor
lens
vitreous humor
retina
blind spot
fovea
choroid
sclera
nerve and sheath

Figure 14-8 A vertebrate eye. The fovea of man is densely packed with cones. It has the best acuity in good light. When you look straight at an object its image falls on the fovea. Where the optic nerve leaves the eye there is a blind spot containing no visual receptors.

Figure 14-9 A. Lizards, birds, and mammals accommodate by changing the shape of the lens. This is done by the ciliary muscle that controls the tension around the edge of the lens. When the tension is decreased, the lens becomes thicker and bends the light more. Fish, amphibians, and snakes accommodate by moving the lens further from the retina for close objects instead of changing its shape. B. When we focus our eyes on an object, the rays of light reflected in various directions from each point on that object are bent by the cornea and lens so that they converge to form a corresponding point on our retina. In this way an inverted image of the object is formed on the retina, but with the aid of the brain we perceive the object right side up. In farsighted people the cornea and lens cannot bend together the light rays reflected from nearby objects enough to focus them on the retina, and a convex lens is needed in front of the eye to help refract the light. Distant objects appear blurred to nearsighted people because the light entering their eyes converges to a focal point in front of the retina. A concave lens is needed to make the light diverge just enough before entering the eye to focus on the retina.

To bring near objects into focus fish, amphibians, and snakes move the lens farther from the retina (Fig. 14–9). This process is called **accommodation**. In lizards, birds, and mammals accommodation is brought about by the contraction of certain muscles connected to the ligament suspending the elastic lens. This allows the lens to become rounder in shape and more convex, bringing its focal point nearer. In myopic (near-sighted) people the retina is just a little too far away from the lens for sharp focus of distant objects. The cavity of the eyeball between cornea and retina is filled with transparent fluid—**aqueous humor** in front of the lens and **vitreous humor** between the lens and retina.

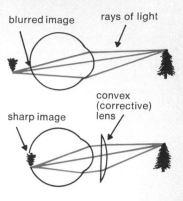

FARSIGHTED EYE
blurred image   rays of light
convex (corrective) lens
sharp image

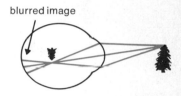

NEARSIGHTED EYE
blurred image

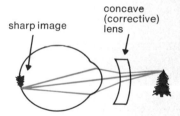

concave (corrective) lens
sharp image

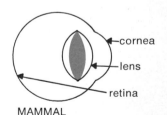

cornea
lens
retina
MAMMAL

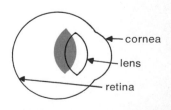

cornea
lens
retina
FISH

Figure 14–10 Visual pigment is located in the outer segment of rods and cones. It is thought to be contained in the stack of membranes that fill this part of the cell, as shown in the drawing of the rod and in the electron micrograph of a portion of the outer segment of a rod from the eye of a rat.

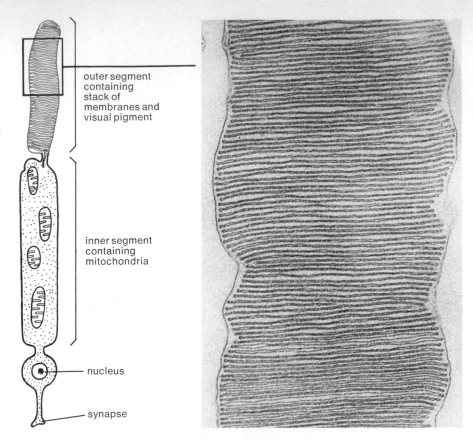

outer segment containing stack of membranes and visual pigment

inner segment containing mitochondria

nucleus

synapse

Light forming an image on the retina must first pass through several layers of ganglion cells and axons before it falls on the close array of photoreceptors. Each photoreceptor cell (Fig. 14–10) consists of a rounded **inner segment**, from which a short process extends into the ganglionic layer, and an **outer segment** that is elongate in the case of the rods and spindle-shaped in the case of the cones. The outer segments are minutely corrugated into many folds, or **lamellae**, and are the sites where the energy in light quanta initiates photochemical reactions leading to **generator potentials**. These are local, graded potential changes that occur across the membrane of a receptor cell when it is stimulated. They spread electrotonically over the cell and are the first step in the generation of action potentials. The rods, sensitive to low light intensities, are more numerous than the cones and are more widely distributed over the surface of the retina. The cones reach a maximum density in a central region of the retina directly opposite the lens. This region is called the **fovea**. Here the cones crowd out the rods. Images falling on the fovea are seen in color and in the greatest detail when the light is moderate to bright. Extrafoveal regions of the retina are most effective in low light intensities and are particularly sensitive to movement. Thus, the rods require for their excitation a small number of light quanta while the cones require more light and provide us with color vision.

At first all of this may seem like a very impractical arrangement. After

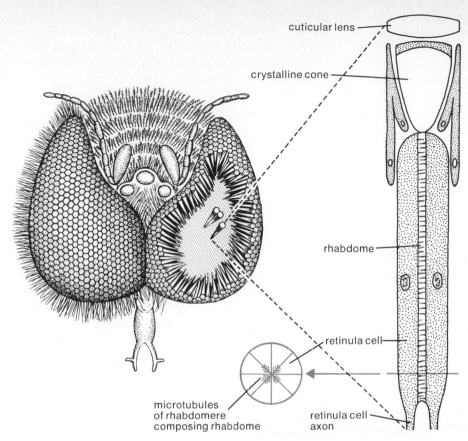

cuticular lens

crystalline cone

rhabdome

retinula cell

microtubules
of rhabdomere
composing rhabdome

retinula cell
axon

Figure 14–11 A honeybee's head contains a pair of very large compound eyes. The surface of each compound eye is made up of many facets, which are cuticular lenses of underlying ommatidia. Together with the crystalline cone, this lens focuses light on the central portion, or rhabdome, of the eight retinula cells where the visual pigment occurs.

passing through the clear vitreous humor, light has to travel through a tangle of blood vessels, axons, and the cell bodies of second- and third-order neurons before it strikes the light-sensitive outer segments. These intervening structures seem transparent, but it is hard to imagine how much brighter the world would look if the retina were turned inside out! The explanation of this curious arrangement lies far back in the way vertebrate central nervous systems develop.

The optical arrangement of the highly developed eyes of cephalopod mollusks such as the octopus and squid is very similar to ours. These animals have excellent form vision along with highly developed brains, and they can be trained to discriminate a variety of geometrical shapes when the reward is a small crab.

Arthropods are the only other invertebrates with highly developed vision. They include crabs, lobsters, spiders, and insects and contain a greater number of species than the rest of the animal kingdom put together. Arthropod eyes are built on an entirely different optical plan.

The compound eye of a fly or bee viewed under a low-power microscope appears to be composed of a geometrical pattern of thousands of tiny facets of cuticle (Fig. 14–11). On the hemispheric surface of the eye each facet faces a slightly different direction and is the lens of an individual visual unit that contains its own optical system, photoreceptor cells, and shielding pigment. Each of these units is called an **ommatidium** and extends downwards as a narrow column into the eye. Below the cuticular lens of each ommatidium is a **crystalline cone** that directs light among an elongated cluster of 6 to 12 **retinula cells**. The retinula cells are arranged around the optical axis of the ommatidium much like the segments of an orange, each sending an axon from its inner end to optic ganglia connected to the brain. The central part of each retinula cell —where it meets the other retinula cells of the ommatidium—is highly and complexly folded into **microtubules** and is called a **rhabdomere**. The rhabdomere is the light-sensitive part of the retinula cell. The rhabdomeres may meet closely or loosely at the "central core of the orange," as it were. Here they form a semitransparent column called the **rhabdome** down which light is directed from the lens and crystalline cone.

Thus, each ommatidium appears to be a minute but complete eye with only a few sense cells. It is commonly surrounded by pigment cells limiting the amount of light that can reach it from neighboring ommatidia. In many insects, particularly those of nocturnal habits, this pigment screen may be withdrawn, increasing the light-gathering power of the eye.

Before discussing how vertebrate and arthropod eyes provide their bearers with detailed information about form in the outside world, we must consider what is known about **phototransduction**. How does light falling on rods or cones or retinula cells give rise to generator potentials and become translated into the language of the nervous system?

Phototransduction

The outer segments of vertebrate rods and cones and the rhabdomeres of arthropods contain a light-sensitive substance called **visual pigment**. In the rods of terrestrial vertebrates and marine fish this pigment is a reddish color and is called **rhodopsin**. When one quantum of light falls on a molecule of rhodopsin its energy is expended in causing the molecule to bend or change its shape into what chemists call a different isomer. This change in shape starts a sequence of reactions in which the twisted rhodopsin splits into a colorless protein, **opsin**, and a yellow molecule, **retinaldehyde**. The change in color of the complex from reddish to yellow is known as **bleaching** of the visual pigment (Fig. 14–12). Energy is released in the bleaching of rhodopsin and somehow alters the permeability of the visual cell's membrane so as to give

Figure 14–12 When a quantum of light strikes a molecule of rhodopsin it causes retinaldehyde to bend. The rhodopsin undergoes a series of reactions that result in its splitting into two molecules: opsin and retinaldehyde. This process, called bleaching, changes the permeability of the rod's membrane, and an electrical signal is transmitted toward the brain. Enzymes play an important role in recombining retinaldehyde and opsin into rhodopsin again.

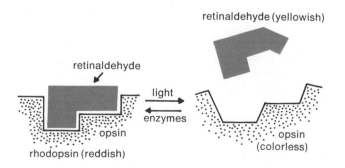

rise to a generator potential. This generator potential triggers action potentials in the ganglion cells connected (via other neurons) to the sense cell in the manner of an e.p.s.p. or e.p.p. The mediator mechanism at this point is unknown.

The breakdown of rhodopsin into opsin and retinaldehyde must be reversible if the photoreceptor cell is to recover its sensitivity to light. Recombination of the end-products can be partial in lower light intensities or complete in the dark and is promoted by special enzymes. The sensitivity of the eye depends in part on the proportion of visual pigment that is bleached at any given time. Thus, in continued bright illumination the retina is less sensitive because a larger proportion of its visual pigment is kept in the bleached condition, and the eye is said to be **light adapted**. Kept in darkness the eye becomes extremely sensitive and is said to be **dark adapted**. Under these conditions one light quantum is sufficient to stimulate a single rod, although six or seven rods must be stimulated simultaneously for light at this low intensity to be detected by the brain.

Light of a wavelength of about 500 nanometers has maximum quantum efficiency in stimulating human rods, which decrease in sensitivity to longer and shorter wavelengths. This corresponds with the wavelength maximally absorbed by rhodopsin. The cones appear to be associated with a related pigment, **iodopsin**. Other pigments, each absorbing light maximally at a slightly different wavelength, have been associated with rods and cones in a wide variety of vertebrate species. Color vision is thought to be mediated by cones each having one of three different types of visual pigment and absorbing light maximally at different wavelengths. Conditioning experiments have demonstrated the ability to discriminate among different colors in some fish, turtles, frogs, birds, squirrels, and primates. Invertebrates known to perceive color differences include some crustaceans, insects (especially honeybees), and cephalopod mollusks. There can be no doubt that the colors of many animals and flowers exist because of their adaptive value.

FLICKER, DISCRIMINATION, CONTRAST, AND FORM

What do we actually *see* as we regard a complex scene? It is obviously impossible to notice every detail, for example each of the individual leaves on a tree. We must, therefore, abstract the scene, picking out certain salient details for inspection.

The answer to this question depends in part on what we are looking for, that is, whether we have a particular search image in mind. But what we see is also determined by the built-in properties of the photoreceptor cells in the retinal array and the manner in which they are "hooked up" to higher centers in the brain. Students of animal behavior are particularly interested both in the search image and in the performance of this hook-up in different species because they reveal much about the perceptual worlds different animals live in. Many volumes have been written on this subject from the viewpoints of art, philosophy, psychology, and neurophysiology.

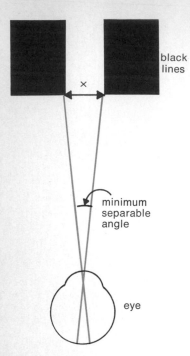

black
lines

×

minimum
separable
angle

eye

Figure 14–13 Visual acuity is determined by measuring the angle subtended at the eye by the minimum distance (x) between two lines that allows them to be seen as separate lines. This angle is called the minimum separable angle.

Movement and flicker

One aspect of the question can easily be answered for animals with image-forming eyes. Movement, flicker, or novelty suddenly introduced into an otherwise static scene immediately attracts our attention. In part, this can be explained by the rapidly adapting property of the photoreceptor cells. **Flicker**—such as frame-by-frame viewing of a motion picture film—at a rate of about 10 per second is intensely stimulating and disturbing to man, but if movement is too rapid or flicker exceeds a rate of about 30 per second—such as movie frames projected normally—we hardly notice it. This frequency is defined as the **flicker fusion frequency**. Some insects have flicker fusion frequencies in excess of 100 per second; honeybees get significant visual stimulation from the flicker of flower petals as the bees cruise low over a patch of blossoms. The flicker fusion frequency depends on the time constants of the photoreceptor cells.

Visual acuity

Visual acuity is a measure of the detail that can be discriminated in a scene. It is determined by the smallest angular distance separating two lines when they can just be distinguished as being separate (Fig. 14–13). Since the eye behaves optically as a camera, this distance might be expected to be proportional to the average denseness or closeness of packing of the rods and cones on the retina, like the graininess of a photographic film. This turns out to be the case, but the explanation is more complicated because each photoreceptor cell does not have an isolated labeled line all the way to the cerebral cortex. Many complex transactions take place in between.

Form vision

In addition to movement, we are particularly attentive to the borders, contrasts, and edges in a scene (Fig. 14–14). This faculty requires a more extended explanation.

Behavioral experiments have been carried out in which animals must discriminate objects of different shape for a food reward. White rats, the favorite of psychologists, are nocturnal animals for which vision is probably of secondary importance. Rats are able to recognize differences among a variety of simple geometrical shapes, although a circle and a square of equal area give them difficulty. The flicker sensitivity of bees leads them to discriminate figures by their degree of "brokenness" (Fig. 14–14). The octopus can discriminate vertical from horizontal bars but fails to discriminate right-sloping diagonal bars from left-sloping ones.

The rods and cones of vertebrates occupy the outer layer of the retina. Between the photoreceptors and the inner surface over which optic nerve fibers converge to the blind spot and leave the eye, there are two additional layers formed by the cell bodies of interneurons (Fig. 14–15). Separating these three layers are two networks formed by the interlaced processes of these cells. The rods and cones send short processes into the middle layer of cell

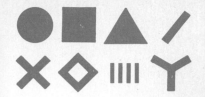

Figure 14–14 Familiar contrasts of light and dark play an important role in our ability to identify objects. Do you think you would have been able to identify the negative version of the bust of Einstein if we had not included the positive version? Honeybees can easily distinguish between two of the above shapes when one is taken from each row; but they have difficulty distinguishing among the shapes within a single row.

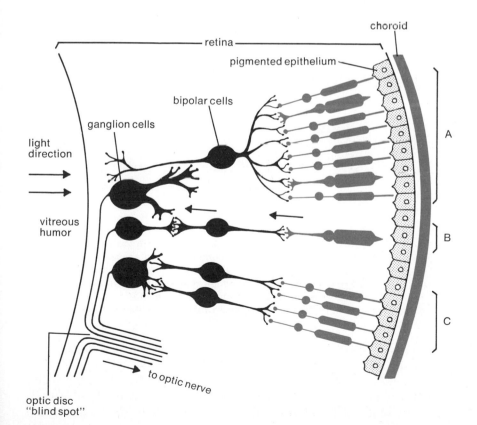

Figure 14–15 This schematic diagram shows three types of connections between photoreceptors and ganglion cells in the vertebrate retina. A represents a ganglion cell that receives its input from a number of rods and cones via one bipolar cell. B shows a ganglion cell receiving its input from a single cone, an arrangement found only in the fovea. C is a ganglion cell receiving input from several rods through more than one bipolar cell. The axons of the ganglion cells travel across the inner surface of the retina to the blind spot, where they converge and form the optic nerve. There are also neurons that send their processes through the retina at right angles to the direction of light. These association neurons are not shown.

bodies. Many fibers forming the intervening networks travel between these layers of cell bodies, making a variety of synaptic connections. Other fibers (not shown in Fig. 14–15) travel laterally, that is, parallel to the plane of the retina. Interneurons of the innermost layer are called **ganglion cells.** Their axons form the fibers of the optic nerve which is actually a part of the brain.

The complexity of the neuronal transactions carried out in these layers of interneurons is suggested by the fact that while there are more than 150 million rods and cones spread over the outer layer of the retina, only about one million axons from the ganglion cells converge at the blind spot and form the optic nerve.

Some of these transactions have been worked out by moving over the retinal surface a spot of light small enough to stimulate only one or a few photoreceptor cells at a time. As the retina is scanned, the responses of one of the ganglion cells are followed with a microelectrode. Each ganglion cell is excited not by a single photoreceptor but by a small population of photoreceptors. This population is known as the ganglion cell's **receptive field** and lies roughly opposite it (Fig. 14–16). There is considerable overlap in the receptive fields of neighboring ganglion cells, for not only does each ganglion cell get convergent signals from several photoreceptors, but each photoreceptor response serves to affect several ganglion cells.

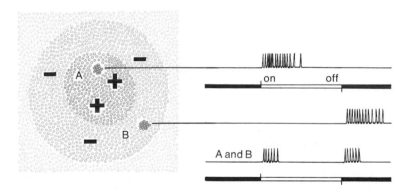

Figure 14–16 The area of the retina within these two circles is the receptive field of one ganglion cell. A light (A) shown on the central area (+) causes the ganglion cell to fire a train of spikes. A similar spot of light (B) on the surrounding area (−) causes the cell to fire only after it is turned off. When both lights are used there is a small discharge at both on and off, but this discharge is smaller, indicating that there is inhibitory interaction between receptors in the two areas of the receptive field.

One important consequence of these overlapping interactions is that they involve inhibition as well as excitation. Light falling off center on a ganglion cell's receptive field may suppress its activity, while light falling on the center of its field may have a stimulating effect. At the same time, the light beam is falling on the center of the receptive field belonging to a neighboring ganglion cell and exciting it. Thus, each receptive field has an excitatory center and an inhibitory surround. In other cases the center of the receptive field may be inhibitory and the surround excitatory. The receptive fields of individual retinal ganglion cells are mostly circular. The nerve connections responsible for these interactions lie in the fiber network extending laterally in the outermost layer of fibers in the retina.

Why should part of a ganglion cell's receptive field be inhibitory? Doesn't this gathering together from several photoreceptors at the ganglion cell negate the visual acuity conferred by the close packing of photoreceptor cells in the retina? Part of the answer to these questions seems to be that the excitatory–inhibitory arrangement accentuates the contrast at borders between bright and less bright areas. If such an intensity border falls on the region of overlap of the receptive fields of neighboring ganglion cells, one of these will dominate the other, discharging more strongly while the other is suppressed. Which ganglion cell has dominance may still be determined by the relative size of the generator potentials in only one or two photoreceptors shared by both ganglion cells. This accentuation of contrast would not take place if the two ganglion cells were not coupled by mutual inhibition.

This "edge effect" is evident in our subjective sensations of vision. A surface having uniform grayness does not hold our attention and the eye strays to spots, edges, and lines in search of information.

These interactions were worked out using the eyes of cats and are thought to be typical of mammals. If we pick up visual signals two synaptic steps further "downstream," that is, in neurons belonging to the cat's visual cortex, and stimulate the retina in the same way, we find a wider variety of complex recombinations. Here certain cells combine signals from the same "line of attention" of both the right and left eyes. In other words they are binocular. Most cortical interneurons have elongate receptive fields, responding best to slits, bars, or edges only if these images are oriented at specific angles to the vertical. When a bar of light is rotated, the discharge of spikes decreases to a minimum and may cease when the bar is at right angles to the "preferred" orientation (Fig. 14–17). Other cortical neurons are stimulated only by moving bars and edges falling anywhere within a large area of retina, provided their axes are appropriately oriented. Still others are sensitive to rate of movement, position in the visual field, and dimensions.

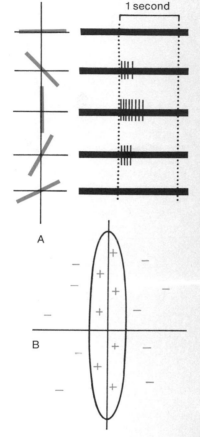

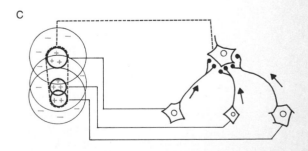

Figure 14–17 The receptive field of this cortical cell is mapped by a bar of light shone onto the retina while a recording electrode is on the cell (A). The strongest discharge is obtained when the light is confined to the vertical excitatory area (B). If the bar of light is oriented horizontally, so that most of it falls on the antagonistic areas on each side, the cell's response is inhibited. We can imagine how three interneurons with adjacent concentric receptive fields might endow a cortical cell on which they converge with an elongate receptive field (C).

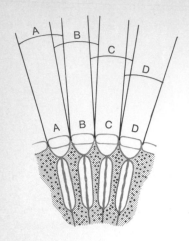

Figure 14–18 Since the surface of the compound eye is curved, each ommatidium looks at (or accepts light from) a slightly different part of the environment. The acceptance angles of four adjacent ommatidia are shown diagrammatically. Notice that each overlaps its neighbor slightly. Objects in the region of overlap may be "seen" by both ommatidia.

Lower vertebrates, such as frogs, seem to do much of their signal processing in their retinas. Ganglion cells may respond only to sharp boundaries located anywhere in the receptive field. Other units respond to curved boundaries of small, dark, moving objects, or to changing contrasts, or to general dimming as by a shadow falling on the visual field. In the frog's brain there are certain units that respond when a small, dark object travels first across the visual field but cease if it retraces the same path. Also, there are other units that lock onto a specific object moving in the visual field and respond to any deviations in its velocity or direction. A little thought will tell you what an important part mechanisms of this kind might play in a frog's life as it lies in wait for moving flies or attempts to avoid capture by a passing heron.

Much less is known about the neural processing of visual signals in the only other large group having image-forming eyes, the arthropods. The microscopic anatomy of their optic ganglia suggests that this may be very complex. It used to be thought that each ommatidium registered the average brightness of a narrow segment of the scene surveyed. This segment is the optical **acceptance angle** of the ommatidium (Fig. 14–18). There are no more than 40,000 or 50,000 ommatidia in the compound eyes of insects having the best vision. This is a small number compared with the number of rods and cones in the vertebrate eye. Therefore, this mosaic theory predicts that such insect eyes have a comparatively crude visual acuity or coarse grain, the image being composed of dots like a poor-quality newsprint photo.

Behavioral experiments suggest that insects have much sharper vision than the mosaic theory predicts. It seems possible that each ommatidium has some image-forming capacity, each of the 6 to 12 retinula cells looking at a slightly different part of the scene covered by the acceptance angle of the ommatidium. If these acceptance angles overlap and the overlapping retinula cell signals are neuronally recombined in the optic ganglia after the fashion of the vertebrate system, then we would expect much better visual discrimination.

HEARING AND EQUILIBRIUM

A variety of sounds and ears

Sounds perceived in the water, or as vibrations through a solid surface, or as compression waves of the air play an important part in the lives of many animals. Ears appear to have evolved only once in vertebrate animals, but a dozen or more separate times in arthropods, especially in insects. Insects are also highly sensitive to vibrations through sensors on their legs.

Probably the most widespread use of sound in animal behavior is enabling the opposite sexes of a species to identify one another as members of the same species and then to locate each other. The songs of the multitude of crickets, grasshoppers, and cicadas in summer serve this purpose. The same is true about frog and bird calls, and to a lesser extent the cries of certain mammals. Second in importance are sounds made in defense of a territory, common among birds, mammals, and certain insects. Some insects make hissing noises like snakes, possibly a protection against small mammalian predators. Certain moths make trains of clicks when being chased by bats, apparently to advertise their distastefulness before being snapped up. Many young birds and mammals make distress calls, thereby attracting the parents. Bats produce a series of high-pitched chirps as they fly through the darkness, finding their way and their insect prey by means of a most sophisticated system of sonar.

Nearly all of these animals have ears and can detect the sounds made by their fellows. However, this sound production and communication seem to be little more than expressions of mood such as readiness to mate or feed, or discomfort, or merely to announce, "Here I am" to other members of a flock. Probably such sounds are akin to laughing or weeping or shouting "Help!" in human behavior and have little in common with the complex sounds we call language.

The outer and middle ear

The ear of mammals consists of three distinct regions, each playing a separate role in hearing (Fig. 14–19). The **outer ear** includes the external flap or **pinna**, and the **auditory canal**. The pinna is enlarged, horn-like, and mobile in many mammals and is very important to them as a directional collector of sound. The pinna is lacking in the lower land vertebrates.

The beginning of the **middle ear** is marked by the eardrum or **tympanic membrane** closing off the auditory canal. The tympanic membrane is relatively light and large in area, and is readily displaced by sound waves. Its inner surface is connected to a chain of three small ear bones, the **malleus**, **incus**, and **stapes**. The stapes is in turn connected to a small membrane, the oval window, which marks the beginning of the fluid-filled inner ear. The middle ear is air-filled, and is connected to the mouth cavity by the **eustachian**

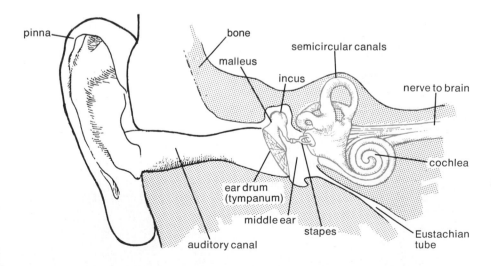

Figure 14–19 The human ear and vestibular system.

tube, which serves to equalize the air pressure on either side of the tympanic membrane and so prevent its rupture by sudden pressure changes. The tympanic membrane and chain of ear bones solve the problem of efficient transfer of mechanical energy from the light and compressible air to the dense fluid of the inner ear.

A sense of balance

The **inner ear** (or membranous labyrinth) contains the auditory sensing mechanism, but it evolved as an organ of equilibrium in fish and only later acquired an auditory function in the land vertebrates. The portion still concerned with equilibrium in mammals consists of several interconnected membranous sacs and tubes embedded in the temporal bone of the cranium and filled with fluid called **endolymph** (Fig. 14–20). One set of sacs contains patches of **hair cells,** each extending a minute cilium into the cavity and an axon from its outer end. A small crystalline "pebble" of calcium carbonate, the **otolith,** lies within the cavity and rests upon a patch of cilia. If the axis of the head is changed, the relatively heavy otolith shifts in position and bends the cilia belonging to a different group of hair cells. This causes a change in the spike pattern generated by both groups. These signals provide us with a sense of the direction of gravity. They also integrate with the spinal mechanisms of posture discussed earlier and assist in the automatic regulation of stance.

The labyrinth also contains the **semicircular canals,** three liquid-filled tubes

Figure 14–20 The vertebrate inner ear, or labyrinth, is filled with fluid. The otoliths rest on hair cells and monitor the position of the head with respect to gravity. Rotation of the head is sensed by hair cells in the cupola of each semicircular canal. The cupola consists of a gelatinous cap covering a cluster of hair cells (B). The stapes in the air-filled inner ear rests on the oval window and transmits sound vibrations to the hair cells in the cochlea.

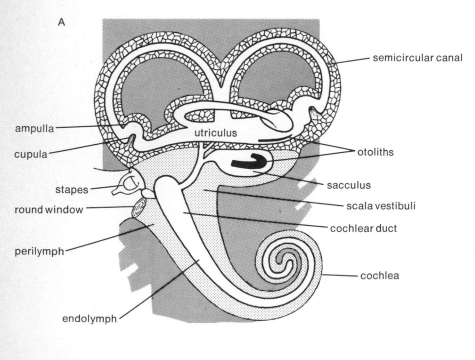

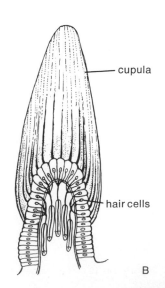

Figure 14-21 The cochlea and Organ of Corti. A shows a cross section through the cochlea revealing the Organ of Corti on basilar membrane. B illustrates the middle and inner ear to show how sound vibrations cause basilar membrane to oscillate. C shows hair cells from the Organ of Corti. Tips of cilia touch tectorial membrane and are bent when basilar membrane moves.

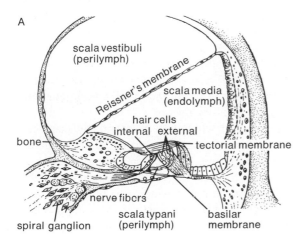

A

scala vestibuli (perilymph)

Reissner's membrane

scala media (endolymph)

hair cells internal external

tectorial membrane

bone

nerve fibers

spiral ganglion

scala typani (perilymph)

basilar membrane

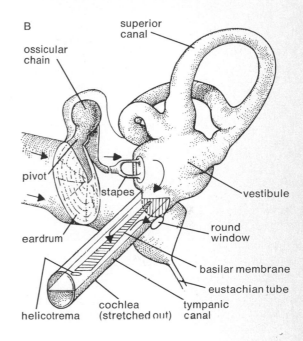

B

ossicular chain

superior canal

pivot

stapes

vestibule

eardrum

round window

basilar membrane

eustachian tube

helicotrema

cochlea (stretched out)

tympanic canal

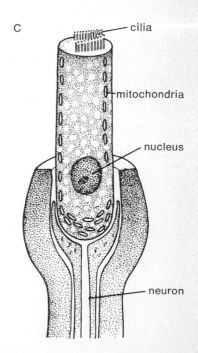

C

cilia

mitochondria

nucleus

neuron

connected to one of the sacs at each end and arranged at right angles to one another, corresponding approximately with three dimensions in space. At one end each canal is enlarged into an **ampulla**. Each of the three ampullae contains a patch of hair cells whose cilia are embedded in a gelatinous cap—the **cupula**. The semicircular canals provide us with a sense of change in the *rate* of rotation of the head—of accelerated or decelerated turning in any direction. When such a displacement takes place, the inertia of the endolymph in one or more of the canals near the plane of the displacement causes it to lag behind during the acceleration. As a result, the endolymph tends to flow relative to the cupula and to displace both it and the embedded cilia. This causes a change in the spike pattern generated by the hair cells in specific canals, which collectively provide information about the direction and the rate of displacement of the body. These parts of the labyrinth have changed very little in the course of vertebrate evolution.

The hearing organ of vertebrates

The sense organ of vertebrate hearing is also part of the inner ear, a part called the **cochlea** and consisting of a tube divided into three parallel compartments by two longitudinal partitions (Fig. 14–21). The central compartment of the cochlea, called the **scala media**, is filled with endolymph. It connects with the other cavities of the structure. The outer parallel compartments on either side are called the **scala vestibuli** and **scala tympani**. They are filled with perilymph and are connected at the top of the spiral by a small hole, the **helicotrema**. At the base of the spiral the scala vestibuli and scala tympani are separated from the middle ear by small membrane-covered openings called respectively the **oval window**, against which the stapes rests, and the **round window**.

The auditory receptor organ is called the **organ of Corti**. It consists of four or five orderly parallel rows of hair cells arrayed on an elastic spiral sheet, the **basilar membrane**, that forms the wall between the scala media and the scala tympani. The array of hair cells can be likened to the treads of a spiral staircase that becomes narrower at the top. The hair cells have fine cilia projecting into the cavity of the scala media. The cilia are graded in length, the longest touching the **tectorial membrane** which arches out and forms a ledge covering all the hair cells. The base of each hair cell is in synaptic contact with a dendrite whose cell body lies outside the organ of Corti and in the **spiral ganglion**. Axons from these cell bodies form the auditory nerve.

When the stapes presses in on the oval window, it momentarily displaces the fluid in the scala vestibuli. This displacement is transmitted through the flimsy partition, called **Reissner's membrane**, to the scala media where it presses on the basilar membrane. From there the displacement reaches the scala tympani where it eventually causes the round window to bulge outward. Such displacements follow one another at the frequency of the sound. Since the tectorial membrane in contact with the tips of the cilia is anchored firmly to the wall of the cochlea and at a different place from the elastic basilar membrane, the bodies of the hair cells are vibrated in a sliding or shearing fashion with respect to the tips of their cilia. This relative displacement of the cilia is believed to alter the membrane permeability of the hair cells and to depolarize them. This in turn excites the auditory neurons and changes their firing rate in the fibers of the auditory nerve.

A game in darkness

Bats and moths compete for survival after dark. The maneuvers in this game are determined entirely by ultrasound (beyond the range of human hearing) detectable by both organisms. The reward for the bats is food and for the moths survival. Much of the bats' story was worked out by Donald Griffin and his students.

The little brown bat, *Myotis*, is common during the summer in the northern part of America. As it flies in darkness it emits high-intensity cries about 10 to 20 times per second (Fig. 14–22). Each cry, or chirp as it may be called, is entirely ultrasonic. It begins with a frequency of up to 80 kHz and drops to about 30 to 40 kHz at the end. While the bat is cruising in open territory and searching for prey, each chirp lasts between 10 and 15 milliseconds.

The minimum size of an object capable of casting back an echo depends on the wavelength of sound striking it. The high frequencies and short wavelengths of bat chirps can, therefore, echo from quite small objects. Bats have large, movable ears and a most sensitive and sophisticated sense of hearing,

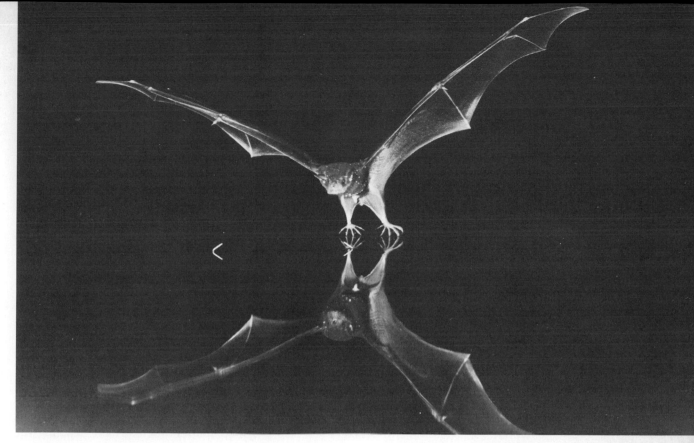

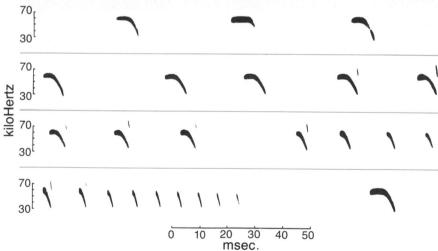

Figure 14–22   ABOVE: This tropical bat (*Noctilio leporinus*) catches fish as well as flying insects. It flies low over the water and with its sharp claws spears small fish swimming at the surface. The bat locates prey by echolocating ripples produced by fish or a dorsal fin breaking the surface. The photograph shows a bat being tested for its ability to discriminate between similar wires projecting at an angle from the water. A dip at the "correct" wire is rewarded with food. BELOW: Sonagrams of the sequence of ultrasonic orientation pulses emitted by a fishing bat as it caught food. Pulses were produced in sequence from left to right beginning in the top line. Most pulses begin with a constant frequency followed by a downward frequency modulated sweep. As the bat approaches its food, the pulse repetition rate increases and reaches a maximum at the instant the food is caught (near the middle of the bottom line).

for they are able to determine by echolocation both the distance or range (from the time for the echo to return) and the direction or bearing of quite small objects with amazing precision. They use echolocation to detect and avoid obstacles in their flight path and to determine the range and bearing of their prey, which consists entirely of flying insects. This is precisely the principle of sonar.

A moth is quite a small object. Moreover, it is generally moving in an erratic path through the air. A bat probably gets its first echoes from a moth when the range is less than 10 feet. It turns in flight toward the echo source and begins to track it. Remember that the bat is not receiving a continuous image of its prey as we would when tracking an object by sight. The bat's acoustic image is a discontinuous series of echoes. By extrapolating from this string of echoes, it has to estimate the next move of its prey. Accordingly, as the bat closes the range it shortens the duration of each chirp and increases their repetition frequency to as much as 200 per second (Fig. 14–22). This increase lessens the time interval or distance flown between echoes and increases the bat's accuracy as it gets closer to its target. If the insect is small it ends up directly in the bat's mouth.

Much about this performance remains mysterious. How can a bat detect the faint echo from a small object immediately after it has just uttered an extremely loud cry? How can bats distinguish between a pebble tossed in the air and a moth of equal size? Griffin and his students have shown that bats flying in a darkened laboratory can avoid colliding with many wires strung from floor to ceiling when they are only 0.1 mm in diameter, and that the bats continue this avoidance even when the room is flooded with ultrasonic noise.

Bats do not have it all their own way in this game played in the dark. Moths of some families have a countersonar system warning them of the approach of a bat. Moths of the family Noctuidae have a pair of ears or **tympanic organs** just below the second pair of wings. A thin tympanic membrane is coupled to two minute acoustic sense cells. Both respond best to short pulses containing the ultrasonic frequencies present in bat cries. While one is sensitive to faint sounds, the other begins to respond at the sound intensity at which the first reaches its maximum firing rate. There is no way in which this simple ear can discriminate pitch, yet it appears to have evolved solely as a bat-warning system. The more sensitive receptor cell begins to generate a train of spikes to each bat pulse when the bat is still 100 feet away (Fig. 14–23). Therefore, the bat-warning system of the moth gives advance notice that a bat is approaching long before the bat's sonar could detect the presence of its potential prey.

Experiments were carried out in the field in which the tracks of moths were recorded as they flew near a mast bearing an ultrasonic loudspeaker. The loudspeaker could be made to generate trains of bat-like ultrasonic pulses on command. Moths showed two kinds of behavior when the loudspeaker was switched on. If they were far from the fake bat they turned and steered a flight path away from the sound source. If they were close by and received intense acoustic stimulation, they showed a bewildering selection of loops and dives, flying mostly downward and to the ground (Fig. 14–24).

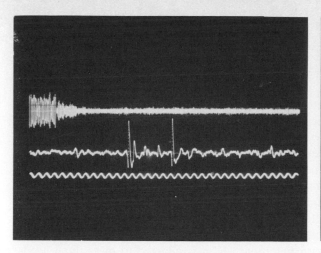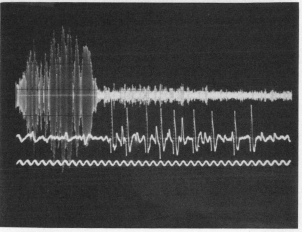

Figure 14–23 The cries of a bat flying outside the laboratory recorded through an open window by an ultrasonic microphone (upper trace) and an acoustic interneuron in the brain of a noctuid moth (middle trace). The sine waves in the lower trace mark 1 msec. intervals. At left, the bat was evidently more distant, as shown by the smaller amplitude of the microphone signal and the fact that the interneuron discharged only two spikes. At right, the bat was closer to the window, causing a larger microphone response and nine more closely spaced spikes in the brain interneuron. The delay in the nerve response was mostly due to the time taken for impulses to be conducted through two synapses to the moth's brain.

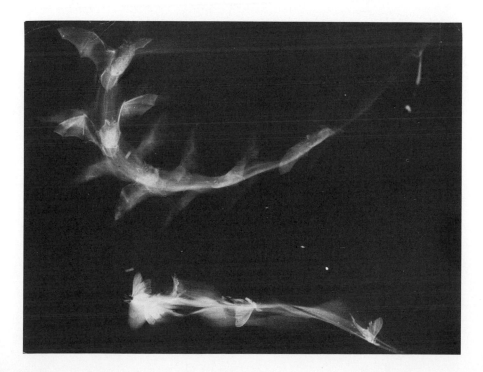

Figure 14–24 Evasive action can be traced in this multiple exposure photograph as the moth, initially flying toward the left, reverses direction to avoid the bat's dive and flies groundward.

These two types of reaction make sense for moth survival. The turning-away reaction occurs only when the moth could not have been detected by the bat, and it takes the moth to a safer area. The unpredictable dives and turns occur when the moth may be in tracking range of the bat's sonar. At this point it would not be of much value to the moth to fly away from the faster and heavier bat. The best protection is to be as unpredictable as possible and "hit the deck." These behavior patterns are steered by the spike trains in only four acoustic receptor cells, two in each tympanic organ.

These skirmishes between moths and bats illustrate once again the survival value of an ability to respond rapidly and with precise coordination of many muscles. In the precision timing these aerial combats require, a few milliseconds can make the difference of life or death for the moth and of satisfaction or hunger for the bat. Selective pressures such as these have been important factors shaping the evolution of the nervous system, and from the preceding pages we can begin to appreciate how well it is adapted to meet these needs. There are, however, important biological processes that occur over much longer periods and require a different mechanism for their long-term timing and coordination. The reproductive cycles of animals are a good example. The regulation of such processes is largely under control of the second major integrative system in the body—the endocrine system—which we will consider in the next chapter.

1 Since action potentials reaching the brain from the ear are just like those arriving from the eye or nose, how does the brain determine what kind of sensory modality the action potentials represent?

2 How would the stereochemical theory of olfaction explain the fact that chemically unrelated molecules sometimes have a very similar odor?

3 What effect does a quantum of light have on a molecule of visual pigment such as rhodopsin?

4 A generator potential is a special kind of graded, local potential. What is there about the nature of its origin that distinguishes it from endplate potentials and excitatory postsynaptic potentials?

5 Describe what is meant by the term "receptive field" as applied to a ganglion cell in the retina. What shape is characteristic of most cat ganglion cell receptive fields? How might these be combined to produce an elongate receptive field for a cell in the visual cortex?

6 Hair cells in the cochlea and stretch receptor neurons in the muscle spindle organ are both mechanoreceptors. One of these is a nerve cell; the other is not. How is each adapted to perform its special function? Contrast their adequate stimuli and the way in which they transmit excitation to the brain. What other sense organs use hair cells as transducers?

7 What are some ways in which the discharge of the moth's tympanic organ can tell the moth whether the bat is at a distance or very close?

SELECTED READINGS

Griffin, Donald R. *Listening in the Dark*. New Haven, Conn.: Yale University Press, 1958. A thorough, articulate account of early studies on echolocation by bats, blind people, and other animals.

Roeder, Kenneth B. *Nerve Cells and Insect Behavior*. Cambridge, Mass.: Harvard University Press, 1963. A delightful little book which describes various studies on insect nervous systems in terms of the behavior of the insects. For a shorter article in the same vein, see "Episodes in Insect Brains," *American Scientist,* vol. 58, no. 4 (1970), pp. 378–389, by the same author.

Smith, C. U. M. *The Brain. Towards an Understanding*. New York: G. P. Putnam's Sons, 1970. This lively book includes a discussion of sense organs, perception, and higher nervous activities.

Gregory, R. L. *Eye and Brain*: *The Psychology of Seeing*. New York: McGraw-Hill Book Co., 1966. A very interesting introduction to the psychology and physiology of visual perception. A useful bibliography is included.

15

THE ROLE OF HORMONES

HORMONES: THEIR EVOLUTION AND FUNCTION

Chemical transmission was probably the earliest method of communication, occurring first in single-celled organisms by diffusion within the cell and later between cells of multicellular organisms. The evolution of multicellular organisms required that the increasingly complex activities of millions of cells be coordinated with a speed, efficiency, and flexibility greater than that possible by simple diffusion (Fig. 15–1). The nervous system was one adaptation that retained chemical diffusion for message transmission from cell to cell. At the same time, evolution of a circulatory system provided the multicellular animal with an efficient means of removing wastes and supplying nutrients, and with an alternative pathway for the distribution of chemical messages throughout the body. Cells specializing in releasing into the general circulation chemicals that affect cell function at distant sites evolved into a second integrating system, the **endocrine system**. The components of the endocrine system sometimes occur as separate organs or glands, such as the thyroid, but they may also be only a portion of other organs. Endocrine glands are distinguishable from **exocrine** glands, such as the mammary glands, by the absence of a system of ducts for transport. **Hormones**, the chemical messengers of the endocrine system, use the circulatory system as a communication pathway.

Numerous endocrine tissues, each having one or more secretions and a variety of effects, make up the endocrine system of mammals (Fig. 15–2). Hormones not only coordinate the separate, specialized functions of cells, tissues, and organs but also regulate appropriate responses to changing conditions in the external and internal environments. Hence the endocrine system has a homeostatic function. During the course of evolution when animals moved out of the sea onto dry land and into freshwater, the composition of the fluid bathing their individual cells remained similar to that of the ancient sea, especially with regard to sodium and water. In the higher vertebrates, the kidney conserves or excretes water and sodium, and hormones from the **adrenal cortex** regulate these functions. Consequently, animals without adrenal cortical hormones become sodium-depleted and die unless they are supplied with additional dietary salt and protected from stress.

METAMORPHOSIS: In insects, hormones are involved with the series of developmental changes called **metamorphosis**. Most insects pass through an immature stage as **larvae** into the adult stage after spending several weeks or months as quiescent **pupae**. The larva itself may molt several times before it

Figure 15–1 The internal environment responds to external environmental stimuli and so readies the animal for action.

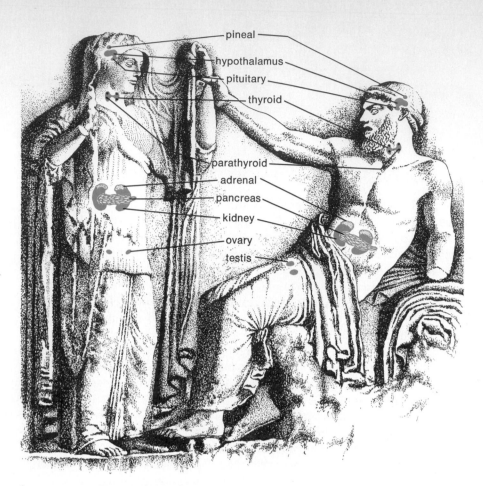

Figure 15–2 Endocrine glands in humans.

Labels on figure: pineal, hypothalamus, pituitary, thyroid, parathyroid, adrenal, pancreas, kidney, ovary, testis

forms a pupa. Research by V. B. Wigglesworth, C. M. Williams, and others has determined that the molting process is under indirect control by a hormone secreted in the brain of the larva, and under direct control by a second hormone, ecdysone, which is produced in the thorax. The "brain hormone" stimulates the gland that produces ecdysone. Ecdysone diffuses throughout the larva, beginning at the head and continuing to the rear, and induces the formation of a new exoskeleton. Thus, the insect is allowed to grow.

At some point in its development, however, the larva must be induced to metamorphose into an adult. This is accomplished by the repression of a third hormone, called the **juvenile hormone**, which is present in all but the last larval stage. When juvenile hormone is absent, the cellular processes leading to metamorphosis into an adult occur.

REPRODUCTION AND BEHAVIOR: In addition to its role in survival in a changing environment, the endocrine system is essential for the survival of the species. To this end, hormones control a wide range of morphological and physiological processes involved in reproduction and the courtship, mating, and parental behavior of pairs of animals. Pituitary hormones (**gonadotropins**) mediate environmental signals that activate the ovaries and testes in seasonal

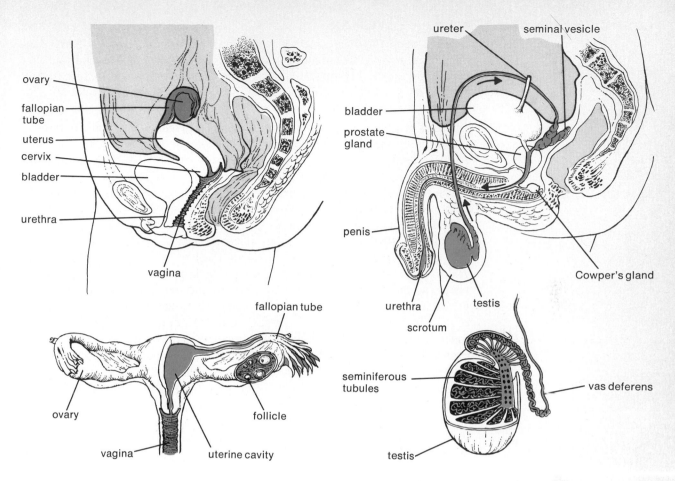

breeders and modulate cycles of gonadal activity in both seasonal and continuous breeders. Gonadal effects include growth and maturation of egg or sperm and secretion of the sex hormones **estrogen** and **progesterone** in females and **androgen** in males. In turn, the sex hormones stimulate growth and secretion of the ducts through which egg and sperm respectively are conveyed (**oviduct** and **vas deferens**), the compartment in which a developing embryo is nourished (**uterus**), and the organs of intromission by which internal fertilization is accomplished (**penis** and **vagina**). (Figs 15–3 and 15–4.) In addition to their effects on these and other sex accessories, hormones control the development of secondary sex characteristics, which first appear at sexual maturation and become most prominent when the gonads are actively secreting hormone. In some species males develop brilliant coloration and/or other dramatic accessories such as the bright red comb and wattles of roosters and the antlers of deer, adaptations that enable sexually active individuals to identify each other and are an integral part of, and sometimes trigger, courtship and mating behavior. The actions of hormones on peripheral tissues thus affect behavior.

Although the actual movements and postures comprising sex behavior must be attributed to integration by nerves, sex hormones acting directly on the nervous system condition the cellular substrate upon which neural messages

Figures 15–3 and 15–4 Human female and human male reproductive systems.

act and release behavior patterns characteristic of one sex or the other. In rodents, when the ovaries or testes are removed, mating behavior ceases but can be restored by injection of sex hormones. When hormone crystals are implanted in discrete hypothalamic areas of the brain, sex behavior reappears but not the morphological or physiological changes that would indicate that the hormone had reached the general circulation.

Sex as determined by genetic constitution as well as the embryonic hormonal environment are additional factors that modulate patterns of behavior in adult animals. Short exposure to a hormone, if given at the right time, produces a change in developing cells for the duration of the life of the animal. In rats, in which nervous system maturation continues for a few days after birth, one injection of male hormone into female pups under five days of age activates a male-type center for gonad control in the brain. At maturity, instead of manifesting the rhythmic gonadotropin secretion characteristic of females, the pituitaries of these animals have a steady level of gonadotropin output, like males. Consequently, cycles of alternating follicle growth and ovulation do not occur, so sterility results. Further, females injected with androgen show a greater frequency of male rather than female sex behavior. The same injection of male hormone after five days of age has no effect on development of sex behavior or gonadal control. Effects of hormones on development should be an essential consideration when hormones are administered to pregnant women or when oral contraceptive hormones are used during early pregnancy.

Hormones are influential in the development of certain behavior patterns even for some time after birth. It is not surprising that urination as an expression of territoriality in animals is sex-related. Female and immature male dogs crouch for urination, but after maturation and the initiation of testicular androgen secretion, a male dog urinates by lifting its leg. Subsequent castration does not alter its behavior. Thus, the presence of a hormone during learning can influence the behavior pattern that ensues although the hormone is no longer required. Persistence of sexuality in humans after castration may be explained, in part, by this effect.

Estrogens and androgen are not the only hormones that influence the developing brain. A deficiency of thyroid hormones before or immediately after birth affects maturation of the nervous system and produces permanent impairment of intelligence and other neural functions. The syndrome is called **cretinism** and can be produced experimentally by feeding the pups of pregnant rats a substance that blocks thyroid hormone synthesis or by removing the thyroid in newborn animals.

Other behavior patterns of individuals and societies of animals, while not so obviously sex-related as courtship and mating, are also affected by male and female sex hormones. Aggressiveness and dominance are aspects of territoriality and are illustrated in the establishment of social hierarchies. A group of female hens kept together for a period of time will sort themselves out into a peck order. The most dominant hen is most aggressive and pecks all the others. The most peaceful hen is pecked by everybody and pecks no one. Each of the other hens has a fairly stable position somewhere between these two extremes. Male birds, or cocks, also sort themselves into social hierarchies—but with a violence sometimes resulting in death. A castrated cock drops rapidly to the bottom of the peck order while injection of androgen into a hen will improve her social position. Injection of estrogen tends to lower the rank of hens or cocks. Peck orders are common among many species; however, in mixed male and female societies, aggressiveness is usually related to possession of the available females.

CHARACTERISTICS OF THE ENDOCRINE SYSTEM

Hormones as messengers

Hormones are organic molecules that may be divided into two classes. **Steroids** are lipids produced in a variety of forms by the adrenal cortex, the gonads, and the placenta. Each of the steroid-forming endocrine tissues has a capability of manufacturing the hormones of other steroid-producing glands under normal and certain disease conditions. For example, a rich source of female sex hormone is the stallion testis. When some kinds of adrenal tumors occur in genetic females, excess production of androgens has masculinizing effects.

The second class of hormones are those that are either amino acid derivatives or amino acid chains of various lengths (polypeptides and proteins). Among this group are hormones that resemble neurotransmitters. Some of the amino acid sequences of polypeptide and protein hormones are known. Insulin, for example, has 51 amino acids comprising two polypeptide chains.

Some hormones have inhibitory effects. Experimental results indicate that pituitary **MSH (melanophore stimulating hormone)** synthesis and release occur spontaneously and that the hypothalamus has an inhibitory influence. Frogs change color in response to environmental stimuli, turning light on a light background and dark on a dark background. When the pituitary is removed from juvenile frogs, light colored or "silvery tadpoles" result. However, when the pituitary is transplanted away from the sphere of influence of the hypothalamus, or when the connection between hypothalamus and pituitary is severed, the tadpoles become very dark (Fig. 15–5).

The molecular structures of hormones that are homologous (serving the same function) throughout vertebrates are very similar. In the case of the ovarian hormones progesterone and estradiol and the thyroid hormones, molecules are identical. Estrogens and other sex steroids have also been isolated from invertebrate and plant tissues and thus are extremely widely distributed molecules. There are some species differences, however, especially in the peptide and protein hormones. **Somatotropic hormone (STH)** from domestic animals such as sheep and cows is not effective in promoting growth in primates (monkeys and humans). Some suggest that during the course of evolution it was not the molecular structure of hormones that changed, but the uses to which hormones were put. If this hypothesis about the evolution of hormonal effectors is correct, it is not surprising that the same hormones in different animals have widely different actions. While **prolactin** stimulates milk secretion in animals with mammary glands, the hormone affects crop sac secretion and

Figure 15–5 The tadpoles left and right of the center animal (the control) had their pituitaries removed. While the one at left shows retarded growth and failed to develop pigmentation, the one at right became gigantic and developed dark pigmentation after its pituitary was reimplanted (irregular mass on side of tail). (WILLIAM ETKIN)

maternal behavior in pigeons, water drive in amphibia, and salt and water balance in fish and reptiles, to cite just a few examples.

The communication pathway: hormones in circulation

The communication pathway for endocrine messages is the blood. A number of factors act simultaneously and affect circulating hormone levels: rate of synthesis and release from endocrine tissue, quantity of binding protein available for transport, and rate of inactivation.

SYNTHESIS AND SECRETION: Hormonal synthesis and secretion are separate processes and may occur independently. In general, the rate of secretion depends on the need for the hormone; however, each hormone has specific mechanisms that control its rate of synthesis and/or release. Synthesis of hormones occurs on or in the membranous network of the cell cytoplasm from raw materials present in the diet or from products of other cells. The use of radioactive isotopes has enabled endocrinologists to study the step-by-step synthesis of many hormones from labeled precursors and the specific enzymes catalyzing each step. In the biosynthesis of steroids, there are intermediates common to all hormones belonging to this category. Relative differences in activity of specific enzymes in the ovaries, testes, placenta, and adrenal cortex determine the predominant pathway and end product.

To some extent all endocrine cells store their products or precursors, which are then visible in the cytoplasm as membrane-bound granules (polypeptide hormones and protein) or lipid droplets (steroid hormones). Variations in the quantity of these materials are indicative of cycles of activity and inactivity; however, it is sometimes impossible to determine whether the absence of cytoplasmic granules can be attributed to decreased synthesis or increased release. Secretion is released from the cells when a granule or droplet adheres to the cell membrane which, without rupturing, fuses behind it. The hormone passes first into the spaces surrounding the cells and then diffuses into the rich capillary and lymphatic network characteristic of all endocrine tissues.

TRANSPORT: Once in the blood, hormones are distributed between the cells and plasma according to their molecular size and ability to diffuse across membranes. Thus red cells act as a reservoir for plasma steroids. In the plasma, thyroid and steroid hormones and insulin are transported in loose combination with specific "carrier" proteins. These not only prevent diffusion out of the capillaries but also protect against metabolism as the blood passes through the liver and kidney. There is an equilibrium between free and bound hormone in plasma; only the free is biologically active, the bound serving as a reservoir. The levels of binding protein determine the capacity of the plasma for steroid transport. In humans, for example, there is a specific binding globulin, transcortin, for the major secretion of the adrenal cortex (**cortisol**), which functions in adjustments to stress. Estrogen increases the level of transcortin by influencing its synthesis in the liver, thus leading to an elevated level of cortisol in females compared to males. The usefulness of this adaptation is unproven, but it may be related to the increased stress associated with reproduction in females.

The effective levels of hormones in the blood and at active sites in the tissues are extremely low. For example, in mammals the concentration of estrogen in plasma is as low as 0.00005 micrograms per milliliter. The nature and intensity of the response elicited by each hormone at the periphery are primarily a function of its concentration in the blood. As little as 0.0125 micrograms of estrogen per rat injected systematically produces significant growth of the immature uterus.

METABOLISM: Some degree of hormonal inactivation occurs within all tissues; however, both liver and kidney have special enzymes that metabolize hormones in the blood passing through them. The end products of metabolism are then excreted in the urine or feces. The quantity of hormone metabolic products lost in the urine is used as an index of endocrine activity and also as a source of hormone for purification and experimental or clinical use.

Responses to hormones

PROPERTIES OF THE MESSAGE: In the nervous system, extension of the neuron itself all the way to the site of action, and application of the chemical component of the final message directly to the cell membrane, assures rapid transmission to a specific effector. The response is of brief duration, however, since neural transmitters are enzymatically destroyed at their site of action immediately following release.

Hormones are dependent upon the circulatory system for transport of the message to the site of action and are distributed randomly throughout the blood, lymph, and extracellular fluid. In contrast to nervous control, changes in the organism produced in response to hormonal signals occur more slowly, are of longer duration, and may be diffuse, occurring in many widely separated cells simultaneously. While a response to a nervous stimulus can be measured in milliseconds, hormonal responses must be measured in minutes, hours, or even days. **Adrenocorticotropic hormone (ACTH)**, one of the hormones released by a stress, stimulates a measurable increase in adrenocortical hormones in blood within one minute of injection. In contrast, a single injection of thyroxin will elicit a response measurable by an increase in basal metabolic rate beginning 30 hours later, long after the hormone has disappeared from the blood. Some hormones thus act as triggers for lengthy responses.

Not only is the effect of a single pulse of hormone of longer duration than that of a nervous impulse, but the level of many hormones in blood is fairly constant within a short time span producing a sustained effect. Thus, endocrine regulation is ideally suited for physiological and behavioral processes spanning days or even months. Developmental changes such as growth, metamorphosis, sexual maturation, and their related behavior patterns are all hormone-controlled. Migration is an example of a hormone-controlled behavior pattern. The spotted newt *Diemyctylus* is an amphibian that, after the first metamorphosis (red eft stage), lives on land for three to four years and then returns to water and matures sexually. The motivation to return to life in the water is initiated by prolactin, a pituitary hormone, and maturational aspects of this metamorphosis have additional hormonal controls.

Figure 15–6 *Rana pipiens* tadpoles show localized metamorphic changes (tail fin resorption) induced at the point of implantation by pellets of thyroid hormone analog. The top photograph was taken 6 days after implantation. The one below was taken 20 days after implantation; hence resorption covers a larger area.

Hormone effects can be localized, but only when the hormone does not enter the general circulation. The classic experiment of C. Williams in which the larva of the *Cecropia* moth was divided into head and tail by constricting ligatures demonstrated that metamorphosis could be confined to body parts exposed to the appropriate sequence of hormones. Similarly, local metamorphosis can be induced in tadpoles by implanting thyroxin pellets. Presumably the hormonal concentration reaching the general circulation is too low to induce complete metamorphosis (Fig. 15–6).

In view of the ubiquitous distribution of hormones within an animal, how is specificity of action achieved in hormone-regulated processes? No cells are affected by all the hormones with which they come in contact; rather, different tissues have different sensitivities to the action of each hormone. Those tissues most sensitive to a hormone are called its **target tissues**. Virtually the entire cell population is sensitive to growth hormone, insulin, and the thyroid hormones. Other hormones act almost exclusively on specific target tissues: **FSH (follicle-stimulating hormone)** and **LH (lutenizing hormone)** on the gonad, **TSH (thyroid-stimulating hormone)** on the thyroid, and ACTH on the adrenal cortex. Most endocrine tissues are insensitive to their own secretion; however, this does not preclude sites of action in adjacent tissues in the same organ. Androgen produced by the Leydig cells of the testes is essential for sperm production by testicular tubules. Similar localized actions of estrogen on ovarian follicular development have been reported.

Many hormones have multiple target tissues that respond simultaneously. In lizards, increased secretion of estrogen during the sexually active phase induces synthesis in the liver of protein destined for deposition in the yolk of the growing egg, releases calcium from storage in bone for shell formation, stimulates growth of the oviduct in preparation for receipt of the egg, and initiates the appropriate behavior for mating to occur so that sperm and egg are brought together at just the right time (Fig. 15–7).

Stress acting via neural pathways stimulates the secretion of large quantities of adrenal medullary hormones. The "fight or flight" response that follows involves many different organs: increased heart rate, increased depth of respiration, increased blood sugar, increased blood flow through the muscle, decreased blood flow through the skin, decreased intestinal motility. All these adjustments are useful in preparing the animal to respond physically to stress and are accompanied by a heightened emotional state. A multiplicity of target tissues enables the endocrine system to coordinate complex, interrelated responses simultaneously by the secretion of a single hormone.

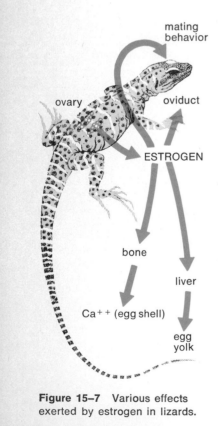

Figure 15–7 Various effects exerted by estrogen in lizards.

RECEPTORS: What confers hormone sensitivity on a particular cell type? Hypothetically, the molecules composing different cells have receptor sites that fit like a key to a lock with a molecular component of a particular hormone. Formation of a hormone–receptor complex is the first, essential step in the fundamental action of a hormone at the molecular level. Thus, the absence of tissue sensitivity to a hormone may be explained by the inability of a hormone to bind to appropriate receptors. Experimentally, target tissues or intracellular receptor sites are identified in animals injected with radioisotopically labeled hormone if all of the following criteria can be established:

1) at a specified time after injection (say, two hours) concentrations of radioactivity occur in selected tissues; 2) these tissues lose their radioactivity more slowly than other regions, indicating hormonal "binding"; 3) administration of the same, non-radioactive hormone prior to injection of the radioactive hormone reduces the quantity of radioactivity taken up, implying that available binding sites are already filled and indicating receptor specificity; 4) removal of a natural source of the hormone under investigation increases the amount of radioactive hormone taken up, indicating a greater percentage of vacant binding sites. Selective uptake of labeled hormone can be demonstrated in tissue samples by microdissection and analysis of radioactivity in separate samples. Another method, autoradiography, makes possible the intracellular localization of receptor sites. Thin sections of whole tissue are exposed to photographic film sensitive to radiation, and then the film is compared with adjacent thin sections of tissues prepared in the usual way for microscopic observation (Fig. 15–8).

Hormone binding sometimes occurs in clumps of cells that have not yet been established as hormone-sensitive. Separate hormone–receptor complexes, although not yet chemically isolated and identified, are thought to account for the multiplicity of effects elicited by a single hormone.

MECHANISMS OF ACTION: A fundamental question that must still be answered for most hormones is what happens at the molecular level following formation of the hormone–receptor complex. The primary action of a hormone—a single cellular or subcellular biochemical or physical change—must be distinguished from the numerous secondary effects that occur as a result of that change. Thyroid hormones, for example, have wide-ranging effects: in adults, on rate of metabolism and oxygen consumption, especially in muscle and liver; in juveniles, on growth and maturation, especially of bone and nerve tissue; in warm-blooded animals, on heat production and regulation of body temperature; in amphibia, on a multitude of changes associated with the transformation of the aquatic larval form, the tadpole, into the terrestrial adult form, the frog. For many years, the lag period between administration of thyroid hormone and observed effects puzzled endocrinologists and suggested that unknown events occurring during this time might account for all of these metabolic and growth changes. Recent research has revealed a number of intracellular changes in response to thyroid hormones, all of which are associated with protein synthesis, especially in liver.

Hormones do not initiate any new processes but affect the level at which the molecular apparatus characteristic for each cell type functions. Because so little is known about these intracellular events, it is difficult to determine precisely how they are regulated by hormones. Nevertheless, the primary mechanisms of hormonal action may be grouped into several categories. For instance, hormones are known to act on enzyme systems by increasing the synthesis or activity of an enzyme or by serving as an essential component of a reaction. According to this concept, by favoring one metabolic pathway hormones may depress an alternative route.

Another site of hormone action is the cell membrane. In some instances, hormones appear to alter cellular metabolism by affecting the permeability of

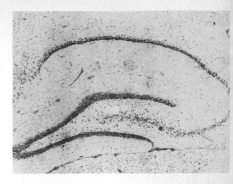

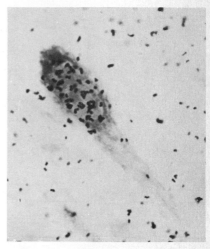

Figure 15–8 Radioautogram illustrating localization of hormone in rat brain after injection of labeled corticosterone. In the top radioautogram, a longitudinal section, the contrast between dark and light areas is partly due to intensity of labeling of hippocampal neurons. Below, at greater magnification, silver grains indicating exposure to radioactive hormone can be observed clustered primarily over the nucleus of a single neuron. Surrounding areas are relatively free of labeled hormone. (From *Science*, Vol. 175, pp. 1133–1136, Fig. 1 by J. L. Gerlach and B. S. McEwen. Copyright © 10 March, 1972. American Association for the Advancement of Science.)

structural membranes surrounding the cell or the organelles contained within it. Theoretically, formation of a hormone–receptor complex positioned on a membrane may initiate a rearrangement of the molecules comprising the membrane and alter its properties as a barrier. Thus, hormones may control the supply of substrate or other components of intracellular reactions and thereby regulate the rate of occurrence of those reactions. Growth hormone, for example, probably stimulates protein synthesis and resultant growth by increasing the rate of entry into the cell of amino acids, which are protein building blocks. Similarly, insulin markedly increases the rate of entry of both glucose and amino acids into most cells, accounting for its effects in lowering blood sugar and increasing intracellular energy metabolism and growth. A number of other hormones alter transport of inorganic ions, water, amino acids, and sugars across membranes. This type of hormonal action can be demonstrated only in cells with membranes intact.

Other hormones act on gene-controlled metabolism within the cell. It is generally recognized that the chromosomal components of the cell nucleus regulate the day-to-day processes characteristic of any particular cell and the direction of development from a juvenile, undifferentiated cell to the definitive adult type. Genes govern cell function by controlling the synthesis of enzymes and other proteins within the cell. In addition to the thyroid hormones, growth hormone, estrogen, testosterone, and adrenal corticoids bind specifically to sites within the nuclei of their target cells and affect protein synthesis. In vertebrates that produce large, yolked eggs, for example, the yolk protein vitellin is synthesized in the liver and transported via the blood to the developing follicle in the ovary, where the vitellin is deposited as yolk. One of the numerous effects of estrogen is a shift in protein synthesis in the liver to vitellin, a gene-induced act. In theory, hormones act directly or indirectly on genes by activating or suppressing their function. However, the reactions occurring in both the nucleus and cytoplasm that lead to completion of a specific protein molecule are complex, and a number of the steps during synthesis may be hormone-sensitive. It is tempting to speculate that hormonal actions on genes account for many of the known effects of hormones in development.

HORMONAL INTERACTIONS: Although in theory specific actions may be attributed to individual hormones, in life these actions occur within a general hormonal milieu consisting of secretions of all the endocrine glands. In the endocrine system there is, in fact, an interdependency that sometimes makes it difficult in a living animal to separate the effects of one gland from the function of others. The secretory activity of many endocrine glands is affected directly by other hormones, which, in turn, depend for their effects on simultaneous or sequential secretions of other endocrine glands. **Glucagon**, a hormone that effects an increase in blood sugar, acts directly on the pancreas by stimulating secretion of **insulin**, the hormone that *depresses* blood sugar. Thus, while glucagon directly influences insulin secretion, the two hormones are mutually **antagonistic**.

Hormones that promote a change in the same direction, on the other hand, are termed **synergists**. A special example of synergism occurs when a single hormone has no readily detectable effect of its own but enhances the effectiveness of a second hormone. The first hormone is said to be permissive. Progesterone, for example, has little influence on sex behavior but increases the effect of estrogens. For some processes the appropriate sequence of hormones is critical. Estrogen followed by progesterone is essential for maximal uterine growth and secretion. The delicate balance of complex hormonal interactions is best illustrated by menstrual cycles, which involve at least six hormones in appropriate sequence.

ENDOCRINE CONTROL SYSTEMS

All endocrine glands have a basal rate of secretory activity that compensates for use and metabolism and maintains a constant level of hormone in the blood. In addition, acute changes in circulating hormone occur in response to external or internal environmental signals. Control mechanisms maintain levels at a predetermined "set-point" and adjust the set-point as required.

Feedback control

CIRCULATORY CONTROL OF HORMONE SECRETION: Like many other biological phenomena, steady state activity of the endocrine system is controlled by negative feedback systems, each gland being autoregulatory. The components of these feedback loops are analogous to the reflex arcs of the nervous system. Briefly, excitation of a sensor stimulates the release of hormones into the blood, whereby they reach a responsive target cell, an endocrine effector, which produces a response that negates the stimulus and shuts off further hormone secretion.

In contrast to the nervous system, the sensory circuit of simple endocrine feedback systems is foreshortened, and the reception of stimuli and output of effector signals are both functions of the endocrine tissue itself. A comparable neural reflex in which the brain receives stimuli directly before relaying signals to effector organs is that for temperature regulation. In the endocrine system there is no equivalent of the special receptors that are part of the central nervous system. All endocrine tissues function as receptors in feedback loops and are sensitive to chemical and sometimes physical changes in the blood.

One of the simplest endocrine control systems is that governing blood calcium (Fig. 15–9, bottom). Calcium ions are important for certain chemical reactions such as blood coagulation and hormone–receptor interactions, and they control the irritability of membranes. In the absence of adequate blood calcium ions nerves fire spontaneously and muscle cells have a lower threshold for stimulation. In skeletal muscle, fibrillations or twitchings may progress to sustained, painful spasms and convulsions. This condition is called **tetany** and can result in death, often from asphyxiation due to spasm of the laryngeal muscles. Total body calcium must be replenished continually in the diet as calcium is lost through the urine and feces, and a readily available source of blood calcium is the bone.

Dissolved calcium in the blood is in equilibrium with stored calcium in bone.

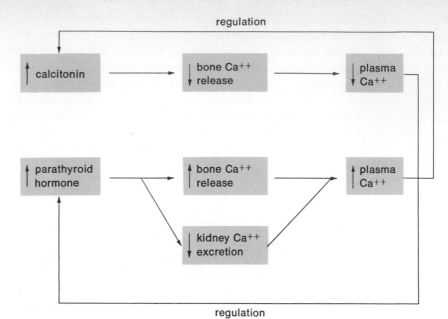

Figure 15–9 Feedback regulation of blood calcium.

A decline in plasma calcium provokes parathyroid hormone secretion which mobilizes calcium from bone and diminishes calcium loss via the kidney filtrate. As blood calcium rises, the stimulus to further parathyroid hormone secretion is reduced. This simple feedback loop functions in parallel with a second system involving **calcitonin**, a hormone secreted by cells intermingled with definitive thyroid tissue in response to increased blood calcium. Calcitonin has effects on bone and kidney opposite to parathyroid hormone (Fig. 15–9, top), effectively lowering blood calcium and negating its own further secretion but providing a stimulus for parathyroid hormone release. These two hormones regulate serum calcium between the normal limits of 9 to 11 mg/100 ml. A "push–pull" principle whereby two antagonistic hormones operate via interconnected feedback loops in the regulation of a single blood parameter probably provides a more precise control mechanism than would be possible with a single loop. The two pancreatic hormones insulin and glucagon, which are secreted in response to fluctuations in blood glucose, also operate on a push–pull principle.

Two additional endocrine organs, those that regulate water and sodium content of body fluids, are sensitive to blood changes in these parameters. The **zona glomerulosa**, the outer layer of the adrenal cortex, produces **aldosterone**, which acts on the kidney tubules and decreases loss of sodium in the urine. **Anti-diuretic hormone (ADH)**, synthesized in the hypothalamus, enables the kidney tubules to reabsorb water, thus diminishing urinary loss. All endocrine glands that have a homeostatic function are directly responsive to the substance being regulated. While fairly rapid, this type of negative feedback system is relatively inflexible; the predetermined set-point or threshold sensitivity does not vary in the course of normal operation. Since the survival of the animal depends on the internal environment's being maintained within narrow limits, the adaptive significance of rigidly controlled homeostatic regulators is apparent.

The balance between the components of a single feedback system is clearly illustrated by pituitary control of ovarian growth. Follicle-stimulating hormone (FSH) from the anterior pituitary stimulates dramatic growth of the ovarian follicles about every 28 days in females. The maturing follicles secrete increasing amounts of estrogen which, in turn, shut off pituitary FSH output. The balance between these two hormones is such that if one ovary is removed, reducing estrogen output to one half, FSH secretion continues unchecked until the size and hormone output of the remaining ovary have doubled. This phenomenon is termed **compensatory hypertrophy** and occurs in other endocrine tissues. The same principle may be illustrated in animals injected with estrogen. After a while, the ovaries of these animals undergo atrophy (regression), the exogenous source of hormone effectively replacing the endogenous source by shutting down pituitary FSH secretion and, thus, follicle growth. Any source of estrogen, including birth control tablets, can potentially block FSH. Similarly, the indiscriminate use of androgenic substances by athletes to build up muscle strength may suppress normal testicle function.

Because of the variety of tropic hormones secreted by the anterior pituitary, for many years this gland was considered the "master gland" or "conductor of the endocrine orchestra." Feedback control systems for the glands regulated by pituitary hormones emphasized the importance of this gland and were called the pituitary–gonad, pituitary–adrenocortical, and pituitary–thyroid axes. In fact, these relationships are more complex than the simple feedback loops that control the hormones of homeostasis, because the pituitary itself is regulated by a part of the brain immediately overlying it, the **hypothalamus**. When techniques became available for transplanting the pituitary away from its bony chamber at the base of the brain to another site—beneath the kidney capsule, for example—the adrenal cortex, thyroid, and gonads atrophied to the same extent as we would expect if the pituitary had been removed entirely. However, these glands were restored to their original size after the pituitary was retransplanted back under the hypothalamus. Normal tropic hormone secretion, therefore, depends on a functioning hypothalamic–pituitary complex.

Although the pituitary itself is relatively insensitive to fluctuating levels of estrogen and other target-organ hormones, we can locate feedback-sensitive areas in the hypothalamus experimentally. A very small pellet of crystalline estrogen placed directly into the hypothalamus will effectively block FSH secretion and induce ovarian atrophy; however, similar quantities of estrogen implanted under the skin or even directly into the pituitary are not effective. A much greater quantity of estrogen is required to block FSH when the estrogen is injected into the general circulation. Discrete hypothalamic areas concentrate and bind estrogen and other target-gland hormones such as thyroxin and cortisol. In addition, rate of spontaneous discharge and firing patterns of individual hypothalamic neurons have been related to the hormonal status of the animal. Hormone-induced sex behavior patterns are probably mediated by electrophysiological changes in hypothalamic neurons also.

The feedback loops of which the tropic hormones are components consist of two separate endocrine tissues, the hypothalamus and the anterior pituitary, functioning in series and regulating a target tissue or third endocrine gland

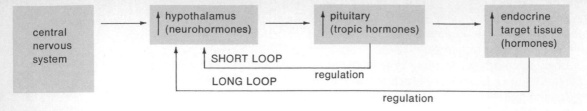

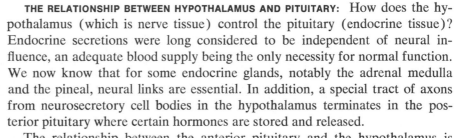

Figure 15–10 Feedback control of tropic hormone secretion by the pituitary.

(Fig. 15–10). The hypothalamus detects fluctuations in target organ hormones such as estrogen (long feedback loop) and also in tropic hormones such as FSH (short feedback loop).

THE RELATIONSHIP BETWEEN HYPOTHALAMUS AND PITUITARY: How does the hypothalamus (which is nerve tissue) control the pituitary (endocrine tissue)? Endocrine secretions were long considered to be independent of neural influence, an adequate blood supply being the only necessity for normal function. We now know that for some endocrine glands, notably the adrenal medulla and the pineal, neural links are essential. In addition, a special tract of axons from neurosecretory cell bodies in the hypothalamus terminates in the posterior pituitary where certain hormones are stored and released.

The relationship between the anterior pituitary and the hypothalamus is not neural but vascular (Fig. 15–11). When the blood vessels linking these two organs are destroyed and prevented from regenerating, tropic hormone secretion ceases. Blood flows from the hypothalamus to the pituitary through portal vessels. Blood entering the primary capillary bed of the hypothalamus collects in separate vessels that carry it to a second capillary bed in the anterior pituitary. Thus, any materials diffusing into the blood in the hypothalamus are carried a short distance directly to the pituitary. In some instances, point-to-point vascular pathways between discrete areas of the hypothalamus and pituitary occur. A combination of anatomical and physiological observations support a neurovascular theory of tropic hormone control stating that neurosecretory cells in the hypothalamus synthesize and release into the portal circulation hormones that regulate anterior pituitary function.

The relationship between the brain and the anterior pituitary has considerable value to the animal, since it serves as an important link between the nervous and endocrine systems. Certain areas of the hypothalamus are sensitive not only to hormonal feedback but also to neural input from nerve tracts connecting the hypothalamus and other brain areas, including the cerebral cortex. Thus, the hypothalamus is a transducer for the conversion of neural messages into hormonal signals, and the pituitary portal system is the "final common pathway" for both types of messages.

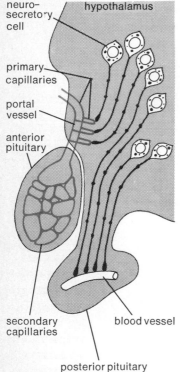

Figure 15–11 The pituitary has a double relationship with the hypothalamus. While nerve fibers link the hypothalamus with the posterior pituitary, in mammals blood vessels carry neurohormones from the hypothalamus to the anterior pituitary.

Brain-endocrine interaction

Although chemicals transported in the blood regulate long term hormonal secretion, nerve-mediated stimuli control acute changes in endocrine activity. In general, the set-point for circulating hormone is determined by the need for that hormone. This in turn depends on what is happening outside the body and at distant sites within the body. Most animals, for example, have yearly cycles of breeding activity, which means that hormones integrating reproductive functions must be responsive to environmental signals such as day length, temperature, rainfall, or food supply.

Receptors of the nervous system detect sensory stimuli and include special sense organs such as the eye and ear and receptors for pain and temperature. Although the endocrine system is without such sensory devices, there are several pathways between the nervous and endocrine systems by which environmental information monitored by neural receptors can influence endocrine-regulated processes (Fig. 15–12). Control systems having both neural and endocrine components are termed **neuroendocrine reflex arcs**.

ENVIRONMENTAL CUES AND HORMONE ACTION: The vascular link between brain and anterior pituitary is the route by which the nervous system exerts the greatest variety of endocrine effects. All tropic hormones respond to one or more environmental changes: STH, ACTH, and LH to day–night cycles; TSH to environmental temperature variations; ACTH to physical and emotional stress; and so on. The controlling influence of the nervous system on FSH and LH secretion and associated reproductive functions have been especially well studied.

The onset of reproductive activity in the springtime in a wide variety of species is one of the oldest known examples of the external environment influencing hormonal secretion. One of the major factors involved in this process is increasing day length which acts via the nervous system to stimulate the secretion of gonadotropin by the pituitary. In birds, this stimulates the testes of the males to secrete androgens under the influence of which they begin courting the females.

Once the behavior patterns in a male are altered by its own (endogenous) androgen acting on its brain, the induced change in behavioral responsiveness

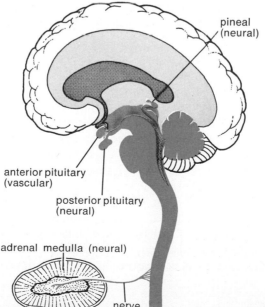

Figure 15–12 Neural and vascular connections between the central nervous system and the endocrine system.

presents a new stimulus to the females. If female ring doves are kept together with castrated males, it is extremely unlikely that they will ovulate. If, however, the males are injected with androgen, they show increasing amounts of various elements of courtship behavior in proportion to the dosage of androgen which they have received. The proportion of females that ovulate in this situation is directly related to the dose of androgens which the *males* received. Thus a hormonally-induced behavior change in the male is converted to a hormonal change in the female. This ovarian response in the female thus depends on complex processes involved in recognition of particular sensory patterns (such as visual and auditory) which then stimulate her pituitary gland, and thereby stimulate her ovary.

Clearly courtship behavior by males has a potent effect in stimulating ovarian development in the females toward which the courtship is directed, and the female's already basally-stimulated ovaries (also under the influence of increasing day length) are rapidly stimulated to develop and secrete more estrogen and progesterone. These increasing levels of ovarian hormones stimulate nest-building behavior and mating readiness in the females, and these changes in her behavior in turn influence the male to change his behavior toward the female. Thus a sequential interaction develops in which the external environment changes the hormonal levels in an individual, resulting in a change in its behavior and reproductive condition; the change in behavior then induces a change in hormonal condition in the mate, and this induced hormonal change alters the mate's behavior and reproductive state. This change in behavior then acts back on the first individual, and the mutual interaction proceeds through the stages of mating, nest-building, egg-laying, incubation, and caring for the young.

Man-made alterations in the environment often produce dramatic effects. For example, the starlings that roost under the brilliantly lit billboards of the West End in London have significantly larger testes than their suburban counterparts. Nor is the human species immune to such influences. It has been suggested that the earlier onset of menstrual cycles in girls in this century, compared to the last, is associated with the invention of the incandescent bulb!

OVULATION: The senses of sight, sound, smell, and touch have all been shown to modify hormone secretion. For example, chickens lay eggs almost entirely during the daytime. But if the light cycle is reversed so that it is light at night and dark during the day, the chickens soon lay their eggs almost exclusively during the light night period. Ring doves (see also Chapter 22) ovulate if they are placed in a cage with another dove—male or female—or with a mirror, but they do not ovulate if they are alone. So visual stimuli can activate secretion of gonadotropin by the pituitary. Parakeets and doves can be made to ovulate if the recorded sounds of other birds of their species are played to them, indicating the importance of auditory stimuli for endocrine processes. If female mice are raised in cages together with male mice, they attain puberty and start the ovulatory cycle at a significantly younger age than if they are raised only with females. If female mice merely smell the odor of male mice of a strain different from the one with which they mated, their pregnancy can become blocked, but their pregnancy persists if their olfactory bulbs are removed. Thus, odors also play a significant role in hormonally-controlled reproductive processes. In some animals touch also plays an extremely important role in certain endocrine processes, especially ovulation.

In most mammals except humans copulation and release of the egg from the ovary are synchronized, increasing the probability that fertilization will take place. This occurs in two ways. Animals that ovulate spontaneously at about the midpoint of the cycle at this time also exhibit behavioral **estrus**, the time when the female is "in heat," or receptive to advances by the male. In animals with estrous cycles (for example, dogs, rats, and domestic animals), secretion of the ovulating hormone LH and estrogen effects on receptivity are governed both by intrinsic hypothalamic rhythms and hormonal feedback.

In other animals, copulation itself is the stimulus required for LH release. The rabbit, cat, and ferret are **reflex ovulators**, the ripened follicle remaining in a state of suspended activity until copulation occurs. In the rabbit, stimuli are transmitted to the brain by peripheral sensory neurons from the genital area within 30 seconds after copulation. Within 90 minutes, sufficient hormones have been secreted to begin the physical and biochemical changes in the ovary leading to ovulation. The total time elapsing from stimulus to ovulation is about 10 hours. Electrical stimulation of appropriate hypothalamic areas will trigger ovulation in the absence of copulation. Although human females ovulate spontaneously at about day 14 of a 28-day menstrual cycle, there is evidence that, in some individuals, ovulation can be induced by copulation during the first half of the cycle. This may partially explain the unreliability of rhythm as a contraceptive method. While mating behavior in spontaneous ovulators is hormone-regulated, in reflex ovulators mating behavior itself induces the hormone-controlled event. These two phenomena clearly illustrate that there are reciprocal relationships between the nervous system and the endocrine system.

NEUROHORMONE PATHWAYS: The neural link between the hypothalamus and posterior pituitary is a second pathway for brain–endocrine interaction. At this site, neural input acting directly on neurosecretory cells signals the synthesis of vasopressin and oxytocin. Nonspecific sensory stimuli including pain, stress, and other sensory stimuli can elicit release of these neurohormones. The milk ejection reflex is a familiar example. In a lactating female, the stimulus received during suckling of the infant is transmitted along sensory nerves to the brain, and **oxytocin** is released. This neurohormone produces contraction of the muscle cells surrounding the milk sacs in the mammary glands, which results in the release of milk into the ducts. This reflex can be conditioned; a mother thinking of her baby or a cow hearing milk pails rattling may produce the same effect as suckling.

Although the exact sequence of hormonal events leading to the birth process itself is not clear, oxytocin is known to be involved in a positive feedback loop resulting in uterine contractions and, ultimately, expulsion of the fetus. In humans, both uterine contractions and milk ejection occur in response to sensory stimuli during copulation, probably as a result of oxytocin release.

1 What are the major differences between neural and endocrine integration? What similarities are there? What processes are controlled by each?
2 How do hormones act?
3 How do hormones affect the nervous system and influence behavior? Give specific examples.
4 Is there a reciprocal relationship between the two integrating systems, nervous and endocrine? Discuss.
5 Which hormones are independent of nervous control? Which are affected by nerve-mediated signals? What is the adaptational significance of these two types of hormone control systems?
6 Diagram a negative feedback loop. How is it autoregulatory?
7 Diagram the pathways by which environmental lighting affects the female reproductive tract.
8 What is neurosecretion? What is the importance of the pituitary portal system?

SELECTED READINGS

Frieden, E., and Lipner, H. *Biochemical Endocrinology of the Vertebrates.* (Foundations of Modern Biochemistry Series). Englewood Cliffs, N. J.: Prentice-Hall, Inc., 1971. This is a concise and up-to-date compilation of hormone biochemistry. It is especially useful for information about mechanisms of hormone action and chemistry of hormone molecules.

Gorbman, A., and Bern, H. A. *A Textbook of Comparative Endocrinology.* New York: John Wiley & Sons 1962. Although dated, this book is valuable because it provides a clear and readable treatment of endocrinology in general and documents many fascinating aspects of hormones in non-mammalian species. The value of a comparative approach for a better understanding of the endocrine system becomes apparent on reading this book.

Turner, C. D., and Bagnara, J. T. *General Endocrinology.* 5th ed. Philadelphia: W. B. Saunders Co., 1971. This is a basic textbook that follows the classical approach to study of the endocrine system. Mammalian systems are described in detail, and more important aspects of hormones in lower vertebrates and invertebrates are discussed. This edition includes much of the latest research.

Young, W. C. *Sex and Internal Secretions.* 3rd ed. Vols. I and II. Baltimore, Md.: Williams and Wilkins Co., 1961. This is a research-oriented reference work. The two volumes contain a comprehensive and in-depth review of all aspects of gonadal function including extensive coverage of hormones and behavior.

Part 4
MAINTENANCE

In Part 3 we discussed the mechanisms by which
behavioral activity occurs, emphasizing two
elements—integration and control. In Part 4
we introduce the body functions that support this
activity. In discussing nutrition, respiration,
circulation, excretion, cell structure, and metabolism,
we focus on two major roles served by these body
functions: the intake, distribution, and use of
metabolites by cells in the production of energy,
and the homeostatic mechanisms involved
in ensuring a constant internal environment.

16
SUPPORTIVE FUNCTIONS: NUTRITION AND RESPIRATION

All single-celled and multicellular organisms must obtain and take in from the external environment raw materials needed as a source of energy and substance for nutrition, maintenance, and growth (Fig. 16–1). The harnessing of biologically useful energy, the synthesis of proteins, and the transport of nutrients to all living parts of an organism are essential to life. In the following chapters we will examine a number of ways an organism processes and delivers raw materials from the external environment to its cellular systems. In this chapter we will concentrate on two complex organ systems: the **digestive system**, which processes food ingested; and the **respiratory system**, which acquires oxygen and eliminates carbon dioxide in aerobic organisms.

The digestive system

Essentially, there are four major activities involved as an organism processes the raw materials it takes up: 1. ingestion (to carry in); 2. digestion (to take apart); 3. absorption (to take in); and 4. egestion (to carry out). Collectively, the processes by which an animal obtains food are called **alimentation.**

THE CALL FOR NUTRIENTS

Before discussing the mechanisms underlying alimentation, we should understand what animals require in the way of food. The most well known necessities are proteins, carbohydrates, and fats. The last two kinds of compounds contain carbon, hydrogen, and oxygen; proteins contain nitrogen as well. Proteins are, in fact, the main source of dietary nitrogen and provide a number of animals, including humans, with certain amino acids which the animals cannot make for themselves. These three chief food classes provide the main raw materials organisms use in the construction of molecules. A number of minerals such as calcium and magnesium are also needed, as are **vitamins**, which can be defined as low molecular weight compounds that, though required in many cellular chemical reactions, cannot be synthesized by the organism itself. Thus a vitamin for one animal is not necessarily a vitamin for another. Ascorbic acid can be made by most higher animals from glucose, but we (and the guinea pig) cannot synthesize it. Hence, ascorbic acid is a vitamin (vitamin C) for us, but not for those organisms able to produce it themselves.

It appears that primitive protists may have required very little in the way of an external food supply. Apparently synthetic capacity has declined with the passage of time. Molds are far more versatile in making organic molecules

Figure 16–1 *The Peasant Wedding* by Pieter Bruegel, 1568.

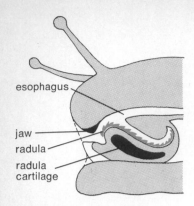

Figure 16–2 This section through the head of a gastropod mollusk shows the radular saw-like mechanism used in grinding food.

esophagus

jaw
radula
radula
cartilage

than men are. Hence they have need of only a very few types of nutrient, while most animals need a wide variety of these substances. The first problem for most animals is to physically lay hold of the materials containing these nutrients, then to take them into their bodies in some manner. This is accomplished by ingestion.

Ingestion

Some animals consume large parcels of food, others small ones. The former we refer to as **macrophages**, the latter as **microphages**. Among microphages, **filter-feeding** is a common practice in which the organism brings into play a filter of some type through which the ambient medium is strained. Cells and organic matter accumulated by filtration may later be attacked by digestive juices. A number of crustaceans and mollusks, such as clams and oysters, use the filter-feeding method. Protozoans such as *Paramecium* and *Amoeba* commonly employ their locomotor organelles to capture and ingest food. *Amoeba* engulfs its prey in its pseudopodia and then stores it in a food vacuole. Coelenterates (animals such as hydra) have stinging hairs that paralyze the victim and tentacles that later bring the stunned organism into the body cavity.

The variety of ingestive mechanisms in the animal kingdom, involving both morphological and behavioral adaptations, is very great. Certain animals even digest their prey outside the body! The young *Dytiscus* (water beetle) squirts a bit of juice out through tubes in its mandibles and into the prey it captures. The juice dissolves both hard and soft tissue and the beetle sucks up a prepared meal.

Trituration

Once inside the animal, food usually must be ground up before it can be processed any further. Microphages acquire their nutrients in such a small form that this step may be omitted, but the grinding down of food particles—called **trituration**—is essential to most macrophages.

Certain insects use their mandibles for trituration. Mollusks such as snails use an organ called the **radula**, a rasp-like structure (Fig. 16–2) that grinds down food by "sawing" it. In mammals, teeth are the structures used for mashing and tearing food. When food has been sufficiently ground it is ready for further treatment, this time by chemical as well as physical means.

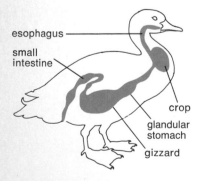

Figure 16–3 Birds swallow their food whole and store it temporarily in the crop. Trituration takes place chiefly in the gizzard.

esophagus

small
intestine

crop

glandular
stomach

gizzard

Digestion

Except for the lower invertebrates, most animals have a well defined **alimentary tract** that consists of mouth, esophagus, stomach, and intestine, along with associated glands. It is also called the **gastro-intestinal tract**, or **GI tract**. The **esophagus** usually serves solely as a passageway and does not act on the food passing through it. It may, as in birds, contain an enlarged region that serves as a storage area, the **crop** (Fig. 16–3). Its size is generally greater and its function more prominent in the invertebrates than in birds. In some invertebrates the mechanical breakdown of food occurs in the crop.

THE MECHANICAL PHASE OF DIGESTION: Not many animals have evolved oral structures capable of mashing food so finely that it can immediately be further processed in the digestive tract; trituration is often accomplished by structures placed more posteriorly in the GI tract. Birds have **gizzards** located between the crop and intestine (Fig. 16–3). The gizzard stores small pebbles, sand, and similar materials eaten by the animal. The food entering the gizzard is then ground against these "artificial teeth." Crayfish have a **gastric mill** that contains real teeth and does for crayfish what the gizzard does for birds.

In the absence of an internal pulverizing apparatus, some animals rely entirely on the kneading action of the digestive tract itself. The tract is basically a hollow muscular tube that contracts and expands, and because it can exert considerable pressure, it is able to grind up a large variety of materials.

Pythons and boa constrictors rely almost entirely on chemical methods for digesting their food. These snakes ingest their victim by unhinging their jaws and swallowing the entire animal; then they simply loll about and wait for it to be chemically digested before taking up the hunt once more.

THE CHEMICAL PHASE OF DIGESTION: Once food materials have been ground down to a fine enough consistency, they are attacked by enzymes that operate either intracellularly or extracellularly. In single-celled organisms digestion must, of course, be intracellular, and it occurs within organelles called **lysosomes**. These structures contain a number of digestive enzymes. In higher animals, digestion occurs principally within the **lumen** (hollow) of the intestine into which enzymes are poured by various types of cells and glands. Extracellular digestion is much more rapid than the intracellular type and it is not accidental that in most active animals digestive processes tend to be carried out primarily in the lumen of the GI tract.

Enzymes, the chemical agents of digestion, are basically similar throughout the entire animal kingdom, their relative concentrations differing in accordance with various animals' diets and living conditions. These enzymes are chiefly **hydrolases** that break molecules apart by adding water to them. (Enzymes are always designated by the suffix -*ase*.) There are three main classes of enzymes—**carbohydrases**, **lipases**, and **proteases**. The first attack sugars and starches; the second break down fats; and the third, proteins.

Since cellulose is by far the most plentiful organic compound on Earth, it is strange that virtually no animals have the enzymatic equipment to cope with it. In cases where it is consumed, the consuming animal usually depends on the activity of micro-organisms living in its gut to digest the cellulose. Wood-eating termites play host to protozoa that contain cellulases capable of doing the job required. Grass eaten by ruminant animals is stored in a complex stomach, the **rumen** (Fig. 16–4), where bacteria break down the cellulose. The material is then regurgitated, chewed, and fully digested in more posterior

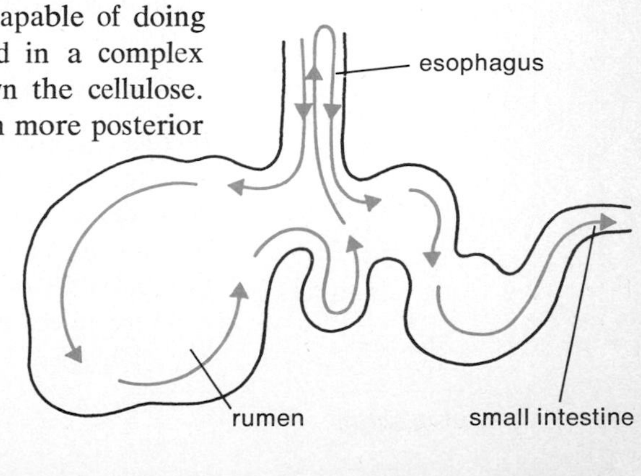

Figure 16–4 Food swallowed by a cow is stored in the rumen and later brought back into the mouth for chewing. Bacteria in other parts of the stomach carry on cellulose digestion, for which a cow has no enzymes.

regions of the GI tract. With only a few exceptions, the digestive process tends to be similar among all animals. Because this is so, we will present the best understood case known to physiologists—that of man—to familiarize you with the more salient details of this important mechanism.

DIGESTION IN HUMANS

Our urge to eat is controlled by many factors. The concentration of glucose in the blood is one; psychological factors are also of great importance, as many people suffering from obesity are well aware. Gourmets and professional workers in the field of nutrition agree that well prepared and esthetically appealing food is usually preferred because it makes the digestive fluids "run better" and so facilitates the entire process of alimentation.

Figure 16–5 shows the major components of the human GI tract. Digestion begins within seconds after food is taken into the mouth. Three pairs of **salivary glands** (**parotid**, **submaxillary**, and **sublingual**) pour juices into the oral cavity through ducts. The saliva lubricates the food before it is swept into the **pharynx**. Saliva contains the enzyme **ptyalin**, a kind of amylase or starch-splitting enzyme that yields the sugar **maltose**. However, food usually remains in the mouth too short a time for a thorough enzymatic workover. Once shunted past the **fauces**, the area between the mouth and pharynx, food enters the esophagus and then the **cardiac** end of the stomach.

For millennia the function of the stomach was debated. Some considered its action mainly mechanical, others chemical. The stomach does in fact knead food to a certain extent. It also secretes (from **parietal cells**) hydrochloric acid and the enzyme **pepsin**. The acid (pH 1.0) kills many foreign organisms and provides a pH under which the pepsin can attack proteins. (The expression p**H** designates a quantitative range of acidity or alkalinity graded from 0 to 14, anything less than pH 7 being acid and anything more being alkaline.) In addition to pepsin, the stomach of infant mammals contains **rennin**, which through a series of reactions converts the important milk protein **casein** into curds and whey. The curd is susceptible to further action by other enzymes.

In many ways, the stomach is a mystery organ. It contains an acid sufficiently powerful to kill most organisms unfortunate enough to be in that inhospitable hollow. It is an acid so strong that it can break down most proteins on contact. Yet only under unusual conditions does it ever inflict a wound on the lining of the organ in which it floats. A detailed explanation of why the stomach doesn't digest itself has yet to be worked out by physiologists.

The intestinal phase

Just as a **sphincter** (a circular muscle) at the upper end of the stomach permits food to enter, a muscle at the lower or **pyloric** end permits food to leave the stomach in the form of juice. The entrance of this chemically processed material into the first region of the small intestine (**duodenum**), triggers a complex series of events.

Three juices are secreted in the duodenum when food enters. One is the

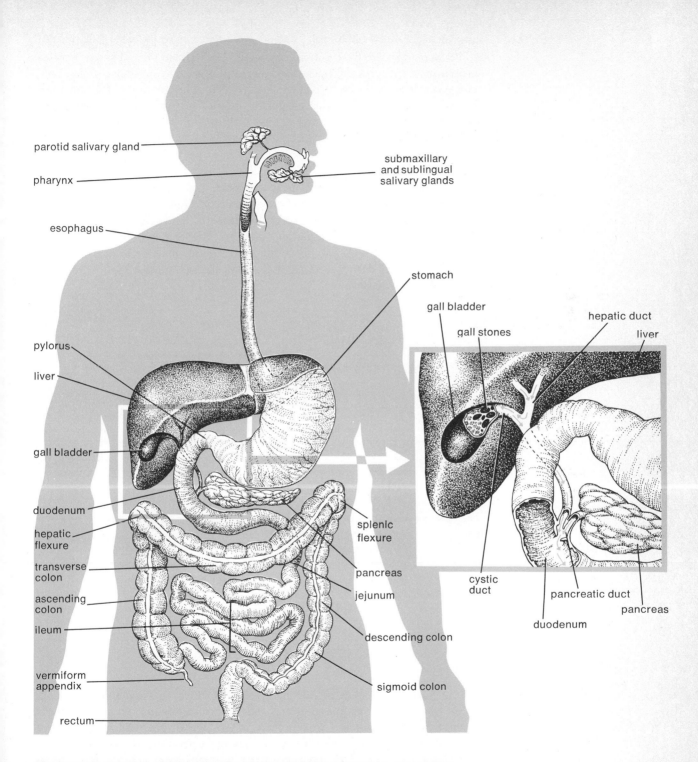

parotid salivary gland

pharynx

esophagus

submaxillary
and sublingual
salivary glands

stomach

gall bladder

gall stones

hepatic duct

liver

pylorus

liver

gall bladder

duodenum

hepatic
flexure

transverse
colon

ascending
colon

ileum

vermiform
appendix

rectum

splenic
flexure

pancreas

jejunum

descending colon

sigmoid colon

cystic
duct

pancreatic duct

duodenum

pancreas

Figures 16–5 and 16–6   The human digestive system. The magnified view shows
linkages between gall bladder, liver, pancreas, and duodenum. Insoluble particles
called gallstones sometimes form in the gall bladder and block the cystic duct.

intestinal juice proper. Another is the secretion of the pancreas, and the last is bile formed in the liver but stored in the gall bladder (Fig. 16–6). The intestinal juice contains enzymes that split fat, sugar, and proteins; it also contains **enterokinase**, which activates certain enzymes originating in the pancreas. Fats within the small intestine trigger the release of the hormone **cholecystokinin**, which in turn triggers the release of bile from the gall bladder. Notice in Fig. 16–6 how the liver, gall bladder, and pancreas all feed into the small intestine through ducts.

It is fairly common for "stones" to form in the gall bladder. Stones can block the gall bladder's tubule, the **cystic duct**, and cause severe pain. When operating normally, the duct transmits its secretion into the **hepatic duct** leading from the liver and into the duodenum. Bile has the function of emulsifying fats, breaking them into fine particles that are further dealt with by enzymes. Table 16–1 lists the enzymatic components of the pancreatic and intestinal juices, as well as other secretions, and shows the substances upon which they act and the products evolved.

SOURCE OF ENZYME	ENZYME	SUBSTANCES ACTED UPON	PRODUCTS OF DIGESTION
salivary glands	salivary amylase	polysaccharides (cooked starch and glycogen)	disaccharide (maltose)
stomach glands	pepsin	proteins	peptides
	rennin	milk casein	clotted casein (curds)
pancreas	trypsin chymotrypsin carboxypeptidase	proteins and peptides	amino acids
	pancreatic amylase	starch	maltose
	lipase	triglycerides	fatty acids, glycerol, and monoglycerides
small intestine	peptidase	peptides	amino acids
	sucrase maltase lactase	disaccharides	monosaccharides

Table 16–1 Some digestive enzymes in man.
Source: G. G. Simpson and W. S. Beck, *Life: An Introduction to Biology,* 2nd ed. New York: Harcourt Brace Jovanovich, 1965.

Absorption

By the time the processed food has passed through the **jejunum** and **ileum** (Fig. 16–5), most of the nutrients have been absorbed. It was formerly thought that starches were broken down to the level of hexose sugars and proteins to that of single amino acids by enzymes operating extracellularly, but this is not the case. The inner layer, or **mucosal layer**, of the intestine is covered with **epithelial** cells. Arranged in pleats and folds, they provide greater surface area for absorption (Fig. 16–7). This surface area can amount to as

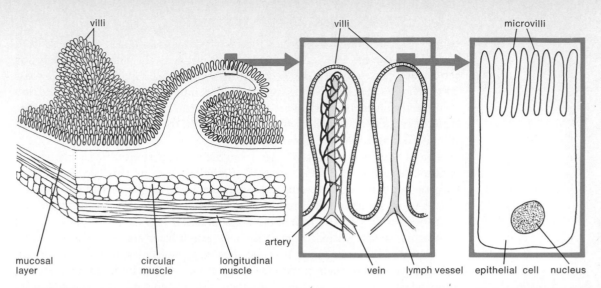

villi   villi   microvilli

mucosal layer   circular muscle   longitudinal muscle   artery   vein   lymph vessel   epithelial cell   nucleus

Figure 16–7 Enormous enlargement of mammalian small intestinal surface is provided by villi and microvilli. Details of the villi are shown in the first large square. An epithelial cell from such a villus is enlarged at far right.

much as 75 square meters in an average human. While glucose and galactose are transported by active means across these cells and into the blood stream, requiring the operation of a hexose "pump," other hexoses must migrate by diffusion alone.

Extracellular digestive enzymes—those working in the lumen of the intestines—convert at most 20% of the carbohydrate ingested (the total is about 500 gm/day in men) to the level of hexoses. The remaining 80% must be converted by intracellular carbohydrases in the mucosal epithelium. A similar picture is emerging for proteins.

Finger-like projections of the mucosal surface of the gut (**villi**) contain both blood and lymphatic vessels. While amino acids and hexose sugars enter the blood vessels easily, fats, in general, do not. Fats can be taken into the epithelial cells by being broken down by lipase to free fatty acids and glycerol, or by a process known as **pinocytosis**. During pinocytosis a particle in contact with the outer surface of a cell membrane is pinched off and "swallowed" into the cell, later to be broken down and integrated with the cytoplasm. If the fats are broken down by lipase, the resulting fatty acids and glycerol that pass through the cell wall can be recombined within the cell. Special vessels (called lymph vessels) absorb the products of fat digestion. These products eventually find their way into the blood stream, however, because the lymph vessels ultimately feed into the circulatory system.

The release of digestive enzymes and muscular movement of the GI tract are both under nervous and hormonal control. Analysis of a number of animal types shows that the more anterior structures (such as the esophagus) tend to be chiefly under nerve control while the posterior ones (such as the large intestine) tend to be more subject to hormonal influence.

Elimination or egestion

After nutrients have been extracted from it, the food passes through a valve and enters the large intestine, actually shorter than the small intestine (2 m as opposed to 7 m), but wider (8 cm as opposed to 5 cm). The large intestine consists of three main segments (Fig. 16–5): the **ascending, transverse**, and **descending colons**. The right-angle junction between the first two stretches is the **hepatic flexure** (for it lies beneath the liver, whose Greek name is *hepar*). The junction between the transverse and descending colon is the **splenic flexure** (for it lies near the spleen). The descending colon becomes the **sigmoid colon**, then the **rectum**, and finally a sphincter, the **anus**, through which the undigested food is eliminated in the form of **feces**.

The large intestine absorbs water from the fecal substance. Feces contain, in addition to undigested food, cast-off epithelial cells, mucus, and usually a thriving population of bacteria, the type depending on the diet of the individual. It takes about one day for food to make its way from mouth to rectum with food leaving the stomach about six hours after ingestion.

Whether we are speaking about man, or crayfish, or ameba, digestion in all accomplishes the same thing. It transforms large molecules, usually specific ingested organisms or their parts, into smaller ones. These basic building stones, upon which all life is founded, are then assimilated and incorporated once more into larger structures, specific to the consuming animal, which can be used for any one of a number of purposes, including the evolution of useful energy.

THE CALL FOR OXYGEN

Oxygen is as necessary for the "fires" of life as it is for burning wood. Glucose, "food" transported by the blood to the body cells, is the hexose sugar derived by digestion from larger molecular weight compounds. Oxygen is required for that breakdown process, as it is for the breakdown of lipids (fats).

$$C_6H_{12}O_6 \quad + \quad 6O_2 \quad \longrightarrow \quad 6CO_2 \quad + \quad 6H_2O$$

| glucose | molecular | carbon | water |
| (hexose sugar) | oxygen | dioxide | |

Without molecular oxygen, aerobic organisms would not be able to break down the large, unusable molecules they ingest and would starve to death.

Respiratory techniques

How do organisms obtain this essential life-sustaining gas? The answer varies with the physiological life style of the animal. In simple protists, diffusion answers the organism's requirements.

Gas molecules, like liquid ones, move in response to concentration gradients. If one phase of a system is richer in a given gas than another, the gas tends to move from the more plentiful to the less plentiful region. Air pressure at sea level will support a column of mercury 760 mm high. Since 21% of our air is oxygen, the **partial pressure** of O_2 is $.21 \times 760$ or about 160 mm. This means that if air at sea level were placed in contiguity with a gas mixture containing 160 mm partial pressure of O_2 the latter would not lose O_2 to the air or acquire any more from it because the two gases would be in equilibrium.

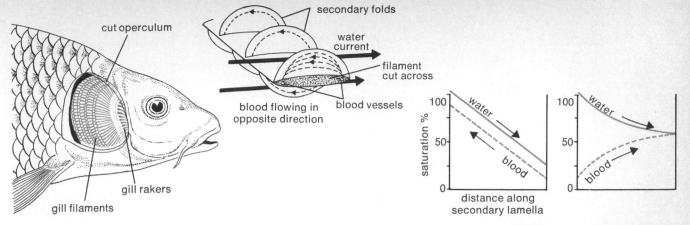

If the partial pressure in the mixture were greater than 160 mm, it would lose O_2 to the air, and if the pressure were less than 160 mm the mixture would absorb O_2 from the air.

A very small animal, an ameba or a paramecium for example, can satisfy its oxygen requirements by simple diffusion. As a result of metabolic activity, the partial pressure of O_2 within the cell declines while that of CO_2 increases. Consequently CO_2 diffuses out of the cell while O_2 dissolved in the surrounding water diffuses into it. The technique is also effective for flatworms because they are relatively thin, but it is not the answer for large animals. Complex animals require the intermediation of special respiratory organs to obtain an adequate supply of oxygen and to rid themselves of waste carbon dioxide. The chief types of respiratory devices are gills, tracheal systems, and lungs.

GILLS: Most aquatic organisms take in oxygen by means of **gills** (Fig. 16–8), which are tissue structures with a large surface area and a rich supply of blood vessels. The water forced over the gill structures has a higher partial pressure of oxygen than the blood in the capillaries of the gill filaments. Hence the oxygen moves into the blood vessels; similarly, CO_2 exits. Crustaceans and a number of organisms other than fish also have gills. Some crabs are able to "breathe" both in water and on land. When in the water they use a specialized leg to force water past the gill. If the leg is removed the animal can survive on land but not in the sea!

In general, gill-bearing animals must keep water moving past their respiratory organs for at least two reasons. Water contains far less oxygen than air, one estimate being 210cc of O_2 per liter of air and 7cc O_2 per liter of water (and that is clean water, not the polluted water of so many lakes and streams). Secondly, the diffusion of oxygen in water is far slower than it is in air. When the oxygen content of the water decreases, the animals living in it are quick to sense the change. One general reaction is that they begin to move about vigorously. Some aquatic animals—water beetles and their relatives, for example—use a bubble instead of gills. The insect carries around a bubble of air, and the oxygen within it diffuses into the insect's respiratory system as needed. Eventually, the animal resurfaces and snatches a new bubble. Structures called **plastrons** (Fig. 16–9) work in very much the same way as the bubble but are more enduring. They consist of unwettable hairs that trap a layer of air to supply the animal with oxygen.

Figure 16–8 Gas exchange in the gills of fish occurs between the capillaries in the secondary lamellae (folds) and water passing over them. The blood flows through these lamellae in the direction opposite the flow of surrounding water. This allows more oxygen to diffuse into the blood because, as the blood passing through the lamellae gains oxygen, it comes into contact with water from which less and less oxygen has been removed. This "counter-current" arrangement maintains a concentration gradient between oxygen in the blood and in the water, and oxygen continues to diffuse into the blood along the entire length of the lamellae. The advantage of counter-current flow over parallel flow is illustrated by the two graphs.

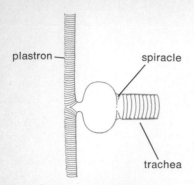

plastron — | — spiracle

— trachea

Figure 16–9 The plastron present in some insects consists of non-wettable hairs on the animal's cuticle that trap a layer of air to be carried under water. This air covers the insect's spiracles, providing oxygen in the same manner as does the air bubble carried down by other diving insects. As the oxygen is used by the animal, its partial pressure decreases and oxygen from surrounding water diffuses into the air layer, which thus functions temporarily as a gill. A plastron with its air layer differs from a simple air bubble in that hairs over the spiracle further protect the tracheal system from water entry. (AFTER J. A. RAMSAY)

The air contains a far more dependable supply of oxygen than the water does, but in order to tap it new kinds of respiratory techniques had to evolve. A respiratory surface is usually very thin, contains large numbers of blood vessels, and must be kept moist. Yet such a structure usually lacks structural rigidity; gills collapse when exposed to air.

LUNGS: The solution that evolutionary processes chanced upon is an interesting one. The basic nature of the respiratory apparatus itself was changed only in small ways—more surface area and more blood vessels, for example— but its location was changed from outside the body to within. Invariably, **lungs** are located deep within the animal and have access to the external environment through tubular extensions. Very few water animals have internal respiratory organs, though there are some exceptions. Sea cucumbers have an internal "respiratory tree" supplied with oxygenated water by way of the anus. Frogs have lungs, but much of their respiratory exchange takes place through the skin. When a frog is partly submerged—with head above but body below water—oxygen is taken primarily from the air and moved into the lungs; but CO_2, which dissolves in water more readily than O_2 does, is expelled through the skin. Diffusion through skin to support respiration is also the process in earthworms.

TRACHEAL SYSTEMS: Insects have quite a different respiratory system serving their oxygen needs. It is called a **tracheal system**. Circular spiracles (Fig. 16–9) transmit air from the outside into a collection of tubes called **tracheae**, which branch into **tracheoles** that communicate directly with the body tissues. In contrast to lungs, a fluid (the blood) does not transport the oxygen to the cells, although there are some exceptions. In order to illustrate the general mechanism of operation of a respiratory system, let us once more focus on humans and examine the mechanism by which we breathe.

RESPIRATION IN MAN

The human respiratory system is shown in Fig. 16–10. The lungs, the main organs of breathing, are located in a protective cage, the **thorax**, and are surrounded by a lining called the **pleura**. The ribs surrounding the lungs provide protection and rigidity. The tent-like diaphragm divides thorax from abdomen.

When the diaphragm moves down, it increases the volume and decreases the pressure in the thorax. As a result, air from the outside rushes in and fills the lungs. When the diaphragm recedes to its former position, and the volume of the thorax is reduced, the air rushes out, and the elastic lungs collapse (Fig. 16–11). Air rushing into the nasal cavity sweeps past a series of moist surfaces then through the pharynx and into the trachea. The trachea is ringed by a series of cartilagenous hoops that provide strong support.

Food destined for the esophagus, which lies behind the trachea, is kept from entering the trachea by a lid of tissue called the **epiglottis**, which seals the tracheal opening during swallowing, but as you know from personal experience the mechanism is not foolproof. Once past the trachea, air moves through the

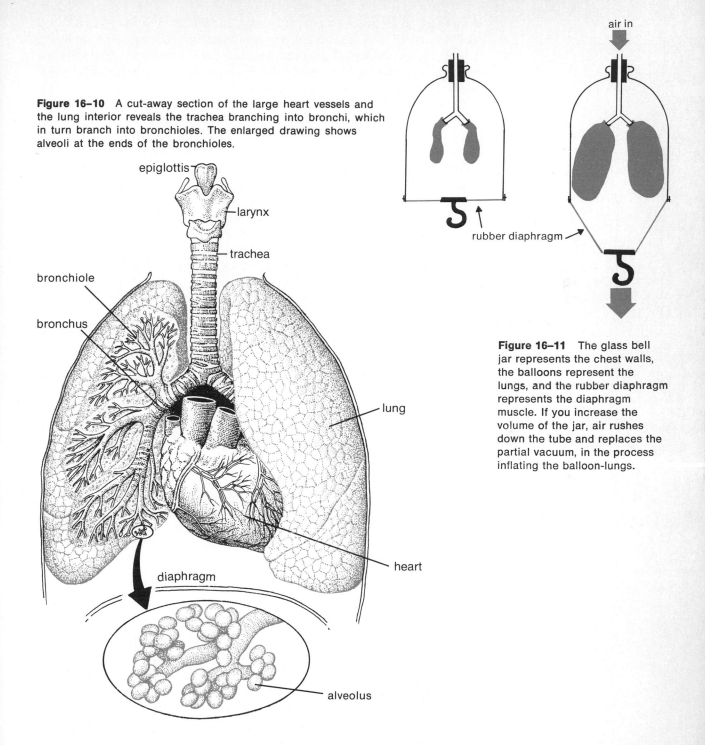

Figure 16–10 A cut-away section of the large heart vessels and the lung interior reveals the trachea branching into bronchi, which in turn branch into bronchioles. The enlarged drawing shows alveoli at the ends of the bronchioles.

epiglottis

larynx

trachea

bronchiole

bronchus

lung

heart

diaphragm

alveolus

air in

rubber diaphragm

Figure 16–11 The glass bell jar represents the chest walls, the balloons represent the lungs, and the rubber diaphragm represents the diaphragm muscle. If you increase the volume of the jar, air rushes down the tube and replaces the partial vacuum, in the process inflating the balloon-lungs.

bronchi to the finer **bronchioles** and finally to millions of little pockets called **alveoli** (Fig. 16–10). The alveoli are richly supplied with capillaries and it is here that gas exchange takes place. At this point the first stage of respiration (external respiration) is complete. To what extent gas exchange takes place is determined by partial pressure differences and diffusion rates.

Air just inhaled is rich in O_2 and low in CO_2. Venous blood supplying the lungs, on the other hand, is low in O_2 and rich in CO_2. Hence, O_2 moves into the blood and CO_2 leaves it. During exhalation, CO_2-laden air is given off (along with much moisture, as you can tell by breathing onto a mirror).

The control of respiratory movement is voluntary in part, but it is impossible to asphyxiate yourself by holding your breath. When the CO_2 level of your blood builds up sufficiently, it stimulates specialized centers in the blood vessels that in turn influence the stem of the brain in such a way that respiratory muscles, such as the diaphragm, resume their activity. In that way the pattern of breathing is sustained and made responsive to conditions of both the external and internal environments, another example of homeostatic regulation.

Oxygen transport

The inhalation–exhalation cycle is what physiologists call external respiration.

Figure 16–12

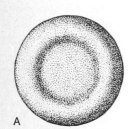

A

HEMOGLOBIN AND OXYGEN TRANSPORT

The presence of hemoglobin in mammals enables the blood to transport 60 times more oxygen than would be possible were hemogloblin not present in the red blood cells, or **erythrocytes** (Fig. 16–12A).

Each erythrocyte carries nearly 300 million molecules of hemoglobin, a hemoglobin molecule consisting of a globulin protein made up of four protein chains (Fig. 16–12B). Within each protein chain is a complex iron-containing compound called **heme**, represented by the disks in Fig. 16–12B, and the structure of which is shown in Fig. 16–12C. Each of the four iron atoms (the sphere in each disk) can form a weak bond with an oxygen molecule (O_2), so one hemoglobin molecule (Hb) can carry eight atoms of oxygen (Hb+$4O_2$).

The oxygen concentration in the lungs is high enough to cause hemoglobin to form bonds with the oxygen. The hemoglobin, now called **oxyhemoglobin**, transports oxygen to capillaries throughout the systemic circulation. A lower concentration of oxygen in the capillaries outside the lungs next causes the oxyhemoglobin to give up its oxygen. The "dissociation curve" in Fig. 16–12D shows how the oxygen-carrying capacity of human hemoglobin varies with the oxygen concentration in the lungs and in the body tissues.

The movement of the relevant gases by the cells, along with the breakdown of substrate, is called **internal respiration**.

The blood occupies a unique place in the physiological scheme of things. It is the medium of transportation between all parts of the organism. In it are dissolved not only the two chief gases of respiration (O_2 and CO_2) but also hormones, enzymes, agents that ward off foreign interlopers, and cells serving a number of other functions. Once a fresh supply of air has been admitted to alveoli, O_2 diffuses into the surrounding capillaries and CO_2 moves out of them. Some O_2 dissolves in the blood, but not enough to satisfy the needs of most organisms with lungs, or any other specialized respiratory organ for that matter.

Almost all animals have as part of their blood certain pigments that have a special affinity for oxygen. In most organisms the pigment is **hemoglobin**, whose molecule contains iron as one of its components. It is the iron that combines with oxygen in the alveoli and carries the gas to the cells. Figure 16–12 illustrates the structure of hemoglobin and the oxygen-carrying capacity of the hemoglobin molecule. Humans subjected to low oxygen tensions react by producing more red blood cells. Somehow the lack of O_2 triggers the release from the kidneys of a special material that stimulates the formation of additional red cells by the bone marrow.

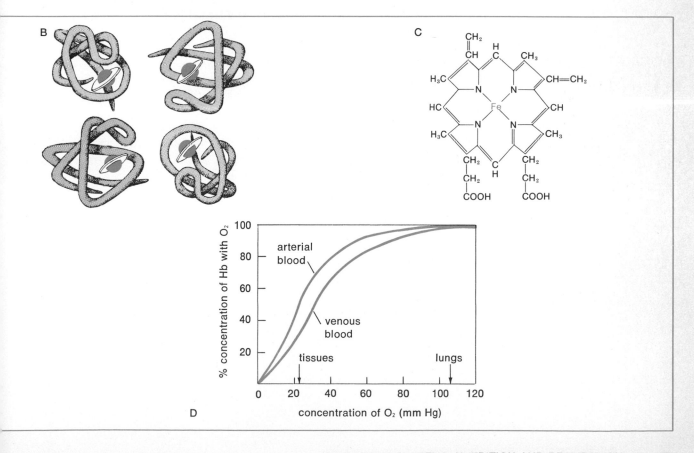

Transport of carbon dioxide

The movement of oxygen to the cells through the blood stream is only half the circulation story. The other half consists of waste CO_2 being returned to the lungs. Some of this waste CO_2 is carried away from the cells by the hemoglobin. In general, when CO_2 is in aqueous media it undergoes the following reaction:

$$CO_2 \ + \ H_2O \ \xrightarrow[\text{anhydrase}]{\text{carbonic}} \ H_2CO_3$$
$$\text{carbon} \qquad \text{water} \qquad\qquad\quad \text{carbonic}$$
$$\text{dioxide} \qquad\qquad\qquad\qquad\qquad \text{acid}$$

The carbonic acid then produces hydrogen and bicarbonate ions:

$$H_2CO_3 \ \rightleftharpoons \ HCO_3^- \ + \ H^+$$

When bicarbonate reaches the lungs, the reactions listed above are reversed so that CO_2 is generated; it is subsequently blown out during exhalation. The chemical occurrences near the respiratory surfaces are thus exactly opposite those taking place at the surfaces of other cell masses of the body. Some carbon dioxide moves in combination with proteins other than the protein component of hemoglobin, and a certain amount is dissolved in solution within the blood, but the main means of transportation is accomplished by the ubiquitous bicarbonate ion.

We have seen that to fire the furnaces of cellular metabolism, the participation of three organ systems is required: the digestive system brings the fuel for the fire; the respiratory system provides the spark; and the blood, which is part of the circulatory system, transports all of the ingredients to the right places at the right times. The blood also removes the ashes. It is a cyclic phenomenon that operates without interruption until the organism dies.

With an understanding of the broad outlines of how nutrition and respiration help maintain the organism, we are now in a position to move on to two other supportive functions—circulation and excretion.

1 What are the main means by which animals acquire their food?
2 Name the three major classes of nutrients.
3 What are vitamins?
4 Compare and contrast the structure and function of gills, lungs, and trachial systems.
5 Differentiate between external and internal respiration.
6 What function is served by hemoglobin?
7 In Chapter 5 we discussed how the morphology of an organism and its behavior often interact, having evolved together. Describe several examples of ingestive mechanisms in animals wherein a physical structure and a particular behavior are associated.

SELECTED READINGS

Carlson, Anton J., Johnson, V., and Cavert, H. M. *The Machinery of the Body*. 5th ed. Chicago, Ill.: University of Chicago Press, 1961. An introductory text on human physiology, requiring little previous training in the sciences.

Clendening, Logan. *The Human Body*. New York: Alfred A. Knopf, Inc., 1945. Written in a highly entertaining manner, this classic text presents human physiology from a physician's point of view.

Gordon, M. S., Bartholomew, G. A., Grinnell, A. D., Jorgensen, C. B., and White, F. N. *Animal Functions: Principles and Adaptations*. New York: The Macmillan Company, 1968. The emphasis is upon how vertebrate organ systems function and how these functions relate to the organism's external environment. Behavioral mechanisms receive some attention as well.

Jennings, J. B. *Feeding, Digestion and Assimilation in Animals*. London: Pergamon Press, 1965. The approach of this brief text is unusual in that it integrates natural history, classical biological concepts (including evolution), and detailed laboratory observations in its discussion of feeding mechanisms and digestion.

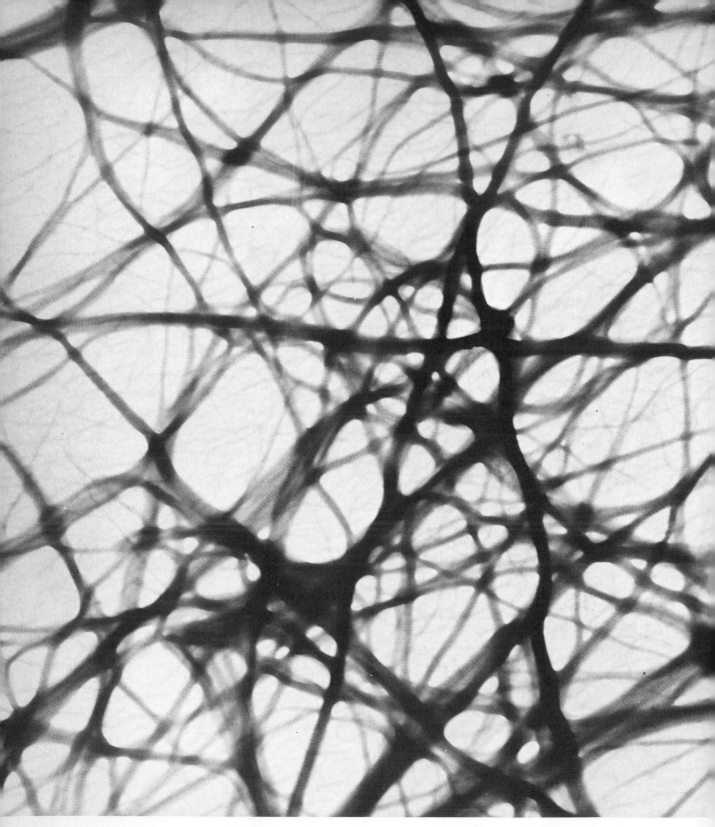

Figure 17–1 Blood clotting takes place when fibrinogen, a soluble blood protein, is converted to fibrin threads (seen here greatly enlarged), which are an insoluble protein gel.

17
SUPPORTIVE FUNCTIONS: CIRCULATION AND EXCRETION

EVOLUTION OF CIRCULATORY SYSTEMS

As in the previous chapter dealing with supportive functions our discussion in this chapter must also touch on the process of diffusion. The circulatory system is essentially a convection mechanism—a mechanism that takes up where diffusion leaves off. In protozoans, diffusion *almost* unaided can stir up the cytoplasm enough to allow an adequate distribution of metabolites and other important substances. We say "almost" because even in protozoans a special motion of the cytoplasm—called **cytoplasmic streaming**—is needed to supplement diffusion if the cell is to sustain itself.

We do not find a clearly defined circulatory system in either hydra and its kin (Fig. 17–2) or in flatworms. In both cases the cellular populations that need to exchange gases and receive nutrients are usually very thin, so diffusion satisfies their needs. Because they do not have a general distribution system, flatworms must also get along without benefit of anatomically localized functions. Instead of having a single digestive apparatus, they have a multiple one that repeats itself over and over again throughout the animal. And without a circulatory system to pipe blood and so distribute the products of digestion, the digestive organs must themselves deliver their contents to all the elements that require the products of digestion. Flatworms, it would seem, have missed out on the benefits associated with division of labor.

Even in some of the larger animals, for example the sea anemones, sea urchins, and sea stars, a true circulatory system is lacking, and those animals are larger than some that have well developed circulatory systems. In the case of sea urchins and sea stars, however, much of the bodily mass consists of inanimate mineral constituents with only a few cells. Sea anemones (which, like hydra, are coelenterates) are generally inactive. While a frog may consume 120 to 170 mm³ of O_2/gm/hr., an anemone will probably use no more than a tenth of that amount and about a sixth as much as most earthworms. So, in considering the need for true circulatory systems we must take into account the mass and shape of the living elements and the level of activity of the particular organisms under consideration.

CLOSED CIRCULATION: With six times the O_2 consumption of sea anemones and a great proportion of "live tissue," earthworms apparently require a well-developed circulation, although they are no faster than sea anemones. Figure 17–3 shows the circulatory system of the earthworm. A dorsal and ventral blood vessel are connected in the anterior portion of the worm by five lateral

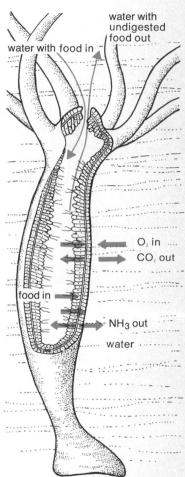

Figure 17–2   The movement of water, food, oxygen, and wastes in *Hydra*, which lacks a specialized transport system. The animal obtains oxygen and rids its cells of CO_2 and ammonia (NH_3) via the water in its cavity as well as the water surrounding it. The cavity is thus part of *Hydra*'s environment.

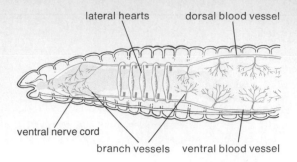

Figure 17–3 In the circulatory system of the earthworm, peristaltic waves move the blood anteriorly in the dorsal blood vessel, ventrally through the hearts, and posteriorly in the ventral vessel. Valves increase the efficiency of circulation. In the skin capillaries, blood takes up O_2 and expels CO_2. It picks up digested foods from the intestine and transports them throughout the body while delivering wastes other than CO_2 to the excretory organs.

hearts. Through muscular movements of roughly the same sort that occur in our digestive tracts, the hearts pump blood into the ventral vessel, transmitting the fluid to all segments of the animal; then, through a threadwork of fine branches, blood is transferred once again to the dorsal vessel. The system is a completely closed series of tubes and for this reason constitutes what biologists call a **closed circulation**. In many annelids, which are segmented worms, blood moves in an ebb and flow fashion back and forth through the same vessels.

OPEN CIRCULATION: Insects have an **open circulation** system instead of a closed one. Figure 17–4 shows some of the blood vessels of the grasshopper. By mammalian standards, an insect's heart exerts only minuscule pressure. It is, however, forceful enough to propel the blood forward into the head region where it spills over into the general body cavity of the animal. It must then find its way back to the heart, which beats within a puddle of blood, as it were. What has happened is that during development the cavity destined to form some of the major blood-conveying structures in vertebrates and annelids became, in insects and certain other animals, the general body cavity. In insects, the tubes that developed into the body cavity became much reduced in size.

An open circulatory system is not as efficient a conveyor as a closed one is, but an insect has no need to worry about this. Figure 17–4 explains why. Notice how the respiratory system is distributed throughout the insect. The several air sacs are serialized in a way similar to the digestive apparatus of the flatworms. Here is another instance in which division of labor has been sacrificed, in that organs are repeated in each segment. An animal cannot have it both ways; either it has an efficient circulatory system, or it has a repetition of serialized structures.

Figure 17–4 Grasshoppers and other insects use tracheal tubes instead of blood for the transport of O_2 to the cells and CO_2 away from them and outside the body. Blood flows toward the head from the heart through a single blood vessel. In all other parts of the body, the blood flows freely through spaces among the organs.

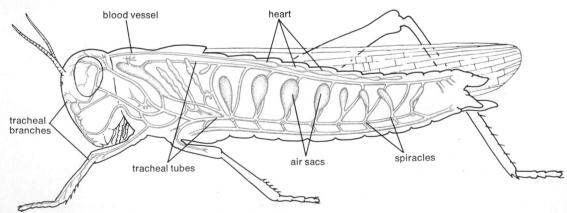

THE CIRCULATORY SYSTEM IN HUMANS

Historians variously date the beginning of recorded history between five and eight millennia ago. It might seem surprising, then, to learn that we have known how blood moves through our bodies for only three centuries. Aristotle supposed the arteries to be air-laden passageways while the veins carried the blood, a mysterious material thought to be concocted in the liver. About 500 years later, the physician Galen refuted the idea that the arteries contained air. Veins and arteries alike, he claimed, were conveyors of the blood; blood in the right side of the heart was blackish while that on the left was a lustrous red. He further supposed that the transformation occurred when the blood "sweated" from the right side to the left side through the septum that divides them. He could not see any pores—but neither could one see them in skin, yet they undoubtedly were there. Galen assumed the blood ebbed and flowed in man as we now know it to do in certain of the worms. In honor of the ancient physician, such movement is called "galenic," and Galen's view held sway for more than 14 centuries.

In the 1600s William Harvey, physician to King Charles and the father of modern physiology, carried out experiments to determine the true nature of circulation. Harvey's experiments were thoroughly quantitative and although the quantities he determined were imprecise, they were accurate enough to lead him to the correct conclusions.

The heart as a pump

In one of the most important of his analyses, Harvey measured the amount of blood flowing through the heart in a given time. He also knew the total amount of blood in the body. "Consider the capacity of the heart," he wrote. "Suppose the ventricle holds but two ounces. If the pulse beats 72 times in a minute, in one hour the left ventricle will throw into the aorta no less than $72 \times 60 \times 2 = 8,640$ oz $= 38$ stone 8 lb [540 lb], three times the weight of a heavy man! Where can all this blood come from? Where can it all go to?"

Harvey knew the veins contained valves that permitted blood to move toward the heart. Galen must have been in error. The blood travels in one direction only and it must move again and again through the heart—in effect it *circulates*. The arteries carry it away from the heart, due to the heart's pumping action, while the veins return it to the heart. These fundamental principles formed the basis not only of the field of medicine to which they specifically relate (cardiology) but also of all modern physiology.

Figures 17–5 and 17–6 show the structure of the human circulatory system. The heart has four chambers (in fish there are only two; in amphibia, three). The lowermost chambers are the **ventricles**, the uppermost ones, the **auricles** (or **atria**). The heart is a muscular organ about the size of your clenched fist. The segment on the right—both right auricle and ventricle, which are shown at left in the diagram—supplies blood to the lungs, and the segment on the left pumps it to the rest of the body. Referring to Fig. 17–7, we can follow a drop of blood through one full cycle.

Blood returning from the upper and lower portions of the body moves

A

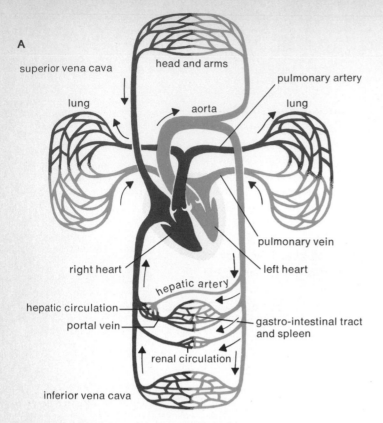

superior vena cava

head and arms

lung

aorta

pulmonary artery

lung

pulmonary vein

right heart

left heart

hepatic artery

hepatic circulation

portal vein

gastro-intestinal tract
and spleen

renal circulation

inferior vena cava

Figure 17–5 The schematic diagram shows oxygen-
deprived blood in the human circulatory system entering the
right heart through the superior and inferior vena cavas. It is
then pumped to the lungs where it becomes oxygenated
(indicated by color), re-enters the heart, and is then pumped
out through the aorta and supplies oxygen to the cells through
an extensive system of capillaries.

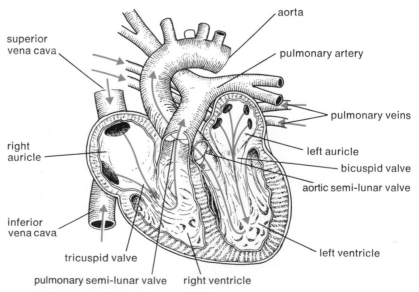

aorta

superior
vena cava

pulmonary artery

pulmonary veins

right
auricle

left auricle

bicuspid valve

aortic semi-lunar valve

inferior
vena cava

left ventricle

tricuspid valve

pulmonary semi-lunar valve

right ventricle

Figure 17–6 Arrows show the direction of blood flow through
the human heart.

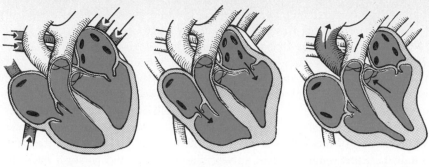

DIASTOLE   AURICULAR SYSTOLE   VENTRICULAR SYSTOLE

Figure 17-7 Between contractions (diastole) blood enters the auricles from the veins. During auricular systole, blood is pumped from the auricles into the ventricles. During ventricular systole it moves from the ventricles into the pulmonary artery and aorta. Note open and closed positions of various valves. Compare this diagram with Fig. 17-6.

through the **superior** and **inferior vena cava** into the right auricle. From there it moves into the right ventricle and then to the lungs through the **pulmonary artery**.

In the lungs oxygen is picked up and carbon dioxide discharged, causing the blood to change color from dark to bright red. Next the blood moves through the **pulmonary vein** into the left auricle and finally to the left ventricle, largest of the four chambers. The left ventricle is a thick-walled and powerful structure. During contraction, the action phase called **systole**, it pumps blood into the **aorta**, the body's chief artery. The aorta carries blood to all the organs and tissues by means of finely branching extensions—first the **arterioles** and then the **capillaries**. It is through the capillaries, tubules so small they are visible only microscopically, that the important exchanges between blood and cells occur. Once this is accomplished, the blood now laden with the waste products of cellular metabolism moves into venules, then veins, and finally back to the inferior and superior vena cava.

The capillaries have extremely thin walls with pores, in effect selectively permeable membranes. Relatively small molecules such as oxygen, sugars, amino acids, salts, and carbon dioxide can readily penetrate the capillary walls, thus permitting the vital exchange of materials between the blood and cells of all body tissues. Since materials can pass through the capillary walls, why isn't there a net movement of fluid into or out of the capillaries? Two mechanisms prevent such a net fluid movement (Fig. 17-8). One is blood pressure, which remains at an average of 25 mm Hg in the capillaries. Although that pressure

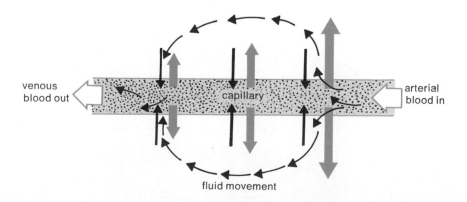

venous blood out   capillary   arterial blood in

fluid movement

Figure 17-8 The movement of fluid through the capillary wall depends on the balance between blood pressure and osmotic pressure.

is high enough to move fluid out of the capillaries, a second force prevents any net loss. Because of the presence of relatively large protein molecules in the blood plasma—molecules that cannot pass through the pores of the capillary walls—the osmotic pressure in the blood plasma is maintained at a higher level than the osmotic pressure in the extracellular fluid, the result being a tendency for extracellular fluid to be drawn into the capillaries. Since the osmotic pressure of the blood plasma is about 25 mm Hg, although there is a liberal exchange of fluid between capillary blood and cells, a steady state is maintained.

Coordination of blood flow depends on the work of valves within the heart. Without the functioning of these valves, blood would tend to slosh back and forth between the region it just came from and the region it should be going to. When the right auricle contracts, blood is forced past the tricuspid valve (Fig. 17–7) into the right ventricle. When the right ventricle moves the blood into the pulmonary artery, the tricuspid closes and prevents back-flow. On the left side, the bicuspid valve serves the same function, and when we reach the great vessels we find more valves. During the resting phase, called **diastole**, the semilunar valves plug the breach between ventricle and vesssel in both the aorta and the pulmonary artery. Heart murmurs are due to defective valves and are so called because of sounds heard through the stethoscope when hearts with diseased valves are examined.

Though cardiac tissue is able to beat without a nerve supply, the rhythm itself is sustained by nerves. Some of the nerves speed the beat and others slow it; hence the heart is said to have reciprocal innervation. Also, blood pressure at various points within the circulatory system is sensed and the information is transmitted to the brain stem, which can control heart-beat rate and make it responsive to a particular condition an organism may be facing. Details of many agents controlling the heart have yet to be discovered, and since we do not understand them fully it is impossible at the present to build an artificial heart with capacities even remotely approaching those of the natural organ. This is why Christiaan Barnard and others of his school feel it necessary to take the risks involved in heart transplantation. In some situations, where extensive cardiac damage has been done, the physician has no real option save that between possible life and certain death.

Blood gets back to the heart through the veins by the action of muscles (Fig. 17–9). When active the muscles press against the veins and, aided by

skeletal muscle contracts

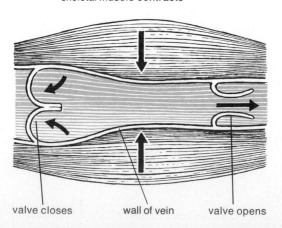

Figure 17–9 Venous valves make it possible for muscular pressure exerted on veins to force blood in a one-way direction back to the heart.

valve closes   wall of vein   valve opens

valves within the veins, push the blood along. Since the valves prevent back-flow, the forward motion of blood occurs even when there is the slightest muscular activity. Nevertheless, the absolute muscular rigidity of military attention often results in fainting spells if sustained for a long time.

The importance of circulation is clearly illustrated by the fact that disturbances to it account for more human deaths than any other group of diseases. Much is expected of our hearts: To keep us alive they must beat an average of three billion times during an average human life span, and they must act continuously, deprived of rest for as long as we are alive. The brain can be deprived of blood (including oxygen) for only a very brief time before suffering permanent injury. If its blood vessels become clogged, a stroke follows. If the coronary arteries, which feed the heart tissue itself, become blocked, heart attack occurs.

Many medical problems are caused by the blood vessels instead of the heart. When we are young our arteries are very elastic; as a result, the pressure produced when the heart pumps blood into them is moderate. As we age, the vessels become more and more fibrous, lose their elasticity, and react to pressure change more like fragile steel tubes than rough elastic ones. Blood pressure tends to rise in the vessels (hypertension) and causes the heart to work harder to overcome the back force. The arteries also become plugged with deposits of cholesterol and minerals of various types, which only aggravate an already bad situation.

Wondrous organ though it is, the heart cannot perpetually cope with such conditions. Like the long-distance runner, the victim of acute circulatory malfunction becomes short of breath and perhaps a bit blue in the face. The skin may swell and the pulse flutter, signs that the end is near. Life and circulatory function are this closely related.

THE CONSTITUENTS OF THE BLOOD

Blood is a unique fluid. It is a tissue and like other tissues consists of cells steeped in matrix. But here the matrix is liquid, not solid. You can see it for yourself when you get a cut (Fig. 17–1). Let the blood stand exposed and it separates into two phases, one solid, the other fluid. Within the solid phase are cells enmeshed in a gel—the **coagulum**. These cells make up 45% of our blood and are of three main types: red blood cells, white blood cells, and platelets (Fig. 17–10). While the red cells are responsible for the transport of the respiratory gases, the white cells combat germs and other foreign bodies on entering the circulatory system. They do so by engulfing the foreign bodies in a process called **phagocytosis**. There are at least five varieties of white cells, each carrying out specific functions.

Foreign bodies, known as **antigens**, introduced into the blood are immediately attacked by a variety of **antibodies**, which either destroy or neutralize the invading foreign particles. It is through the action of specific antibodies, including the proteins known as globulin, that we develop immunity to various diseases. Antibodies are also involved in the likely rejection of foreign tissue during a skin graft. When the host receives transplanted tissue his cells

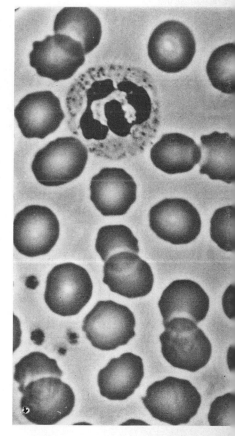

Figure 17–10 The numerous bodies without nuclei are red blood cells, or erythrocytes. The larger body with the segmented nucleus is a white blood cell, or leukocyte. Another kind of leukocyte has a large round nucleus. The small disc-shaped bodies are platelets.

recognize the foreign cells and immediately specific antibodies are produced, with the result that the donor cells are destroyed. Great care must be taken to match blood groups during a transfusion to avoid antibody reactions, which can cause severe illness or death.

Antigen–antibody reactions

But what are antibodies and how do they operate? They are globulin protein synthesized by the blood. Whenever an antigen (a bacterium or virus, for example) enters the circulatory system, receptor cells called **lymphocytes** begin dividing. Some differentiate into **plasma cells**, which secrete the antibody specific for the invading foreign body. Although we have much more to learn about the antigen–antibody reactions that produce immunity, we can make certain generalizations that appear valid. For example, as Fig. 17–11 shows, an antibody molecule specific for an antigen seems to have identical paired surfaces. On combining with two antigens, the antibody neutralizes the antigens. Still other antibodies tend to isolate and concentrate an antigen, thus making the antigen easier to be filtered out of the circulatory system (by the lymph nodes); other antibodies attack and destroy a bacterium's cell wall thus destroying the organism itself, and still others seem to increase the rate at which white cells engulf and destroy antigens by phagocytosis.

The large question about antibody specificity is how do the plasma cells "know" what kind of antibody to synthesize for the specific invading antigen? At the present time, the most workable hypothesis is one suggesting that an organism has an enormous variety of lymphocytes, enough to match billions of different kinds of foreign protein. An invading antigen links up with its corresponding lymphocyte receptor cells, thus stimulating profuse cell division among those lymphocytes. More of the appropriate lymphocytes are formed and mass-produce plasma cells, which in turn mass-produce the antibody specific for the invading antigen. As difficult as it is to accept the notion of a near infinite variety of lymphocytes being present in an organism and ready to go to work, the "clonal selection hypothesis," as it is called, is the most promising one available.

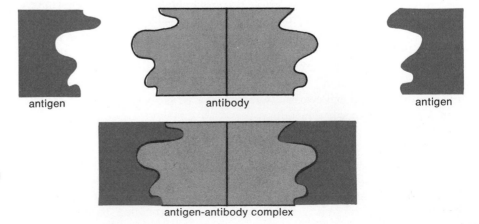

antigen antibody antigen

antigen-antibody complex

Figure 17–11 Antibodies are specific for antigens, a given antibody molecule having paired identical surfaces that react with and inactivate two antigens.

The blood cells are produced chiefly in the marrow of the long bones. The red cells live about four months and are thought to be ultimately destroyed in the spleen. In mammals, they are about $7\mu m$ (7 micrometers) in diameter, have the form of biconcave discs (Fig. 16–12), and lack a nucleus. By contrast, the red blood cells of other vertebrates tend to be spindle shaped and nucleated. In certain amphibians they may be as much as $75 \mu m$ in diameter. The fluid portion of the blood mentioned earlier in association with the capillaries is called **plasma** when it contains materials necessary for the coagulation process. When it lacks these materials it is called **serum**. Plasma constitutes 55% of the blood volume and contains a number of agents that remain to be discovered. In view of the many organs blood touches, and the many functions it serves, gaps in our knowledge about it are not surprising.

Blood clotting

Blood clotting, common among all vertebrates and some invertebrates, is a physiological adaptation that prevents excessive blood loss through damage to the veins and arteries. At one time it was thought that blood clotted on exposure to the air, but investigations have shown that clotting is stimulated by the release of a substance from the damaged region of a vessel and by the destruction of the little-understood blood platelets on contacting such damaged tissue. As the platelets break down, they release quantities of the same substance released by the damaged tissue—**thromboplastin** (Fig. 17–12). However, three additional substances are required before clotting will occur: calcium ions (Ca^{++}), a soluble plasma protein called **fibrinogen**, and a plasma globulin protein called **prothrombin**. A clot will not form, however, until prothrombin has been acted on by Ca^{++} and thromboplastin and converted to **thrombin**, which is the agent that alters fibrinogen from its soluble form to its insoluble (gel) form known as **fibrin**. The fibrin mesh of fibers (Fig. 17–1) contracts, squeezes out the fluid-serum, and hardens as a clot.

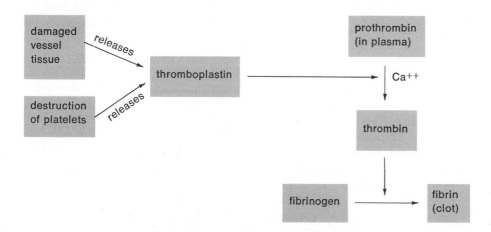

Figure 17–12 Sequence of events and substances leading to the formation of a blood clot.

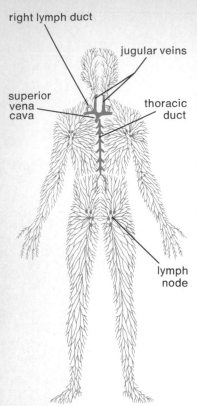

right lymph duct

jugular veins

superior vena cava

thoracic duct

lymph node

Figure 17–13 Lymph ducts drain water and dissolved substances from the extracellular spaces, returning them to the blood. This vast system of lymphatics converges to form two main ducts. The right lymphatic duct, which serves the right side of the head, neck, and thorax, and the right arm, empties into the junction of the right internal jugular and subclavian veins. The thoracic duct drains the rest of the body and empties into the corresponding venous junction on the left side. The nodes filter out foreign bodies.

THE LYMPH

The heart, acting as a pump, imparts great pressure to the blood and drives it through almost every tissue of the organism. Across the diaphanous walls of the minute capillaries the life-giving stuff of the blood is transported to the body's cells.

The portion of the capillary nearest a supplying arteriole bears a higher pressure than that near the venous exit. This circumstance causes fluid to be driven out of the capillary (Fig. 17–8). It is basically a modified plasma, some of which re-enters the capillary at the low-pressure venous end, but not all. The organism requires a mechanism that can recover the modified plasma, which might otherwise be lost. This material is called **lymph** and most vertebrates have a system of vessels capable of receiving it; they are the **lymph vessels** (Fig. 17–13).

The walls of lymph vessels are exceedingly permeable and through them the lymph gains access to the vessel's lumen. Once there, the lymph is transported to one of the great veins in the thorax and so regains admission into the circulatory system. While outside that system, lymph has served the cells well; it has, in fact, provided them with another "internal environment." About half of the volume of the blood is lost to the tissues and regained in a single day. So critical is the function of the lymphatics that they are acted upon, in certain lower vertebrates, by **lymph hearts**. There are animals with two hundred of them! We do not have these structures. However, we do have small enlargements called **nodes** that are part of the lymphatic system and apparently filter out foreign particles from our systems when we have been infected. They are prominent in the neck and under the jaw, and you have probably found them to be swollen when you become ill with flu, common cold, or an infected tooth.

WATER HOMEOSTASIS AND EXCRETION

Without food, a person may live two or three weeks, but when deprived of water a person will die in a matter of days. In view of our need for water, it is easy to understand why it must be under strict homeostatic regulation. The mechanisms controlling water balance become more prominent as one ascends the evolutionary tree. Primitive organisms of long ago and those presently living in the ocean apparently have little need for carefully operated water-balancing mechanisms. The reason for this is clear.

The circulatory fluids of the primitive life forms are almost identical in composition to sea water; consequently they live in a huge pool of "circulatory fluid"—the ocean. We, on the other hand, "carry the ocean within us" but are forever in danger of losing it, living as we do in the arid confines of our terrestrial environment.

When primitive organisms left the sea and invaded land and fresh water, a water-regulating system became essential. We are interested primarily in seeing how our ancient *émigrés* evolved in the face of situations that would either flood them and deprive them of quantities of minerals and salts, or desiccate them and increase their salt concentrations beyond tolerable limits.

Some of the protozoans, for example, moved from salt water to fresh, where we find them today. Here are cells with selectively permeable membranes. They contain a relatively high concentration of salts and macromolecules. What happens to such organisms if they are placed in water of low salt concentration, such as they encounter in inland streams and pools? The "law" of osmosis tells us that the cells must swell. Water must move into them and if there were no way of stopping the flood, the protozoan would eventually burst. How is this end averted?

The contractile vacuole

If you have ever watched a living paramecium under a microscope, you probably noted a pulsating organelle located toward the posterior of the protist (Fig. 17–14). Called a **contractile vacuole**, this little organelle is responsible for the survival of many protozoans, including the familiar ameba. If you place a paramecium in water of increasingly higher salt concentration, the pulsation frequency of the vacuole declines. The more salty the water becomes, the less frequently the vacuole pulsates. One interpretation of this event sees the contractile vacuole acting as a bilge pump bailing out the excess water. We can test this supposition easily. If we stop the vacuole's pulsation, the animal swells up, apparently deprived of the regulating mechanism. The kinds of compounds that can "stall" the contractile vacuole are interesting. They are, in general, chemicals that are able to inhibit the evolution of energy by the cell. In other words, the contractile vacuole requires an energy input in order to operate properly. Why this should be so will become apparent when we examine the mechanism responsible for the formation of material within the vacuole.

The fluid in the contractile vacuole is *much less* concentrated than the organism's protoplasm but *somewhat more* concentrated than the external medium. In other words one could say the ameba, the paramecium, and other organisms that have contractile vacuoles and live in fresh water are producing a dilute "urine," for the material in the vacuoles is less osmotically active than is the protoplasm itself. The basic question is how the vacuolar fluid becomes less concentrated than the protoplasm in the first place. We think this occurs by a process of active transport. Active transport requires energy, and this would account for the fact that poisons that block energy generation also interfere with the work of the contractile vacuole.

The contractile vacuole is a homeostatic organelle. Through active transport it preserves water balance for paramecia, amebas, and other protozoans. Homeostasis, then, is not exclusively a property of higher organisms, but is found in many protists. Like other vital processes, it evolved in primitive unicellular organisms. Often, differences between higher and lower life forms are those of degree rather than kind.

The multicellular organisms that invaded fresh water habitats include a large variety of evolutionary types that had to avoid excessive water influx as well as water loss. They did this chiefly in two ways—by evolving hard and semi-impenetrable structures that kept water out, and by developing organs that removed excessive water that would tend to dilute the organism's salt reserve.

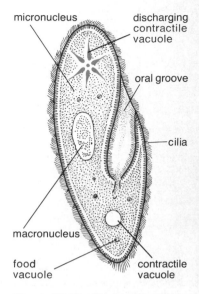

Figure 17–14 Contractile vacuoles present in *Paramecium* function as homeostatic regulators maintaining water balance. Many common species have two contractile vacuoles. Note the star-like appearance of the upper contractile vacuole, which is discharging its contents outside the cell. The other contractile vacuole is collecting water prior to discharging it.

Antennary glands

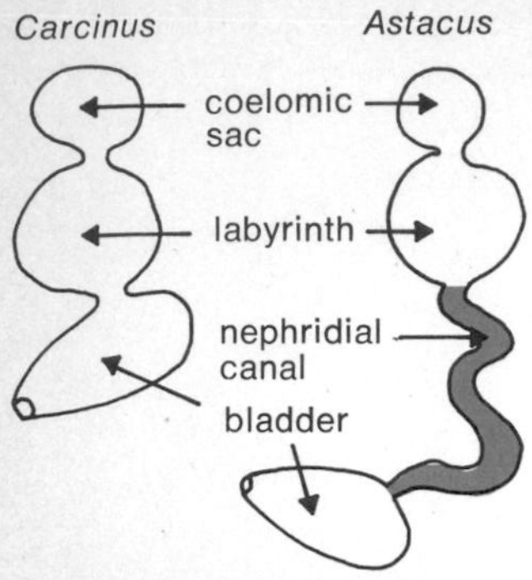

Carcinus *Astacus*

coelomic sac

labyrinth

nephridial canal

bladder

Figure 17–15 The antennary gland of *Carcinus*, a marine form, is compared with that of *Astacus*, a fresh-water form.

Crayfish, crabs, and their relatives have near their antennae a gland that is roughly analogous in function to the kidney of the higher animals. Because of its location, it is called the **antennary gland**. It is this organ that helps fresh-water crustaceans control water balance. Removing an antennary gland from a seashore crab and comparing it with one from a fresh-water crayfish reveals a striking difference (Fig. 17–15). Both glands contain a coelomic sac, a labyrinth, and a bladder. However, in the case of the fresh-water form, notice the addition of a segment called the **nephridial canal**. This structure is responsible for the excretion of a relatively dilute urine accomplished by active transport of much-needed salts back into the animal's system. So crayfish produce a copious and dilute urine just as paramecia do. Although the anatomical arrangements are different, the basic process, active transport, is similar and the end results the same. Now that we have seen homeostasis at work in a single cell and in a relatively advanced multicellular invertebrate organism, let's turn to homeostatic regulation of water balance in mammals.

Mammals and the kidney

The situation encountered by most mammals was exactly opposite the one crustaceans and protozoans encountered. Mammals invaded terrestrial habitats and so were continuously faced with the problem of desiccation, or drying out. Some have handled the problem passably, some are adept at it, and still others have become masterful. The masters of the situation are, of course, those mammals that successfully inhabit the deserts.

One of the complications involved in the study of mammalian water balance techniques is the supposition by many experts that primitive vertebrates evolved in fresh-water habitats. In essence, they developed organs that operate in much the same way as the contractile vacuole and antennary gland. In the vertebrates of Paleozoic times, the structure was what we call a **glomerulus** (Fig. 17–16). It is in reality a tuft of small-caliber blood vessels lying close to a tubule that leads to the external environment. Fresh-water vertebrates of old dealt with excessive water by expelling it through their glomeruli. But what happened to the animals that moved onto the land and had to conserve water? And what happened to those that returned to the salt of the sea?

In some of the fresh-water vertebrates that left their fresh-water habitats and took up life in the sea, the glomerulus degenerated. The sea horse is one such animal. Others drank the sea water and expelled excess salts through cells located in their gill filaments. This process, operating against a concentration gradient since the external environment is more concentrated with salt than is the internal environment, requires an energy source. Again we find a basic theme running through the evolutionary hierarchy—energy driving active transport and homeostatic regulation. The animals that conquered the land elaborated on their glomeruli.

The glomerulus is located in the outer region of the human kidney. Tubules extend from the glomeruli and empty into the ureter (Fig. 17–17). The glomerulus is really a continuation of a blood vessel (the afferent arteriole). As

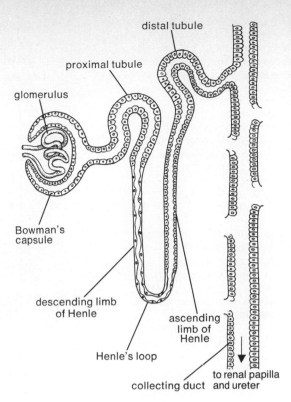

distal tubule

proximal tubule

glomerulus

Bowman's
capsule

descending limb
of Henle

ascending
limb of
Henle

Henle's loop

collecting duct

to renal papilla
and ureter

Figure 17-16 A nephron is the functional unit of the kidney. It consists of a cluster of capillaries (a glomerulus), a Bowman's capsule, and a tubule to the collecting duct.

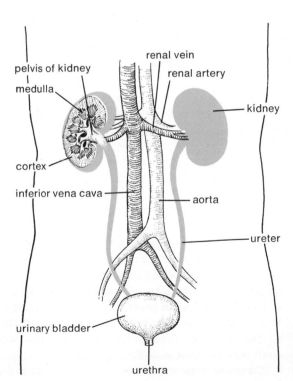

pelvis of kidney

medulla

renal vein

renal artery

kidney

cortex

inferior vena cava

aorta

ureter

urinary bladder

urethra

Figure 17-17 This ventral view of the human urinary system shows the position of the kidneys, ureters, and bladder.

Figure 17-18 The kidney possesses a countercurrent multiplier that enables it to produce concentrated urine and conserve water. Sodium ions are actively transported out of the proximal and distal tubules and from the ascending limb (AL) of the loop of Henle, which is impermeable to water. Sodium leaving the ascending limb enters the descending limb (DL). Thus there is a countercurrent exchange of sodium between these limbs, causing sodium to become very concentrated in the tubule and in extracellular fluids at the bend of the loop of Henle. As the collecting ducts (CD) pass through this region, water is passively reabsorbed out of the ducts into the extracellular fluid. The amount of water reabsorbed is controlled by the hormone ADH, which affects the permeability of the duct. The longer the loop of Henle, the higher the concentration of sodium and the greater the amount of water that can be reabsorbed from the urine. The longest loops of Henle are found in desert mammals that secrete extremely concentrated urine. The numbers in the diagram represent the relative osmotic concentrations along the tubule, and the arrows indicate the movement of sodium and water. The heavy arrows indicate active transport of sodium. Some evidence suggests that the entry of sodium into the descending limb may also be by active transport rather than by diffusion.

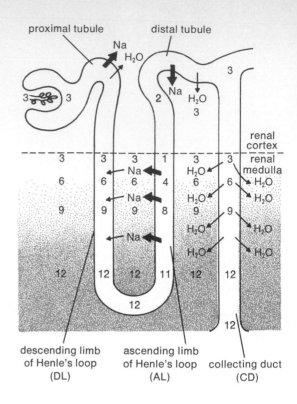

Figure 17-19 A variety of animals, apparently including man, use an arterial-venous countercurrent heat exchanger to conserve heat and rewarm blood returning from the cold limbs to the body core. This figure shows how, in the dorsal fin of the bottlenose porpoise, the arteries are closely surrounded by veins. Most of the heat lost by the warm arterial blood is "captured" by the cooler venous blood and returned to the body. Part C of the figure shows a hypothetical temperature gradient.

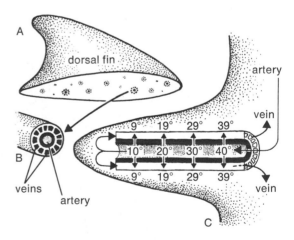

blood moves through the glomerulus, blood pressure forces fluid through pores in the vessel walls. In effect, the straining action produces an **ultrafiltrate** of the blood, a clear fluid that contains everything the blood contains except cells and protein molecules. The fluid produced moves through the tubules (which have walls no more than a single cell thick).

Notice in Fig. 17-16 that the glomerulus lies within a *double layer* of material, as opposed to a single layer. This structure is called **Bowman's capsule**, and along with cells making up the capillary walls of the glomerulus it strains the blood into the kidney tubule. The entire tubular system, including the glomerulus, is called a **nephron**.

The nephron of the kidney of mammals performs three basic functions: filtration of blood, reabsorption, and secretion. Filtration is the screening out of large molecules by the glomerulus. Reabsorption is a vital process for the animal because it helps save essential body chemicals. What happens to glucose will illustrate our meaning.

Glucose is not a very large molecule and penetrates the glomerulus, entering the tubular fluid. Because of the importance of glucose to the organism, it would be very inefficient to lose tremendous amounts of the material. The kidney helps conserve glucose by reabsorbing it. Measurement of the concentration of glucose as a function of the distance that the tubular fluid moves down the nephron, establishes that most of it is absorbed in the segment lying close to the glomerulus, the **proximal tubule** (Fig. 17–16). People with diabetes excrete and lose large amounts of glucose because it is not completely reabsorbed. Absorption of glucose requires the mediation of another agent to transport it through the cell membrane. We refer to such agents as carriers. If too much glucose is present in the kidney fluid, the carrier is "swamped" and glucose is lost as part of the urine. Eating a very large amount of sugar causes excretion of glucose in urine even though diabetes does not exist.

Secretion of materials into the nephron is another important function performed by the kidney. This operation is the opposite of tubular reabsorption. The mechanism is useful when the organism needs to rid itself of foreign or dangerous materials. For example, when penicillin (an antibiotic) is injected into the blood stream, it is swiftly excreted through the kidneys. The penicillin is pumped across the tubular wall and is then lost in the urine. Reabsorption and secretion are both carrier-dependent, differing only in direction.

Water conservation

To understand how water conservation is achieved, study Fig. 17–18. The diagram is arranged in much the same way as the tubules of the mammalian renal system in Fig. 17–16, channels AL, DL, and CD being equivalent to the **ascending limb of Henle, descending limb of Henle,** and **collecting duct.** Such an arrangement is called a **countercurrent multiplier** because of the direction of flow. To discover what such a multiplier can do, look at Fig. 17–19. Here we are dealing with the transfer and conservation of heat energy rather than a fluid. When the veins and arteries follow separate courses through a limb, each loses a large amount of heat to the cold environment. When the venous return channels surround the arteries, however, much heat from the arterial blood is transferred to the venous blood and retained in the body. Vascular heat exchangers maintain a steep temperature gradient in the appendage. The appendage is kept cold, but less heat is needed to maintain a constant temperature in the rest of the body.

Concentrations of solute can be handled by the kidney in much the same way as heat is handled by the countercurrent system shown in Fig. 17–19.

Notice how in Fig. 17–18 sodium is continuously being actively transported out of tubule AL and into tubule DL. In effect, as fluid moves through the kidney system and is pushed out through AL, its concentration becomes lower and lower, as the numbers in the diagram indicate. Eventual depletion of the ions is averted, however, by the active movement of sodium into tubule DL. Hence, at the turn in the U-tube (called **Henle's loop**), a high content of sodium is redelivered to tubule AL. In the absence of such a return supply, sodium would eventually be depleted.

In addition to the ionic concentration taking place in tubule DL, the fluid between the tubules is also becoming rich in sodium. Thus, a concentration gradient is being established with respect to channel CD. As the fluid in channel CD moves down, its concentration increases, as indicated by the numbers. Because of the heightened ionic gradient built up by the counter-current system, the concentration of ions in the kidney's collecting ducts (channel CD) increases as fluid progresses from top to bottom in the diagram. The collecting ducts, which eventually connect to the ureters, join the bladder, and the urethra transports the contents of the bladder (Fig. 17–17) out of the body. In other words, if the contents of the collecting ducts are concentrated, the urine will also be concentrated. The fluid in the collecting ducts increases in concentration due to the gradient set up outside the walls of the ducts. The water within the tubules moves out and tends to smooth out the gradient. In so doing, it leaves behind a solution with a very large number of ions. The water thus removed from the collecting ducts is conserved, a vital physiological adaptation enabling terrestrial mammals to avoid desiccation.

Virtually no other organisms besides birds and mammals can form urine that is much more concentrated than their blood. The ability to make such urine is tied specifically to the interesting kind of kidney we have been discussing. Desert-dwelling mammals have very long loops of Henle and other mechanisms that enable them to form a highly concentrated urine. The camel produces an extremely concentrated urine; so do desert rodents. As a matter of fact, rodents produce the most concentrated urine known and have among the longest loops of Henle. The fat sand rat, *Psammomys obesus*, produces a urine which is about six times as concentrated as ours is. Some desert mammals have such efficient kidneys that they can drink salt water. This is also true of a number of birds that have, in addition to long loops of Henle, accessory glands that excrete high concentrations of salt.

Humans are relatively inefficient at dealing with desiccating environments. Consider a man lost at sea. He cannot drink sea water because he cannot produce a sufficiently concentrated urine. Even before the dehydration produced by drinking such water sets in, the GI system becomes extremely inflamed. That is actually the immediate cause of death from drinking ocean water. What, then, to do? To eat fish which contain some barely drinkable water is not the answer because the breakdown products of fish protein must be eliminated from the body. To eliminate them requires water and depletes the water gained from eating the fish in the first place. Without accessory equipment, the best thing to do is lap up the fluid around the fish's muscles since the fish maintains a salt concentration lower than that in sea water. However, only a meagre supply of suitable water could be gained in that manner.

Artificial kidneys

The kidney, like the contractile vacuole and the antennary gland, is a homeo-static regulator and is essential to our survival. Although artificial kidneys have been designed for use during certain operating room procedures, they are very primitive machines compared with the genuine article. In artificial kidneys, a person's blood is passed into a series of channels whose walls are made of cellophane. The walls have small pores, so many of the waste products the kidney normally removes can be absorbed from the system through the pores in the cellophane walls. Although many lives have been saved with artificial kidneys, a cellophane membrane is not able to drive active transport or facilitate diffusion. We still have much more to learn before we can make an entirely satisfactory replica of the living kidney.

The body functions we have discussed in the preceding two chapters are "supportive" in the sense that they are essential if an organism is to maintain life-sustaining energy. This energy, of course, is converted into usable form by cells, and it is to cells that we now turn our attention.

QUESTIONS FOR REVIEW

1 How was Harvey able to tell that the blood circulates? Why did his experiments have a major influence on all biological science and not just on the study of the heart itself?

2 How does the circulatory system of the annelids differ from that of insects?

3 Marine fish often drink salt water in which they live, yet their problem is to rid themselves of salt and to get water. How do they do it?

4 If a paramecium were placed in a very dilute solution would you expect the rate of contractile vacuole pulsation to decrease, increase, or remain the same compared to its rate when the cell is in pond water? Explain.

5 Some fish have lost their glomeruli. What advantage would this offer?

SELECTED READINGS

Cannon, Walter B. *The Wisdom of the Body*. New York: W. W. Norton & Co., 1932. Discusses the general principle of homeostasis and the maintenance of stability in an organism's internal environment. The work was written at a time when the many relationships between stabilizing processes and the autonomic nervous system were just becoming clear.

Ramsey, James A. *Physiological Approach to the Lower Animals*. 2nd ed. London: Cambridge University Press, 1968. This short discourse on functional aspects in lower vertebrates is certain to make one aware of the importance of studying the simpler metazoans to gain a proper perspective upon human physiology.

Smith, Homer W. *From Fish to Philosopher: The Story of Our Internal Environment*. Summit, N. J.: CIBA, 1959. This is a most readable book which explains how the kidneys have come to function as they do and relates the evolutionary pressures that have been brought to bear on their development.

18
CELL CHEMISTRY AND ENERGETICS

CELLULAR ENERGETICS

To act or react in the physical sense, an organism requires fuel as a source of energy. The branch of science concerned with energy relationships is called thermodynamics. It is an extremely important discipline for the biologist because living matter, it turns out, obeys the laws developed by thermodynamicists just as faithfully as inanimate matter does. There are no exceptions to thermodynamic rules—they are straightforward and irrevocable.

Laws of thermodynamics

Electricity, light, and certain chemical reactions were all known by 19th-century scholars to be capable of performing work—hence, all contained that invisible something called energy. Through some ingenious studies on heat phenomena, Hermann Helmholtz and Robert Mayer arrived at an important conclusion: Energy is never created or destroyed. It may be converted from one form to another, as from the chemical energy of a car battery to the electrical energy needed to start a car, but the sum total of energy remains constant. We call that statement the first law of thermodynamics. As Albert Einstein was later able to show, energy and matter are interconvertible. That is, energy can be created at the expense of matter (and vice versa) according to the formula $E = mc^2$. This modification in no way undermines the first law, but only makes it more general.

In a living system involving cells, organisms, and populations, the first law of thermodynamics tells us that energy from the Sun (light) or from food (chemical) can be converted into energy which is usable within the system. It may be passed from one organism to another (as when the first organism is eaten by the second), and within one organism from the energy of one chemical bond (sugar, let's say) to another (proteins which are synthesized within the cell). A living system would operate as a self-sustaining web, according to the first law, except that energy is constantly being lost to the environment through heat loss, through excretion, and because of the second law of thermodynamics. According to the second law, "Whenever a reaction occurs, the usable energy in the reaction system must decline." In other words, the level of energy within a system tends to run downhill. The system becomes more random, and the amount of energy available at the next level is less than before. To keep matters simple, we may say that not all the energy in a waterfall or in a tank of gasoline can be harnessed for purposes of doing work. We do not refer here to the type of energy eventually lost as heat in the bearings of an

Figure 18–1 Solar radiation, used by green plants in the production of glucose, is the source of energy for all living organisms on Earth. Organisms at all trophic levels ultimately depend on the plant-producers as a source of energy to drive chemical reactions on the cellular level.

engine. Even if there were such a thing as an ideal frictionless machine, *all* its energy still could not be converted into work. The part not available for the performance of work is called **entropy**.

Here thermodynamics gives us some real direction. It tells us (through the second law) that a reaction is possible only if the reaction leads to an *increase* in entropy or randomness. (The discussion of food webs and chains in Chapter 6 provided examples of how energy is lost in going from the level of plants to that of herbivores to carnivores.) A perfect crystal at a temperature of absolute zero has no entropy. The crystal is a model of perfect order for it can exist (at absolute zero) in one state only. As temperature increases, atomic and molecular motion increase. When molecules move rapidly, as in a gas, the chance of their ever existing in perfect order is slimmer than if those molecules were moving more slowly. Their entropy is now said to be high.

Remember that the second law tells us entropy is ever on the increase. That means order is being transformed into disorder. The only way a tendency toward disorder can be averted is by tapping some other energy source. One can keep a mechanical alarm clock operating by winding it. The clock's works

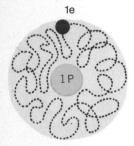

hydrogen atom

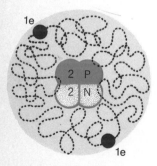

helium atom

Figure 18–2 Atoms are composed of three basic building blocks—protons and neutrons that make up the nucleus, and electrons that move about the nucleus in specific regions. The looping dotted lines represent movements of the electron over the invisible surface of a nonexistent shell, all points of which are uniformly distant from the nucleus.

ATOMS AND HOW THEY COMBINE

All matter in the universe is composed of minute structural units called atoms. An atom consists of three basic building blocks, the atoms of each chemical element having a specific number of **protons** and **neutrons** in the nucleus (or core) and a number of **electrons** (equal to the number of protons) situated at one or more energy levels from the nucleus. Because protons carry a positive electrical charge and electrons carry a negative electrical charge, and because their number is the same in an ordinary atom, the atom is electrically neutral. Neutrons do not have an electrical charge.

Protons and neutrons, just about equally massive, make up almost the entire mass of an atom, a proton being 1,845 times more massive than an electron. The hydrogen atom (Fig. 18–2) is the simplest member of the atomic family, consisting of a single proton and a single electron. We can picture an electron as a mobile unit in continuous motion this way and that over the "surface" of one or more "shells" enclosing the nucleus. Each shell, or energy level, progressing outward from the nucleus, is designated by a letter (*K, L, M, N, O, P, Q*) and can accommodate a specific number of electrons. Notice in Fig. 18–2 that the *K* orbital of the helium atom contains two electrons (maximum for that orbital) and that the *L* orbital of sodium contains eight (maximum for that orbital). More complex atoms, such as those of uranium, have numerous protons, electrons, and neutrons, one form of uranium having 92 protons and 146 neutrons. Combining the numbers of protons and neutrons, we say that the atom has an **atomic weight** of 238 and write it in chemical shorthand as U_{238}.

The electrons of an atom are not bound permanently to their orbitals;

are drawing on energy from the individual who does the winding, and as a result, the entropy level of the individual has grown. Orderly systems can do more work than disorderly ones, but as a result of that work the orderly systems themselves undergo an increase in disorder. The essence of life, as a state, is organization and order. Without them there is no life. While alive, an organism is a very low entropy system. How can such a system endure for long if the second law holds? How does the biotic world persist in so inhospitable a physical framework?

Experimental work over many years has shown that, like a clock, organisms draw their energy from sources of relative abundance. The foods we eat are rich sources of energy—in the form of carbohydrates, such as sugars and starch, and fats. Animals tap the foodstuffs synthesized by plants during photosynthesis by breaking down the foodstuffs through a series of chemical reactions. In order to achieve either the synthesis or the breakdown of foods, cells require the work of enzymes. To understand how organisms obtain energy from the foods they consume, we must first know a few chemical details about carbohydrates, fats, and the enzymes that act on these molecules.

they may jump back and forth from one energy level to another. For instance, ultraviolet radiation striking certain substances provides energy capable of causing electrons in the outer orbital to jump to an orbital of a higher energy level. Because such a situation is an unstable one, the electrons fall back to their former energy level. In the process of returning, they emit a small packet of energy that we may see as visible light.

When atoms dissociate or combine during a chemical reaction, only the electrons in the outer orbitals are involved, and it is the number of electrons in the outer orbital of an atom, **valence electrons** as they are called, that determines one atom's "willingness" to combine with another and form a molecule. Atoms with full outer orbitals, such as helium, neon, and argon, do not combine with other atoms and are said to be inert. Atoms such as sodium and chlorine (Fig. 18–3) combine readily since their outer orbitals are not full.

Atoms are held together as molecules by **chemical bonds**. For instance, a bond may be formed when two atoms come so close together that their outer electron shells overlap and they share an electron. In other cases, such as that of a sodium and chlorine atom combining, an electron from one atom (sodium) is transferred to the other atom (chlorine). When such a transfer takes place, each atom becomes electrically charged and is called an **ion**. In the case of NaCl, the Na atom loses its outer-orbital electron (thereby being left with a charge of $+1$) and is written Na^+, while the chlorine atom acquiring the electron is left with a charge of -1 and is written Cl^-. Such a chemical bond involving the *transfer* of an electron is called **ionic bonding**. When two atoms —such as two H or Cl atoms—combine as a molecule by *sharing* an electron, the bond is said to be a **covalent bond** (Fig. 18–4).

Figure 18–3 The sodium atom transfers its single outer orbital electron to the outer orbital of the chlorine atom, giving the Na atom a positive charge and the Cl atom a negative charge. The electrostatic attraction of their opposite charges forms an ionic bond that holds the two ions together as a molecule of sodium chloride (NaCl).

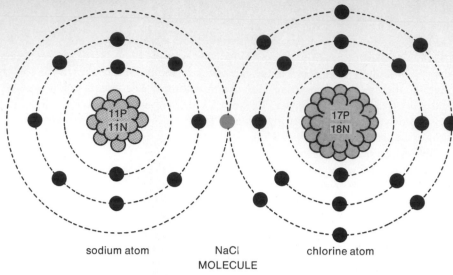

sodium atom   NaCl   chlorine atom
MOLECULE

Figure 18–4 Two hydrogen atoms (H + H) are bonded as a molecule (H_2) by sharing electrons.

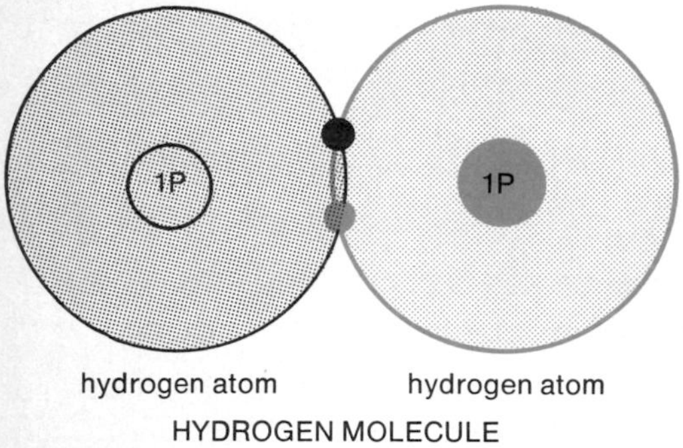

hydrogen atom   hydrogen atom

HYDROGEN MOLECULE

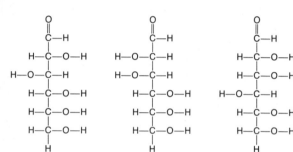

Figure 18–5 The three six-carbon sugars shown here, identical in composition but different structurally, are called isomers.

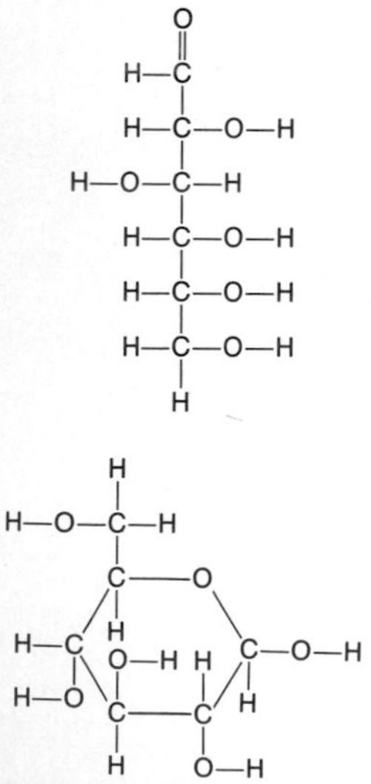

Figure 18–6 Chain structure (top) and ring structure of a six-carbon sugar.

BIOMOLECULES

The carbohydrates

Sugars, or carbohydrates, are materials consisting of carbon, hydrogen, and oxygen only. Carbohydrates are biologically important compounds since they play a vital role in satisfying the energy requirements of cells. Although the carbohydrate of greatest concern in our present discussion is glucose ($C_6H_{12}O_6$), sugars with other numbers of carbon atoms are also important biological compounds. **Starches** and **glycogen** are the principal storage compounds in higher plants and animals respectively, while **cellulose**, an extremely non-reactive carbohydrate, is the major supporting material in plants. All these and other carbohydrates can be represented by the general formula [CH_2O]. Different forms of sugars, each with the same number of carbon, hydrogen, and oxygen atoms, are known. Although similar in composition, these sugars are distinctive structurally. Such compounds are known as **isomers** (Fig. 18–5). As shown in Fig. 18–6, sugars can also exist as either a straight chain or a ring structure.

Because glucose contains six carbons it is referred to as a **hexose**. Sugars with five carbons are **pentoses**, and those with three, **trioses**. When one sugar sub-unit constitutes a complete molecular structure, the molecule is said to be a **monosaccharide**; with two sub-units, a **disaccharide** (Fig. 18–7); with many sub-units, a **polysaccharide**. Glycogen, with a great number of sub-units and often called "animal starch" since it is stored in liver and muscle cells, is an example of a polysaccharide.

In order to utilize the energy contained in the chemical bonds of the glucose molecule, cells must break down these molecules through a series of oxidative reactions, known as **cellular respiration**. Oxidation occurs when molecular oxygen combines with a substance or when hydrogen is removed from a molecule. Cellular respiration takes place in small steps, with the glucose molecule giving up more and more of its total energy at each succeeding step. The end products, if oxygen is available, are carbon dioxide and water.

If respiration occurs in the absence of oxygen (an anaerobic environment) the chemical reactions involved are known as **glycolysis** and **fermentation**. Glycolysis is the general term which describes the oxidation of glucose or other carbohydrates to form pyruvic acid, in the process generating two molecules of the energy-rich compound known as **ATP** (adenosine triphosphate). If the reaction is allowed to continue in the absence of oxygen, pyruvic acid is reduced (hydrogen atoms are added) to form alcohol or lactic acid through the process of fermentation. Although we will go into this pathway in greater depth later, two points should be emphasized here: (1) the purpose of glycolysis and fermentation is to build energy-rich ATP molecules, which the cell can then use in its metabolic pathways, and (2) this process can take place in an atmosphere totally lacking in oxygen.

If oxygen is present in the cell environment another process, known as **oxidative phosphorylation**, occurs. Cellular respiration can thus take place in two different directions depending on the availability of molecular oxygen. This second process, because it is able to make more efficient use of the glucose molecule, produces three times the ATP produced in glycolysis.

Lipids

Like carbohydrates, lipids are composed of carbon, hydrogen, and oxygen (Fig. 18–8), but unlike carbohydrates, lipids assume a number of seemingly

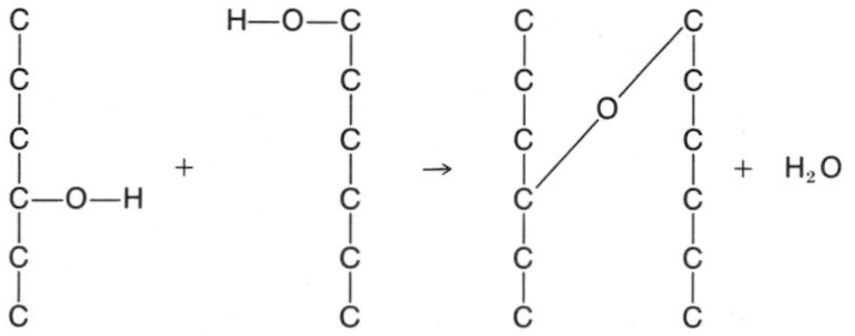

Figure 18–7 A disaccharide can be formed by the combination of two monosaccharides and the removal of water.

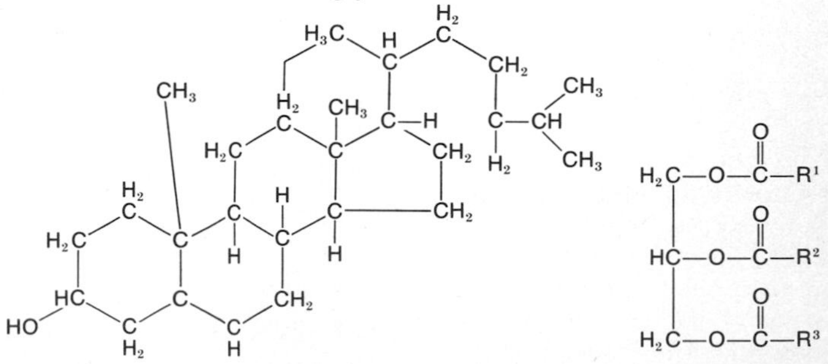

cholesterol

triglyceride

Figure 18–8 Two typical lipid molecules. The "R" groups in triglyceride are long-chain fatty acids.

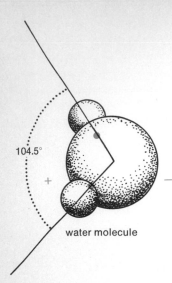

104.5°

+

−

water molecule

Figure 18–9 Because the shared single electron of each hydrogen spends most of its time on the oxygen side of its nucleus in a covalent bond, a water molecule has an electrically (+) and electrically (−) end and is said to be a polar molecule.

O
H
H

Figure 18–10 The geometry of water molecules is such that the positive hydrogen "end" forms a bond with the negative oxygen "end" of a neighboring molecule. The resulting bonds are called "hydrogen bonds" and are responsible for the cohesive force of water.

unrelated chemical configurations. The only common denominator for fatty substances is that they dissolve in organic solvents such as toluene or xylol. Fats have several very important physiological functions. For one, they are rich sources of energy that can be stored over comparatively long periods of time. They also serve as building blocks for hormones and for cell membrane systems. Certain sex hormones are basically steroids, a class of lipids.

Water

The necessity of maintaining water balance was emphasized in the previous chapter. Without water, life as we know it would not exist on Earth. Water serves the cell in a number of ways. It enters into many of the chemical reactions which occur in the cell; it facilitates chemical reactions through its capacity for ionizing other molecules in the cell; it acts as a good conductor of heat and operates to cool the cell and the organism.

Because of its geometry (Fig. 18–9), the water molecule has a positive "end" and a negative "end." Such a molecule is said to be **polar**, a feature that is important in determining the efficiency of a substance as a solvent. The charged "ends" of such molecules interact with oppositely charged "ends" of other molecules or with ions (Fig. 18–10). Common NaCl goes into solution easily because water is a polar molecule. The NaCl dissociates into Na^+ and Cl^- ions, the Na^+ reacting with the negative pole of the water molecule and the Cl^- combining with the positive pole.

Water, then, is a basic biomolecule because it provides cells with a measure of constancy. At the same time it is able to bring physiologically important molecules and membranes into a common framework, so that when the need arises they can interact. The molecules and membranes involved in energy procurement are part of that framework.

Protein and enzymes

The protoplasm of animal and plant cells alike is largely made up of a class of giant molecules called **proteins**. These important molecules are also present in cell organelles, the blood, cell membranes, and chromosomes, and they form the antibodies mentioned earlier. In addition to serving in a structural capacity, proteins also serve regulatory functions in cells and tissue. Insulin, for example, is a protein hormone that regulates the amount of sugar reaching our tissues through the blood.

Unlike the carbohydrates and lipids, proteins contain nitrogen in addition to carbon, hydrogen, and oxygen. So complex are these molecules that a single one may contain tens of thousands of atoms. At this stage you might do well to review the text and related figures (Figs. 2–3 and 2–4) in Chapter 2 that describe how protein molecules and amino acids are synthesized and how amino acids are bonded to form long spiral-shaped polypeptide chains (proteins) held together by hydrogen bonding.

ENZYME–SUBSTRATE INTERACTION: One special class of proteins—the enzymes—are essential to the chemical reactions taking place within cells.

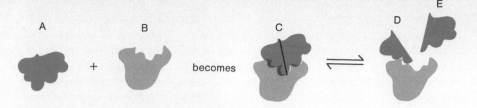

Enzymes operate as agents, called **catalysts**, that speed up a chemical reaction without themselves becoming chemically altered during the reaction. This may seem odd, since an enzyme actually combines with the substance, called the **substrate**, that it transforms. It does so by binding the molecules of the reactants—like the antigen–antibody reaction in the previous chapter—placing them in close proximity and contributing to the synthesis of a new molecule. This reaction can work either way, depending on the pressure, temperature, and concentration in which the reaction takes place. Either the new molecule is synthesized, or it again breaks into its reactant parts.

As more substrate is added to a reaction medium, the limited amount of enzyme present becomes progressively involved and eventually will reach a stage where all of it is "tied up." At this point, the addition of more substrate does nothing to increase the overall reaction rate. Substrates apparently interact with a specified part of enzymes known as the **active site** (Fig. 18–11), a relatively small area on the enzyme molecule. The great efficiency of enzymes—above that of inorganic catalysts like platinum—is explained by their ability to "seek out" specific reactants and bind them, at the active site, for the purposes of reacting.

The role of phosphate

Enzymes were first isolated by investigators interested in fermentation and the biochemical activity of yeasts. Later Arthur Harden and W. J. Young conducted a very important piece of experimental work with yeast. They noticed an extremely curious phenomenon. In a fermenting system, CO_2 and ethanol would be produced for a time, but then the rate of output of the two

$$C_6H_{12}O_6 \longrightarrow 2CO_2 + 2CH_3CH_2OH$$

glucose   carbon   ethanol
                dioxide   (ethyl alcohol)

compounds would decline. However, if simple inorganic phosphate were added to the medium, the process would be reversed and, instead of a decline, an intensification of the fermentative reaction was observed. This could be repeated over and over again. Clearly, phosphate played an important part in fermentation. The best idea early investigators could come up with, and one which subsequently proved to be correct, involved the participation of the inorganic phosphate in the formation of an organic compound. Subsequently this organic compound would be broken down and yield carbon dioxide and ethanol. The material was called fructofuranose 1,6-diphosphate.

Many of the reactions occurring in muscle tissue and operating in the absence of oxygen are broadly similar to those in fermenting systems. **Glycogen**, a polysaccharide made up of many units of glucose, is broken down in actively functioning muscles. The series of reactions producing the breakdown of the polysaccharide glycogen is called **glycolysis**. The role of energy in muscle contraction has been a source of perpetual interest to physiologists, so when investigators realized that fermentation and glycolysis were similar processes, information from both fields could be used in piecing together the chemical puzzle. As a result, the entire complex pathway could be set down for both glycolysis and fermentation. The initial stage of glycolysis and fermentation consists of the phosphorylation of sugars. One important aspect of the process is the splitting of the fructose 1,6-diphosphate molecule so that the six-carbon fragment is simplified to two three-carbon fragments. One of these three-carbon fragments is an acid, meaning that it has gained a carboxyl (COOH) group through oxidation. When any substance is oxidized or reduced, one of three things must occur. Either oxygen has been transferred or hydrogen has been transferred or electrons have been transferred. In any case, the energy levels of the reacting compounds have undergone a change; energy has been made available for use by the cells. But how can cells lay hold of the energy that has changed hands as a result of oxidation and reduction?

GENERATION OF ATP: Near the end of the glycolytic pathway, a compound occurring in every living organism and in every living cell is synthesized. It is ATP (adenosine triphosphate) whose universal role is energy storage and supply (Fig. 18–12). Although investigators of the last century realized that cells and organisms require energy to remain alive, how this energy was delivered remained unknown. In what form, they asked, is it supplied to muscles, to glands, to the heart? We now know that ATP is the chemical conveyor of biologically useful energy.

In Fig. 18–12, notice the presence of three phosphate groups. The last two are the "chemically gifted" ones, for they are able to shuttle energy back and forth from one molecule to another. Since all three phosphate groups are negatively charged, they tend to repel one another, so they separate rather easily. Biochemists describe this state of affairs by saying that ATP undergoes **hydrolysis**; that is, during the reaction water absorption takes place. Figure 18–13 shows how useful biological energy is liberated from ATP in the form

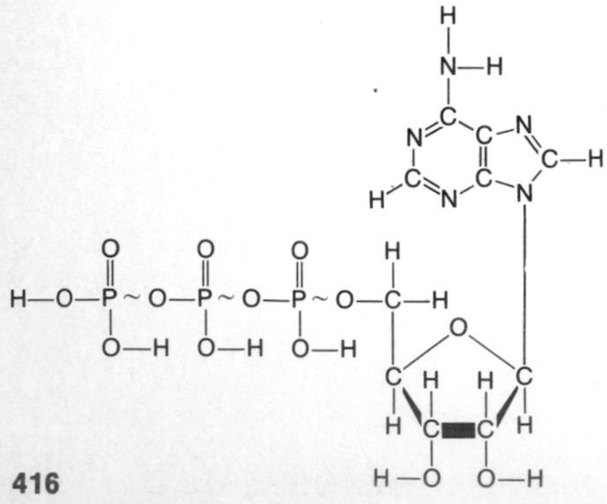

Figure 18–12 The structure of adenosine triphosphate (ATP).

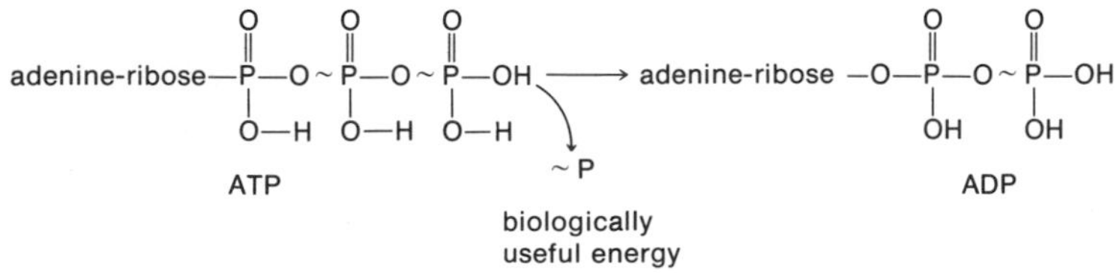

Figure 18–13 The conversion of energy-rich ATP into ADP is required to drive all biological reactions.

of an energy-rich phosphorous bond when ATP is converted into ADP (adenosine diphosphate). Chemists say that ATP exists at a "higher free energy level" than ADP does. ADP is left when the terminal phosphate of the three phosphates on the ATP molecule is removed.

ATP's ready breakdown to ADP is only one of its profoundly essential features. Another is that ATP, by undergoing hydrolysis, can *transfer* energy to other molecules that happen to be energy-poor. ATP has been called the "energy currency of life" because it contains a very convenient parcel of energy from the standpoint of cell chemistry (Fig. 18–14). When sugar is burnt by routine methods, it too yields energy, but the conditions attending its breakdown could not possibly occur in a living cell. What is more, the quantity of energy set free is too great a dose to be efficiently harnessed to chemical conversions that must proceed "uphill" (that is, require energy). By contrast, the free energy of hydrolysis of ATP and ADP matches these kinds of demands quite closely. The extreme effectiveness of ATP in energy transactions is emphasized by the fact that every living form so far studied makes use of it!

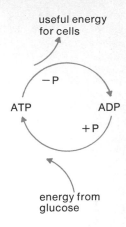

Figure 18–14 Each living cell derives its energy from the breakdown of glucose and subsequent synthesis and breakdown of ATP.

METABOLISM

The biochemical pathways of glycolysis and fermentation are parts of what is called **metabolism**, which can be defined as the sum total of all chemical reactions within the cell. Metabolism involving the breakdown of materials is usually termed **catabolism**, while metabolism leading to the synthesis of molecules is termed **anabolism**. The breakdown of sugar in fermentation and glycolysis is an example of catabolism; the synthesis of glycogen from sugar represents a type of anabolism.

The respiratory chain

When researchers first realized that oxygen was "activated" mainly within cells and not in the blood or the lungs, they quite understandably wished to unravel the mechanism by which the gas was actually "captured." Eventually, certain oxygen-activating compounds, the **cytochromes**, were discovered. Although there are a great number of cytochromes, only one, cytochrome A_3, interacts with molecular oxygen. The cytochromes are reminiscent of hemoglobin, for they contain iron in chemical combination with proteins. In addition to the cytochromes, a number of other substances are involved in the process of capturing, transferring, and accepting electrons in the Krebs cycle. The most important of these carriers are flavins (FAD and FMN) and nucleotides (NAD and NADP), the former related to riboflavin and the latter to niacin, both essential vitamins.

ATP is generated at three well defined points along that biochemical pathway called the respiratory chain. The process by which the ATP is formed has been called **oxidative phosphorylation**. Pasteur knew that yeast cells could grow under either anaerobic or aerobic conditions, but he reported that they invariably multiplied more frequently when air (oxygen) was present.

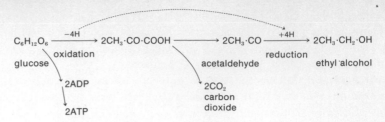

Figure 18–15 The process of fermentation as carried out by anaerobic organisms is summarized here. Notice that oxidation and reduction are involved. For every molecule of glucose processed, three molecules of ATP are produced, but there is a net gain of only two since one molecule is spent in driving the chemical reaction.

We know now why Pasteur observed this. In the absence of O_2, yeast uses the fermentation pathway (Fig. 18–15), in which a profit of only 2 ATPs is realized for each glucose molecule broken down to the level of CO_2 and ethanol. By contrast, for each pair of electrons "riding" the respiratory chain, three phosphates are yielded and one atom of oxygen is reduced. Hence, biochemists refer to a *P/O ratio* of 3. Let's set down the classic formula for respiration.

$$C_6H_{12}O_6 + 6O_2 \longrightarrow 6CO_2 + 6H_2O$$

With a P/O ratio of 3 we should, therefore, evolve 36 atoms of high-energy phosphate by respiratory means ($P/O = 3$; $6O_2 = 12$; and $3 \times 12 = 36$). Thirty-six ATPs represent considerably more energy than two ATPs. Pasteur was observing, at first hand, the importance of energy for survival.

THE CARBON PATHWAY AND THE HYDROGEN PATHWAY: Although cell physiologists and biochemists have some ideas about the mechanism behind oxidative phosphorylation, we do not yet understand all the details of its chemistry. All we are certain of is the close association of oxidation–reduction reactions, electron transport, and ATP generation. Enzymes are involved, but investigators have been embroiled in debate over the exact nature of enzyme roles.

Two distinct kinds of molecular changes occur in both glycolysis and aerobic respiration. In one, the numbers of carbon atoms are being varied. In the other, the hydrogen atoms are being manipulated. These two types of transformation can, in a sense, be considered two separate types of pathways. The **hydrogen pathway** is concerned chiefly with ATP manufacture while the **carbon pathway** enables cells to make a great variety of different metabolites. The staged release of energy through oxidation and reduction reactions is a major theme in biological systems.

The mitochondria

The respiratory chain does not float in a formless intracellular soup. Instead, it is firmly knit into the walls of a long-known cellular organelle called the **mitochondrion**. Some cells contain thousands of mitochondria, others no more than a dozen. Most mitochondria are about 2 μm long and under the electron microscope are seen to have a characteristic shape (Fig. 18–16). They are sandwiched by a double membrane with a space between. The outer membrane offers little resistance to the movement of molecules, but the inner one is much more selective about the substances it permits to migrate into the **lumen** (internal space) of the organelle.

As you can see in Figs. 18–16 and 18–17, the lumen is crisscrossed with a large number of membranous folds called **crista**, which provide mitochondria with a very great surface area. It is greater, in fact, than that of the membrane surrounding the entire cell. During the 1940s and 1950s, biologists successfully isolated mitochondria from cells by the technique known as differential centrifugation. Tissue such as liver was ground up and then centrifuged. Of the various inclusions, one of the first to be separated out was the mitochondrion. After centrifugation the organelle could be identified by electron microscopy. Chemical tests showed beyond doubt that mitochondria contained *all* the machinery for oxidative phosphorylation. The electron transport materials are found in minute assemblies located in the crista and inner membranes, while some of the enzymes and substrates are localized in either the matrix of the organelle or the outer wall.

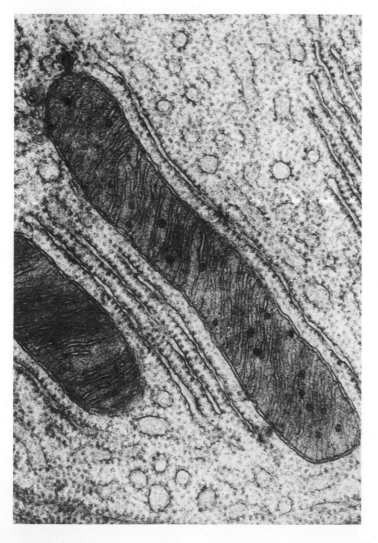

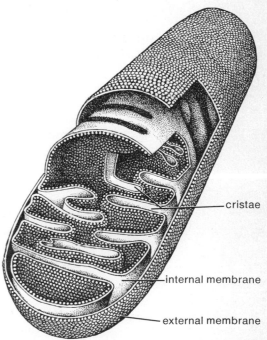

cristae

internal membrane

external membrane

Figures 18–16 and 18–17 A photomicrograph of a mitochondrion of a bat pancreas is shown at left, while a reconstruction of a mitochondrion is shown at right. The external and internal membranes and structures called "cristae" are clearly visible. All three structures are covered with thousands of sphere-shaped particles thought to be associated with the synthesis of ATP. (Figure 18–16 from D. W. Fawcett, *The Cell*, © 1966. By permission of W. B. Saunders Co.)

When mitochondria are taken to pieces by ultrasonic treatment, small chunks of the organelle are capable of sustaining electron transport and in some cases oxidative phosphorylation. Certain organized bodies or clusters found in the chunks are believed to represent a complete set of cytochromes and other electron carriers, capable of carrying out respiration via the Krebs cycle. While this claim has been debated, it seems plain that in mitchondria oxidative phosphorylation occurs in the substances composing the membranes. It is as if the bricks in the walls of a factory also acted as drill presses, conveyor belts, and circular saws. The essence of respiration lies in the mysterious relationship between membrane structure and oxidative phosphorylation.

PHOTOSYNTHESIS

So far, we have concentrated on biochemical pathways involved primarily with the breakdown of complex compounds. In fermentation, glycolysis, and respiration sugars are broken down to smaller substances. If there were no way to make sugar (or some similar compound) in the first place, these metabolic mechanisms could not have evolved. Early workers in the field knew that carbon dioxide and water reacted within plants, in the presence of light, and produced organic molecules plus oxygen. But how? The only way foodstuffs can be generated in appreciable amounts is through the use of solar energy, which can drive chemical reactions "uphill." And "uphill" is precisely the way carbon dioxide and water must travel in order to combine as sugars.

The importance of photosynthesis is not restricted to production of the world's food supply, but includes the renewal of oxygen in our atmosphere. Photosynthesis is indeed the *only* natural source of O_2 and is one reason why destruction of plant life by pesticides and contaminating chemicals is of such concern these days. As you found in Chapter 2, in the early stages of Earth's history the atmosphere was without free O_2. Cosmic radiation could penetrate easily and initiate numerous chemical reactions at Earth's surface. Some of these reactions yielded the organic materials needed for life to evolve. It might at first seem logical to suppose that the first living cells to evolve should have been photosynthetic ones. This now seems unlikely because rather sophisticated biochemical and structural qualities are required for photosynthesis.

The first cells were probably heterotrophs, not autotrophs. The heterotrophs could well have fed upon organic materials in the Precambrian "soup," then after countless eons had passed environmental conditions (scarcity of foods, for example) may have provided sufficient impetus for the emergence of an autotrophic life style. It is not surprising, therefore, to find many **prokaryotes** (cells without nuclei or nuclear membranes) with photosynthetic capabilities. Blue-green algae, for example, and a number of different bacterial forms can be counted in this group. Considering that photosynthesis was evolved by *single cells*, it is remarkable that this means of energy production was carried along through evolutionary pathways and integrated with the extreme structural specializations of the land plants, which invaded every conceivable terrestrial habitat. The whole physiology and anatomy of higher plants had to develop around the photosynthetic machinery available. It is not surprising, then, that there are only very slight differences in the photosynthetic patterns observed in different organisms.

Photosynthetic mechanisms

In 1905, the English biologist F. F. Blackman discovered what he called the **light** and **dark reactions** of photosynthesis. When exposed to light of low intensity, a green plant's rate of photosynthesis did not change when the temperature was increased from 0°C to 30°C. At high light intensities, on the other hand, the rate of the reaction did increase with an increase in temperature. Blackman believed these findings could be explained if one assumed the existence of the two processes mentioned above. Reactions dependent only on light are not very sensitive to changes in temperature, whereas chemical reactions generally double with each increment of 10°C.

When light was in short supply, he reasoned, the light-dependent conversions could not, of course, be expected to proceed rapidly. If the products of these reactions were required for dark-phase *chemical* conversions, Blackman's results could be readily understood. When light was not a limiting factor, temperature rise would cause an increase in photosynthetic rate because sufficient quantities of light-phase reactants would be available to the cell. Blackman's interpretation has not had to be changed significantly since he worked it out more than 60 years ago. Today we view photosynthesis as a combination of two sets of processes.

THE LIGHT REACTION: At first plant physiologists thought that sunlight broke down the CO_2 molecule. Carbon, set free by this reaction, would combine with the H_2O, yielding $[CH_2O]$.

$$CO_2 + 2H_2O \xrightarrow{\text{light}} [CH_2O] + O_2 + H_2O$$

Work with certain photosynthetic bacteria, however, contradicted this notion. The microorganisms do not use water. Instead, their hydrogen donor is hydrogen sulfide, H_2S. So instead of evolving oxygen as higher plants do, these prokaryotes excrete sulfur.

$$CO_2 + 2H_2S \xrightarrow{\text{light}} [CH_2O] + 2S + H_2O$$

If photosynthetic chemistry is basically similar in different organisms, then we should observe the above conversion reaction involving CO_2 and H_2O in higher plants. Sunlight should cause the **photolysis**, or breakdown by light, of water, the oxygen evolved coming from the H_2O, not the CO_2. This prediction was confirmed by labeling water with isotopic oxygen (O^{18}). During photosynthesis, then, only radioactive oxygen is released by plants dosed with O^{18} labeled water. Water donates hydrogens (it is a reducing agent) and CO_2

accepts hydrogens (it is an oxidizing agent). Here once again is a case of oxidation and reduction.

To do work, light must be absorbed. In green plants the pigment called **chlorophyll** is responsible for light absorption. Being green, chlorophyll is most efficient at absorbing red light, and in certain cells red light is best for photosynthesis. The chlorophyll molecule is very much like the cytochromes and hemoglobins. However, instead of containing iron, chlorophyll contains magnesium.

When light is absorbed by a chlorophyll molecule, an electron is displaced and usually is attracted by a protein called **ferredoxin** (Fig. 18–18). With its newly captured electron, ferredoxin is a strong reducing agent. If it can "find"

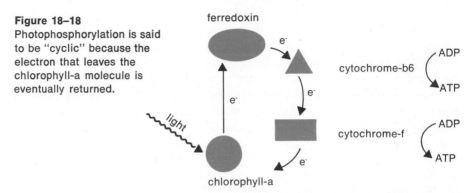

Figure 18–18
Photophosphorylation is said to be "cyclic" because the electron that leaves the chlorophyll-a molecule is eventually returned.

other materials whose reducing potentials are not as great as its own, it can pass on its electron to them; and that is what usually occurs. For instance, ferredoxin gives its electron to cytochromes. Electrons are passed through two cytochromes and the same electron which left chlorophyll now returns to it. The chlorophyll is now ready to perform its task again. During the process— called **cyclic photophosphorylation**—two ATPs are generated from ADP. By another slightly more complex route, O_2 is also evolved. The pathway is non-cyclic because the electrons that leave chlorophyll do not find their way back to it. The electrons that do, however, come from water during the photolysis reaction.

The reactions we have described can all take place in an isolated **chloroplast** (Fig. 18–19), which is as much a photosynthetic unit as the mitochondrion is a respiratory unit. The light reaction is not yet understood as well as biologists wish; a number of reducing agents besides ferredoxin are currently being studied. Also, several varieties of chlorophyll seem to be involved in light capture. During the light reaction phase of photosynthesis, then, some light energy is absorbed by chlorophyll and used to split molecules of H_2O, and some is stored in the form of ATP. The second part of the photosynthesis story takes place in the absence of light as an energy source.

THE DARK REACTION: During the reactions that occur in the dark, which were worked out largely by Melvin Calvin, ATP and other high-energy hydrogen compounds react with CO_2. Calvin used radioactive labeling techniques to trace the materials generated by photosynthesizing plants. Such a

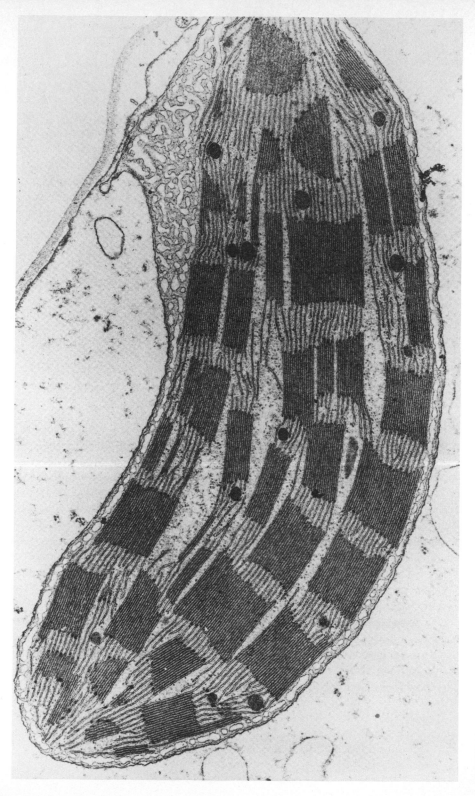

Figure 18–19 A normal chloroplast from a mature mesophyll cell of a green portion of a maize leaf. (From L. K. Shumway and T. E. Weier, *American Journal of Botany,* Vol. 54, No. 6, 1967.)

process is complex and involves dozens of steps. Finally, reactions driven by chemical energy stored by the plant result in half the hydrogen atoms split from the H_2O during the light reaction combining with an appropriate number of oxygen atoms from the CO_2 and again producing water. The remaining hydrogens that were split off during the light reaction combine with the remaining CO_2 and produce carbohydrate. That carbohydrate is a store of chemical energy deriving originally from light energy and now available for use by the plant itself and by all heterotrophs.

Some of the dark reactions are identical to those in the fermentative pathway, but there is also a difference to be reckoned with. The direction in which the pathway is traversed is all *uphill* in the dark phase of photosynthesis whereas it is *downhill* in fermentation. If the reactions are downhill, energy can be drawn off the pathway by the cell. If the reactions are uphill, energy has to be invested. Where does the energy to fulfill this requirement arise? The answer is from the photophosphorylation reactions during the light phase: For every molecule of CO_2 engaging in hexose sugar synthesis, three molecules of ATP are required; and to integrate six hexose molecules into starch requires an additional ATP.

Photosynthesis and respiration are similar in that both lead to ATP formation. Plants use some of the ATP to form storage materials available when needed. Much of this material is consumed by animals that, through respiratory metabolism, lay hold of the energetic coinage that the plants minted by using solar energy.

Chloroplasts

Although the photosynthetic prokaryotes are usually without chloroplasts, these organelles are common in the higher plants. The chloroplast is a very complex structure consisting of numerous membranes, channels, and granules (Fig. 18–19) and is the site of chlorophyll. Chlorophyll is found in two membrane structures of the chloroplast and the light reactions of photosynthesis are associated with these membrane structures. The dark reactions may run their course in a region characterized by the presence of relatively few membranes. So similar are mitochondria and chloroplasts that some cell physiologists have suggested the evolution of one organelle from the other.

In the present chapter we have considered a number of the important biomolecules required by cells as a source of energy and building materials. We have also examined energy-production and maintenance mechanisms that keep a cell alive and functioning. In the following chapter we will concentrate on a structure common to all cells, the cell membrane, and find out how this organelle maintains a more or less constant internal environment for the cell.

1 Distinguish between entropy and energy.
2 What are the differences between an oxidant and a reductant?
3 What organelles are the cellular sites of photosynthesis and oxidative phosphorylation?
4 Discuss the similarities and differences between photosynthesis and respiration. Which process do you think is the more ancient? Why?
5 How does a covalent bond differ from an ionic bond? Give examples of compounds containing each.
6 How does an enzyme influence the velocity of a chemical reaction?

SELECTED READINGS

Lehninger, Albert. *Bioenergetics*. 2nd ed. New York: W. A. Benjamin, Inc., 1971. Written by a pioneer in research on mitochondria, this book starts with an imaginative approach to thermodynamics and, through the ATP–ADP system, relates thermodynamics to energy-dependent activities of cells—respiration, fermentation, photosynthesis, active transport, contractility, and the like.

Lowey, Ariel G. and Siekevitz, Philip. *Cell Structure and Function*. 2nd ed. New York: Holt, Rinehart & Winston, 1969. Emphasis in this excellent survey text is on interaction between the microstructure of the cell and the metabolic and synthetic processes that occur within the cell. Highly recommended for those wishing to pursue cell biology.

Rothstein, Howard. *General Physiology: The Cellular and Molecular Basis*. Lexington, Mass.: Xerox College Publishing, 1971. Physical and chemical bases for vital processes are examined and a historical approach to each problem is taken, together with the presentation of decisive experimental data.

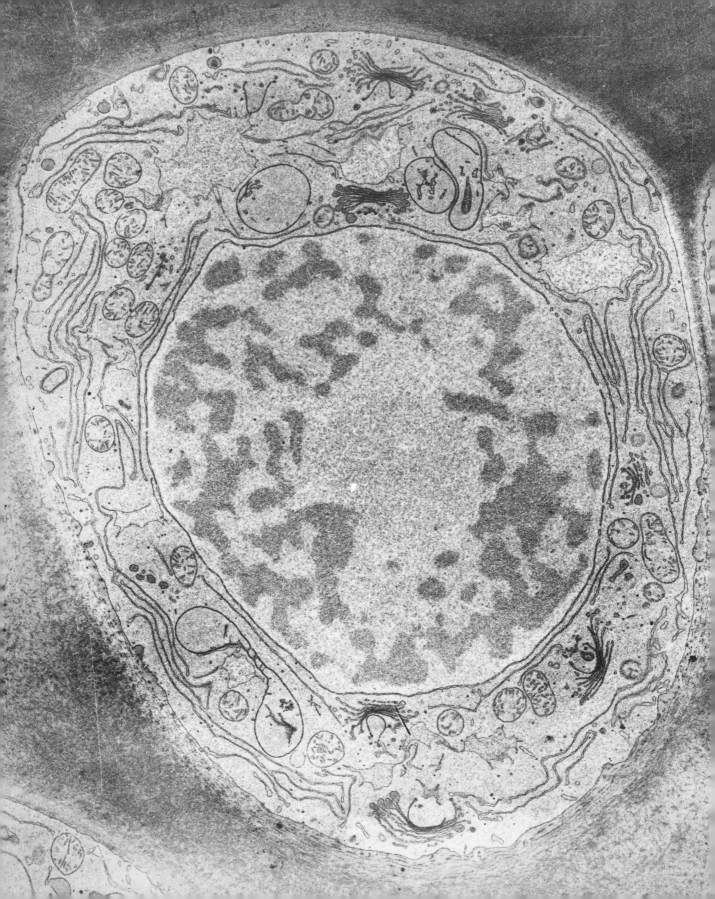

19
CELL MEMBRANE SYSTEMS

Exchanging materials with the environment

The composition of cells and whole organisms is clearly different from the composition of the external environment, yet the lives of cells and organisms depend on the transport of materials from and back to the external environment. How do living things reconcile this apparent paradox?

In almost all cells that we know of, intracellular concentrations of many ions and other substances differ strikingly from the concentrations of these same substances in the external environment. How a cell selects, imports, and exports materials has long interested biologists. The cell's "problem" is basically a thermodynamic one. On theoretical grounds a cell shouldn't even exist. Being highly organized (for organization is one of the characteristics of life), it is a low-entropy system and continuously susceptible to loss of order. We might imagine that a cell would retain its sophisticated organizational patterns much more easily if it were cut off from the environment. The fact that this is not the case follows from very simple principles.

In order to drive many of the reactions essential to its life, the cell must produce ATP, and it can do so only by taking in foodstuffs from its external environment, so on the one hand a cell must constantly exchange materials with the outside world, and on the other it must maintain a unique kind of constitution. How it does so is our chief concern in this chapter.

SUBSTRUCTURE OF THE CELL

When biologists of the late 19th century began to use lenses of high quality to observe eukaryotic cells, they saw a bewildering variety of organelles (Fig. 19–2); furthermore, considering the large quantity of membranous material seen, they concluded that a cell has a large surface area. As one biologist put it, "Part of the secret of life is the immense internal surface of the cell." The reason for this general belief was simply that large surfaces were considered excellent sites for the execution of chemical reactions.

Equilibrium processes

A system containing numerous partitions can manifest patterns of behavior quite different from those found within a simple tumbler, for example, containing a sodium chloride solution. The processes of diffusion and osmosis (see Chapter 12) become particularly important to examine when we deal

Figure 19–1 Contrary to the rather static view often portrayed in diagrams of a "typical cell," cells are highly complex and dynamic in their organization. Compare this photomicrograph with the diagram on page 428 to identify some of the major organelles. Their number and distribution within the cell are constantly changing.

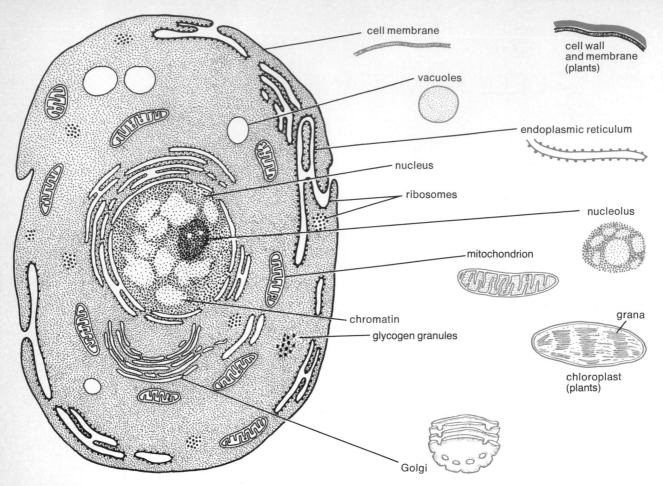

Figure 19–2 A generalized animal cell.

with a system containing large numbers of membranes. Diffusion and osmosis are natural tendencies of systems and manifestations of the second law of thermodynamics in operation. For the concentration gradient in Fig. 12–3 to remain for very long is inconsistent with thermodynamic reasoning. It will not occur if the system is relatively low in entropy, and as soon as the opportunity arises the entropy level will increase. The entropy is low originally because there is order in the system. There are a relatively large number of sodium chloride molecules (or the ions which form from them on dissociation) in one part of the system and none, or very few, in other parts of the system. Osmosis and diffusion are the processes that operate to "even up" molecular concentrations and increase entropy.

A relevant question we must ask sooner or later is whether osmosis and diffusion *alone* can explain the unique properties of cells. In fact they cannot. Osmosis and diffusion are both what we call equilibrium processes, which do not require an input of energy from an external source. They are merely accomplishing what the second law demands must be accomplished in any physical system. But remember that while it lives, the cell *apparently* runs

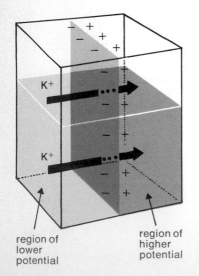

region of lower potential

region of higher potential

Figure 19–3 A hypothetical example of net movement against an electrochemical potential gradient. If potassium, for instance, moved as indicated in the diagram, we would have to assume that energy was driving the process.

FUNCTIONS OF CELLULAR ORGANELLES

Cell Wall   Provides mechanical strength for plant cells (not present in animal cells).

Cell Membrane   Regulates the passage of molecules and ions into and out of the cells; also called plasma membrane.

Smooth Endoplasmic Reticulum   A storage depot for various kinds of intracellular materials.

Vacuoles   Digests foods and foreign particles and may also regulate water contents in some cells.

Ribosomes   Small cytoplasmic particles, the sites of protein synthesis.

Mitochondria   These organelles are intimately associated with the respiratory activity of the cell. Provided with suitable substrates, they can generate ATP, which is the energy currency of living things. Mitochondria are called the "powerhouse of the cell."

Rough Endoplasmic Reticulum   The membrane system involved in circulation of materials through the cell. Its outer surface is studded with ribosomes.

Nucleolus   A structure found within the nucleus. It is usually attached to a particular chromosome and is believed to be the region at which ribosomal precursors are built up.

Nucleus   Usually located at the cell's center, it contains the chromosomes that in turn contain the genes. It is surrounded by a double membrane, the *nuclear envelope*, which regulates the passage of substances between nucleus and cytoplasm.

Chromatin   This term is used to refer to the material of the chromosomes. When the latter are not engaged in the process of cell division, the chromatin exists in a relatively dispersed state. When the cell begins to divide the chromatin condenses and appears as a well defined group of "rodlets," the chromosomes.

Golgi zone   A membrane system usually occupying a characteristic position within the cell. It is involved in the packaging of proteins and in the synthesis of carbohydrates. Secretory products usually are seen in association with it.

Chloroplast   These organelles are found only in green plants and are the main sites of chlorophyll localization. They are heavily interlaced with membranes and are involved in the process of photosynthesis.

Grana   Stacks of membranes observed within chloroplasts.

Food Inclusions   Consist mainly of glycogen, which is carbohydrate (starch), and lipids, which are fats.

counter to the second law. The following example will illustrate our meaning.

Suppose we have a cation with a valence of $2+$. We can call this cation C^{2+}. If we found the cation moving across a membrane with a positive charge as shown in Fig. 19–3 into a region containing a greater concentration of C^{2+} than that from which the C^{2+} in question originally came, we would be confronted by much the same situation that occurs in the cell. Thermodynamic laws seem to be overridden by the phenomenon. The only way the cations can move "uphill" against the electrochemical potential gradient is if energy is introduced into the system—and that is precisely what cells do. They "spend" energy, mainly ATP, and so attain their unique concentration profiles. The cell maintains important differences from its environment, and yet communicates with it, by employing different types of membrane systems as energy transducers.

OPTICAL AND ELECTRON MICROSCOPES

The sophistication of the microscope over the centuries has strongly influenced our view of cell structure, as shown by Figs. 19–4 and 19–5. Figure 19–4 is a light micrograph, while Fig. 19–5 is an electron micrograph.

The early microscopists who used only optical methods could see some half a dozen structures within the cell; the electron microscope reveals many more. This is not to say that light microscopes were made obsolete. They are still important instruments for inspection of fixed

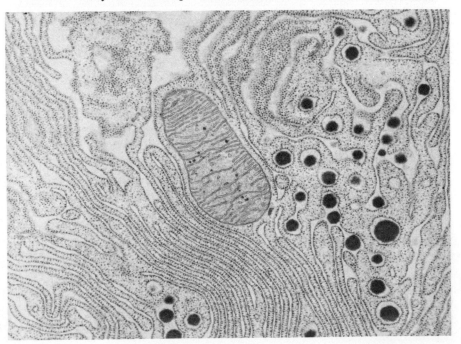

Figures 19–4 and 19–5 The light micrograph at left shows a stentor, a protozoan, several hundred times natural size. Although a number of cellular structures can be identified, none can be seen in much detail. By contrast, the electron micrograph showing part of a bat's pancreas reveals great structural detail due to magnification by a factor of many thousands.

Structure of the cell's surface

By the 19th century the cell periphery was considered to consist of oily or fatty materials. Fat-soluble substances were known to penetrate membranes more easily than water-soluble substances. It was natural to assume a high fat content for the cell membrane. Investigators then began to study the penetration properties of a wide variety of compounds. If the entrance rate of many classes of substances could be determined, they reasoned, the chemical architecture of the membrane might become apparent. In the first half of this century, experiments revealed two important aspects of cell membrane lore: 1. Large molecules do not penetrate as fast as small ones; 2. The higher the electric charge on a substance, the lower its permeability (quantified as its rate of movement across the membrane).

and stained material, for inspecting living cells, for helping to determine whether there are areas within cells that contain many molecules oriented in the same way, and for "weighing" substances within cells. The electron microscope has by no means replaced the light microscope; it has merely supplemented it and empowered biologists to examine a broader spectrum of entities within the cell.

Recently, the scanning electron microscope (SEM) has been employed for a number of cellular investigations. The SEM is particularly useful in operating over an extremely broad spectrum of magnification and studying surface characteristics (Fig. 19–6).

Figure 19–6 This scanning electron micrograph, 1,500 times actual size, shows with remarkable clarity and detail structural features of the under-surface of a green leaf.

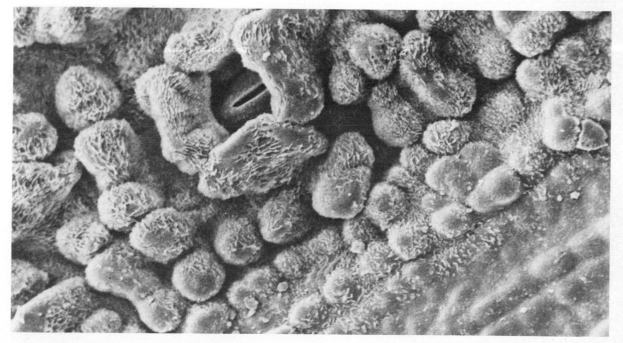

The "cell membrane" observable by 19th-century investigators was seen to have at least two and possibly three different structures. The outermost portion of animals cells is called the **glycocalyx** and is made up largely of complex sugar molecules. The cell membrane, which measures only 75Å in thickness, lies beneath the much thicker glycocalyx. A third part of the cell membrane is a somewhat amorphous gelled substance called the **cortex** whose composition is largely unknown, although it probably contains proteins and lipids. The cortex adds considerable mechanical strength to the cell periphery and is particularly evident in the egg cells of echinoderms—sea urchins and starfish, for example. Unlike animal cells, plant cells have a rigid cellulose **cell wall** forming a surface outside the cell membrane. The cell wall can be considered a type of glycocalyx. As you can see, the cell surface is a complex affair, a combination of structures each of which carries out essential functions. Being selectively permeable is only one function of a cell membrane.

STRUCTURE OF THE CELL MEMBRANE

In 1925, E. Gorter and F. Grendel extracted the fatty materials from the surface of red blood cells. When the extract was spread out in a very thin layer (1 molecule thick), its total area was found to equal *twice* that of the cells from which it had been removed. The inevitable hypothesis saw each cell ensheathed by a double lipid membrane.

Fats could not be the sole component of cell membranes since membrane surface tensions seemed to be lower than those characteristic of fats. Since protein can lower surface tension, it seemed reasonable to suppose the cell membrane (also called the plasma membrane) to be a mixture of fats and proteins. During the 1950s, electron microscopists had started to collect large amounts of data on cell membranes from many different organisms. One such microscopist, J. D. Robertson, who spent much of his time observing nerve cells, saw many structures of the type shown in Fig. 19–7. Notice that the arrow tip separates two membranes and that a central light area is sandwiched between two darker zones in each of the membranes. Robertson presumed the darker areas to be protein and the lighter ones lipid. The neural tissue he investigated is particularly favorable because of the peculiar properties of myelin, which is actually a whole collection of plasma membranes surrounding the nerve cells.

On the basis of his own experience, Robertson suggested that the plasma membrane, which measures about 75 Å wide, is representative of a whole class of membranes of roughly similar width which are found within cells. This out-

Figure 19–7 This electron micrograph shows a section of two plasma membranes separated from each other (by the black arrow). The lipid zone is sandwiched between two zones of protein, all three zones collectively forming the "unit membrane." (From E. L. Benedetti and P. Emmelot in *The Membranes,* ed. A. J. Dalton and F. Haguenau. Copyright © 1968 by Academic Press.)

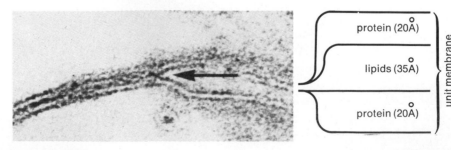

protein (20Å)

lipids (35Å)

protein (20Å)

unit membrane

text continued on page 433

BIOLUMINESCENCE
Organisms That Make Their Own Light

The ability of various organisms to emit light has been known for many centuries. If dead salt-water fish or the flesh of animals is left unattended, it soon becomes luminescent, emitting an eerie blue glow (Figs. A and B). More than 2,000 years ago, Aristotle wrote ". . . some things though they are not in their nature fire nor any species of fire, yet seem to produce light." In 1668, Robert Boyle discovered that the light emitted from decaying fish ceased if air was removed from the container. Although oxygen had not been discovered, we now know that his experiments demonstrated the requirement of oxygen for bioluminescence.

In 1742, Baker suggested that the light of dead fish comes from "animalcules." Of course, today we know that the blue light is due to the growth of luminous bacteria on dead flesh. Since the 1700s, much scientific work has been done on these organisms. We know how to culture the luminous bacteria in the laboratory and consequently have been able to identify the chemical processes involved. We know that the luminescence process is closely related to the general metabolism of the bacteria, but we have much more to learn about its value to the organisms.

 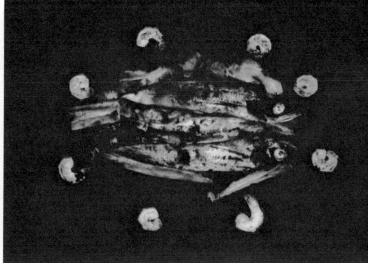

Figures A and B   The photograph at left showing a plate of dead salt-water fish and shrimp was taken in ordinary light. When infected with luminous bacteria after a day or two, the dead organisms emit a very bright bluish light, as shown at right. (FRANK JOHNSON)

B

C

D

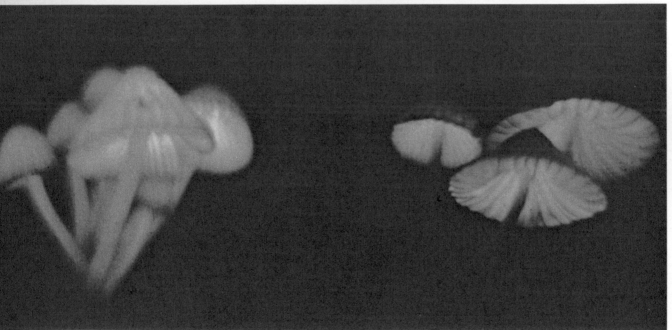

Figures C and D The top photograph of luminous toadstools was taken in ordinary light while the one below was made in light emitted by the toadstools. Luminous molds are often seen in rotting logs, but it is rare for luminescence to persist into the fruiting stage, as here. (YATA HANEDA)

The property of bioluminescence is distributed among a wide variety of organisms. There are luminous bacteria, fungi (Figs. C and D), jellyfish-like animals, crustaceans, clams, squid, earthworms, insects, and fish. There is no apparent development of bioluminescence along evolutionary lines; rather it is randomly distributed among many forms of life. There are no self-luminous forms of reptiles, birds, mammals, or higher plants. Very few fresh-water organisms are luminescent, yet many of their salt-water counterparts are. With this great diversity of luminous forms with different chemical mechanisms, it is difficult to understand why luminescence evolved and how it benefits the organism. However, we do know that in certain organisms—fireflies, for example—bioluminescence is part of the organism's mating behavior. In certain other organisms, bioluminescence seems to have the function of defense, warning would-be predators away, much as coloration does in certain butterflies.

Color of light

The color of light emitted by most bioluminescing organisms is blue, but fireflies emit a yellow-green light. A beetle found in South America and a salt-water squid are the only known examples of organisms that emit red light. The color of the light emitted tells us something about the nature of the molecule that emits light. By using these characteristics, we have been able to isolate the substance from the organisms and study the chemistry of the light reaction in the test tube.

LUCIFERIN AND LUCIFERASE: Probably the most important early experiments on the chemistry of bioluminescence were those of Raphael DuBois in 1887. DuBois was studying a luminescent clam, *Pholas dactylus*. *Pholas* is from the Greek and means "hidden, or lurking in a hole." The luminescent clam *Pholas dactylus* has the habit of boring into soft rock. DuBois found that if he chopped the clams into small pieces and then ground them until a paste was formed, he could demonstrate two important substances. One was enzyme which he called **luciferase**. The other was a substance that came to be called **luciferin**, meaning "light bearer." Luciferin is an organic molecule and it, like luciferase, is different for each bioluminescent organism. In many cases, we know what the structure of luciferin is, and in some cases the luciferase has been purified and studied. The general requirements for bioluminescence appear to be the same for most systems—an enzyme, luciferase, a luciferin, and oxygen.

Fireflies and other luminous beetles

A familiar luminescent organism in North America is the firefly (Figs. E and F). At about dusk during the summer months, many of these creatures can be seen flying and flashing in the grass and bushes. There is a definite ritual. For the most part the females remain on the ground while the males fly around emitting short flashes of light at regular intervals. If a male flashes within three to four yards of the female, she waits a certain period of time and then flashes a response. This flash pattern is repeated several times as the male flies toward the waiting female. If they recognize through their flashing pattern that they are the same species of firefly, the male lands and mates with the female. Each species of firefly has a characteristic flash pattern that the female of the species can recognize. The recognition is apparently based on two factors: the time lag between flashes and the "shape" of the flash.

The click beetle is another interesting luminescent insect. It is found mostly in sub-tropical and tropical regions and is larger than the American firefly. Because these beetles have two oval green luminescent "head lights," they

Figures E and F The top photograph (courtesy of J. M. Bassot) shows the glowing organ of a common male American firefly *Photinus pyralis.* The photograph below (courtesy of William Vandivert) shows the largest known firefly in the world, with a small American firefly beside it. The photograph was made in Jamaica and initially taken in the dark while the firefly was walking along flashing. The flashes are reflected from the leaf. After the two flashes a strobe light was used to photograph the firefly in ordinary light.

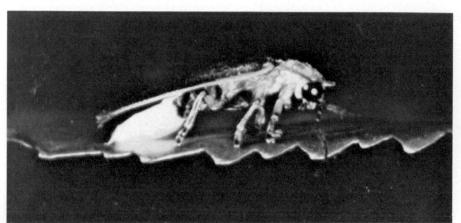

E

F

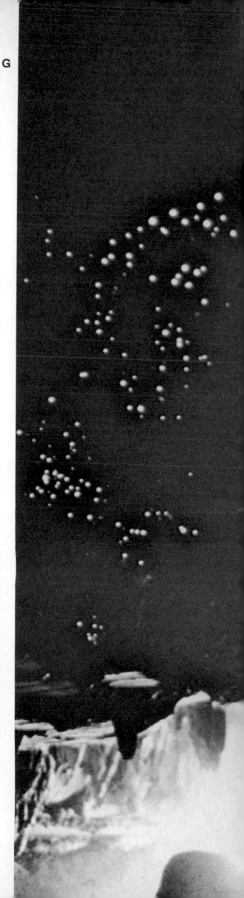

Figure G Luminous larval forms of gnats hang from a cave ceiling by a silken sheath excreted by the larvae. A sharp noise, which disturbs the larvae, turns off the luminescence. The photograph was taken in Waipu Cave, North Island, New Zealand. (YATA HANEDA)

G

have been called "automobile bugs." They also have an orange luminescent spot on the ventral part of the abdomen, visible only when the beetle is flying. These organisms are greatly attracted to small glowing lights. During the evening, if you hold up a glowing stick, click beetles from several hundred yards away fly toward the light.

In Malaysia there are famous glowing trees that house many fireflies. At night the tree is lighted with hundreds of them. At first the flashing is random and unorganized. Then some of the fireflies begin to cluster on a single branch and flash in unison. Soon other fireflies pick up the rhythm until finally the whole tree is flashing on and off in perfect synchrony. Probably only the males flash in this pattern and the synchrony may be a means of attracting females with an efficiency that solitary flashes lack.

In some of the underground caves of New Zealand, the ceilings are covered with thousands of glow-worms (Fig. G). These larvae extrude several luminescent threads which are covered with droplets of a sticky material. The bright luminous strands attract insects, which are then trapped in the threads and are devoured by the worm. Any noise in the cave causes the lights to go out immediately, but after a period of silence, the glow begins again. The sight of hundreds of these worms glowing in the darkened caves is spectacular.

FIREWORM OF THE SEA: On his first voyage to the new continent, Columbus wrote of seeing lights in the water; they were probably fireworms of the sea, *Odontosyllis enopla* (Fig. H), a polychaete type of worm. The behavior of

H

Figure H This photograph of luminescing fireworms of the sea was taken through a microscope in the dark. (YATA HANEDA)

these organisms is most remarkable. Three days after the full moon, one hour after sunset, the females appear at the surface of the water swimming in circles and emitting a greenish light. The light attracts the male worm, which first appears as a dimmer light 10 to 15 feet from the female. The males swim directly to the center of the circle of light, and often several males and a female will rotate together releasing eggs and sperm in a luminous cloud. The display can last from 20 to 30 minutes. For these worms, the identification of the female by the male appears to depend on the light emission process.

CRUSTACEANS: *Cypridina* (Figs. I and J) are small crustaceans that live near shore in Japan and Jamaica. They feed at night and if you dangle a fish head in the water, these creatures collect on the head and appear as pinpoints of blue light. The luciferin and luciferase are excreted into the water, where they react with dissolved oxygen and produce the luminescence. These creatures can be preserved indefinitely in the dried state and are very useful for studying the chemistry of the light reaction. The excretion of the luciferin and the luciferase into the water may be useful in inhibiting predators from eating the cypridana, thus giving survival value in the light system.

DINOFLAGELLATES: The legendary "sea fire" reported by many sailors is the blue glow sometimes seen in the wake of a ship traveling in ocean waters. When examined more closely, the apparently homogeneous light is seen to

Figures I and J *Cypridina,* about 3 mm in diameter, as seen in ordinary light (below left) and as photographed in light of their own making. (YATA HANEDA)

I

J

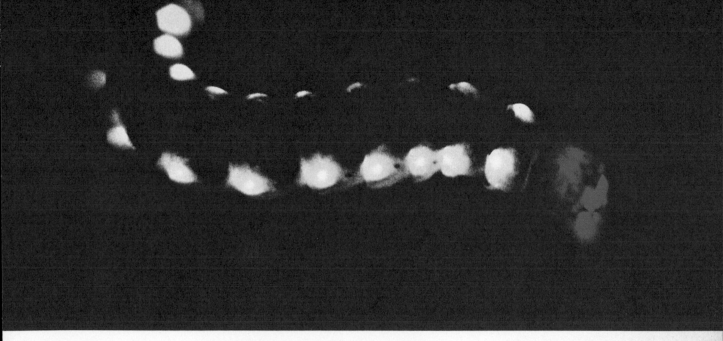

come from many tiny sparks. The bioluminescence is due to single cell dinoflagellates that give off light when disturbed. These organisms can multiply very rapidly and give rise to high concentrations of cells in the ocean. Any mechanical disturbance of this bloom produces an intense blue light. A related non-luminescent dinoflagellate is what causes the "red tide" which is toxic to fish. On occasion large fish kills are caused by these organisms.

In certain bays where conditions are just right, large permanent blooms of luminous dinoflagellates may occur. These so-called phosphorescent bays are famous tourist attractions. One of the most spectacular is a bay near Falmouth on the north coast of Jamaica. At night every fish that makes the slightest movement in the water is outlined with a blue "fire." The light produced by a boat moving through these waters is bright enough to read by. It is not surprising that the early sailors were enchanted and mystified by the "burning of the sea." These organisms have now been grown in the laboratory, although the chemistry of light emission is still not known.

RAILROAD WORMS: Perhaps one of the most remarkable of all luminescent forms is the South American railroad worm (Fig. K), the larval form of an insect. There are 11 pairs of yellow-green luminous spots running along the sides of the organism. On the head are two red luminous spots. When the worm is at rest, no light is visible. If it is slightly disturbed, it turns on the red head lights and in the dark looks like a glowing cigarette. A greater disturbance produces a glow of the yellow-green lights and the creature indeed looks like a railroad train with red beacons.

Figure K When disturbed, the South American railroad worm lights up dramatically and gives the appearance of a railroad train with red beacons. (NATIONAL GEOGRAPHIC SOCIETY)

LUMINOUS FISH: There are a number of luminous fish. Some have
luminous spots along the side while others have ventral lights. There are a
number of remarkable luminous fish that depend on the harboring of
luminous bacteria for their light. These harmless luminescent bacteria are the
cause of the glowing dead fish mentioned earlier. The light emitted is usually
blue or blue-green. Often, reports of luminous organisms are really due to
cultures of these bacteria living symbiotically with a host. For example, the
Indonesian fish *Photoblepharon* has under each eye a white spot (Fig. L) in
which luminous bacteria grow. The fish has a fold of skin much like an eyelid
that can be closed over the luminous spot to turn the light off. Thus, it is
possible for the fish to swim along flashing a light made of luminous bacteria.

It should be evident from this brief description of some luminous organisms
that biolumsinescence is a remarkable biological process, in some cases
involving behavioral adaptions. It has fascinated scientists, poets, and
philosophers for centuries and will undoubtedly continue to do so even after
its chemical basis and value to organisms endowed with it are thoroughly
understood.

Figure L   *Photoblepharon*, found in the Banda Sea near the eastern end of
the Indonesian Archipelago, has a sac of luminescing bacteria beneath each
eye. A fold of skin similar to an eyelid enables the fish to swim along in the
dark flashing a light of luminous organisms. (YATA HANEDA)

L

look is called the **unit membrane hypothesis**. Virtually all membranes in the cell have been hypothesized to be unit membranes consisting of a lipid–protein "sandwich" in which each surface is a continuous layer of lipid molecules whose electrically charged polar regions are directed outwards and whose non-polar ends are oriented toward protein molecules forming the interior of the membrane.

If all membranes have this same structure and are covered by a continuous sheet of lipids, it is difficult to see how different membranes or different parts of the same membrane can behave differently and perform special functions. A primary function of membranes is to distinguish among very similar ions and molecules by allowing some to enter the cell while excluding others. It is frequently suggested that this differential permeability, to ions for example, may be explained by postulating the existence of electrically charged pores through the membrane which act as a sieve. However this hypothesis does not adequately account for the permeability properties of membranes. Although membrane permeability is not yet fully understood, the biophysicists J. Diamond and E. Wright have shown that its main features can be accounted for in terms of the electrical forces acting between molecules and atoms of the membranes and of the permeating substances. While the basic structure may be that of a unit membrane, there is evidence that in at least some membranes globular protein molecules interrupt the lipid surface layers at irregular intervals. These proteins could provide lipid-free routes across the membranes and confer special properties on the membrane. Perhaps these protein components are almost continually on the move within the surrounding lipid phase. We have every reason to believe that membranes are dynamic and not static structures. The molecules composing the plasma membrane are probably in a continual state of flux.

Active roles of membranes

We know of at least five ways by means of which substances can travel into and out of the cell: simple diffusion, active transport, facilitated diffusion, phagocytosis, and pinocytosis. The first three phenomena are more or less continuous. Not only can we sometimes detect the occurrence of phagocytosis (Fig. 19–8) and pinocytosis by simple microscopic inspection, but we can recognize them because they visibly alter the entire cell surface.

ACTIVE TRANSPORT: The essential difference between *diffusion* and *active transport* involves energy flow. On theoretical grounds alone, diffusion cannot be the only mechanism responsible for determining the cell's chemical concentration profile. If it were, we could write the equation: cell = environment. But that equation tends to be obeyed only after the cell has died. Active transport maintains concentration asymmetry within the cell relative to its external environment. For it to do so energy—usually in the form of ATP—must be used by the cell.

The expulsion of sodium from the cell is a good example of active transport. For Na^+ to move out of the cell it must be "pushed" against an unfavorable electrochemical gradient. ATP must be consumed in order for transport to

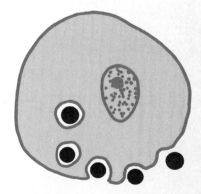

Figure 19–8 Progressive stages in phagocytosis are shown in a hypothetical cell, as it first comes in contact with a solid particle and then engulfs the particle in stages until it is entirely within the cytoplasm.

occur. Sodium expulsion by energy derived from ATP has been shown to occur in many cells other than neurons. It usually involves the enzyme, ATPase, which splits ATP. If the enzyme is prevented from functioning, transport cannot take place. We now believe that transported materials link up with special **transport proteins** located on the cell surface; some of these proteins have been isolated and crystallized. Proteins associated with the transport of several amino acids, sugars, and ions have been identified. Transport proteins probably function in concert with ATP and ATPases, the cooperative reaction resulting in transport against a gradient. After permeation has been accomplished, the system becomes recharged; that is, ADP generated as a result of the transport is reconverted to ATP.

FACILITATED DIFFUSION: Facilitated diffusion is much the same as active transport so far as the role of carriers is concerned. The important difference between the two mechanisms relates to the concentration gradient. In facilitated diffusion net movement is always *with* the gradient, whereas the reverse characterizes active transport.

PHAGOCYTOSIS AND PINOCYTOSIS: Phagocytosis and pinocytosis are very much alike. When a cell membrane comes in contact with certain solid objects or with certain liquid substances, the entire surface of the cell may be thrown up into finger-like projections. If a solid object becomes entrapped, the activity is called **phagocytosis**. If fluid is entrapped, the process is termed **pinocytosis**. We do not yet understand what causes these phenomena although we know that phagocytosis is an important feeding behavior among protists. In higher organisms such as the vertebrates, phagocytosis among many white blood cells operates as an effective means of dealing with foreign interlopers.

LOCOMOTION AND THE CELL SURFACE: Cell biologists have long felt that the cell surface exerts an important influence on locomotion, the influence possibly being determined by electrical charges. When cells are grown in tissue culture, we can observe their surfaces taking part in very curious types of behavior. When a cell is not surrounded by companion cells, it tends to migrate about until it meets one or more other cells. When meeting between two cells occurs, the cells stop moving, a phenomenon called **contact-inhibition**. In some way we do not understand, the surface of each cell informs its owner of the other cell's presence and issues a halt command. Since cells stalled in this way usually do not divide very frequently, we refer to a contact-inhibition of mitosis as well as of motion.

The nature of the cell surface is of particular interest in cancer research because cancer cells apparently have surfaces insensitive to their neighbors' existence. Such cells move about ceaselessly, failing to control their reproductive activities. The ultimate death of most organisms with malignant growths bears strong testimony to the importance of the cell surface, not only to cell survival, but to organismal survival as well. The electron microscope reveals a variety of spaces and structures between cells in communal tissue. There also are a number of cell surface structures that, presumably, have an equal variety of functions. Despite the tendency toward cell surface specialization, despite the presence of intercellular macromolecular adhesives, and despite the surface itself, all reliable studies tell us that cells in a tissue community communicate freely with one another. Only in cancer is this communication upset.

The electron microscope shows the plasma membrane to be connected to other membrane structures within the cytoplasm. The cell membrane of muscle cells (sarcolemma), for example, is continuous with a series of internal membrane structures, an association that is essential to the process by which muscle excitation and contraction are linked. Besides the fact of their physical linkage, the plasma membrane and internal membranes share certain anatomical and physiological attributes. Their dimensions, though not identical, are in the same range; furthermore, diffusion and the various transport mechanisms occur across their surfaces. Overall, the basic function of the internal membrane systems, like that of the plasma membrane, seems to be the preservation of a unique chemical concentration profile within the cell. We will now discuss some of the properties of the cell's inner membranes.

INNER MEMBRANES OF CELLS

The endoplasmic reticulum and Golgi zone

ENDOPLASMIC RETICULUM: At the turn of the century, a cytologist observed a "reticular" (Latin for "little net") apparatus in cells of human salivary glands. Later, the system came to be called the **endoplasmic reticulum** (**ER**). The ER contains a series of tubules and vesicles delimited by membranes that superficially resemble the plasma membrane. The ER is broadly divided into two categories. One type is studded with ribosomes, the function of which is the manufacture of proteins. This part of the system is called the **rough** ER because of its appearance under the electron microscope (Fig. 19–5). The second type is the **smooth** ER, which lacks ribosomal material. While the rough reticulum is concerned with protein synthesis, the smooth reticulum seems to be involved in storage of various kinds of substances and in the metabolism of steroids. Steroids contribute to the formation of such molecules as sex hormones, cholesterol, and certain membrane-associated macromolecules (phospholipids).

The rough ER produces proteins on ribosomal elements. While the protein being prepared is for export from the cell, ribosomes are quite capable of making proteins for use within the cell itself. It seems as if "export" cells contain a large proportion of ribosomes directly attached to the endoplasmic reticulum, whereas cells making proteins for internal use contain many ribosomes that are not attached to the reticulum. Immature blood cells do not have an endoplasmic reticulum. The mammalian red blood cell happens to be the only eukaryotic cell known so far not to contain endoplasmic reticulum.

Cells of the pancreas manufacture precursors of the digestive enzymes, which are proteins. If we supply such cells with radioactively labeled amino acids, we can determine the labeled material's precise location within the cell. Initially, the label is localized over the ribosomes themselves, then it is found in the interior channels of the rough endoplasmic reticulum. Still later, the label moves to a region of the cell known as the **Golgi zone**. Here the label is modified and subsequently transposed to the cell surface, where it combines with the plasma membrane and is finally ejected by a process of reverse pinocytosis. At no time is the newly forming protein ever exposed to the protoplasm outside of membranes. It is surrounded by membranous material from the time it is first formed on the ribosomes to the time it is ejected from the cell. The precursors of the digestive enzymes formed in the pancreatic cells are known as **zymogen granules**. After release from the pancreas, they travel to the intestine where they are converted into active forms of various "proteolytic" enzymes able to break down proteins ingested by the animal.

The reticulum also seems to be involved in some type of electron transport, a feature shared with the mitochondria, but what contribution to the total energy holdings of the cell is made by the endoplasmic reticulum still eludes researchers. The membranes of which the ER is composed apparently are able to transport substances and are in effect selectively permeable. Even so, the ER and plasma membranes are not identical. For instance, the proteins and phospholipids each contains differ; their thickness is dissimilar as well, the plasma membrane being about 75 to 100Å in diameter while the membranes of the reticulum have a diameter in the order of 50 to 60Å. The ER membranes are much closer in structure to those of the mitochondria than to the plasma membrane.

One interesting experiment with mammals shows that the smooth reticulum responds vigorously when the animal is given large concentrations of drugs, such as those commonly found in sleeping pills (phenobarbital). An overdose of the drug stimulates a striking increase in the number of membranes in the smooth reticulum. Apparently the drugs are rendered harmless by enzymes located in the smooth reticulum and so, in response to large concentrations of these potentially fatal substances, the number of membranes in the smooth reticulum grows, thereby increasing the concentration of enzymes to deal with the administered drugs. The smooth reticulum may originate from rough

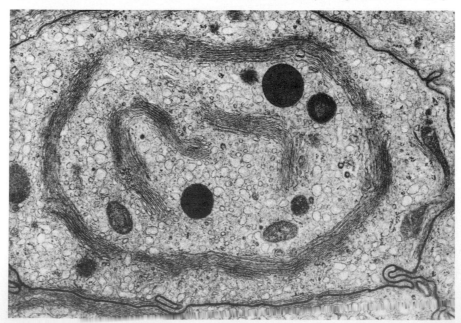

Figure 19–9 This electron micrograph of the Golgi zone reveals the elongated membranes known as saccules (circular and "broken" strands) and the vesicles (dark, round structures).

reticulum, and the rough reticulum itself may be generated by the nuclear envelope, which in many respects is similar to the rough reticulum.

THE GOLGI BODIES: The smooth reticulum is thought to give rise by a process of "membrane flow" to the Golgi bodies. To the uninitiated viewer of electron micrographs, the Golgi apparatus looks very much like smooth endoplasmic reticulum; however, it has a number of elongated **saccules** that lie in a characteristic position relative to the cell nucleus. In association with the saccules are small **vesicles** that also lie in characteristic positions (Fig. 19–9). The organization of the Golgi is very well defined and its function is rather well known. Apparently the main body of the Golgi zone has a concave face and a convex one (Fig 19–10). After proteins have been manufactured in the rough endoplasmic reticulum, they wend their way to the Golgi zone. Here they are modified and finally shunted away and out of the cell. The proteins apparently enter the Golgi complex at the convex zone and undergo condensation and chemical change; for instance, it has been shown that carbohydrates can be added to proteins in the Golgi zone of intestinal cells.

While proteins are thought only to be modified in the Golgi zone, carbohydrates and certain complex fatty materials may actually be synthesized there. It may be that the addition of carbohydrate to proteins is necessary for the protein to penetrate the cell membrane; apparently, the addition of sugar makes membrane permeation easier. A diagram summarizing some of the functions of the Golgi zone is shown in Fig. 19–11. In the future we may expect still more information on this very important portion of the cell's macromolecular synthesizing machinery.

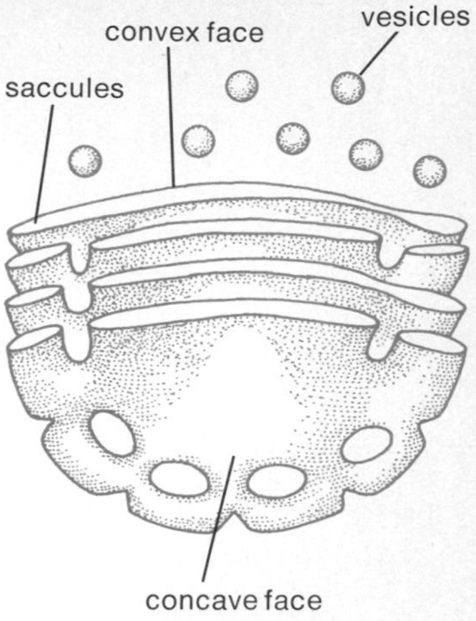

The lysosomes

One of the enzymes located within the Golgi is called **acid phosphatase**. As the name suggests, the enzyme is able to break down phosphate groups when

Figure 19–10 A diagram illustrating details of the Golgi bodies. (From D. W. Fawcett, *The Cell*, © 1966. By permission of W. B. Saunders Co.)

convex face · vesicles · saccules · concave face

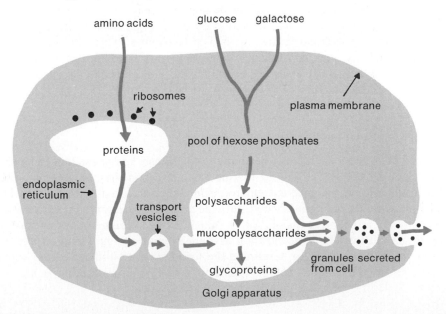

amino acids · glucose · galactose · ribosomes · plasma membrane · proteins · pool of hexose phosphates · endoplasmic reticulum · transport vesicles · polysaccharides · mucopolysaccharides · glycoproteins · granules secreted from cell · Golgi apparatus

Figure 19–11 In this summary of the role played by the Golgi bodies in the cell, notice that the amino acids, glucose, and galactose enter the cell from the outside through the plasma membrane.

the hydrogen ion concentration is relatively high. However, the enzyme is found not only in the Golgi but also in another cellular organelle called a **lysosome**. Because the lysosomes were first convincingly identified with the help of staining reactions specific for acid phosphatase, the lysosomes are thought to be generated from the Golgi region. The function of these cellular organelles is mainly digestive and hydrolytic; they contain large numbers of enzymes capable of breaking down proteins, nucleic acids, and other substances found within the cell. They are surrounded by a single "unit membrane" and we now think that their contents may not be released during the entire lifetime of the cell. Indeed, if their contents were released, the cell would perish.

For a long time biologists were puzzled by the fact that a cell contains enzymes capable of digesting the cell itself, yet during its lifetime the enzymes did not engage their usual substrates. When dead, a cell suddenly contains the machinery to dissolve itself, but not when alive. The lysosomal membrane would provide an answer to this problem. During the lifetime of the cell the membrane would simply not permit lysosomal enzymes to escape into the cytoplasm. However, after cell death and possibly in some pathological situations, the lysosomal materials could be released and thus destroy the tissue in which they existed.

It was not until a few years ago that we even knew of the existence of the lysosomes. The reason for this was that certain characteristics of the lysosomes are very close to those of mitochondria. Since their discovery in the 1950s much has been learned about lysosomes. These organelles contain comparatively large numbers of hydrolytic enzymes seen to be involved in digesting materials imported into the cell. This occurs during pinocytosis and phagocytosis. It is now apparent that these imported substances eventually end up, at least in part, in lysosomal particles and are partially digested there. In some cells, the waste products may be released; in others they tend to accumulate in the lysosomes. It may be that the continuing accumulation of wastes eventually leads to the senescence and/or demise of a cell.

Lysosomes have the ability of acting on other organelles in the same cell. For example, mitochondria are digested in lysosomes. This kind of process, called **autophagy**, may be extremely important to cells because it could serve as a kind of regulatory system controlling the concentration of cytoplasmic membranes. The factors determining when a particular organelle would be gobbled up are not known to us.

Significance of cellular membranes

Cell membranes constitute the machinery the cell uses to oppose the tendencies expressed by the second law of thermodynamics. It is these membranes that accumulate from the external environment materials needed inside the cell. The membranes, acting in concert, provide a microcirculatory system for each cell and are largely responsible for the manufacture of high-energy substances by the cell. Basically, concentration asymmetry and energy evolution are the most important factors for sustaining the living system. Without energy input and a chemically unique composition, there could be no such thing as life.

1 The endoplasmic reticulum and Golgi apparatus are both membrane systems yet they differ in important ways. Discuss these differences.
2 Describe the various means by which materials enter and leave cells.
3 Name and describe the structures found at the cell surface.
4 What is meant by contact-inhibition?
5 Relate the membrane systems of the cell to the cell's ability to "stay" the fate predicated for it by the second law of thermodynamics.
6 To what extranuclear system does the nuclear envelope bear the closest resemblance?

SELECTED READINGS

Lima-De-Faria, A., ed. *Handbook of Molecular Cytology*. New York: American Elsevier Publishing Co., 1969. A compilation of 53 review articles by selected experts on various aspects of subcellular evolution, ultrastructure, and biochemistry. This book provides the interested student with an excellent introduction to the status of specific problem areas in the study of the cell.

Margulis, Lynn. "The Origin of Plant and Animal Cells," *American Scientist*, vol. 59, no. 2 (1971), pp. 230–235. This paper summarizes the author's view that eukaryotes may have arisen from a symbiotic arrangement. Put simply, the theory supposes that chloroplasts and mitochondria originated from the symbiosis of an anaerobic heterotroph and an aerobic prokaryote.

Picken, Laurence E. R. *The Organization of Cells and Other Organisms*. London: Oxford University Press, 1960. This is an advanced work that provides a synthetic view of how cells are structured at the macromolecular level. In dealing with changes in concepts of the cell, the author provides a valuable historical perspective as well as an awareness of the ever-changing nature of "facts." Each chapter begins with a review that can be used to gain access to related literature.

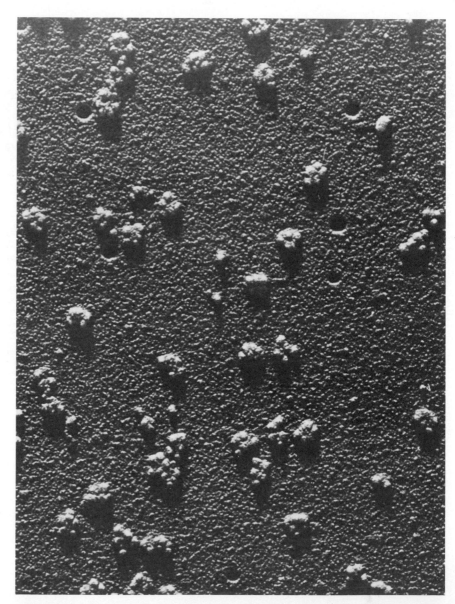

Figure 20–1   Polyribosomes. Each consists of a cluster of several ribosomes, and at these sites within the cell proteins are synthesized. How does this take place? Where does the information calling for synthesis of one protein, and not another, come from? How does this process relate to the molecular structure of genes within the nucleus?

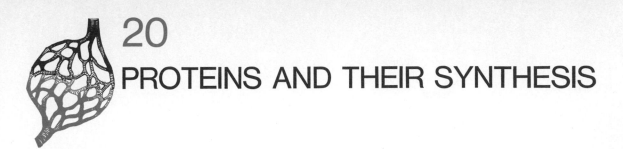

20
PROTEINS AND THEIR SYNTHESIS

A MOLECULAR BASIS FOR DIVERSITY

In Chapter 5 we were concerned with morphological, physiological, and behavioral diversity among organisms. The focus of the present chapter is the molecular basis for such diversity—the nucleic acids and the synthesis of proteins accomplished by these nucleic acids. Genetic material housed in the chromosomes in some way must be able to manipulate the physicochemical characteristics of the cell, and hence the organism. The genes must be in command of "information" of some sort and express its presence in such a way that a green heron, for instance, displays courtship signals of its own species and not those of a herring gull.

In the year 1869, a recently graduated medical student named Friedrich Miescher isolated a cellular material that contained large amounts of phosphorus. This was an unusual finding for the times because phosphorus had not yet been discovered in many substances of biological origin. Since Miescher's substance had come from nuclei, he called it "nuclein." Eventually nuclein was found to consist of nucleic acids and proteins, so its name was changed to **nucleoprotein.**

Nucleic acids have three components—bases, sugars, and phosphate groups. The bases, of which there are five, are called **adenine, guanine, thymine, cytosine**, and **uracil** (Fig. 20–2). The two kinds of sugar molecules both have five carbon atoms in the ring configurations organic chemists called "pyranoses." The sugar called **deoxyribose** has one less oxygen atom than the sugar called **ribose.** Phosphate occurs in all nucleic acids. Nucleic acids with deoxyribose are deoxyribonucleic acids (DNA), while those with ribose are ribonucleic acids (RNA). The structure of a portion of a molecule of DNA is

adenine

thymine

Figure 20–2 The structures of the five base components of nucleic acids.

guanine

cytosine

uracil

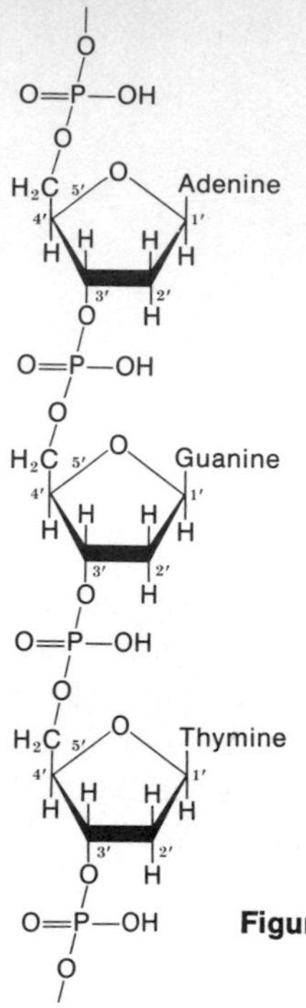

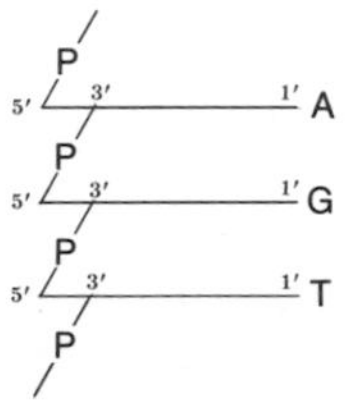

Figure 20–3 The structure of a "stretch" of DNA.

shown in Fig. 20–3. In general, DNA is without uracil, and RNA lacks thymine, but there are a few rare exceptions.

Combination of one base with a sugar and phosphate produces a **nucleotide**, which may contain either one, two, or three terminal phosphates. When the energy-carrier ATP is converted to ADP, the ATP loses one phosphate group; when it loses two phosphates, AMP (adenosine monophosphate) is produced. The nomenclature for nucleic acids is presented in Table 20–1.

BASES	RIBOSE FORMS	DEOXYRIBOSE FORMS	NUCLEOTIDES
adenine	adenosine	(deoxyadenosine)	adenylic acid (AMP)
guanine	guanosine	(deoxyguanosine)	guanylic acid (GMP)
cytosine	cytidine	(deoxycytidine)	cytidylic acid (CMP)
thymine	(ribo) thymidine	(deoxythymidine)	thymidylic acid (TMP)
uracil	uridine	(deoxyuridine)	uridylic acid (UMP)

Table 20–1 Nomenclature for nucleic acid components.

Figure 20–3 shows how nucleotides are combined to form nucleic acids. The chemical bond holding the nucleotide units together is called a 3'-5' phosphodiester linkage because the phosphate joins the number three carbon of one sugar to the number five carbon of another. The 3'-5' phosphodiester bond of nucleic acids is thus analogous to the peptide bond in protein molecules.

The general nature of protein syntheses

DNA is the stuff of the genes and operates as a kind of overseer of protein synthesis. It is the protein component of a skunk or a tulip that determines, for

Figure 20–4 X-ray diffraction diagram of DNA. (Courtesy of M. H. F. Wilkins, Medical Research Council, King's College, London.)

the most part, the organism's characteristics; the basis for taxonomic diversity is thus determined by the diversity of protein assemblies. Both DNA and RNA are able to produce exact copies of themselves. The RNA, which exists in several forms, associates with those cytoplasmic organelles called ribosomes. If free amino acids are available to the ribosome–RNA complex, proteins can be built up by joining these amino acids together in a highly specific manner. Therefore, under appropriate conditions DNA makes DNA or RNA, and RNA makes proteins. In order to understand the details of the process, it is necessary to become familiar with the physical makeup of DNA.

A model for the structure of DNA

During the early 1950s in England's Cavendish Laboratory, a young post-doctoral student named James D. Watson was working on the problem of nucleic acid structure. He collaborated with the British biophysicist Francis H. C. Crick. They were especially interested in X-ray diffraction analyses of DNA. This technique involves the bending of X-rays by crystals, the way in which the rays are bent being related to the structure of the crystal. The

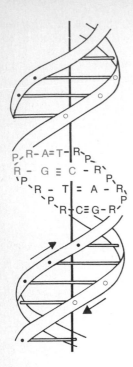

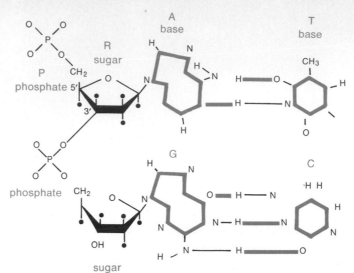

Figure 20–5   The DNA double helix (left) showing the sequencing of phosphate groups, sugar groups, and base pairs: A, adenine; T, thymine; G, guanine; C, cytosine; P, phosphate; R, sugar. At right, the bonding of the groups in color at left is shown.

phenomenon is vaguely similar to what happens when an object is placed in front of a light source. The shadow projected can tell you something about the object's shape. The diffraction pattern of a crystal also reveals much about the crystal's molecular structure.

The X-ray diffraction diagram for DNA shown in Fig. 20–4 suggests to the trained eye that DNA has a number of molecules stacked on top of one another and arranged in a helical configuration. With this sort of data, plus some important chemical information, Watson and Crick began to make hypothetical models of DNA and came upon several interesting relationships. In the model system, adenine could bind *only* with thymine, and guanine could bind *only* with cytosine. The model proposed was a **double helix** in which the sugars and phosphates would exist on the outside and the bases would point inward (Fig. 20–5). It is much as if the sugar–phosphate groups form the uprights of a ladder while the bases form the rungs, the uprights being flexible while the rungs are not. If one end of the ladder is anchored firmly and the other end rotated, a Watson–Crick double helix will be generated (Fig. 20–6). The Watson–Crick proposal suggested an explanation not only for how DNA replicates itself but how it may generate proteins. Before we come to grips with the details of protein synthesis, we should evaluate the implications of some of the points already developed.

The base compositions of DNA molecules from different species were known to be different. Only 2,500 bases of four kinds, it was calculated, could account for 10^{1500} different macromolecules—different at least in base sequence. Most DNA molecules contain far more than 2,500 bases, so the variety of possible polymers is enormous, more enormous than the number of species of organisms, more enormous even than the number of different proteins in all the organisms constituting all the species!

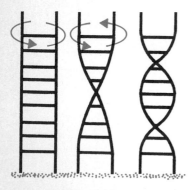

Figure 20–6   A double helix, such as that forming a DNA molecule, can be formed by twisting the top of the ladder, as shown.

DNA synthesis

The bases adenine and thymine always attach to one another by means of hydrogen atoms (Fig. 20–5). The same is true of guanine and cytosine. The G–C pair, however, has one more H group than the A–T pair. The structure of the helix repeats every 34Å units. In each 34Å there are 10 bases, so each base occupies 3.4Å. The double helix is 20Å in diameter. Adenine could not be matched with guanine, in models, because the bonds between the bases would be too long. On the other hand, bonds between thymine and cytosine would not reach one another if placed in the helix as defined by the X-ray studies. With such specific base pairing rules, a mechanism for generating new DNA from old becomes apparent.

The two chains of which DNA is composed should separate. After separating, the individual bases should pair with the correct partners (or complements). If one had the sequence of base composition shown as the left member below, the sequence should yield the following:

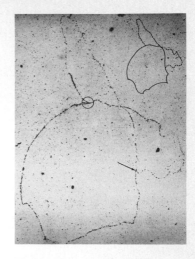

Figure 20–7 Autoradiograph of an intact duplicating chromosome of *E. coli*. The growing region is indicated by an arrow and the starting point for duplication is circled. The inset indicates the location of labeled (———) and unlabeled (- - - - -) strands. The two longer sections are essentially equal in length and therefore must be the two daughter helices, while the short section is the parent helix. The growing region may be identified as the junction at which the parent helix is only half labeled. The other junction is the starting point for duplication. The location on the parent helix where the intensity of labeling is seen to double indicates the point in the division cycle at which the label was introduced. (From J. Cairns, *Cold Spring Harbor Symposium on Quantitative Biology*, Vol. 28, 1963. By permission of Cold Spring Harbor Laboratory.)

```
A . G . A . A . G        A . G . A . A . G        T . C . T . T . C
|   |   |   |   |   | ——→ |   |   |   |   |   |  and |   |   |   |   |   |
T . C . T . T . C        T . C . T . T . C        A . G . A . A . G
```

In other words, the fact of complementarity leads us immediately to a mechanism for the synthesis of new DNA from old. Experimental evidence provided strong support for the idea. Arthur Kornberg was able to isolate an enzyme from the intestinal bacterium *E. coli* which can stimulate synthesis of DNA from the four major nucleotides. To be operative the enzyme requires DNA in the reaction mixture. The freshly synthesized DNA faithfully reflects the base sequence of the old DNA. By physical and chemical criteria the two macromolecules appear to be identical. Proof for *biological* identity was not presented in the initial studies but has lately become available. Kornberg, in collaboration with the virologist Robert Sinsheimer, was able to reproduce a bit of viral DNA capable of eliciting the same kind of infection as native DNA. In a sense life was created or at least copied in these dramatic excursions into molecular biology. The accuracy of the replication process is very great. According to the most reliable figures we have, the probability of an error arising when a new base pairs with a "parent" one is of the order of 10^{-8} to 10^{-9}. An error is committed only once in one hundred million to one billion times. Surely this is the kind of copying fidelity one would expect of the genetic substances.

When DNA replicates, the hydrogen bonds holding the two strands together are ruptured. As the bases "let go" of one another, new bases are attracted to the old ones, putting each type of base next to its proper partner. Hence, if we label both strands with a radioactive isotope, the resultant DNA duplexes will have a label in one strand but none in the other. After the next division, only two of the total of eight strands would be labeled, and so on.

By placing isotopic elements into molecules of *E. coli* DNA and following them as replication proceeded, Matthew Meselson and Franklin Stahl were able to prove the case for this mechanism. When DNA was completely

Figure 20–8 This schematic diagram of the DNA double helix shows the specific pairing of the bases (colored boxes), which are linked by hydrogen bonds (solid lines between boxes). "R" groups are sugars and "P" groups are phosphates. Broken lines represent bonds linking nucleotides. The two halves of the helix are "antiparallel" since the positions of the carbon atom (3's and 5's) on the sugar groups in one chain are opposite the other chain.

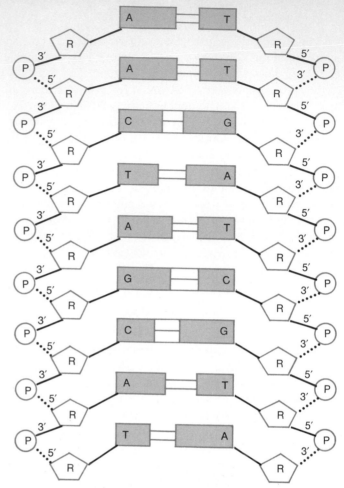

saturated with heavy nitrogen, and then allowed to replicate in its absence (for example, in the presence of conventional, light nitrogen), hybrid DNAs began to appear. After a complete cycle of replication, bacterial chromosomes were found to be composed of 50% "heavy" DNA and 50% "light" DNA. Similar results were obtained by J. Herbert Taylor who worked with the chromosomes of higher plants. In Taylor's case the site was chromosomal. Starting with uniformly labeled chromosomes, he observed label after replication in only half of a chromosome (Fig. 20–7). This is the pattern demanded by the Watson–Crick model.

If you look carefully at the structure of DNA (Fig. 20–8), you will see that the two halves of the double helix are oriented in opposite directions; that is to say, they are antiparallel. Notice how the chain on the left has a number 3′ at its uppermost end and 5′ at the lowermost one. The orientation of these numbers, which signify positions of carbon atoms in the deoxyribose sugar component of the DNA, is opposite in the chain on the right. Apparently, chain growth can occur in both the 5′ → 3′ and 3′ → 5′ directions. However, DNA polymerase is known to guide construction only in the 5′ → 3′ direction, which suggests the existence of additional DNA-synthesizing enzymes.

The role of RNA

DNA has been looked upon as a kind of cellular master-molecule. It is the repository of information used eventually to guide the synthesis of proteins. But DNA itself cannot be the "template" or mold upon which protein molecules are synthesized. In recent years it has been possible to construct protein molecules *in vitro* in the complete absence of DNA. Amino acid condensation has to be considered the basic reaction in protein synthesis, but on chemical grounds there is no obvious way for amino acids to interlock directly with DNA. Some years ago, Crick suggested the participation of certain "adapter" molecules, a view that proved correct. The adapter molecules are a type of RNA called **transfer** RNA (**t-RNA**) able to combine with an amino acid. The reaction requires ATP and occurs in two steps:

(1) ATP + AA + E $\rightleftharpoons$ E (AMP ~ AA) + PP

adenosine triphosphate | amino acid | | activating enzyme (amino acyl synthetase) | amino acyl adenylate pyrophosphate

(2) E (AMP ~ AA) + t-RNA $\rightleftharpoons$ t-RNA AA + E + AMP

amino acyl t-RNA | adenosine monophosphate

The reactions just noted were known to occur as long ago as the late 1950s. Even before then a strong relationship was believed to exist between protein synthesis and RNA content. Cells active in synthesizing proteins always seemed richer in RNA than those that made relatively little protein.

Most (90%) RNA exists in the cytoplasm in the form of ribosomes, which contain about as much protein as they do RNA. In eukaryotes the RNA is derived ultimately from the nucleolus. That small body within the nucleus has long been known to contain RNA. The RNA within the ribosomes is called **ribosomal** RNA (**r-RNA**).

When amino acids are labeled with a radioactive isotope such as carbon-14, the label appears first in association with t-RNA, then *later* in r-RNA. This suggested that each kind of amino acid has a specific t-RNA adapter. After the amino acid attaches itself to its adapter molecule, it is carried to the ribosome, which is the actual site where amino acids combine with one another and form protein molecules.

Though the general mechanism given for protein synthesis seemed plausible enough, many doubted the role assigned to r-RNA. It did not seem to be metabolized rapidly enough and did not seem to qualify as a template. Many ingenious experiments suggested the existence of still another type of RNA, which came to be called **messenger** RNA (**m-RNA**). As its name implies, the substance actually carries the message of the genes. M-RNA is synthesized on DNA in very much the same way DNA is. The role played by DNA in protein synthesis, then, is to serve as a template, and the composition of the newly created RNA reflects the composition of that template. Unlike DNA, most RNAs so far studied are single-stranded and linear rather than double-stranded and circular. Though RNAs other than the ones we have mentioned have been

Figure 20–9 The structure of t-RNA-alanine.

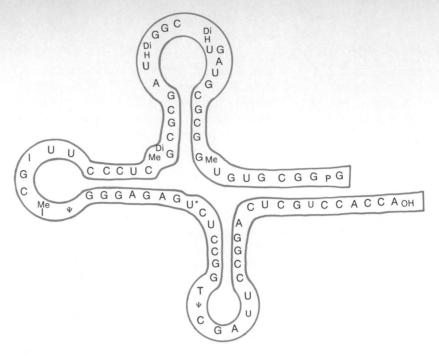

described by molecular biologists our cast of characters is now sufficiently complete to give you an idea of how proteins are put together.

Protein synthesis

Amino acids become bonded to t-RNA molecules through a chemical reaction. The specificity of these conversions lies largely in the enzymes stimulating the conversions—amino acyl synthetases. Following the attachment of an amino acid molecule to its t-RNA adapter, the resultant amino acyl t-RNA migrates to the ribosomes. Before we analyze what happens at that point, we should consider the versatile nature of t-RNA molecules.

These intermediaries *par excellence* form the link between proteins and nucleic acids. Complete analysis of the chemical structure of certain t-RNA molecules (primarily from yeasts) reveals that the molecules have about 80 nucleotides and a molecular weight of about 25,000. They are also shown to have a rather large number of types of bases, not usually found in nucleic acids. The shape of t-RNA molecules seems to be like that shown in Fig. 20–9. The cloverleaf configuration may increase the molecule's function considerably. Somehow the t-RNA molecules are able to pick the correct amino acids, partly through the action of the enzyme that causes the two molecules to combine in the first place, and probably also through some inherent ability of the t-RNA molecule itself.

In addition to an ability to recognize the proper amino acid, the t-RNA must also be able to correctly read signals sent from the DNA of the cell in which it operates. Obviously then, though they are not large molecules, t-RNA molecules are very versatile ones. The only way we can completely understand them is by determining their three-dimensional structure, which should soon be possible through X-ray diffraction procedures. Because DNA is usually confined to the nuclei, in eukaryotic cells, or the nucleoid in prokaryotic ones, the DNA is unable to instruct the t-RNA "in person"; the alternative is to send an intermediary in the form of messenger-RNA. The m-RNA and t-RNA come together on the ribosomes, the actual site of protein synthesis.

Ribosomes are composed of two sub-units, one larger than the other. A m-RNA attaches itself to the smaller of the two sub-units. After a t-RNA molecule enters the ribosome at specified "entrance" sites, it attaches itself to the m-RNA, the physical linkage being between the m-RNA and t-RNA, while the t-RNA is still bonded to its amino acid. The linkage is accomplished by hydrogen bonding of base pairs, bases on the t-RNA recognizing complementary bases on the m-RNA. The ribosome has several kinds of sites, or holes. In addition to the entrance site, another is the "condensation site," at which the first attachment of an amino acyl t-RNA molecule to the m-RNA takes place. In short, the amino acyl t-RNA is transferred from entrance to condensation site, after which a second such molecule moves onto the entrance site and then gives its amino acid to the amino acyl t-RNA (now known as peptidyl t-RNA) located at the condensation site. The RNA portion of the original peptidyl RNA is then released, and RNA from the newer amino acyl t-RNA molecule attaches at the condensation site. This phenomenon recurs with the result that a growing chain of amino acids is eventually built up as summarized in Fig. 20–10.

When the chain of amino acids has grown long enough, it leaves the ribosome and enters the cytoplasm. The two halves of the ribosome are then thought to separate. A new m-RNA may take up occupancy in the smaller sub-unit, after which a large sub-unit combines with it, but not necessarily the same large sub-unit with which it was associated previously. Ribosomes thus facilitate the production of large numbers of copies of a particular protein or group of proteins.

Properties of RNA molecules

Although all three types—messenger, transfer, and ribosomal—of RNA molecules are made on DNA templates, the properties of the three are quite different. It is apparent that m-RNA and t-RNA must contain "information" in

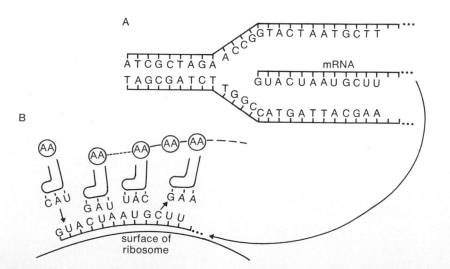

Figure 20–10 Schematic view of protein synthesis. In A, the messenger RNA is copied from a segment of DNA, according to the base-pairing rules, except that uracil takes the place of thymine. Then in B, the m-RNA migrates to the cytoplasm where it becomes attached to a ribosome. The t-RNA–amino acid complexes then wait their turn to line up on the m-RNA template. When the amino acid (AA) has been joined to the growing protein chain, the "empty" t-RNA is released. (From *Cell and Molecular Biology: An Appreciation* by Eugene Rosenberg. Copyright © 1971 by Holt, Rinehart and Winston, Inc. Reprinted by permission of Holt, Rinehart and Winston, Inc.)

their base sequences. What is termed a **codon** in m-RNA dictates the identity of the t-RNA partner. Similarly, t-RNA must have bases in order to participate in such binding. The recognition sequence is called either the **anticodon** or **nodoc**. But what of r-RNA?

Ribosomal-RNA accounts for the greatest quantity of ribonucleic acid in the cell, in eukaryotes as well as in prokaryotes. Undoubtedly it is part of the protein synthesizing machine we call a ribosome, but its precise role remains to be discovered. It is the black box of protein synthesis.

The genetic code

Many of the phenomena described in this chapter depend on the transmission of information. A knowledge of how this information is coded is essential to our understanding of protein synthesis. For example, suppose you have 20 amino acids and four code letters that you can arrange in various sequences to identify each acid. The four symbols in the alphabet we're concentrating on here are of course A, G, C, and T for adenine, guanine, cytosine, and thymine.

Since there are 20 amino acids, we want at least 20 symbols. A singlet, or one-letter, code is insufficient to provide us with that many; so is a doublet code. The first would give us only four labels, the second only 16. A triplet code, however, gives us 64 as shown here.

SINGLET CODE (4 WORDS)	DOUBLET CODE (16 WORDS)				TRIPLET CODE (64 WORDS)			
A	AA	AG	AC	AU	AAA	AAG	AAC	AAU
G	GA	GG	GC	GU	AGA	AGG	AGC	AGU
C	CA	CG	CC	CU	ACA	ACG	ACC	ACU
U	UA	UG	UC	UU	AUA	AUG	AUC	AUU
					GAA	GAG	GAC	GAU
					GGA	GGG	GGC	GGU
					GCA	GCG	GCC	GCU
					GUA	GUG	GUC	GUU
					CAA	CAG	CAC	CAU
					CGA	CGG	CGC	CGU
					CCA	CCG	CCC	CCU
					CUA	CUG	CUC	CUU
					UAA	UAG	UAC	UAU
					UGA	UGG	UGC	UGU
					UCA	UCG	UCC	UCU
					UUA	UUG	UUC	UUU

The proof of this theory emerged primarily in two different ways. One approach was genetic and was pursued largely by Francis Crick and his colleagues in England. The object of their study was a bacteriophage, called T4. Crick and his colleagues subjected T4 to various kinds of mutagenic agents, materials which could produce mutations in these organisms. The mutagens functioned by adding or deleting bases to the viral DNA. Crick found that additions or deletions of three bases (or multiples of three) upset only the region in which the change had been effected. Deleting or adding one or two bases, however, produced very conspicuous effects involving large stretches of the genome. This could be averted by creating a mutation of opposite type. In other words, one deletion could be balanced by one insertion. Two insertions could be balanced by two deletions. In these cases only the region between the two types of mutation would be thrown out of balance. The conclusion was that the code was read in groups of three symbols without overlap. The strong effect of these and similar kinds of experiments upon students of heredity is demonstrated by the terms they used to define certain of the processes in which they are interested. For example, the synthesis of RNA upon DNA templates is commonly called *transcription*. The elaboration of proteins upon ribosomes, under the auspices of m-RNA, is called *translation,* clear evidence of the molecular biologists' involvement in information theory.

The genetic experiments of Crick give us some hints as to the overall nature of the code. The next question obviously concerns the definition of each symbol. In other words, what we would like is to be able to put together a dictionary of code meanings. The road to this goal was taken unexpectedly. A young and gifted biochemist at the National Institutes of Health, Marshall Nirenberg, was working with an enzyme (polynucleotide phosphorylase) which is able to staple together ribonucleotide monomers yielding a polymeric ribonucleotide. With the diphosphates of the various ribonucleotides one can, with this enzyme, generate large numbers of different kinds of ribonucleotide molecules. One of the artificial polymers with which Nirenberg worked was composed only of uridylic acid sub-units. Nirenberg found, quite to his surprise, that this polymer stimulated the formation of another one. But the new one was not a polynucleotide. It was instead a *polypeptide*, polyphenylalanine —a miniature protein composed of only one type of amino acid. This finding could mean UUU is defined as phenylalanine. Using this kind of approach, Nirenberg, Severo Ochoa of the New York University College of Medicine, and others started to work out all the code words.

What was necessary to do this was to make great varieties of artificial messenger RNAs. After these were prepared one could see which amino acids they called for. The techniques were sophisticated later so that instead of dealing with large polymers, one was able to utilize *trinucleotides*. The advantage of this is quite simple to see. One could, in essence, work with just a particular codon and find out which transfer RNA molecule it beckoned. UUU would call for the transfer RNA molecule which transports phenylalanine. Similarly, other materials could be identified. One investigator, H. G. Khorana, took a different tack. He synthesized artificial m-RNAs whose sequence was known precisely and from this he was able to suggest the codons specifying particular amino acids. By 1967 the code for protein synthesis had been broken, a cryptographic breakthrough of considerable proportions. A working "dictionary" of code meanings is shown in Table 20–2.

UUY phenylalanine	CUN leucine	AUY isoleucine	GUN valine
UUR leucine		AUA isoleucine	
		AUG methionine	
UCN serine	CCN proline	ACN threonine	GCN alanine
UAY tyrosine	CAY histidine	AAY asparagine	GAY aspartic acid
UAR gaps	CAR glutamine	AAR lysine	GAR glutamic acid
UGY cysteine	CGN arginine	AGY serine	GGN glycine
UGA gap		AGR arginine	
UGG tryptophan			

U = uracil; C = cytosine; A = adenine; G = guanine;
Y = U, C; N = U, C, A, G; R = A, G.

Table 20–2 The amino acid code.

Notice that each amino acid can be represented by more than one codon on m-RNA. A code characterized by this feature (synonomy) is said to be **degenerate**. Synonomy is part of the reason why there are more than 20 t-RNAs although there are only 20 amino acids. Some students believe that if three letters were used in evolutionarily primitive cells some changes may have occurred over the ages. In most cases where more than a single code word can specify an amino acid, two of the symbols remain constant and the third seems to be replaceable by others. Some of the codons (UAA, UAG, UGA) stand for **nonsense**. They do not specify an animo acid and are believed to be used as termination signals. Mutations usually give rise to **missense** rather than nonsense. In the case of a mutation, incorrect amino acids are inserted into protein molecules. With our knowledge of protein synthesis, including the way nucleic acids combine, proteins that are not foreign to the biological world have been made in the laboratory.

It is possible to make one organism's proteins with the t-RNA and r-RNA derived from another organism. All we have to do is be sure to supply the system with m-RNA derived from the cell whose proteins we wish to prepare. For example, investigators have synthesized the hemoglobin of rabbits by using t-RNA from bacteria. Many such achievements are now matters of record. Collectively, they strongly suggest the universal nature of the genetic code. The coding mechanism, in broad outline at least, occurs in all living matter. Its operation is at once the near starting point and the final proof for evolutionary doctrine.

The protein-generating system described probably existed in quite primitive heterotrophs, which undoubtedly were prokaryotic. Much of what we have learned about protein production stems from laboratory experiments with present-day prokaryotes such as bacteria; we have also learned a great deal from the study of viruses. But we are not made of the same kind of cell that bacteria are composed of. Since our cells are nucleated, it is reasonable to ask whether the information developed for prokaryotes also applies to eukaryotic cells. Such a question is of more than passing interest for it has very practical applications. For instance, if we were adept at manipulating the genetic machinery, we might be in a position to cure some of the most devastating illnesses that plague the human race. To realize this goal we must start on a foundation built largely with data obtained from the prokaryotes. But we will also have to understand the flow of genetic information in cells of the higher forms.

INFORMATION FLOW IN THE EUKARYOTE

The flow of information in prokaryotes can be summarized:

$$\circlearrowleft DNA \longrightarrow RNA \longrightarrow protein$$

The curved arrow symbolizes the autocatalytic function of DNA, while the two straight arrows represent the transcription and translation mechanisms, respectively. Almost all experimental evidence to date shows information transmission to be the same in eukaryotes as it is in prenuclear cells. The main question of interest for cell biologists concerns the manipulation of the process by such structures as the nuclear membrane, the nucleolus, and the chromosomes.

Prokaryotes do not have the first two structures, and their "chromosomes" are strikingly different from those of higher cells. As Fig. 20–11 shows, *E. coli*, for example, has one circular chromosome and is made up entirely of DNA. It has enough DNA to make 2,000 to 4,000 different kinds of protein. By contrast, a eukaryote chromosome may have about 800 times more DNA than *E. coli* has. A cell from a mammalian organism should, on theoretical grounds, be able to synthesize 2,000,000 different types of protein. But this does *not* signify the existence of a direct relationship between taxonomic position and DNA content. Salamander and frog cells may contain 20 to 25 times as much DNA as ours do! While the eukaryotic chromosomes have far more of the "master chemical" than prokaryotic chromosomes have, the relationships between DNA and evolutionary position is far from clear.

The chromosomes of the more advanced cells always contain, in addition to DNA, considerable amounts of RNA and protein. Some of the protein is acidic and some is basic. The most prominent members of the basic class are called **histones**, and there are good reasons to believe that histones may switch genes on and off. Because prokaryotic cells usually have extremely little protein associated with their chromosomes, some geneticists refuse to call the DNA type of bacteria a chromosome.

Arrangement of DNA in the eukaryotic chromosome

One puzzle worth mentioning concerns the packaging of DNA in chromosomes. We know pretty well how this is accomplished in lower cells, as a circular double helix. But what about the eukaryotic chromosome with 800 times more DNA? Its packaging must be fantastically complicated. If all the

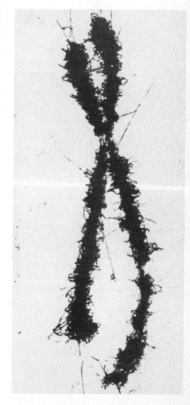

Figure 20–11 A human chromosome magnified several thousand times. (From E. J. Dupraw and G. F. Bahr, *Acta Cytologica*, Vol. 13, No. 4, © 1969. By permission of the International Academy of Cytology.)

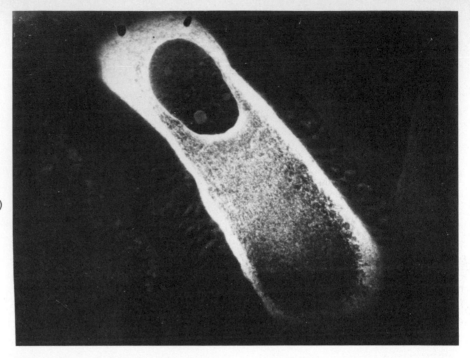

Figure 20–12 This photomicrograph of a *Cecropia* moth's egg shows the cell after being exposed to a protein labeled with fluorescent dye. The material's location within the egg could then be found microscopically. The glow clearly shows fluorescence in the cytoplasm, but not in the nucleus. The protein–label combination was unable to pass through the nuclear membrane. (From C. M. Feldherr and A. B. Feldherr, *Nature, 185: 4708*, 1960.)

DNA it contained were unraveled into a single thread, it would extend a distance of about 2 meters. The problem is to understand how a strand two meters long and 20Å wide can be packed into a structure whose dimensions are measured in micrometers (Fig. 20–12).

The DNA may exist in one long chain folded back and forth on itself many times. The proteins of the chromosome may coat the DNA, or in some way interconnect numbers of the DNA sub-units. In bacteria, DNA synthesis always begins at a specific point on the chromosome, while in metazoan chromosomes it may begin at up to 125 different (and characteristic) sites.

Chromosomes of higher organisms have long been known to contain some regions where the chromatin is packed loosely (and called **euchromatin**) and other regions where it is packed tightly (and called **heterochromatin**). So far as we know, there aren't any chemical differences between the two materials. Heterochromatic regions are easier to observe with the microscope because they are denser. We believe RNA transcription occurs chiefly in the euchromatic regions of chromosomes. The fact that the degree of packing in chromatin on various regions of a chromosome is not constant implies that some regions are more influential than others. It now seems possible that the histones and other nucleoproteins in some way regulate the transcriptive activity of chromatin. This would have important implications for cellular and therefore organismal homeostasis.

Nucleus and cytoplasm

When we consider the cell physiology of higher animals, it becomes particularly important to examine the interaction between nucleus and cytoplasm.

In the lower forms the chromosomes lie within the cytoplasm; in the higher ones a well defined membrane called the **nuclear envelope** separates them.

The nucleus of a cell produces its own ATP and other important metabolites; it also contains enzymes and other materials necessary for the continued life of the cell. Our observations show that there is a heavy exchange of materials between the nucleus and cytoplasm. After formation, RNAs of all three types (and perhaps others) migrate through the nuclear membrane and into the cytoplasm. Proteins shuttle back and forth in both directions, but the membrane is not permeable to all substances. The nucleus can be made to shrink when concentrated solutions of high-molecular-weight compounds are introduced into the cytoplasm. Figure 20–9 vividly shows the cellular distribution of certain proteins that cannot enter the nucleus.

The problem of nuclear permeability is an important one, for the products of the genes must migrate through the nuclear membrane if the cell is to pursue an uninterrupted program of protein synthesis. Electron microscopy of the envelope reveals the presence of very large pores (Fig. 20–13), so large that it is difficult to see how any molecule can be excluded.

The nucleolus

The **nucleolus**, like the nucleus, was first observed in the 18th century in epithelial cells of the eel. These structures are almost always attached to a particular site on a given chromosome and contain a considerable amount of DNA and RNA. The RNA represents precursor molecules destined for the ribosomes while the DNA seems to act as a template for r-RNA synthesis. Recently investigators at the Oak Ridge National Laboratory succeeded in observing these genes in action!

A precursor of RNA (uridine) was labeled with tritium and then analyzed by viewing autoradiograms under the electron microscope. If RNA is synthesized on genes, then we should find precursors of this RNA incorporated right along the genes themselves. And so it was (Fig. 20–14).

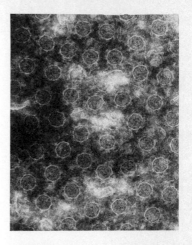

Figure 20–13 This electron micrograph shows the nuclear envelope of a newt cell. The walls of the pores (large circles) are very prominent. (From J. G. Gall, Jr., *Journal of Cell Biology*, Vol. 32, 1967.)

Figure 20–14 This is an autoradiogram of part of a newt gene. The long dark thread is DNA. The fuzzy looking ones extending outward from the DNA are newly-formed RNA molecules, and the dark dots are thought to be RNA polymerase. (Courtesy of O. L. Miller, Jr. and Barbara R. Beatty, Biology Division, Oak Ridge National Laboratory.)

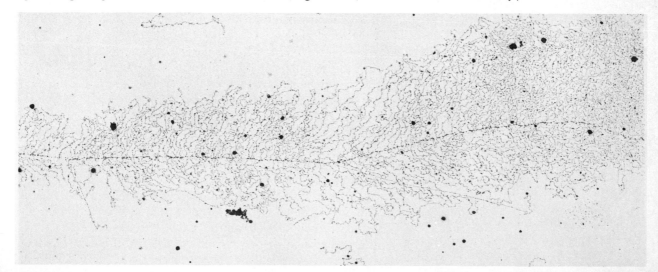

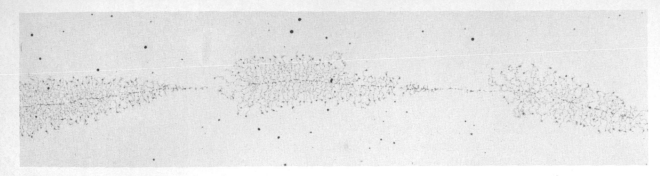

For some reason, many copies of the r-RNA precursors are made in the nucleoli of amphibian egg cells. Apparently, certain sequences of bases are repeated over and over again. R-RNA is not generated in a form immediately usable for ribosome construction; instead it goes through a well defined developmental course, after which it leaves the nucleolus and subsequently the nucleus. Most nucleoli consist of granular and fibrous materials. The duplicate genes are arranged in tandem as the fine electron microscope autoradiograph in Fig. 20–15 shows. This suggests the existence of "spacers" whose function is to keep genes apart.

How do genes "know" when to transcribe?

On theoretical grounds, we know that *E. coli* should be able to make between 2,000 and 4,000 different proteins. Does this mean the bacterium will go ahead and produce *all* such proteins at *all* times? And will each of these proteins be present within *E. coli's* cytoplasm in equal concentration? And will each of them be made regardless of the cell's external environment? The answer is "no" in all three cases. Cells, both prokaryotic and eukaryotic, have means of controlling the quantity and quality of proteins that they are going to manufacture at any particular moment. In other words, the cell itself maintains its internal environment at a steady state. Since the operation of homeostatic regulators is of utmost importance to the cell's survival, we would do well to examine control mechanisms.

Most of the pertinent work in cell homeostasis has been done with *E. coli*, and only a few investigations have been performed with eukaryotic cell types. The bacterium frequently makes use of the sugar lactose, which is composed of the two hexose sub-units, galactose and glucose. In the absence of lactose, many *E. coli* are incapable either of transporting freshly added lactose into the cell, or of breaking it down. However, in a number of forms, the addition of lactose stimulates transport into the cell as well as the synthesis of appropriate enzymes. What is there in the first case that prevents formation of materials needed to break down the disaccharide lactose? Generally, *E. coli* exposed to lactose contain upward of 3,000 molecules of the enzyme needed to split lactose, and this represents about 3% of all the protein within the *E. coli* cell. A very sophisticated kind of control system operates within bacteria. Several "structural" genes seem to control the synthesis of the m-RNAs that eventually supply the code for making the enzymes whose precise role in lactose metabolism is not yet certain. The three structural genes are apparently controlled by an **"operator" gene**. Here is a new concept in biology—genes that control other genes. The conventional gene is the structural gene. The new type is a **regulatory gene** and can be thought of as an off–on switch that causes many of the structural genes to produce their r-RNA molecules. A substance called a **repressor** is a protein that operates the switch. Normally, when the repressor combines with the operator all the structural genes the operator controls are silenced. The repressor is produced by still another type of regulatory gene that lies relatively far from the operator, one called the **regulator**.

So a regulator gene can produce (through the normal channels of protein synthesis) a molecule that binds to the operator and, therefore, limits the transcriptive process in the structural genes. The operator, along with its structural genes, has been called an **operon**. And operators themselves have recently been divided into two new sites: one, the site that binds with the repressor, retains the name operator; the other, responsible for binding RNA polymerase and so starting a transcriptive episode, has been called a **promoter**.

This rather complex control system, which seemed conjectural to some workers, was proven to exist when the **lac operon**—the series of genes involved in handling lactose—was isolated and seen in the electron microscope (Fig. 20–16). Repressor molecules have also been isolated in at least two instances. One of these is the repressor that controls the syntheses of the lac operon. Lactose induces the presence of the required enzymes by acting as an **inducer**. By combining with the repressor, it inactivates the repressor, thus allowing the operator to function in the "on position."

There are also molecules that repress transcription at specific gene sites. These simply act as corepressors; in other words they, like an inducer, join the repressor, but instead of making the repressor less efficient in linking up with the operator, they make it more efficient. These corepressors apparently are common in a number of cells and are very much involved in the metabolism of amino acids. When an amino acid becomes too concentrated within the cell, it may act as a corepressor of its own synthesis.

Modern microbial genetics has also shown us that m-RNA may be produced in copies, each of which stands for a number of different enzymes that are metabolically related. Such RNAs are called **polycistronic** because the basic unit of genetic function is termed a **cistron**. We would imagine that polycistronic-RNA ought to give rise to equal rates of protein synthesis for all the materials it signifies, but this is not what we find. Instead, different portions of the m-RNA tape are read out at different rates, and so in addition to controls existing at the level of transcription we must also imagine controls existing at the level of translation.

The cell, then, has many types of control systems. In the case of the lac operon the regulator gene produces a material whose "temperament" is largely negative in character. The repressor stops transcription. In some cases regulator genes produce substances that actually stimulate the structural genes through interaction with the operator. So at the genetic level we have controls of both positive and negative types and we also have the possibility of more

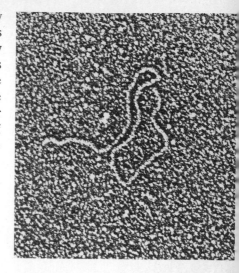

Figure 20–16 An electron micrograph of an isolated lac operon. (Electron micrograph by L. Machattie from J. Shapiro *et al.*, in *Nature, 224:768*.)

immediate kinds of control. This does not mean that every enzyme studied is sensitive to some type of governing agency. There are some in fact (for example, those involved in the handling of certain sugars) that apparently are synthesized regardless of what the environment has to offer, and we do not know why this should be so, since it appears uneconomical.

Not much work on the subject of control (at least at the molecular level) has been done on eukaryotic cells. These cells have far more DNA than the nonnucleated variety. On the basis of rather sophisticated analysis, some biologists believe that much of the extra DNA in the higher life forms is involved in the phenomenon of regulation. It would be almost inconceivable that regulation in these cells is *less* sophisticated than it is in the bacteria. New and better answers to the problem should be forthcoming within the next decade.

As we shall discover, the topic of switch-on–switch-off mechanisms in the cell takes on additional importance in a discussion of the differentiation, growth, and regulation of organisms.

QUESTIONS FOR REVIEW

1   What are the chemical relationships among amino acids, nucleic acids, and proteins?
2   From a cell's "point of view," what is the importance of ATP? How is phosphate involved when ATP is converted to ADP? When ADP is converted to ATP?
3   Give an example of how a DNA molecule can be altered in such a way that a genetic mutation occurs.
4   What is the significance of the "triplet code"?
5   In an earlier chapter, you read that the nucleus is the "control center" of the cell. On the basis of what you have read in this chapter, explain the biochemical significance of that statement.

SELECTED READINGS

Beadle, George W., and Beadle, Muriel. *The Language of Life*. Garden City, N.Y.: Doubleday & Co., 1966. This fascinating book is one of the very few that introduce the chemistry of the gene and mechanisms of gene action at the level of the layman.

Watson, James D. *The Double Helix*. New York: Atheneum Publishers, 1968. The author presents a personal account of the people and events involved in the quest for the solution to the structure of DNA.

————. *The Molecular Biology of the Gene*. 2nd ed. New York: W. A. Benjamin, Inc., 1970. Written for the college student, this fine text provides details of how genes are transcribed and their genetic messages translated. Excellent illustrations are included. See especially Chapters 11–14.

Part 5

MATURATION

In Part 4 our concern with organisms was
on the systemic, cellular, and subcellular levels,
with a view to understanding the basic processes
needed to maintain life. In Part 5 we examine a
number of processes related to the development of
organisms. We will also be looking into the
development of behavior and into some of the
important behavioral roles played by learning.

21

ON BECOMING MULTICELLULAR

Multicellularity—some advantages

Although single cells are able to do some extraordinary things, they are not able to grow very large (Fig. 21–1). Why do cells remain as small as they are? If you increase the diameter of a sphere, the surface grows less rapidly than the volume. A sphere with a radius of 2 units has eight times the volume but only four times the surface area of a sphere with a radius of 1 unit. At first glance this may seem inconsequential, but it is loaded with weighty consequences for cells. The surface through which diffusion can occur becomes gradually more restricted relative to the volume as a cell grows, which means that foods and wastes cannot be as easily exchanged with the external environment by a large cell as by a small one.

The alternative to growth by continued enlargement of a single cell is growth by an increase in the *number* of cells, or multicellularity. Virtually all the organisms you see from day to day are multicellular. Multicellularity endows organisms with more important features than just size. Cellular division of labor, or specialization, in the higher organisms is one. In *Paramecium*, digestion, excretion, respiration, movement, and assimilation must all be centered in the same cell. In multicellular organisms, different tissues deal with these different physiological processes. Cells of the kidney are organized in a particular way in order to excrete body wastes and water. Muscle cells are specialized to allow movement; cells of the eye process light and, through the specialized cells of the brain, allow vision. Cells that become specialized tend to organize into tissues, tissues into organs, organs into systems, and systems into organisms. Whereas the single-celled organism must be a jack-of-all-trades, the multicellular organism has an assembly of specialists.

Another advantage of multicellularity is the capacity of multicellular organisms to occupy ecological niches not available to unicellular organisms and so avoid competition with their unicellular neighbors. The ultimate advantage is a more efficient handling of energy, for the species that can handle energy most efficiently will win the competition for survival.

Unfortunately we do not have quantitative measurements proving that multicellular organisms are more or less adept at energy use than single-celled organisms, which means that we do not understand why there should be *both* multicellular and unicellular organisms flourishing equally well; both lines continue to be evolutionary successes. We measure biological success relative to the particular ecological niche of the organisms under consideration. Multicellularity probably proved extremely important to those forms that emigrated from the salt water environs of early Paleozoic times.

Figure 21–1 An ostrich egg, which is a single cell, is nearly all yolk—stored food for the developing embryo. The volume of protoplasm ("living substance") is not much greater than that of typical cells.

The transition from unicellularity to multicellularity was, we must suppose, a very gradual one. To think on the one hand of an elephant and on the other of a bacterium is to see the two ends of a spectrum, but to look at the algae *Chlamydomonas* and *Volvox* is quite another matter (see Figs. 1–3 and 2–15). Aggregates of cells that live as a colony display integrative behavior; there must be some sort of coordinating system to control the activities of all the individual "citizen" cells. "Colony" is used to describe *Volvox* because its level of integration is not quite so sophisticated as that in higher forms.

Complex organizations require greater absolute investments of energy for their maintenance than do simple ones. A human being, organized as intricately as it is, requires a much greater input of energy than does a *Paramecium* or *Volvox*. We tend to think, however, that the human being's several trillion cells collectively use less energy than an equivalent number of *Paramecia*, and so in the end we may be more efficient than a colony of *Paramecia* equivalent in number to our number of cells. It would seem, then, that there are definite advantages to our architecture. But how is that architecture achieved? And once achieved, how is the multicellular state maintained?

MULTICELLULARITY AND REPRODUCTION

All the functions necessary for life can be carried out in single cells, but to perform more complex behavioral activities necessitates a higher level of multicellularity and specialization of cell function than is found in *Volvox*. Multicellularity and cell specialization in turn require a mechanism for transition from one generation of multicellular adults to the next.

Some of the coelenterates and flatworms reproduce by budding (Fig. 3–11) or fission, and the generations succeed one another without loss of multicellularity. Simple as this is, it carries with it the evolutionary disadvantage that the offspring have only the same genetic potential as the parent, a theme explored in Chapter 3. In most organisms egg and sperm, which are carriers of the genetic material, fuse as a zygote; that single cell then undergoes cell division, increases its protoplasm, and differentiates in a marvelously organized way, becoming a new multicellular adult with a genetic potential different from either of its parents.

Though the zygote has the potential for development, whether or not it will live depends on how well it can survive the demands of the environment. In a sense, it is an independent organism beset by the same problems that adults face. It must have food to provide energy and substrates for growth and maintenance, it must be maintained within a tolerable temperature range, it must be protected from desiccation, and it must be preserved from infection and predation.

Various solutions to these problems have evolved. Limiting reproduction to the time of the year when climatic conditions are most favorable and food sources readily available has been one solution. The problem of death due to predation and infection was avoided in many organisms by protective membranes and production of a sufficient number of zygotes to increase numerically the probability of survival. In the higher vertebrates, the evolution of

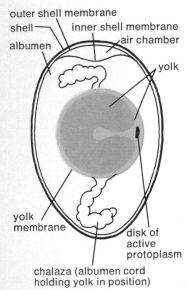

outer shell membrane
shell
albumen
inner shell membrane
air chamber
yolk
yolk membrane
disk of active protoplasm
chalaza (albumen cord holding yolk in position)

Figure 21–2 The hen's egg proper is actually only the central yolky part with the disc of active protoplasm. The albumen, shell membranes, and shell are acquired as the egg passes through the oviduct.

complex behavioral patterns provided care for the young during their more vulnerable periods of life. The problem of food for the developing embryo was solved by incorporating in the egg enough nutrients to last until the time the embryo could assimilate food from other sources.

Desiccation of the zygote and embryo also had to be guarded against in those organisms that took up a terrestrial life. Three solutions evolved. One, adopted by most of the amphibians, is to migrate back to the water and reproduce there—a reproductive technique little advanced over that of fish. A second solution, evolved in the reptilian egg, is a shell that preserves an aquatic environment for the embryo. Birds and egg-laying mammals also share this adaptation. A third solution, which evolved in higher mammals, is retention of the zygote within the uterus until the new individual is ready for birth. This provides still better protection for the embryo and ensures a supply of nutrients, making it unnecessary to incorporate large food reserves within the egg. In addition to its need for protection, a developing embryo requires substrates from which proteins and cellular organelles can be built in the process of growth.

Agents of fertilization

THE EGG: The egg, or **ovum**, is a specialized cell in which reserves of various sorts are stored (Fig. 21–2). Thus, ova tend to be relatively large, spherical cells. The young ovum, or **oocyte**, develops from a diploid sex cell within the ovary. In mammals, each oocyte eventually becomes surrounded by a fluid-filled cavity encased in the **follicle** of ovarian cells. These cells permit the passage of materials to the oocyte from the mother's circulatory system and secrete a protective membrane around the oocyte.

The **yolk** is the main storage product of an egg and is a complex of proteins, phospholipids, and neutral fats. In addition lipid, glycogen, and carbohydrates accumulate as food reserves in some eggs. The final size an oocyte attains is related to the volume of stored reserves. The amount of yolk and the way it is distributed profoundly affect embryonic development. Some eggs, such as those of mammals and echinoderms, have very little yolk evenly scattered throughout the cytoplasm. Others have more yolk that is concentrated toward the lower side of the cell (**vegetal hemisphere**), typical of amphibians, annelids, and mollusks. (The upper half of the egg is called the **animal hemisphere**.) Still other eggs accumulate large masses of stored yolk relative to the amount of yolk-free cytoplasm, typical of many of the invertebrates, fish, reptiles, and birds.

The amount of reserve material does not follow a phylogenetic trend. It is determined by the stage of development of the embryo at which an outside source of nutrition becomes available. Echinoderm embryos develop rather quickly to a feeding stage and do not need much of a reserve to carry them to this point. The mammalian embryo, on the other hand, typically undergoes only a few cell divisions before it obtains added nutrition from the uterus. Birds, reptiles, and fish, which hatch as miniature adults, have to depend on stored food for a relatively longer time than echinoderms and mammals, hence the larger size of birds' and other such eggs (Fig. 21–3).

human egg
0.14 mm

platypus egg
4.5 mm

frog egg
1.75 mm

hen's egg 50.0 mm

Figure 21–3 When we compare egg sizes within a vertebrate series, we can see the relationship of egg size to stage of development at which nutrients other than those stored in the egg are used. A placental mammal (human) receives nourishment from the uterus at the blastula and succeeding stages. An egg-laying mammal (platypus) receives nourishment by sucking after hatching as a fetus, following 12 days of incubation of the egg. An amphibian (frog) feeds on plants as a young larva. A bird (chicken) hatches as a miniature adult, which begins to feed in about 24 hours.

Following the completion of growth, the oocyte is released from the ovary (**ovulation**) and undergoes two meiotic divisions, which reduce the chromosomes to the haploid number. During these divisions almost all the cytoplasm is conserved into a single cell, the ovum. If the ovum is of a species in which development occurs outside, it may accumulate additional membranes as it passes through the **oviduct**, the tube leading from the ovary to the exterior. The jelly layers of frog eggs and the albumen and shell of the hen's egg are familiar examples of such membranes (Fig. 21–2).

THE SPERMATOZOAN: In contrast to eggs, spermatozoa are very small cells. They, too, begin as diploid sex cells but, unlike the egg, do not undergo a protracted growth period. Instead, they undergo two meiotic divisions and become haploid **spermatids** before beginning cytoplasmic differentiation. During differentiation the spermatid loses most of its cytoplasm, and an acrosome located at the anterior end of the nucleus and a flagellum, used for locomotion, develop. Since in some species the **acrosome** is pointed, it used to be thought that it was a device for mechanically piercing the egg membranes during fertilization. We now know that another process is involved.

The process of fertilization

In most species, sperm are simply introduced into the environment of the egg. We may find a clue to the way the two merge if we trace the path of a sea urchin spermatozoan after it has been added to a suspension of eggs. The spermatozoan swims in what appears to be random motion until it happens to make contact with an egg, at which time it then adheres to the egg jelly and becomes quiescent.

In a number of species, the initial union of the gametes involves a special substance on the spermatozoan surface that couples with a corresponding substance on the surface of the egg. The acrosome then releases an enzyme that digests the membranes separating the surfaces of the cells (Fig. 21–4). The two cell membranes break down at the point of contact and permit the sperm nucleus to enter the egg.

Figure 21–4 The entrance of the spermatozoan into the egg takes place in stages: At A, the sperm makes contact with the egg's surface. At B, the acrosome releases an enzyme that digests the egg membrane, and the plasma membranes of egg and sperm fuse. At C, breakdown of the two cell membranes takes place and the spermatozoan nucleus begins to move into the egg cytoplasm.

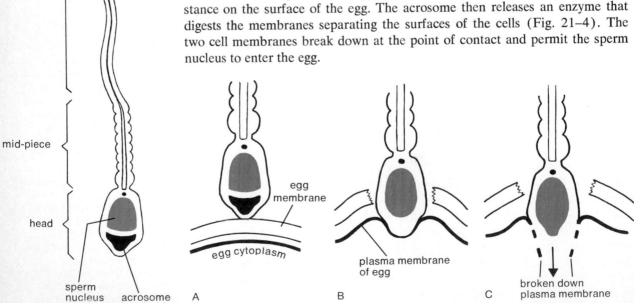

tail-flagellum

mid-piece

head

sperm nucleus   acrosome   A

egg membrane

egg cytoplasm

B

plasma membrane of egg

C

broken down plasma membrane

EARLY CHANGES IN THE FERTILIZED EGG

The entrance of the spermatozoan stimulates the completion of maturation if this has not already been accomplished. Eventually, the haploid egg and spermatozoan nuclei join, thus restoring the diploid number in the zygotic nucleus. The sperm also stimulates the separation of the **fertilization membrane** from the egg surface, which separates the egg from its surroundings and thus serves as an additional protection for the developing embryo. The membrane also helps the zygote maintain its shape, since large eggs tend to flatten if the membrane is removed.

Proceeding at a slower pace, cytoplasmic motion that began after sperm entrance redistributes the stored contents of the egg, movements that signify the beginnings of organization of the new individual. Materials within the cytoplasm next become fixed in position as the zygote becomes partitioned into many smaller cells (**blastomeres**) during **cleavage** (Fig. 21–5). Meanwhile, oxygen consumption of the zygote has stepped up and protein synthesis has been initiated.

Figure 21–5 Cytoplasmic reorganization in frog eggs after fertilization is shown. The unfertilized egg is seen at A. After fertilization the egg is bilaterally symmetrical in its organization (B). C and D show further development, the four- and eight-cell stages respectively. The pattern of division shown here is typical of amphibian eggs and different from the sea urchin, birds, and mammals.

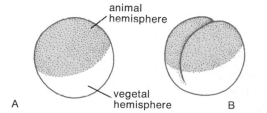
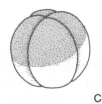

A   animal hemisphere   vegetal hemisphere   B   C   D

The blastula stage

If an egg contains more yolk concentrated near one pole than the other, the rate of mitosis eventually becomes slower in the more yolky regions. At any one time during cleavage, therefore, cells in the vegetal hemisphere will be larger than cells in the animal hemisphere. Yolk, then, decreases the rate of cleavage, very concentrated yolk sometimes inhibiting division of the cytoplasm entirely. This can be demonstrated by centrifuging an amphibian egg so that the yolk is packed at the vegetal pole. Such eggs undergo cleavage, but fail to divide in the region of the vegetal pole. It is not surprising, then, that the very yolky eggs of fish, reptiles, and birds divide only in the region of the yolk-free, active cytoplasm at the animal pole. The bulk of the zygote, containing the large yolk store, does not divide at all.

As cleavage progresses, the inner surfaces of the blastomeres lose affinity for each other and draw apart. As they do, they leave a space—the **blastocoel**—so eggs with little or moderate amounts of yolk are converted into a hollow sphere of cells (the **blastula**) with a central blastocoel (Fig. 21–6). The cells themselves comprise a tissue called the **blastoderm**.

After a few cell divisions, the plate-like blastoderm of avian eggs lifts off the underlying yolk, but remains attached at its periphery where cell division proceeds to form a sheet of tissue that gradually passes down over the yolk

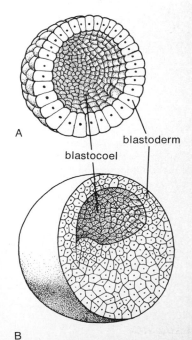

A   blastoderm   blastocoel   B

Figure 21–6 Comparison of forms of blastulae: at A, an echinoderm egg with little yolk; at B, a more yolky amphibian egg. Notice the smaller central cavity and the relatively large ventral cells, which contain the yolky material.

mass. Cells migrate from the blastoderm and form a second layer beneath it. The blastula stage can be thought of as a flattened sphere attached at its margin to a sheet of tissue migrating over the yolk. This tissue is an adaptation for managing a mass of yolk relatively large in proportion to the early embryo. Later it will become very important in regulating use of the yolk; at the present stage the food supply is virtually separated from the cells that will develop into the embryo proper.

At this point the zygote has become multicellular and the position the cells occupy has been largely dependent on mitosis. Each blastomere represents only a small portion of the original cytoplasm and the product of nuclear divisions. The process of cleavage has been a very orderly sequence unique in each species and would appear to be controlled by instructions programmed in the egg.

The study of cleavage rates in a variety of eggs indicates that the instructions for early development come from the cytoplasm rather than the nucleus. Investigators have demonstrated that zygotes are capable of normal development until near the end of the blastula period when they are reared in solutions of Actinomycin D. This antibiotic prevents the synthesis of messenger-RNA, which normally transmits nuclear information to the cytoplasm. The experimental result shows that all the information necessary for development up to this point has been stored in the cytoplasm in the form of stable messenger-RNA during the growth period of the egg in the ovary.

Past the blastula stage, however, development reflects the influence of the genetic information in the blastomeric nuclei, for eggs treated with Actinomycin D are blocked in their development. Thus the genes of the zygote begin to be active in controlling development toward the end of the blastula period.

The gastrula stage

Following the blastula stage, the complexity of the embryo increases through cell movements that result in three tissue layers—an outermost **ectoderm**; a middle layer, the **mesoderm**; and an inner one, the **endoderm** (Fig. 21–7). The movements that bring about this condition occur during the period known as **gastrulation**, during which the endoderm and mesoderm migrate into the interior. The blastocoel provides the space to accommodate the cells.

The first cells to enter the blastocoel in sea urchin eggs are some of the future mesoderm cells that detach from the blastoderm at the vegetal pole (Fig. 21–7). Their migration is followed by a sac-like invagination of vegetal hemisphere cells, comprising the future endoderm and the rest of the mesoderm. Mesoderm cells that have entered with the endoderm subsequently mi-

Figure 21–7 Gastrulation in the sea urchin is shown here. Each of the six stages shown is a section taken along the animal–vegetal axis.

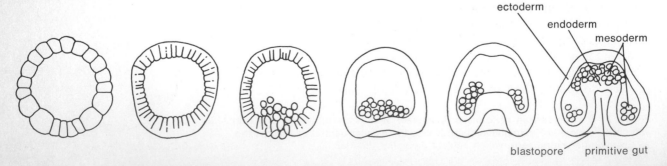

grate away from the endoderm and complete the middle layer. The tube of endoderm cells is the primitive gut, and its opening to the surface later becomes the anus.

Through marking experiments we can locate on the surface of the early gastrula the positions of cells that will later form the basic organ rudiments of the embryo. The early gastrula can thus be visualized as areas of cells destined to follow particular courses of differentiation. Such "fate maps" of a number of amphibians, reptiles, and birds are remarkably similar in the topographical distribution of the areas, indicating a basic similarity in the cell movements that subsequently occur in the several forms. Thus, the physiological aspects of evolution are conservative and we must conclude that once a viable system of cell movements evolved, it was not greatly altered.

Differentiation of tissue layers

By the end of gastrulation, the three main layers from which the organ systems will derive have been established. In the course of development, these tissues fold and thicken as the result of changes in the shape, proliferation, and movement of their cells. As a result, local regions become distinguishable as the rudiments of the major adult organs.

ECTODERM: The first externally discernible organ rudiment in the vertebrate is a thickening of the neural ectoderm that will form the nervous system. The edges elevate, arch over, and fuse, in the process becoming a tube. The wider, anterior end of the tube corresponds to the future brain, while the narrow, posterior end will become spinal cord. Other cells form parts of the peripheral nervous system.

MESODERM: Changes in the mesoderm during this period involve the separation of cells from the original layer. The notochord, one of the first structures to emerge, separates as a narrow strip of cells extending from anterior to posterior in the mid-dorsal part of the mesoderm. While it becomes the main supporting structure in embryos and larvae of lower vertebrates, it is eventually replaced in all adult vertebrates by the vertebral column.

Lateral to the notochord, the mesoderm breaks up into a series of cell masses and sheets and some free cells that migrate to new positions. In general, mesoderm forms the muscles, circulatory, excretory, and reproductive systems, as well as the skeleton, connective tissues, and blood.

ENDODERM: The endoderm forms the lining of the respiratory and digestive systems and their associated glandular tissues such as the liver and pancreas. The other components of these organs (muscle, connective tissue, and blood vessels) differentiate from adjacent mesoderm cells. As the endoderm develops, there is a gradual elongation of the tubular primitive gut, so that eventually the posterior part of the digestive system has to be folded and twisted to fit within the body cavity. Parts of the wall of the gut form the rudiments for the major glands of the digestive system, as well as the respiratory system.

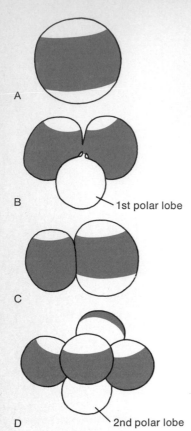

A

B 　1st polar lobe

C

D 　2nd polar lobe

Figure 21–8 Cleavage in *Dentalium*, showing the formation of the first and second polar lobes. The second polar lobe eventually fuses with one of the four cells.

Mechanisms of early differentiation

ROLE OF THE NUCLEUS: Nineteenth-century embryologists thought that genetic information in the zygotic nucleus was distributed to daughter nuclei as the blastomeres formed until eventually each cell contained the specific information necessary for it to differentiate into a particular part of the whole embryo. But this notion was abandoned when 20th-century investigators discovered that any one of the first four blastomeres of the sea urchin, when isolated, was capable of developing into a whole, albeit small, larva. Similarly, each of the first two cells of the frog egg was found to have the capacity to develop into a complete tadpole.

Finally, in the 1950s, when a technique for nuclear transplantation had been developed for frog embryos, it was shown that nuclei taken from late cleavage blastulae contained all the information necessary to support normal and complete development of the larva. It became apparent that nuclei are all alike with respect to the information they contain.

ROLE OF THE CYTOPLASM: On the other hand, evidence that the controlling factors lie in the cytoplasm of the egg and in the interaction between adjacent cells has been accumulating. In the 1920s, E. B. Wilson investigated early development of the mollusk *Dentalium*. Cleavage in *Dentalium* is different from that of the eggs described so far. Just before the first cell division, a large lobe of cytoplasm extends from the vegetal pole and recedes into one of two blastomeres after cell division has been completed (Fig. 21–8). The cell that received the lobe material then produces a second lobe before the second cell division, and its material passes into only one of the four blastomeres.

When Wilson surgically isolated the first four cells, the one that had received the lobe material was the only one capable of forming a whole larva. The other three could form only the anterior half of the larva, suggesting that the lobe material is necessary for the development of the missing parts and that in certain kinds of eggs normal differentiation of the blastomeres is determined very early by virtue of the constituents they contained.

It became apparent, however, that this conclusion could not apply to all eggs, because mild centrifugation of sea urchin eggs yielded normal larvae even though the pigment and other cytoplasmic material had been redistributed. The only structure not shifted by the centrifugal field was the rigid cytoplasm lying closest to the surface. In the eggs of echinoderms and chordates, this material is assumed to play a role in differentiation. In sea urchins, it appears to differ along the animal–vegetal axis. The first two cleavage planes pass through this axis, and blastomeres isolated at this stage can develop into whole embryos. However, if the animal half is separated from the vegetal half, the isolates do not yield whole embryos.

While cell constituents and the superficial cytoplasm are involved in differentiation, interactions among cells also play important roles. Hans Spemann and his collaborators, working in the 1920s with small pieces of blastoderm transplanted to new locations in the early salamander gastrula, found that all but one region would differentiate in accordance with its new surroundings. The unique region was the cells of the dorsal lip of the blastopore, which in normal development forms the roof of the primitive gut beneath the neural region. When transplanted, these cells usually differentiated as notochord. However, the remarkable thing was that the host tissue adjacent to transplanted dorsal lip changed its presumptive course of differentiation to form the parts of a second embryo. Spemann called the dorsal lip the "organizer," since all parts of the embryo appeared to differentiate in accordance with it. If ectoderm or mesoderm was transplanted to the neural region, the transplant differentiated as neural tissue. Similarly, cells normally destined to become neural tissue differentiated as epidermis or mesoderm when placed in association with these tissues. What special kind of cell an undifferentiated cell was to become, it seemed, depended on the cellular company it kept rather than on intrinsic factors within the cell itself. The course of differentiation was not firmly fixed for these cells at the early gastrula stage.

INDUCTION: The phenomenon whereby a group of cells conditions the course of differentiation of another group is termed an **induction**. Chemical exchange between cells is involved. When cells normally destined to become ectoderm are isolated from an early gastrula and cultured alone, they will not differentiate; but when they are isolated and placed in a medium that has contained dorsal lip cells, the ectoderm-destined cells differentiate as neural tissue. However, ectoderm isolated at much later stages develops into structures appropriate to the region from which it has been taken. For chordates, it appears that the destiny of the cell areas of the fate map stems from cells being brought into contact with each other at critical stages during their development. Although we can observe inductive substances at work, their biochemistry remains obscure.

FORMATION OF THE ORGAN SYSTEMS

Nervous system

The formation of the nervous system begins at an early stage. It is one of the primary integrating systems of the body, and its development must necessarily keep pace with the differentiation of other systems. Centers of high

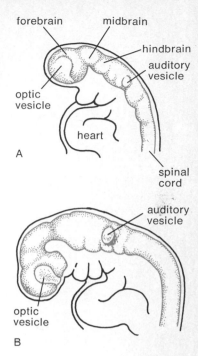

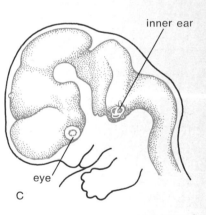

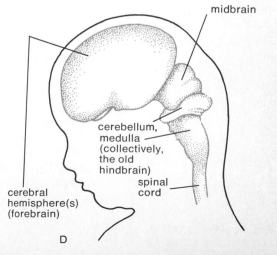

Figure 21–9 Four stages in the development of the human brain. At A, the embryo is about 3.5 weeks old; at B, about 4 weeks; at C, about 7 weeks; and at D, about 11 weeks. Eventually, the midbrain is entirely covered over by growth of the cerebral hemispheres.

mitotic activity and cell death, cell migration, changes in the shape of cells, and foldings of the tissue of the neural tube and adjacent ectoderm gradually delineate the definitive parts of this system and its associated sensory organs (Fig. 21–9).

The extent to which the brain regions develop shows considerable variation among the classes of vertebrates. Generally the anterior part of the brain remains small in fish and amphibians, serving mainly as a center for the sense of smell, which these animals depend on strongly. With increased importance of complex behavioral patterns, the anterior part of the neural tube develops into **cerebral hemispheres** in reptiles, birds, and mammals. In mammals, these constitute the largest part of the brain (Fig. 21–9). Arising from the posterior half of the brain rudiment, the **cerebellum** is especially well developed in active vertebrates, notably the primates and flying and swimming organisms in which a keen sense of body orientation is important.

In most regions, the walls of the neural tube thicken through the proliferation and migration of cells. Some cells develop as neurons, sending out extensions that synapse with neurons at different levels along the tube or that extend outside the tube as motor fibers of the peripheral nervous system. Not all cells in the neural tube differentiate as neurons, however. Some form a lining of the central canal and brain cavities while others differentiate into cells that support nerve tissue and facilitate passage of metabolites between blood vessels and the nerve cells. Sensory neurons differentiate outside the central nervous system, extending and synapsing with neurons within the cord or brain and also extending peripherally, along with motor fibers, as the sensory component of cranial and spinal nerves.

Circulatory system

The circulatory system is the link between respiration and metabolism, providing for exchanges of metabolites between the tissues and between tissues and the environment. For as long as the embryo is very small, these exchanges can take place by diffusion, but diffusion becomes too slow a process as the embryo becomes larger. The circulatory system, then, must develop relatively early so that it is functioning by the time the need for oxygen, nutrients, and elimination of nitrogenous wastes in the other systems exceeds the rate of diffusion.

Among vertebrates, the circulatory system shows a common pattern of development. Variations occur mainly in the size of vessels to and from the sources of food and oxygen. The cells of the avian embryo contain little, if any, food reserve. Hence the first major circulatory routes develop to the tissues surrounding the massive store of yolk. Because the mammalian egg also has little food reserve—and no access to free oxygen—the first major circulatory routes are established early between the embryo and the **placenta** through which an exchange of metabolites takes place.

The heart develops as a tubular, muscular organ that forms by the folding of a sheet of mesoderm anterior to the liver. Rhythmic contractions start long before the heart has achieved its definitive form. Elsewhere, rudiments of the major vessels have begun to differentiate, and development of the system proceeds concurrently in most parts of the body, so that major channels are established by the time the heart beat is initiated. The various parts of the circulatory system undergo continual change and keep pace with the development of other systems.

Respiratory system

The respiratory system in the mammal begins as a bud that pushes ventrally into mesoderm at the junction of the pharynx with the future esophagus. The endoderm bud branches at the tip into left and right halves and becomes tubular. Shaped like the letter **Y**, the tubes form the beginning of the trachea and primary bronchi. As the trachea becomes greatly elongated as the neck develops, the tips of the bronchi branch into smaller channels (Fig. 21–10) within the mesoderm, thus forming the smaller bronchial tubules of the respiratory tree and finally the alveoli (Fig. 16–10).

Tissue culture studies of the endoderm bud in isolation and in combination with mesoderm indicate that the mesoderm from the region of the bud promotes branching, whereas mesoderm taken from other regions is much less effective. So there appears to be local specificity between the two tissues during normal lung differentiation. During final stages of development, the endoderm cells become highly specialized as the thin-walled alveoli in intimate association with the capillaries.

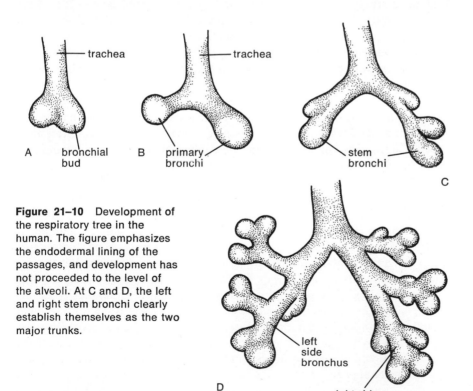

Figure 21–10 Development of the respiratory tree in the human. The figure emphasizes the endodermal lining of the passages, and development has not proceeded to the level of the alveoli. At C and D, the left and right stem bronchi clearly establish themselves as the two major trunks.

Excretory system

The excretory system differentiates from mesoderm situated on either side of the digestive tract. The early excretory system is characterized by the progressive formation of collecting tubules from anterior to posterior. The tubules on each side are united by a longitudinal duct that also differentiates in a posterior direction. In mammals this type of kidney is only temporary and is replaced by the definitive kidney, which originates as a bud from the posterior region of the duct (Fig. 21–11). The bud differentiates as a tube that grows forward and enters the remaining kidney-forming mesoderm. In itself, the tube becomes the ureter of the kidney. The tip of the ureter then begins to branch within the mesoderm and forms the collecting tubules. Meanwhile, cells condense around the tips of the collecting tubules and form the renal tubules, Bowman's capsules, and glomeruli.

POST-EMBRYONIC DEVELOPMENT

Growth and differentiation during the post-embryonic period continue along the patterns that have been established. In amphibians and many invertebrates, the form of the animal at this time is quite different from that of the adult and it is called a larva, the frog tadpole being a familiar example. Animals that develop in this way usually undergo a dramatic metamorphosis in becoming adults, the gradual change frequently entailing a substantial remodeling of the established systems. In the case of the tadpole, the tail and much of the length of the intestine are resorbed, and lungs and limbs develop.

In higher vertebrates, the embryo more nearly resembles the adult. During the extensive growth period that follows the embryonic stages, the young mammal is called a **fetus**. No dramatic change in appearance occurs at hatching or birth in such forms, but changes enabling the new organism to take up a free-living existence may occur. One of the most important of such changes involves the change from a dependency on fetal membranes for respiration to the use of lungs. With the first breath, the compacted lung tissues expand and assume full function. Meanwhile, the vessels leading to the fetal membranes close down by muscular contraction and the accessory organs are discarded.

Less obvious developmental changes continually occur throughout the life of the organism. During early life, growth is the most striking. The newborn infant will increase its body weight approximately 20 times and its height about 3.5 times as it attains adulthood. And growth is not the only change that occurs. We can imagine an infant with the weight and height of an adult, but no one would confuse it with an adult (Fig. 21–12). The difference is clearly not one involving size alone. The proportions of the body change dramatically as differential growth brings about the adult shape. Much of this is due to hormonal stimulation of various organs and tissue, thus giving rise to secondary sex characteristics. With age the systems continue to change, showing the effects of use and altered hormonal levels, and the typical signs of old age (senescence) finally appear.

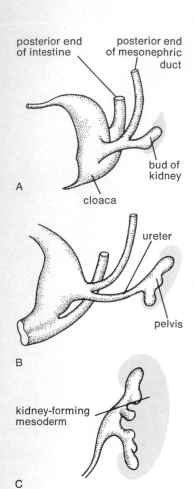
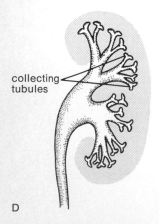

posterior end of intestine — posterior end of mesonephric duct

bud of kidney

A

cloaca

ureter

pelvis

B

kidney-forming mesoderm

C

collecting tubules

D

Figure 21–11 Differentiation of the definitive kidney in the mammal.

Regulation of cell replacement

Many of the gross changes in appearance in a newborn organism are associated with increase in the number of cells. Developmental processes also continue to replace worn-out or lost cells, thus maintaining the proper function of the systems. Replacement of the superficial cells of the skin and growth of the hair are typical examples; blood cells are also continually being replaced. Blood cells arise from undifferentiated stem cells in the blood-forming connective tissues. The stem cells multiply and their division products begin to follow specific paths of differentiation. Some paths lead to the synthesis of hemoglobin and loss of the nucleus, yielding the red cells. Other paths lead to the formation of lysosomes, to phagocytic activity and ameboid movement, or to the ability to form antibodies and result in several types of white blood cells. While the life span of a red cell is about four months before it is destroyed in the liver or spleen, the life of a white blood cell is generally much shorter (approximately 12 to 13 days), so the replacement of both is necessarily a continuing process.

Cell growth

Multicellular organisms have two ways of replacing losses in tissue mass. In one, the cells of the deficient tissue enlarge, a process called **cellular hypertrophy**. The other involves an increase in the number of cells, usually by means of mitosis, and is called **hyperplasia**. Examples of both processes are familiar to you. Hyperplasia occurs during cancer, a case where cell growth has obviously gone out of control. The bulging biceps of a weight lifter, on the other hand, have increased in mass by hypertrophy.

In adult animals, skeletal muscle cells cannot divide and so tissue growth results from an increase in size of individual muscle fibers. When, for one reason or another, a person's heart cannot pump enough blood to satisfy the needs of the tissues, the heart may undergo **compensatory hypertrophy** and enlarge. Enlarged hearts are, in fact, one of the most prominent signs of abnormal cardiac function. So both hyperplasia and hypertrophy take place during certain pathological states, these states affecting growth homeostasis.

Growth processes must, of course, occur in healthy individuals as well. In your skin and intestines, cells are continually dying and being sloughed off. In order for you to continue to have skin and an intestine, you replace the lost cells by means of hyperplasia. Cells in the deeper portions of the intestinal epithelium divide, some migrating to the surface and becoming lost. In other words, in tissue where replacement must occur, there is usually a definite zone —the **germinative zone**—where division takes place.

The processes of cell replacement are not rigidly fixed. If we cut out part of a rat's liver, the organ will, as if directed, restore its normal shape. The residual tissue regenerates almost exactly the same mass that was present before the operation. Such studies have been of great use in clarifying the steps involved in the homeostasis of organ morphology because the kind of reaction occurring in the liver is not confined to that organ alone. Should a kidney be removed, the opposite kidney undergoes compensatory growth involving

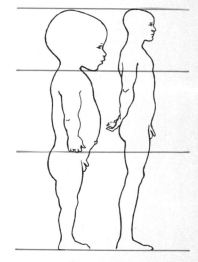

Figure 21–12 Drawn to the same height as an adult, a human infant would never be mistaken for an adult because of the dramatic difference in proportions of body parts, not only in shape but in relative size of brain, skeleton, muscles, and other internal organs and structures.

both hypertrophy and hyperplasia. Similarly, if one ovary is removed from a female mammal, the other ovary compensates for the loss in mass. Obviously, there are sophisticated controls for these responses.

If the lens from an eye of certain amphibia is removed, the eye grows a new lens. The other, healthy eye does not grow an extra lens. This tells us that local factors must be involved in the restitution process. Whether it occurs in conjunction with normal replacement and wound healing depends on a complex series of chemical, physical, and cytological events.

When cells misbehave—cancer

When the homeostatic mechanism(s) governing the interrelationships between cells is undermined, the consequences for the organism are dire ones indeed. Cancer cells respect no boundaries nor do they respect the existence of their neighbors. They move about in places where they should not be at all, exhibiting the property of **invasiveness** with no check on their reproductive tendencies. When we grow normal cells in a tissue culture vessel, they grow in one layer until they fill the dish, then stop. While normal cells recognize boundaries, cancer cells do not. Cancer cells reach the boundaries recognized by their normal counterparts and *continue* to grow. They do not form monolayers but grow right over one another in multicellular conglomerations. When cells become cancerous within an animal, they may eventually spread to various organs by the process known as **metastasis**.

When a group of abnormally dividing cells forms a large enough mass, it is commonly referred to as a tumor. If tumor cells stay where they are, and if the tumor does not involve an extremely sensitive and vital part of the body, it may be removed surgically without undue concern. Such tumors are said to be benign. If, on the other hand, the tumor cells are invasive and disperse and enter various organs, the tumor is said to be malignant; in most such cases tumors are fatal.

Invasiveness implies something unusual about the cell surface. We now have good evidence that the proteins at the surface of cancer cells are different from the proteins in normal cells. Cancer cell surfaces apparently lack a material that accounts for cellular adhesiveness. Where other cells join one another for the communal good, cancer cells do not.

All modern theories of cancer relate somehow to the genetic material and its operation. Many of the leading investigators in this area suggest that viruses are the cause of the several hundred types of cancer known. So far, two DNA-containing viruses and one RNA-containing virus have been strongly implicated in the disease. The viral chromosome apparatus may somehow insert itself into the chromosomal apparatus of the host cell and then harness the cell's metabolic machinery for the virus' own purposes. It has seemed possible to some that malignancy-related genes imported into the cell can somehow be passed on to the progeny. Those who do not believe in a viral cause of cancer suggest the possibility of mutations arising in the victim's own chromosomal apparatus. In any event, it seems there is virtually unanimous agreement about the involvement of the genetic machinery in malignancy. This is only natural if we believe the genes to be the ultimate controllers of the mitotic process. In any event, the results of investigations on wound healing and on tissue regeneration all point to this sort of control.

It is, therefore, of considerable interest to note one of the principal findings virologists have made on cells that have been transformed from normal ones to malignant ones by viruses. When certain tissue culture cells have been infected with viruses, the cell surface changes in composition. New molecules appear and cause the surface to behave exactly the way a cancer cell is known to behave. Another thing we know about cancer cells is their preference for glycolytic metabolism as opposed to aerobic metabolism, the switch to glycolytic metabolism possibly being tied to changes in glucose permeability of the cell surface.

We have, then, an interesting interrelationship between cell surface, chromosomal apparatus, and cell division. This should not be terribly surprising inasmuch as the cell surface is the sensor of the external environment—which includes other cells—for each individual cell. Before we can hope to understand what occurs at a molecular level to regulate the mitotic process during tissue renewal and wound repair, much more demanding research will have to be done. You should realize that we understand only one cell, *E. coli*, in really great detail. The cancer-prone eukaryotic cell is quite a different matter.

Regeneration

Some groups of animals are capable of regenerating a variety of lost parts, an adaptation that serves the animal well in a hostile environment abounding with predators. Members of the lower invertebrate phyla are generally good regenerators, including protozoans, sponges, coelenterates, flatworms, and annelids. A number of arthropods and, among vertebrates, salamanders have the capacity to replace their appendages.

Since regeneration has some interesting similarities to embryonic development, it gives biologists another approach to study development. The regeneration of complex parts does not simply involve the mitosis of one cell type to form another like it, but rather the accumulation of a mass of cells (the **blastema**) at the wound surface followed by their differentiation and organization into a miniature replacement that then grows to normal size. The main difference between regeneration and embryonic development is that the regenerate forms in proximity to adult, differentiated tissues and is subject to the hormonal environment of the adult tissues.

One of the most frequently studied regenerating systems is the salamander forelimb. It may be amputated at any level and a perfect replicate is formed. Immediately after amputation, the epidermis of the limb stump begins to migrate over the wound and closes it within 24 hours. The connective tissues, muscle, and skeleton near the wound lose their structure and liberate free (blastemal) cells with scanty cytoplasm. They are believed to be undifferentiated and somewhat resemble certain embryonic tissue.

The blastemal cells collect beneath the epithelium and begin to divide and cause the end of the limb to bulge outward. As more and more cells are formed, the mass gradually assumes the shape of the missing limb (Fig. 21–13). Differentiation proceeds from the level of the tissues remaining in

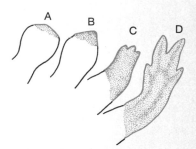

Figure 21–13 Four stages in the regeneration of a salamander's forelimb amputated just above the elbow: A, earliest appearance of regenerating tissue; B, conical outgrowth of new tissue; C, first appearance of fingerbuds; D, complete new section of forelimb.

the stump to the tip of the regenerate, so a continuity of the old with the new is achieved.

Regeneration requires certain conditions not present in the embryo. For example, nerve fibers are not necessary for the development of the embryonic limb bud, but a minimal number are necessary for amphibian limb regeneration. Nerve fibers from the stump extend and branch into the developing blastema. Possibly there are too few fibers present in the limbs of reptiles, birds, and mammals for these animals to be capable of limb regeneration. The adult frog limb will not normally regenerate but can be made to do so if the number of nerve fibers in the stump is experimentally increased.

Each of the stump tissues appears to release blastemal cells sufficient for its own differentiation in the regenerate. But do the blastemal cells "remember" where they came from and re-differentiate into the same kind of tissue? So far, we have not been able to label cells in the stump tissues and trace them through the blastema stage to the re-differentiated tissues. However, if bone and cartilage are removed from the stump at the time of amputation (thus preventing them from contributing cells to the blastema), skeleton still differentiates in the regenerate. Apparently some blastemal cells, at least, are capable of becoming a tissue different from the one they originated from. It is possible that blastemal cells have a very broad spectrum of possible pathways of differentiation.

An individual organism is never precisely the same from one moment to the next, and the way it responds to external stimuli from its environment and internal stimuli from its own body will vary greatly with time. Comparing an immature individual with an adult, we can see how great this variation can be. On one hand, the body of the young individual is not totally developed. Often it cannot respond physically to a stimulus because its muscles and other tissues are incapable of responding. On the other hand the brain, nerves, hormones, and sensory organs of the young individual are immature and imperfect when compared to the adult. They may not be physiologically ready for many stimuli. As the nervous system matures, as more and more information is thrown at and processed by the parts of the nervous system, and as the organism learns to respond correctly to environmental clues, its behavior matures and its chances for survival increase. It is with this process in mind that we turn to the discussion of behavior as it is inherited and as it changes with time.

1 What are the biological advantages of multicellularity?
2 From your reading of this chapter and foregoing chapters, identify some of the major problems species must overcome in order to accomplish successful reproduction. How many of these relate to survival of the embryo?
3 What accounts for the amount of yolk stored in an egg? How does yolk influence early development?
4 Identify the mechanisms that control development from the fertilized egg through the establishment of the rudiments of organ systems.
5 What kinds of developmental changes normally occur throughout the post-embryonic period of an organism?

SELECTED READINGS

Patten, Bradley M. *Foundation of Embryology*. 2nd ed. New York: McGraw-Hill Book Co., 1964. One of the classic introductory texts in descriptive embryology, emphasizing the chick and the mammal. Detailed accounts of the development of the organ systems are presented in separate chapters. Profusely illustrated with semi-diagrammatic drawings. Clearly and interestingly written.

Saunders, John W., Jr. *Patterns and Principles of Animal Development*. New York: The Macmillan Company, 1970. An excellent overview of the field of development for the beginning student, with chapters on the origin of the fertilized egg, the formation of the germ layers, early development of selected systems, concepts of development, larvae and metamorphosis, regeneration, and genetic control of development. A well balanced approach to descriptive embryology and the experimental approach to developmental problems. Concisely written with attractive illustrations and format.

Waddington, C. H. *Principles of Development and Differentiation*. (Current Concepts in Biology Series.) New York: The Macmillan Company, 1966. A clear and interesting introduction to the basic mechanisms that control developmental processes, with chapters on problems of development, the formation of tissues, the origin of the basic plan of the embryo, control of gene activity, and the movement of cells and tissues in the structuring of the embryo. The experimental approach is emphasized with a careful selection of illustrative examples.

Figure 22–1 Play is common among mammals, as with these polar bear cubs, but its behavioral role is far from well understood. It is partly instinctive and partly acquired behavior but seems to lack motivating mechanisms and is non-consummatory. Through play the animal seems to develop patterns which affect its social, sexual, maternal, and emotional behavior as an adult. (OMIKRON)

22

THE DEVELOPMENT OF BEHAVIOR

Behavioral changes that occur as animals mature are among the most fascinating and perplexing in the biology of behavior (Fig. 22–1). The patterns observed during development show striking similarities and puzzling differences in animals of the same species as well as in those of different species. The reasons for the similarities and differences have been hotly debated, some advocating genetic influence as most important, others maintaining that environmental forces are more significant.

Song development in white-crowned sparrows

Before involving ourselves in the controversy, let's begin by tracing the development of a complex behavior studied by Peter Marler, who has investigated song development in the white-crowned sparrow (*Zonotrichia leucophrys.*) Both parents participate in caring for the newly hatched nestlings. The young males begin to sing when they are from 200 to 250 days old, their initial vocalizations consisting of soft, tentative utterances called **sub-song**. These vocalizations become louder and more regular until the adult song is crystallized. The song is quite pronounced and so individualized that it is possible to identify a given male on the basis of his song alone. An interesting aspect of white-crowned sparrow song is that there are distinct regional differences in the pattern of the song; birds from one area of the San Francisco Bay region, for example, sing a distinctly different dialect than do birds from a region some distance away, and the differences in dialect persist over a number of years.

Although all of the songs have an essential similarity and conform to a basic species song pattern, there are small but significant differences between individuals of a given dialect area as well as more pronounced differences between the dialect groupings. How does a given song pattern develop? Is it innate, and the variation the result of inherited differences, or is the variation learned during the individual's social interaction?

GENETIC AND ENVIRONMENTAL INFLUENCES

There has been a lot of nonsense perpetuated in the debate of whether given behaviors are the result of *nature* (aspects of functioning which are the product of inheritance) or of *nurture* (aspects of functioning which are the product of environmental influences). The nature school emphasizes the invariable genetic patterning of behavior and typifies much of zoologists' thinking. Konrad Lorenz has been one of its most articulate spokesmen. The nurture advocates acknowledge that structure is inherited but maintain that most of the significant differences in behavior are the result of experience. This view has typified the thinking of most behavioristically-oriented psychologists since the early 1900s. The most extreme spokesman for this position was John B. Watson, who developed the behavioristic position some 50 years ago.

The controversy has continued over the years and has recently been rekindled by books such as *On Aggression*, by Lorenz, and *The Naked Ape*, by Desmond Morris. These writers maintain that much of what they refer to as the "human dilemma" is the result of inherited behavioral tendencies that we share with other animal species, and that much of man's irrational behavior is the result of evolutionary tendencies over which we have little control or, at best, which can be overcome only by the imposition of societal constraints to counteract such bestial tendencies. The argument has raged over the appropriateness of extrapolating data involving non-human species and using it in a human context, over the aptness of certain analogies, and over the relative extent to which man's language and other distinctly human abilities free him from evolutionary continuities.

Without delving any further into this issue of the biological character of human social behavior, we can look closely at the nature of the basic arguments as they apply to the development of behavior in the maturing organism. In this way we will be able to understand how the different concepts are employed in a simple context and to appreciate the essential differences in the more complex circles of the current debates.

The ethological position

Lorenz's approach and view are based on a detailed examination of ethograms of animals in their natural surroundings. You will recall from an earlier chapter that ethograms are very detailed catalogues of an organism's behavior sequences given a certain physiological condition and faced with various stimulus situations. From the analysis of ethograms, Lorenz has developed the concept of the **fixed action pattern**—a pattern of movements emitted in a regular, mechanical fashion in certain circumstances and genetically programmed into the organism. These fixed action patterns are considered to be released by certain stimuli called **releasing stimuli**, in much the way in which a catalyst activates an enzymatic reaction. The combination of the effective stimuli and the appropriate internal state of the organism is referred to as the **innate releasing mechanism**.

An example is the courtship behavior of the stickleback, which is shown in Fig. 10–7, the entire sequence of individual behaviors depending on the appropriate releasing stimuli being present at each step in the sequence. The stimuli are visual for most of the steps, tactile at the step at which the eggs are released, with perhaps chemical and tactile stimuli playing a role in the fertilization stage. If any link in this chain is broken, the sequence does not continue. So we have a sequence of behaviors genetically programmed but at every step dependent on the proper external stimulation at the proper time in order for the pattern to run to completion. This elaborate interaction of internally programmed and externally controlled behavior sequences is quite common, and the nature of the controlling influences has been studied in careful detail by classical ethologists. Such exquisitely timed patterns ensure that the female and male will be of the same species, since animals of other species would be highly unlikely to perform the series of actions in the same order and with the same timing.

While this notion of fixed action patterns has been useful in developing a full picture of behavior sequences, it has often prompted too rigid and stereotyped a conception of behavior. George Barlow has suggested that, in view of the degree of variability that exists in behavior bouts, we should regard such chains as **modal action patterns**. This view suggests that there is a space–time pattern of organization associated with the "mode," or most frequently occurring event, and it is this modal action pattern that is common to the species. The modal action pattern approach provides a much more adequate expression of the real organization of behavior patterns than does the fixed-action pattern approach, since most fixed action patterns that have been studied show more variability than we would expect on the basis of the concepts of classical ethology. A degree of variability in the responses to external stimuli of different individuals within a species, and even of the same individual at different times, provides the variation necessary for a species to cope with selection pressures brought on by significant environmental change.

The extreme environmentalist position

The extreme environmentalist approach is based on the assumption that the inherited tendencies of organisms are essentially constant for different individuals within a species and that it is experience that produces diversity. Further, this view often emphasizes that complex environmental adjustments depend on the association of stimuli and responses in the light of their immediate consequences. In this way animals learn to respond appropriately to the environment, an association process of prime importance in determining development. The advocates of this position say that minor inherited differences in structure, when combined with major effects as a result of differences in early training, are enough to account for all differences in later behavior.

A compromise position

The late T. C. Schneirla, a psychologist, acknowledged the importance of the innate tendencies stressed by Lorenz but placed more emphasis on environmental influence. Schneirla's position argues that, with more complex organisms, the role of heredity in behavioral development becomes increasingly indirect while the role of environmental influences becomes increasingly important. So, if we want to study the development of behavior patterns in higher organisms, we must focus on the environmental conditions prevailing during development.

It would seem that we are essentially dealing with a useless dichotomy. Although Konrad Lorenz's followers argue that it is not possible to change an instinctive pattern of behavior, they find it necessary to introduce the idea of learned behavior components that are inserted between the purely instinctive and unchangeable sequences of behavior. In this way, they maintain, instincts cannot be changed; at the same time they account for the observation that learning can alter instinctive patterns of action.

Hebb's resolution

D. O. Hebb, also a psychologist, has pointed out that the instinct–environment dichotomy is similar to asking whether or not the area of a rectangle is more the result of its height or of its width. The area would not exist were it not for both. It is obvious that no behavior can exist without having a basic genetic "substrate" and that this substrate is always expressed in an environmental medium. Hebb has offered an alternative scheme for the factors influencing development. He lists five classes:

1. **Genetic factors**: the physiological properties of the fertilized egg.
2. **Prenatal chemical factors**: nutritive or toxic influences in the uterine environment.
3. **Postnatal chemical factors**
4. **Constant sensory factors**: prenatal and postnatal experience that is inevitable for all members of the species.
5. **Variable sensory factors**: experience that varies from one member of the species to another.

Usually, the criterion by which a behavior is classed as an **instinct** is its character as a complex mode of response that is universal for the species and that appears either at birth or in orderly and regular stages of development for all members of the species. When behaviors meet these criteria, there is often the tendency to include them in Class 1, genetic influences. However, such universality could easily be the result of factors of Class 2 (prenatal chemical influences), Class 3 (postnatal influences), or Class 4 (sensory influences), as well. Similarly, a regular series of development could be the result not only of genetic influence but could be due to factors of Classes 1 through 4. Even those responses appearing at birth could be the result of influences of Class 2, as well as of genetic influences. The essential point is that the execution of the genetic program is subject to environmental influences from the moment the egg is fertilized, and attention should be paid to the relative contribution of the various classes of factors rather than to an attempt to pigeonhole a particular behavior exclusively in Class 1, as the instinct school would have it, or in Class 5, in accordance with the environment school.

Song development revisited

How would we find out if song development in the white-crowned sparrow is due primarily to an unfolding of a set of genetic factors totally independent of Class 5 sensory factors? One way would be to isolate the nestlings so that they do not hear any white-crowned sparrow song—called a **deprivation experiment** since the animal is deprived of normal experience. If the behavior then develops normally, we may conclude that the development is independent of variable sensory experience.

White-crowned sparrow nestlings subjected to deprivation experiments do not develop a typical adult song pattern, but sing a quite consistent song composed of a series of modulated whistles but lacking the characteristic buzzes and trills of the adult full song (Fig. 22–2). They do sing, however, and the song is of roughly the proper loudness and the proper length. It seems, therefore, that the birds inherit a tendency to sing a certain type of song but that in this species the tendency requires some sort of environmental input for recognizable adult song to develop.

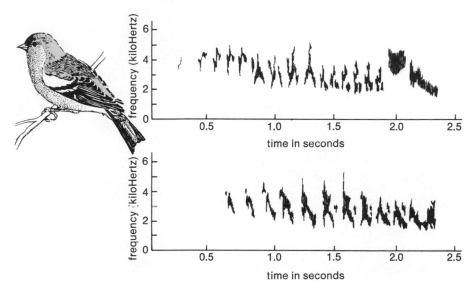

Figure 22–2 At top is a sound spectogram of the song of an adult male chaffinch, while at bottom is a spectrogram of the song of a chaffinch raised in isolation and never having heard the song of any bird.

The next step would be to isolate the nestlings at an early age and to play a song to them, a song in a dialect other than that of their parents. When this is done, the young birds reproduce completely the song played to them. On the basis of such experiments, we can conclude that although the tendency to sing and the basic song pattern are inherited. the specific pattern is learned.

We can carry the experiment still further by exposing the nestlings to the song of a different species, such as that of a song sparrow, to find out if the birds can imitate the song they hear. In this case, it turns out that they can't; the final song is neither that of their own species nor that of the imposed species but is that of a total isolate. There seems to be some built-in mechanism that restricts learning the range of inputs that can be copied. An important point that emerges from such studies is that the development of behavior involves a subtle interaction of genetically controlled biases and of variable sensory input that affects these biases. The birds will not slavishly copy any song that is played to them, but require a certain class of inputs. The tendency to copy certain inputs and not others seems to be universal for the species.

While dialects may not be uncommon among bird species, until recently the only mammal known to have dialects was man. However, a study of a series of breeding populations of the northern elephant seal has suggested dialects in the

Figure 22–3 Threat calls of the northern elephant seal seem to be commonly understood by all members of the species; nevertheless, from one breeding ground to another there are dialects of the call, indicating that environmental as well as instinctive influences are at work.

threat calls of these animals. The northern elephant seal (Fig. 22–3) breeds during a three-month period on a number of the offshore islands that line the coast of California. The males compete with each other for positions in a social hierarchy, which affords the higher ranking males the privilege of mating with many females. One of the behavior patterns used to maintain the social hierarchy is a threat call that consists of loud, low-frequency, guttural sounds. Once a threat has been made, the invading bull seal usually retreats and there is no need for physical interaction. An analysis (using the sound spectrogram technique) of the threat calls made by bulls from the breeding colonies on various islands revealed some consistent differences in the nature of the threat calls from year to year.

Although there are no experiments similar to those performed for the white-crowned sparrows, there is circumstantial evidence that the dialects in the threat call of northern elephant seals are a result of learning. Young male elephant seals are known to move from one breeding island to another, and since the differences in threat calls on each island are remarkably consistent from year to year, such individuals must adopt the dialect of the other males on the breeding island. Again, the question of what is more important, heredity or environment, becomes meaningless once we investigate the development of a series of behaviors.

Genetic factors in behavior

The direct effect of genes on behavior is best documented in animals that show repeated and stereotyped behavior patterns. Most insects fit this characterization rather well and the best examples of direct genetic control of behavior by a few genes are found in this class of animals. W. C. Rothenbuhler studied the genetics of a very specific behavior pattern in certain strains of bees. On occasion the developing larvae of bees die in the wax cells in which they are enclosed. Some strains of bees called "unhygienic" do nothing to the wax cells containing dead larvae. Other strains are termed "hygienic" because they uncap the cells containing dead larvae and remove the corpse. Rothenbuhler studied the genetics of this behavior pattern by crossing bees of the two strains. The progeny of such a cross are all unhygienic. The genetic factor(s) controlling unhygienic behavior is (or are), therefore, dominant to the gene(s) controlling hygienic behavior. Rothenbuhler tested this conclusion by crossing the progeny obtained from the cross of unhygienic and hygienic strains back to the hygienic strain. Among the progeny of this backcross, the experimenters obtained colonies of bees that exhibited not two but *four* different behavior patterns. Approximately one-half of the colonies showed either hygienic or unhygienic behavior characteristic of their parents. One-quarter of the colonies removed the wax cap from cells containing dead larvae but did not remove the corpses. The remaining one-quarter of the colonies could not uncap the wax cells containing corpses but would remove the dead larvae if the cells were artificially opened. These results are exactly as predicted by Mendelian genetics if we postulate that two pairs of genes control these behavior patterns in bees. One pair of genes governs the behavior of uncapping the wax cells. A second pair of genes controls the removal of corpses from uncapped cells. The physiology and anatomy underlying these behavioral patterns in bees are undoubtedly complex and no one would argue that two genes alone are responsible for determining the physiological and anatomical bases for these behaviors. These two pairs of genes most likely act as switches that channel development along a series of alternative steps.

Another example of the genetic control of a behavior pattern has been discovered in a tropical species of *Drosophila*. While experimenting with these flies under laboratory conditions, scientists noticed that an occasional larva would crawl away from the source of food provided. Ordinarily, this type of behavior would prove to be fatal, since the larva would quickly dehydrate once away from the moist food. However, some larvae were able to survive and even produce pupae in which the adult stage of the species develops. Crosses between strains of flies that crawled out of the food and were able to survive and strains that remained in the food and produced pupae showed that this behavior pattern was controlled by a single pair of genes. As in the example with the bees, however, we cannot conclude that a single pair of genes is completely responsible for the presence or absence of this behavior pattern. In fact, the proportion of the larval population that crawls out of the food and pupates can be altered experimentally by artificial selection of parents for the next generation. Most likely, a large number of genes have the potential to affect this behavior in a small way, but one pair of genes acts as a genetic "switch" that directs the action of many other genes.

We can also demonstrate the effect of genes on behavior by attempting to change some of the behavior patterns of a species in a systematic way. In the same way that breeders of dogs, cattle, and other domestic animals have been able to select for the qualities they wanted in an animal, we can select for specific behavior patterns. For example, two strains of rats were selected to show "emotional" or "unemotional" reactions as a response to a frightening stimulus. Selection in these experiments resulted in a strain of rats that was quite at ease even under stress. The other, emotional strain of rats displayed emotion in the presence of a frightening stimulus by remaining fixed in one spot and urinating and defecating.

Jerry Hirsch and his colleagues have successfully demonstrated that strains of fruit flies can be selected and show alterations in their responses to either light or gravity. By forcing flies to move through a maze in which they must make a series of "choices" to go either toward or away from light or either up or down, the experimenters were able to produce strains of flies that were photopositive/photonegative, or that were geopositive/geonegative. Unselected lines of flies usually are neutral in their responses to light and gravity in such situations. These examples are only a few of the many that show that behavior patterns can be changed by altering the genetic constitution of the population of animals showing the behavior.

THE DEVELOPMENT OF SPECIFIC HUNGERS

One general principle influencing behavioral development has been revealed by psychologists who have studied a phenomenon in rats known as **specific hunger**. Rats learn preferences for the taste of foods associated with the rats' recovery from nutritional deficiencies. If a rat is raised on a thiamine-deficient diet, it will prefer a thiamine-rich diet when offered it, while non-thiamine deficient rats will not. Does this mean that the deficient rats recognize their need and, therefore, eat the more adequate diet? Or could it be that the thiamine-enriched food simply tastes better to the deficient rats? It turns out that neither alternative is correct. The rat is reacting to neither nutritional need nor taste. Rather, it is exhibiting a general tendency: Deficient rats prefer new foods, **neophilia**, and show an aversion to familiar ones regardless of what the foods contain! If two new foods are introduced to a thiamine-deficient rat and one is deficient in thiamine while the other is not, there is no preference for either one—both are consumed in equal amounts. Thus, the adequacy of the diet does not play a role; the preference is based on the novelty, and when two novel foods are offered neither is preferred over the other.

Thus, infantile deprivation does not result in a specific preference but causes the animal to adopt a general strategy: In the face of an inadequate nutritional state try some new food—any new food. The adaptive significance of this strategy can be understood quite easily. In the wild, although the rat has a large number of food choices available, we would expect it to sample only one or two during a period of deficiency. If a pronounced deficiency is maintained, then the animal is programmed to avoid the familiar foods and to sample any other available food in the environment. There is a high probability that this novel food will not be deficient in the same elements as is the familiar diet. The deficiency would then be removed, and the animal would continue to eat this now-familiar food in the absence of any deficiency.

The converse strategy is programmed into rats, as well. If a rat eats a poisoned food and becomes ill, it develops an avoidance to *any* new foods, **neophobia**. Since the familiar diet has been safe all of the animal's life, an aversion to the novel-tasting, poisoned bait is protection. Another instance of this is found in wild rat pups. When the mothers of nursing pups were given a choice of two foods—a safe one and a poisoned one—they came to avoid the poisoned one. The pups ate only the safe food as well (possibly because they were imitating their mothers). However, when the pups were weaned and separated from the mothers, they still ate only the safe food. The likely explanation of this phenomenon is that the pups approach areas where adults are located and eat the safe food that the adults are consuming. This safe food becomes familiar to the pups and the innate neophobia of the species results in an avoidance of the unfamiliar poisoned food.

It is possible, then, to achieve a simple general explanation of the development of food preferences without having recourse to any specific association of stimulus and response. The animal is programmed to adopt certain general behaviors and, in the animal's natural environment, such behaviors enhance the possibility of survival.

RESPONDING TO VARIED ENVIRONMENTS

Effects of environmental deprivation

Another important class of factors that alter the course of development are those produced by various kinds of environmental deprivation (Fig. 22–4). If an animal is isolated from normal social contact with others of his species, it exhibits profound effects that influence its general emotional state, its ability to solve problems, and the nature of its social reactions.

R. Melzack and J. P. Scott have studied the effects of social isolation on the emotional behavior of Scottish terrier pups. The isolated pups were reared in cages in which there was normal daylight but from which the pups could not see out. When these pups were released into a room which contained various unfamiliar objects, they showed an extreme degree of emotional excitement, while normally reared control pups responded in a coordinated, well-organized manner. In addition, such isolated pups do not respond appropriately to painful stimuli. When a potentially painful stimulus is held near the nose of the

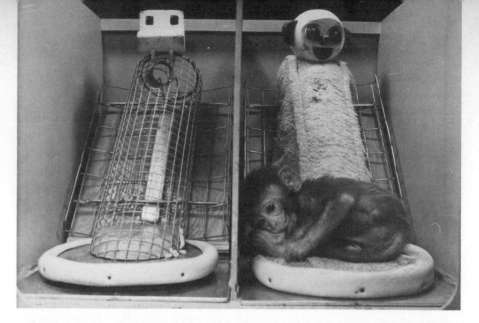

Figure 22-4 Infant monkeys deprived of maternal care and offered a wire model "mother" and a soft cloth model choose the cloth model, even when a nursing bottle is associated with the wire model. Clearly the social bond between mother and infant depends on more than feeding alone. Infant monkeys deprived of even surrogate mothers are much less active by comparison. They explore less, fear unfamiliar objects, and tend to sit in a corner gently rocking, as intensely abnormal human infants may.

isolated dog, for example, it does not withdraw from the stimulus at all and has difficulty learning to do so; normal dogs withdraw at once and quickly learn to avoid contact with the stimulus.

We conclude that experience with the environment is necessary to development of normal emotional reactions to environmental stimuli, even though these emotional reactions *seem* to be so universal as to be innate. It is important that animals have an appropriate range of early experience to develop emotionally in normal directions and to be able to react to specific stimulating conditions in an appropriate way.

Harry Harlow and his associates provide us with yet another clear instance of the importance of early experience on the development of behavior. They have studied the effects of different types of rearing conditions on the social and sexual behavior of the Rhesus monkey and find that the behavior of infants isolated in small wire cages for six months is quite abnormal. Compared with infants who can see and hear other infants, those reared in total isolation for six months show fewer play responses and fewer social threat responses. When infants reared in wire cages are compared with those reared with their mothers, the isolates are usually incapable of normal adult sexual behavior; and when the young isolate females do become pregnant, they fail to display adequate maternal behavior. In general, these isolated monkeys are unable to develop normal social relationships, are hyperexcitable in any situation outside the living cage, and give evidence of a large number of self-directed activities such as thumb-sucking and repetitive movements.

It has been shown that interaction with the mother is quite important to the young monkey if it is to develop normal reactions. Even more important is interaction with other monkeys of its own age. The defects in social, sexual, maternal, and emotional behavior are extremely pronounced if the infant is raised without any experience with peers. Though this conclusion is by no means proved, the intellectual deficits that appear after isolation may be the result of a general abnormality of emotional and motivational mechanisms essential for the performance of the tasks used to assess intelligence.

When we consider these examples it becomes apparent that the development of behavior is not simply a passive unfolding of inherited programs or merely the result of neural and muscular maturation. The type of experiences the animal encounters influence the direction of development profoundly. It is better to characterize the course of development as the expression of predispositions. If these predispositions are not fulfilled then the course of development may be changed in an unalterable fashion.

Imprinting

A good illustration of an animal having predispositions toward certain behaviors is the phenomenon called **imprinting**, which has been observed in ducks, geese, chickens, sheep, and cats (Fig. 22–5). The classic example of imprinting (as well as the term itself) was provided by Lorenz, who observed that newly hatched goslings will at first follow any of a very wide variety of stimuli, but that soon this following response is elicited only by the object initially followed.

Originally, imprinting was considered to have several characteristics. It occurs only within a certain critical period; it occurs with very little practice; once the imprinting takes place, it is irreversible; and if the critical period is passed, the response will not develop at all.

Eckhard Hess has studied imprinting in mallard ducklings. He hatched the ducklings in the dark and isolated them until the time at which they were exposed to the test stimuli. The test apparatus consisted of a circular track and a calling duck model (Fig. 22–6). The response observed was the percentage of positive responses, with a positive response defined as a movement toward the model as opposed to doing something else. The data he obtained are shown in Fig. 22–6. Notice that the percentage of positive responses is related to the ducklings' age in hours. Although there is some imprinting immediately after

Figure 22–5 The term "imprinting" usually is restricted to the "following response" in birds, but certain hoofed mammals—lambs and colts, for example—also exhibit the following response. In those species that do imprint, the response is an adaptation that enhances the survival of the offspring through the juvenile period.

Figure 22–6 Hess' apparatus used to study imprinting in ducklings included a model adult that moved around a circular track. The graph shows the percent of positive responses (successful imprinting) according to the age of the ducklings tested.

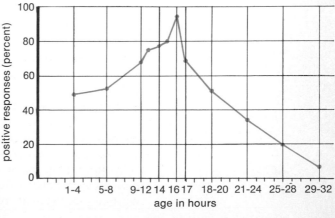

hatching, the degree of imprinting increases rapidly until the duckling is 16 hours old; thereafter the tendency to imprint declines rapidly until there is practically no imprinting at ages 29 to 32 hours.

Recent research has shown that the characteristics of imprinting are not quite so sharply defined as was originally believed. For example, the time of the critical period can be altered and the duration of the period increased by changes in the conditions of rearing and in the nature of the test stimuli. Also, the retention of the imprinted preference seems not to be an all-or-none, irreversible phenomenon as originally believed but depends on the amount of time a duckling or gosling is exposed to the imprinting stimulus. The imprinting process is not automatic and passive but is a much more dynamic behavior involving the animal's initial perceptual preferences (which might be inherited or determined by experience). The responsiveness to the imprinting stimulus is a function of the animal's internal state, the learning process is gradual, and, again, the stability of the imprinting depends on the length of exposure, since in those cases in which the imprinted preferences were maintained throughout the life of the animal, the initial exposure was never less than a week.

Again, we are led to the view that to understand the developmental processes involved in imprinting we must consider the dynamic interactions of the animal's inborn and maturing responses with the constant and variable stimulation provided by the environment.

Regardless of the nature of the processes underlying imprinting, the phenomenon exists and its adaptive significance is apparent. Those birds that leave the nest shortly after hatching are the ones that most readily imprint, an action that assures them of parental care and instruction at a time when the young tend to be most vulnerable. There seem to be some limits to the characteristics of the objects to which a bird will imprint. Objects below a certain size, for example, are treated as food-objects rather than as social-objects. Usually, the first stimulus object with the proper stimulus values to which the young bird is exposed is the parent bird, since the latter tends to remain in the vicinity of the young following hatching. Since the initial parent stimulus will become familiar to the young, this enhances the degree of imprinting even further. However, should the parent bird disappear after a short time, all is not lost; the bird can still accept another bird as mother and so increase its chances of survival.

G. K. Noble has done a simple experiment that demonstrates an imprinting-like behavior in parents rather than in young. Cichlid fish tend to eat the young of other species but not their own. Do they distinguish between their own and alien young on the basis of completely inborn information? Noble resolved this issue by replacing the eggs of a pair of cichlids that were breeding for the first time with the eggs of another species. When the eggs hatched the alien young were accepted and cared for by the pair. Whenever the parents encountered any cichlid young, however, they ate the young. Later, when the pair bred again—and were allowed, this time, to keep their own eggs—they ate their young! They had learned to consider an alien species their own and react to their own as alien. This would seem to be an irreversible and maladaptive imprinting that is unlikely to occur naturally.

Perceptual predispositions

One thread that has been running through our examples of various behaviors is that animals seem to be predisposed to respond to certain stimuli but will not respond to other stimuli—although quite strong—in the same way. Instead the animal tends to behave much as if it had been isolated, as in the example of song development in white-crowned sparrows. You will recall that if an acoustically isolated young bird is presented with the song of an alien species, it sings much the same song when adult as does a bird that has been totally isolated from all songs.

Another clear example of this predisposition is furnished by an experiment involving the tendency of one-day-old chicks to approach either a member of their own strain or a member of an alien strain. Two strains of chick were used; one was yellow and the other black. If no contact had been permitted with other chicks prior to testing, there was no consistent preference for chicks of either color. Social contact with chicks of the same color led to a preference for that color, however, while social contact with chicks of a different color did not lead to a preference for either color. This suggests that the chick is designed so that a particular experience is required to establish a perceptual preference and that other experiences (such as contact with an alien chick of a different color) is not sufficient to establish a perceptual preference. Thus, a complex mechanism is inherited which involves a predisposition to develop in certain ways in response to rather specific environmental conditions, and if these conditions do not occur then the development either proceeds in quite different directions or the entire response system does not develop at all.

Another aspect of development is that an organism has many potentials for behavior. All it needs is the proper environmental stimulus to elicit a particular potential behavior. A striking example of this was found by the famous neurophysiologists D. H. Hubel and T. N. Wiesel. They found that normal visual experience is essential for the establishment of the basic functioning of the individual neurons in the visual cortex. Newborn kittens were treated so that one eye was deprived of normal vision just before the age at which the eyes would open normally. The kittens could see a general light glow through the eye but were not able to distinguish patterns. When this is done, the light-sensitive receptor cells of the eye remain normal in every respect, but this is not so with certain connections that link the receptor cells with detector cells in the visual cortex. While in normal kittens these connections are present at birth as well as at maturity, in the deprived kittens the visual connections, although present at birth, became defective through lack of use. We have a system that operates normally if it is given appropriate stimulation at an appropriate time. If the stimulation is not available at the proper developmental stage, then the functional potential of the system is not realized.

Another instance of the loss of a functional ability through disuse can be seen in normal language development. All normal children learn to talk if exposed to some language community; they don't have to be taught to talk but only have to hear a language being spoken—any language—and they will develop that language with its characteristic intonation and grammar. If a child is born deaf it learns to talk only after a long period of training, and the speech is quite abnormal, especially in intonation. If the child does have a small amount of residual hearing and is fitted with a hearing aid at an early age, the language develops in completely normal fashion. However, if the hearing aid is not fitted until after the normal infantile babbling ceases (the initial babbling being the same for both deaf and normal infants), then the speech which develops is abnormal in many respects. It appears that we have, again, a functional system which operates normally only when given appropriate stimulation at an appropriate developmental stage.

Environmental enrichment

Most of our discussion has focused on the effects produced by the deprivation of normal experience. What is the effect of enriched experiences on behavioral development? Manipulation of the environment in which infant animals are raised affects their later learning and problem-solving ability. Home-reared "head start" rats, for instance, are better adult learners than cage-reared rats.

Researchers at the University of California have demonstrated the importance of experience on even the basic chemistry and anatomy of the brain. Rats raised in enriched environments enjoy many neurophysiological advantages over their less fortunate, isolated-environment littermates. It appears that enriched-environment animals develop a better problem-solving brain than that produced by an impoverished environment. The procedure used in such studies involves enriching the environment by raising animals in a large communal cage and allowing 30 minutes exposure per day to an environment that contains a variety of rat "toys"—ladders to climb, tunnels to explore, levers to press, planks to walk, and so forth (Fig. 22–7). The rats are also trained to run mazes and to perform discrimination tasks. The impoverished animals are

Figure 22–7 Rats reared in an enriched environment, as shown here, develop mental abilities that are measureably and significantly superior to those developed by rats reared in an impoverished environment.

isolated in bare cages in sound-dampened rooms. The conditions are maintained for 80 days from the weaning age, and at the end of this time the rats are analyzed. The enriched animals have an expanded cortex that is deeper and heavier than that of the impoverished animals and the enzyme balance in the cortex of the enriched animals is more conducive to efficient problem-solving. Further, indicatins are that the enriched environment can minimize hereditary disadvantages in problem-solving ability.

There is a large body of evidence indicating that such things as sensory-motor integration, visual perception, and motor development are all influenced by early experiences of developing organisms. Similarly, pronounced effects on later behavior appear if animals are reared in crowded conditions while they are developing, or if they are handled while they are infants. Early experiences of a developing organism can profoundly influence the direction of later development and can strongly influence adult behavior. With an understanding of the important roles played by both genetic and environmental influences, we are now in a position to discuss learning and intelligence and their importance to the survival of the individual and the species.

QUESTIONS FOR REVIEW

1 Compare the concept of a fixed action pattern with that of a modal action pattern.

2 Why is the nature–nurture controversy an unproductive argument?

3 Can you think of any reason why it might be advantageous for animals with complicated behavior patterns and short life spans to have a large part of their behavior genetically programmed?

4 Discuss the effects of sensory deprivation and environmental enrichment on the normal development of an animal. What applications of these effects do you see to a human infant?

5 Is it possible that imprinting behavior and perceptual predispositions exist in men? What might some examples be?

SELECTED READINGS

Moltz, H. *The Ontogeny of Vertebrate Behavior*. New York: Academic Press, 1971. A volume of eleven chapters contributed by thirteen experts. The material covered ranges from a discussion of general principles in behavioral development, through the development of specific behavioral traits, to a discussion of the ontogeny of language.

Munn, Norman L. *The Evolution and Growth of Human Behavior*. Boston, Mass.: Houghton Mifflin Company, 1965. Using animal studies as background information, the author describes clearly and in detail the evolution of human psychological processes and the development of human behavior from birth to death. An impressive survey text by a leading psychologist.

Tinbergen, N. *The Study of Instinct*. London: Oxford University Press, 1951. An extremely readable classic work by one of the most famous European ethologists. While some of the theoretical positions may be dated, the book can be very profitably read since it contains lucid descriptions of many of the important aspects of animal behavior on which our current conceptions are based.

Figure 23–1 Investigative behavior (the "curiosity that killed the cat") is an important part of an animal's learning experience. (The Metropolitan Museum of Art. Gift in memory of Charles Stewart Smith, 1914. Artist Toko.)

23

LEARNING AS A BEHAVIORAL ADAPTATION

If you have ever had a young mammal as a pet, you are doubtless aware that animals do indeed display what can be called curiosity (Fig. 23–1), or "investigative behavior." Laboratory experiments with rats show that a novel object in their environment attracts their attention more than a familiar object. Rats will even learn to negotiate a maze for the reward of exploring a second and more complex maze. These types of behavior patterns are beneficial because they contribute to the organism's knowledge of and, presumably, mastery over its environment. The evolution of such investigative behavior patterns is undoubtedly due to the selective advantage they must confer on their owner, which thus is likely to produce more offspring. In many animals learning contributes enormously to their knowledge of their surroundings, increasing the individual's ability to survive.

THE NATURE OF LEARNING

Learning can be characterized as a stable change in an organism's behavior as a result of experience. Under natural conditions we recognize learning as adaptive changes in an individual's behavior as a result of past experience. The fact that learning produces adaptive alterations in an animal's behavior seems a clear indication of the evolutionary development of learning. Rats that learn not to eat poisoned food live to produce progeny. If this new behavior pattern had to be produced by the action of natural selection on animals that were genetically conditioned to avoid poisoned food, many generations would have to pass before the behavior became a part of the animal's behavioral repertoire.

Habituation

The young of small animals that are threatened by a number of predators show an escape reaction to anything that is large and moves. In many cases this behavior pattern is unadaptive since the individuals may scurry away when leaves blow in the wind or when a large non-predatory bird flies overhead. The animals soon learn which stimuli represent danger and which do not. Eventually they stop responding to stimuli that initially elicited escape reactions but did not result in contact with a predator.

Such behavior is called **habituation** and is common in almost all responses of most animals. W. H. Thorpe defines habituation as the waning of a response

Figure 23–2 Chicks tend to crouch whenever an object passes overhead, a behavior that is instinctive. Through frequency of exposure, a chick soon learns to discriminate between the harmless and potentially harmful shapes. This kind of learning is called "habituation."

predator

non-predator

seed

as a result of repeated stimulation that is not reinforced. This tendency of an animal to respond to a stimulus at the outset and then gradually stop responding to it if the stimulus turns out to be of no consequence has been found in such diverse species as sea mollusks, earthworms, rats, cats, birds (Fig. 23–2), monkeys, and humans. The widespread occurrence of habituation throughout the animal kingdom is evidence of its usefulness as a basic response.

One of the functions of the adult white-crowned sparrow song is to warn off males entering the territory of another male in breeding condition. If a neighboring bird sings at one of the territorial boundaries, a bout of singing and countersinging between the two neighbors takes place. This type of ritualized combat is common among territorial animals and maintains peace without violence—if everyone obeys the rules.

If a tape-recorded song is played to a territorial male, he almost immediately responds by frantically searching for the singing bird, but since there is none he soon abandons the search, perches on or near the speaker, and engages in rapid and vigorous countersinging. If the playback continues, the interval between the real bird's song becomes longer and longer and the bird gradually moves away and resumes his routine activities.

Notice in the above example that an immediate response to the recorded song increased in strength (**sensitization**) then gradually decreased (habituation). If we discontinue playing the song for an hour or so and then begin again, the bird immediately resumes singing at a moderate level, but the singing decreases much more quickly than during the first series of playbacks. We can go one step further and play the recorded song of a different individual of the same species after the response has rehabituated. In such cases there is a sudden but brief increase in the response level. This increase of the habituated response to a novel stimulus is called **dishabituation**.

The rate of habituation depends on such things as the internal state of the animal and the nature of the stimuli used. We can also expect different rates of habituation depending on the location of the intruder in relation to both the nest and the territorial boundary. If the speaker is close to the nest and distant from the boundary, then habituation proceeds slowly; if the speaker is on the boundary, which is also contested by other birds, habituation is rapid.

The "economical" aspect of habituation becomes clear when we realize that the animal continues to respond only to meaningful stimuli and ceases to burden itself by responding to insignificant, repetitive stimuli. Consider an example in your own daily existence. Surely you have been overwhelmed by noise when you arrived at a party in a small apartment, but you quickly adjusted so that the noise was not apparent after a time. Such adjustments involve a type of active "stimulus filtering," a general response that tends to enable an animal to adjust to the situation in which it finds itself.

Environmental triggering

Up to this point we have stressed the importance of the internal state of the organism to its responsiveness to various environmental stimuli. An ingenious set of experiments by D. Lehrman and his associates makes it apparent that the opposite can be just as important: External environmental stimuli are often required to trigger the internal states that elicit behavioral sequences.

Lehrman has studied the reproductive behavior of ring doves, a relative of the domestic pigeon. If a pair of ring doves is placed in a cage with nesting material, courtship follows, then nest building for a week or so, and then egg-laying. A female dove isolated in a cage with nesting material will not display the normal nest-building and egg-laying behavior. A pair of doves isolated from one another for several weeks and then placed in a cage together with a nest bowl containing a nest and eggs will not sit on the eggs. Instead, they ignore the nest and eggs, court, build their own nest, and then lay and sit on their own eggs. This sequence takes the usual five to seven days that the sequence would have taken if the nest and eggs had not been present in the cage, indicating that the pair are not *always* ready to sit on eggs, even if eggs are present. They come into a state of readiness induced by a required sequence of activities.

Lehrman's next step was to find out whether or not the presence of the eggs for a specific period of time was required for the birds to begin sitting on them; in other words, did the eggs serve as a stimulus that changed the "mood" of the birds from a non-sitting to a sitting one? To find out, only nesting material was presented to the pair. The birds courted and built nests, but before they could lay eggs the nest was removed and replaced with one containing eggs. The birds almost immediately sat on the eggs. Therefore, the readiness to sit on eggs was not a result of the egg-laying process or of having the eggs present for any substantial period of time. After the nest-building cycle, the birds are ready and willing to sit on eggs.

Another pair of doves was placed in a cage together without nesting material. Seven days later the birds were given nests with eggs. They did not immediately sit on the eggs, but they did not wait the usual five to seven days. They sat after one day. So pairs of doves do not build nests as soon as they are placed in a cage containing nest material. They will build nests at once if they have spent time together in the cage before being given nest material.

They will not immediately sit on eggs introduced into the cage if the cage in which they have spent time together does not have any nest material; but they will if they do some nest building during the end of their period together.

These results indicate that external stimuli induce changes in the birds' behavior of a kind usually associated with changes in the reproductive cycle. These external stimuli play an important role in inducing a state of readiness to brood; in fact, the birds will not brood at all if the proper external stimuli, both from the partner and the presence of nest material, are not present. Therefore, the organization of the entire reproductive cycle depends, in this instance, on the proper sequence of environmental and behavioral events.

THE STUDY OF LEARNING

What are some of the procedures and techniques commonly used to study learning in the laboratory? Often the discussion of learning is organized in a way that implies that the different experimental approaches represent different types of learning. Let's dispel such a notion at once. The different "types of learning" presented in this section indicate different experimental manipulations used to measure an animal's behavior.

Classical conditioning

One of the most time-honored procedures used to study learning is that of **classical conditioning**, which is also called Pavlovian conditioning and was discussed in Chapter 1 (Fig. 1–8). We suggest that you reread that passage, keeping in mind that this type of conditioning has been demonstrated with a wide variety of conditioned stimuli (such as a bell), unconditioned stimuli (food), and unconditioned responses (salivation). One limitation to such conditioning is that any slight change in the experimental environment tends to disrupt the performance of the conditioned response. On the other hand, if the conditions are repeated exactly, such conditioned responses can be stable over a period of several years.

Many psychosomatic disorders—a physical disorder attributable to psychological causes—are thought to be due to the classical conditioning of automatic functions such as changes in blood pressure and dilation and constriction of blood vessels. The Russians have provided many elegant demonstrations of the conditioning of many responses usually classed as involuntary in both animals and humans. Recently, interest has centered on conditioning faster or slower heart rates. Such conditioning is somewhat difficult to obtain and, when obtained, occurs very slowly. The conditioning model has also been applied to explain certain types of asthma, skin allergies, and gastric ulcers.

Operant conditioning

An investigative approach that has been popular in the United States in recent years is **operant** or **instrumental conditioning**. This approach has become so closely associated with the work of B. F. Skinner that the apparatus used to test

Figure 23–3 A rat presses the food magazine lever in a Skinner box.

an animal's learning ability has come to be called a **Skinner box** (Fig. 23–3).

A typical Skinner box is a sound-dampened and constantly illuminated box with a lever that activates a food magazine. A hungry rat, for instance, is trained to approach the food cup at the sound of the food magazine delivering a food pellet, which the rat eats. The animal then remains in the apparatus until it learns to press the lever and so get food on demand. A number of reward procedures have been used with an equal number of varying results. For instance, if the animal is rewarded every time it presses the lever, we speak of a **continuous reinforcement schedule**. In addition, there are several **partial reinforcement schedules**. If only a certain constant proportion of the lever presses are rewarded, we speak of a **ratio reinforcement schedule**; if the proportion varies randomly around some central value, we speak of a **variable ratio reinforcement schedule**. A slot-machine is one of the best examples of a variable ratio reinforcement schedule. A variable payoff is made on a proportion of the pulls of the handle. If the machine has not paid off for some time, the player knows that the reward is "just around the corner." Animals, including slot-machine players, show very high rates of responding when variable ratio schedules are used. These high rates of responding are also very hard to discourage.

Another partial reinforcement schedule, called the **interval schedule**, is obtained by reinforcing the first response after a fixed interval of time; and there is a **variable interval schedule** in which the time interval is randomly varied around some central time interval value. This schedule produces an uneven rate of responding since the animal usually stops responding immediately after receiving a reinforcement, and, as time passes, it starts responding at a faster and faster rate since the rewarded response occurs only after the passage of a certain amount of time.

There have been a large number of elegant variations of the operant theme. It is possible to condition animals to respond only within a certain time interval after the preceding response, to respond only when a certain stimulus is present, to respond differentially depending on which of two stimuli are present, and so forth.

The operant technique is useful to determine such things as an animal's light-brightness threshold, for example. The animal can be trained to respond only in the presence of light. Then the brightness of the light is gradually decreased, and the point at which the animal consistently does not respond is considered its lower threshold for brightness. Since animals can be trained to perform at stable response levels, these procedures permit us to assess certain behaviors with great precision.

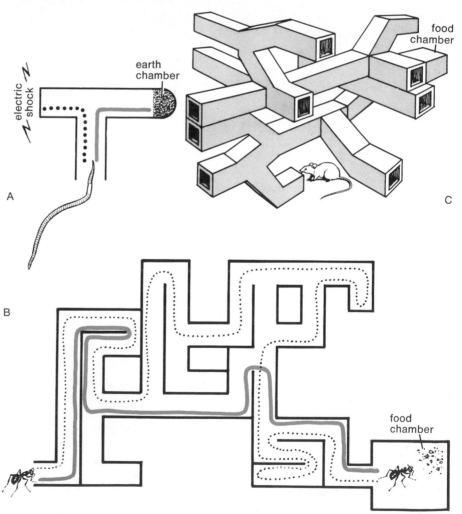

Figure 23–4 Mazes can be used to test the rate at which an animal learns. A simple T-maze (A) is used for earthworms. For making the "correct" turn on reaching the bar of the T, a worm is rewarded by finding a warm, moist chamber. An incorrect turn brings a mild electric shock. More complex mazes (B) are used to study learning in ants, food being the reward for "solving" the maze. Elaborate three-dimensional mazes (C) have been designed for rats.

Maze learning

The rate of learning can also be measured by the use of **mazes** (Fig. 23–4), pathways through which the animal must move in order to obtain a reward at the end of the maze. The pattern of such mazes can range from simple to complex, as shown. It is difficult to analyze an animal's performance in complex mazes since factors other than learning ability can influence performance. We must make a careful distinction between "performance"—the observed response—and "learning." We want to know something about what the animal has "stored" inside as a result of practice. We can never know that directly and must rely on some performance measure. Many things can influence the efficiency of an animal's performance besides what it has learned: Emotional animals do not tend to perform learned responses well; unmotivated animals do not perform well; fatigued animals may not perform well. We must rule out these contaminating factors, or at least estimate their contribution to the overall performance, if we wish to use a performance measure to make inferences about the rate at which an animal learns.

Latent learning

The clearest illustration of the importance of that point is provided by experiments on **latent learning**. In 1930, when E. C. Tolman trained hungry rats to run a complex maze, he recorded the results shown in Fig. 23–5. The error curve for the rats rewarded on every trial shows a progressive and steady decline throughout 17 days. We would conclude, on the basis of this finding, that the rats were showing progressive mastery of the maze.

Consider now the rats that are hungry but do not receive any food reward throughout the 17 days. Their error curve shows a very slight decrease but they are clearly not performing near the level of the rewarded rats. On the basis of this, we might conclude that no learning took place and might make the generalization that it is necessary to reward the animal in order for learning to take place. But let's examine the results for the third group of rats, which were not rewarded for the first 10 days but were rewarded on day 11 and

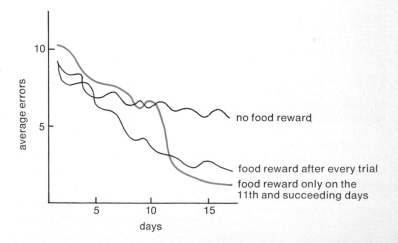

Figure 23–5 Latent learning in rats is shown by the three curves representing reduction in errors made in running a maze. Those animals that were motivated (given a food reward on reaching the end of the maze) performed better than those not motivated.

thereafter. The performance of these non-rewarded rats is comparable to that of the other non-rewarded rats for the first 10 days, but notice what happens to the curve after the 11th day. It is apparent that the rats were, indeed, learning something during the non-rewarded trials, but what was learned remained latent until the animal was strongly motivated to perform! Since many things other than what the animal has learned can influence an animal's performance, we must exercise caution when drawing inferences.

LEARNING AND NATURAL SELECTION

A study of the evolution of learning is an extremely difficult task. While bones may become fossilized, behavior usually does not, at least not directly so. In the evolution of man where the by-products of behavior—such as stone tools and other implements—can be found, anthropologists are able to piece together bits of evidence that suggest only a sketchy outline of the general behavior pattern of past cultures (Fig. 23–6). For groups of animals that do not leave any such clues to their past behavior, evolutionists must try another line of investigation.

One method of attempting to deduce the evolutionary pathways by which learning has evolved is to make a comparison of the anatomy of the nervous systems of various animals. Of course we cannot assume that the nervous system of the presently living great apes is an exact representation of the nervous systems of man's ancestors five million years ago. Both man and the chimpanzee, for example, have continued to evolve since the time when they both had a single common ancestor. Nevertheless, anatomical comparisons of the nervous systems of related groups of animals do tell us that the evolution of these systems was essentially a continuous process. There are no tremendous leaps in the complexity or size of the nervous system as one ascends the evolutionary tree. Man, however, is fond of thinking of himself as qualitatively different from other animals, primarily on the basis of his complex behavior patterns and learning abilities. H. F. Harlow has pointed out that the anatomical evidence may, in fact, be correct; that is, man may differ only quantitatively from other animals in his intellectual capabilities.

This observation leads us to the second method that has been widely used in attempts to characterize the evolution of learning. It rests on a comparative study of learning abilities in various species of animals. Like the anatomical method, this method is beset with the problem of not really having a true phylogenetic sequence of species to use for a comparison. In addition, different species of animals have different kinds of sensory mechanisms. In order to measure the ability of a monkey, a turtle, and an earthworm to discriminate between two stimuli, three different experimental designs and apparatus must be used. We could reward the monkey for a correct discrimination by presenting him with a banana. But how do you reward an earthworm? If you reward the monkey and the turtle with food, is the reward equivalent for both animals? Such questions are difficult to answer.

One of the factors that man recognizes as an important component of his intellectual capabilities is his ability to generalize—to deduce a general pattern

Figure 23–6 Stone-age tools like this weighted digging stick used by Smithfield hunters of the Late Stone Age in South Africa provide numerous clues about the cultural behavior of people of the past.

from a series of specific events. The ability to generalize has been investigated in a number of species using the method of "learning sets." For example, a monkey is presented with a choice between a cup that covers a grape, and a small box that does not contain a reward. After enough tries, the monkey will learn to choose the cup. If the shape of the objects hiding the reward is changed—a triangular piece of wood as opposed to a square piece—the monkey will learn the new discrimination in about the same number of attempts as he made in the first problem. However, when the same animal is presented with a *series* of similar problems, each new problem after the first few is learned more rapidly than the preceding one. The animal is said to have formed a learning set. It has deduced from a series of specific problems one feature that is common to all the problems. A wide variety of animals have been tested for their abilities to form learning sets. Although the rapidity with which the set is learned differs markedly among species, most are capable of forming learning sets. Interestingly, the ability to form learning sets is not restricted to vertebrates; the octopus, a higher invertebrate, is able to form at least one type of learning set.

The lower phylogenetic limit of the ability to learn a simple task apparently occurs in earthworms. These organisms have been trained to choose one arm of a simple T-maze (Fig. 23–4). Each time an incorrect choice was made, the worm was given a shock. The other, "correct" arm of the maze led to a dark, moist chamber, which served as a reward. Although an earthworm is able to learn to choose the correct arm of this maze, an individual requires many trials (about 200) before it chooses the correct arm at least 90% of the time.

While the earthworm has an intellect capable of learning, it is by no means clear how this capability increases the adaptedness of worms under natural conditions. If worms were able to learn a simple discrimination in one or even a very few trials, it is easy to see how natural selection would favor "brighter" worms. Harlow argues that learning in earthworms may be an ability the animals normally do not use. The ability to learn may be simply a by-product of a developing sensory system. For example, the evolution of complex sensory mechanisms, such as color vision in primates, may have played a role in the evolution of learning abilities in primates. Evidence for this supposition comes from the observation that the ability to distinguish color hues is highly correlated with learning ability in primates. It would seem that the development of a nervous system capable of receiving and interpreting the neural signals from a complex sensory organ such as the eye may have provided the basis for a system capable of learning and complex reasoning.

Adaptive significance of learning

The adaptive significance of behavior has been a recurrent theme in many chapters of this book, particularly in Chapter 5. Laboratory scientists, among others, sometimes tend to overlook the adaptive role of behavior when choosing an investigative strategy to explain behavior. There has been a strong tendency to view the organism as a passive associative mechanism, a view that has led to beliefs that we can condition an animal with about the same relative ease to any arbitrarily chosen stimulus, and train it to associate that stimulus with almost any arbitrarily chosen response. This is clearly not the case. Some responses to a stimulus have been enhanced in the species by natural selection.

For example, the ability of rats to learn to avoid stimuli associated with sickness has been investigated. One way this has been done is to inject rats with lithium chloride, a substance that produces nausea following drinking. In some conditions, the water the rats drank contained a distinctive sweet flavor while in others the water-tube was lighted and a buzzer was sounded as the animal drank; hence, "tasty" water and "bright-noisy" water. Following a period of drinking one or the other types of water, some rats were made sick by injections of lithium chloride and some were given a foot shock. The animals exposed to the tasty water as a conditioned stimulus and to the lithium chloride as an unconditioned stimulus learned immediately. Similarly, the rats that drank the bright-noisy water as a conditioned stimulus and received the foot shock as an unconditioned stimulus learned readily. However, neither the animals that drank the tasty-water conditioned stimulus and received the foot shock unconditioned stimulus nor those that had the bright-noisy water conditioned stimulus and the lithium chloride unconditioned stimulus were able to learn at all. This means that the conditioned stimulus and the unconditioned stimulus are appropriately associated in some important way. It is reasonable to expect rats to have the ability to associate tastes with feelings of sickness, and for this ability to be selected in the natural environment. It is as though, when sick, the rat is saying to himself, "It must have been something I ate."

Ethology and psychology: differential strategies

It is also reasonable to expect rats to have the ability to associate visual and auditory stimuli with an external environmental stimulus such as shock. We have, therefore, to consider the appropriateness of a learning situation in order to understand the nature of the learning process and to explain the relative ease or difficulty of the learning. As we have pointed out, some response systems, such as that involving taste and sickness, involve prepared response systems; others, such as that involving taste and foot shock, involve unprepared response systems. In prepared response systems, associations are formed almost instantly. In unprepared response systems, associations are formed gradually and with great difficulty. Typically, the ethologist has studied prepared response systems while the psychologist has concentrated on unprepared response systems.

This simple difference, coupled with the psychologist's emphasis on using standardized behavioral methods such as classical conditioning or operant conditioning, has led to two very different conceptions of the nature of animal behavior. The ethologist usually begins his study with the animal's natural behavior as a primary concern, constructs an ethogram, manipulates some variable or other, and observes the effect of that manipulation on the animal's complete behavior repertoire. His observations permit the ethologist to make some statement about the effects of experimental manipulation on the animal's *whole* system of actions.

The psychologist, on the other hand, has tended to concentrate on arbitrarily selected components of an animal's behavior repertoire and has introduced a high degree of precision in measuring these components in the face of systematic variation of experimental variables.

The ethologist often finds himself adrift on a sea of complexity, since so many aspects of the total response pattern tend to vary as a function of an experimental manipulation. Hence, we often find theory in ethology to be less closely related to an adequate body of data than we would like. Typical psychological theories *are* closely related to a solid data base, but a question arises concerning the significance of the response systems being studied to the animal's total response pattern.

The psychologist, then, has tended to develop a science of behavioral *possibilities*, manipulation of a given variable under some circumstances controlling a given response. What we should develop is a science of behavioral *probabilities* to establish the likelihood that a given variable normally controls a given response. Put another way, this will result in a more adequate *species-probable* science of behavior in place of the elegant but encapsulated *species-possible* science of behavior that we tend to find at present. In order to achieve this goal, we must know more of the natural behavioral tendencies of the animal we are studying (following the lead of the ethologist), and apply sophisticated measurement techniques to these natural behavioral tendencies (taking advantage of the special talents of the psychologist).

METHODS FOR COMPARING BEHAVIOR

One of our goals as biologists is to develop a comparative understanding of animal behavior, a perspective that will help us see how behavior evolves. In this respect our methods of investigation become particularly important.

Laboratory experiments

One advantage of laboratory techniques, described earlier in this chapter, is that they give us a high level of control over quantitative aspects of the behavior we may be investigating. Laboratory studies also permit us to manipulate a particular variable that may interest us while holding all other variables constant. The major problem with laboratory investigations used to the exclusion of field investigations is that they isolate components of the animal's behavior from their natural context. Although such systematic control makes it possible to use precise statistical procedures and to study the interaction of variables, it suffers from artificiality. A science of animal behavior constructed in this manner runs the risk of being *only* a science of species-possible behavior.

Field observation

The most extreme alternative to the use of highly controlled laboratory methods is to use the methods of field observation. With this method we guarantee the naturalness and the representativeness of what we see. With experience it is possible to describe behavior very reliably, and the units of measurement we use to describe it will almost always be natural ones—number of wing beats per second, and the like. However, it is sometimes difficult to keep the experiment "on the track." For example, if we are studying social dominance hierarchies among northern elephant seals, the dominant bull from one group might displace the dominant bull from a second. This fortuitous circumstance would allow us to observe whether the displaced bull rested content with his lot and accepted his diminished status, whether he searched for a group dominated by a bull whom he could displace, or any of a whole host of other possibilities. This occurrence, then, provides a fortuitous experiment and can be extremely valuable. However, it is difficult to construct a comprehensive science if it must be based solely on the collection of fortuitous events; and, due to the inherent complexity of such situations, many things are occurring in addition to the one thing in which the observer is interested.

Field experiments

The obvious compromise is to combine the virtues of laboratory experimentation and field observation. But this depends on our having a detailed description and understanding of the behavior of the animal in the natural context. At that point the field investigator should try to control the behavior in question by changing the environmental stimuli. In the example of habituation of aggressive responses of the white-crowned sparrow to territorial song, one would want to manipulate such things as whether the song being played were that of a close neighbor, a distant neighbor, a member of a different subspecies, or a different species altogether.

At the same time, the response to changes in the stimulus varied can be measured—number of flights per minute, songs per minute, and so on. It is desirable to obtain information about as many of these different responses as possible since they might point the way to certain behavioral aspects not immediately apparent. That point, in fact, highlights one of the serious limitations to many laboratory studies: the investigator's arbitrarily choosing only one aspect of an animal's behavior to the exclusion of all others. Behaviors tend to have interfaces with other behaviors; strip away the interfaces and you risk ending up with a beautifully measurable but artificial behavior. Furthermore, if there were any hierarchical organization of the response systems regulating the behavior we are observing, it would never have a chance to express itself in the laboratory.

INTELLIGENCE

While the pros and cons of laboratory versus field experimentation have occupied many investigators, so has the emotionally loaded controversy over how much of intelligence is inherited and how much of it is due to environmental influences. Again, our nature–nurture controversy is at hand and, as usual, the issue is clouded by ill-defined concepts with overlapping meanings and a misphrased question.

First of all, there are at least two distinctly different meanings of the term **intelligence**. To some it denotes the inherited ability with which an individual is born. This biological meaning implies some internal limiting factor intrinsic to the individual and not influenced by the environment. There are at least two difficulties with such a definition: 1. It is unlikely that there is a single inherited tendency that is unaffected by environmental conditions. Whether an individual realizes his full developmental potential depends on the classes of factors outlined in the previous chapter. 2. Any indication of intelligence we are able to obtain depends on some performance of the animal, and we have seen that the complex state of an organism consists of hosts of related factors other than the one we are trying to measure.

To other people, intelligence refers more to the achievement level the individual has attained. In fact the standard measures of intelligence all imply such a definition, since they are constructed so that an individual is compared in terms of his performance level relative to the level attained by other individuals of the same age. The difficulty with this concept of intelligence is that if we apply the test to individuals from a culture providing a different set of experiences from our own, it is difficult to know what the results mean. Individuals from a "primitive" culture will not score well on the type of intelligence tests familiar to most of us. In fact they may not even perform well in the context of any question-oriented test. On the other hand, such individuals may be able to differentiate between aspects of their environment that are crucial to their well-being in ways that would far exceed the abilities of "intelligent" individuals of our own culture.

Should all intelligence tests be culture-free? It depends on what we are trying to find out. If we are interested in the narrower biological meaning of intelligence, perhaps the tests should be culture-free. However, if we are interested in the broader biological meaning of intelligence—ability to adjust to environmental conditions—then perhaps tests should be culture-specific.

The inheritance of intelligence

One of the major arguments today is the degree to which intelligence may be inheritable. The facts on which the arguments are based are not terribly controversial, but the implication of the facts is. Some evidence strongly suggests that much of the intelligence measured by standard intelligence tests is inherited. The evidence is based on the similarities of the measured intelligence of identical twins (which would have the same gene complement) reared separately or together as compared to the measured intelligence of fraternal twins or of siblings (which would have dissimilar gene complements) reared separately or together. The estimate obtained by most experts in the field is that between 60% to 80% of the total variance in intelligence test scores is accounted for by inheritance. Misunderstanding of the meaning of that statement leads some to believe it implies that it is hopeless to try to eliminate the differences in measured intelligence between (for example) races because the difference in intelligence levels is genetic. Hence, they conclude, environmental intervention is useless.

First of all, there is dispute over the genetic homogeneity of human races;

furthermore, the assumption that the gene pools do not overlap in the polygenic characteristics that determine phenotype "intelligence" is suspect. Secondly, even if a trait is strongly genetically determined, its expression can still be profoundly affected by environmental influences. Even if intelligence is largely inherited, its inheritance (or potential) does not imply fixed (or realized) intelligence. The measurements on which heritability estimates are based are bound to a given set of environmental conditions at a given time.

For example, the correlation of children's intelligence with their natural and with their adoptive parents' intelligence has been studied. Although the rank order of the children's measured intelligence resembled that of their mothers, the children's intelligence was higher. It was distributed in accordance with those of the adoptive parents around an average IQ of over 100, whereas the natural mothers' IQ had an average of only 85. This indicates that even though intelligence might be inherited, a better social environment can raise IQ.

Sandra Scarr-Salapatek has studied population differences in the heritability of IQ scores for racial and social class groups and has reported findings that seem to agree with those we developed earlier when we spoke of developmental processes in general. In brief, she has analyzed twin data by race and social class and has found that there is a profound interaction between the environment and the resulting phenotype. For example, if a child is raised in a "disadvantaged" environment (minimal amount of stimulation conducive to intellectual development), then most of the variability in the child's IQ is determined by environmental influences. This is because the environment does not permit the genetic potential to be expressed to its fullest, and any environmental change will be reflected in the phenotype expression of the existing genotype.

On the other hand, if the child is brought up in an enriched environment, the minimal degree of stimulation will be available for the genotype to be fully expressed, but as in many biological functions, an overdose of enrichment does little more than the "minimal daily requirements" do. Therefore, the variability observed at this level will be due mainly to genetic differences. This research places the question of intelligence solidly on a biological footing about which meaningful research questions can be asked. The old "nature–nurture" argument is properly reduced to absurdity.

What happens when we take a broad comparative view of intelligence? Just how meaningful is it, if at all? Is a wasp intelligent? An octopus? A wasp will quickly learn the location of its nest based on environmental landmarks and will retain this learning over long periods of time (Fig. 23–7). The learning does not depend on particular stimulation by particular landmarks but seems to include the entire pattern of landmarks. This is obviously an intelligent behavior on the wasp's part. However, a wasp would not be a particularly good problem-solver if we subjected it to some of our traditional laboratory tasks. We have to phrase the question, therefore, in terms of "intelligent for what?" Only then can we come to know something of the adaptive significance of the behavior in question. Sheep, for instance, are notoriously poor animals to subject to learning tests involving mazes. Unlike rats, their natural environment is not one of tunnels and holes but of open spaces. Only in terms of the nature of the species, the nature of the ecology, and the specific task, can an animal be judged to be highly intelligent or highly unintelligent.

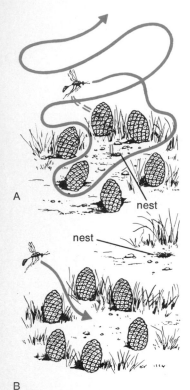

Figure 23–7 Studies performed by Tinbergen show that a digger wasp learns to identify the locality of a new nest with remarkable precision and rapidity. In the situation shown, cones were arranged around the entrance of a new nest when the wasp was inside (A). On emerging, it made a six-second study of the situation, then left. The cones were subsequently moved to new localities 13 different times. Each and every time, on returning to the nest, the wasp missed the real nest entrance, orienting its location in relation to the whole-circle configuration of cones (B).

The basis for intelligence and learning ability in animals is **memory**. Through memory, information is stored in the brain and recalled as that information is required. The capacity of an organism to store and retrieve "bits" of learned information is related to the complexity of its central nervous system. Simple organisms, like planaria, can learn simple avoidance behaviors and recall them when presented with an appropriate stimulus. Planaria can be trained to react to a bright light, followed shortly thereafter by an electric shock, by recoiling in expectation of the painful shock. The response is encoded in the nervous system of the planaria—like programming a computer—and it can be retrieved for some time after the initial training session. This process of encoding forms the basis of all memory, whether in planaria or man.

As the brain evolved, the ability to learn evolved. We have already seen how simple learning tasks can be mastered by earthworms; rats, on the other hand, display a wide range of learning abilities from simple avoidance responses, through discriminations of color, shape, and pattern, to logistic problems involving the manipulation of mazes, ladders, strings, and other equipment provided the test rats. In primates, we see the beginnings of tool-making and symbolic thought, and in man we observe verbal language, problem solving, thinking, and other mental activities. It is the **neocortex**—part of the cerebral cortex in mammals—which is associated with these mental activities.

How is information stored in the neocortex? What is the nature of memory? Researchers in this area are relatively certain of two things: that memory is related to *electrical* patterns in the cells of the neocortex, and that memory is also related to certain biochemical changes in these cells. Recent evidence—first disclaimed, now apparently confirmed—has associated the learning process in rats to changes in the RNA of their brain cells. RNA taken from the brains of rats which had mastered a simple discrimination task was injected into rats with no previous experience with the testing device ("naive rats"). The results show that the naive rats are capable of performing the task despite not having been trained. Whether it is truly the RNA which is directing the behavior or whether it is some other component or side effect of the RNA extract has not been determined with certainty. But it does appear that some biochemical change is associated with learning in rats, and that this change can be transferred from one rat to another.

One possible hypothesis that would reconcile the electrical and biochemical explanations of memory is if *short-term memory*—lasting from seconds to several days—can be explained by the presence of electrical circuits in the brain, and that *long-term memory*—lasting for years—can be explained by the coding of these circuits by RNA, probably in the form of proteins in the cells of the brain. Whether this explanation is plausible should be known soon.

Our inquiry into learning and intelligence could continue into many provocative areas of current research such as the biological basis of language, the expression of emotion, and altered states of consciousness. These areas of investigation hold great promise at present and provide interesting questions because of their broad interdisciplinary sweep. They also lead us into our next and final area of investigation, the ethology of man.

DRUGS
AND PSYCHOTIC BEHAVIOR

Medical researchers often face the difficulty of attacking problems with inadequate technology. Nowhere is this more evident than in attempts to improve our understanding of abnormal states of the mind. Although we have been trying for many decades to produce an "animal model" for the human psychotic state, we have not yet been successful. In fact, with the advent of widespread use of chemical agents such as lysergic acid diethylamide (LSD), we have seen a significant increase in the number of psychotics—with no concurrent expansion of our understanding of how this drug (and other agents with similar pharmacological activities) might be acting.

Hallucinogens or ?

In a recent paper entitled "Pharmacology of Madness—The Hallucinogens," E. Domino classifies a wide variety of drugs as hallucinogens including lysergic acid derivatives, indolealkylamines, phenethylamines, arylcycloalkylamines, glycolate esters, and tetrahydrocannabinols. The diversity of chemical structure among the members of this imposing list precludes any single mechanism of action for all, which only adds to the complexity of a problem that must be approached with the clear understanding that we know virtually nothing about brain function in humans.

For example, we call these drugs "hallucinogens," yet the medical definition of hallucination is a perception without external stimulus, a sensation arising within the individual himself. None of the "hallucinogenic" drugs is capable of producing mental distortion in the absence of external sensory stimuli. In fact, a major portion of the effects of drugs such as LSD in humans appears to be closely interwoven with the action of these agents on sensory input. If, then, we assume that the drugs act by altering the mind's interpretation of sensory input, we might better classify them as "illusionogens," since the medical definition of an illusion is a false interpretation of a sensation, a preception which misinterprets the object perceived.

Whichever term we use to describe these drugs (hallucinogen, illusionogen, psychedelic, psychotomimetic) the crux of the problem facing biomedical research is how to test for their effects and thereby to examine their actions in some convenient laboratory animal. To date, the search has been fruitless; we are unable to answer the question, "Do animals other than man hallucinate (or 'illusionate') when given drugs such as LSD?" The search has been wide, an enormous variety of experimental animals has been tested, and the species studied range in size from ants to elephants and in phyla from insects to mammals. The test systems range from synaptic inhibition to electroencephalographic patterns and from instinctual, unlearned behavior to complex patterns of learned or social behavior. Let us briefly examine some of the animal studies to date.

EFFECTS ON OVERT BEHAVIOR

In vertebrates

More than 20 years ago, P. N. Witt found that psilocybin, LSD, and mescaline caused spiders to change web-spinning patterns. The species *Zilla-x-notata* was of particular interest; low doses of LSD decreased the frequency of web making and reduced the number of oversized sectors in the web, while increasing the regularity of the angles between the radial threads of the web as well as the regularity of the sticky spiral thread. Since the regularity of the web pattern is determined by the spider taking the shortest path when spinning, a behavioral pattern that is adversely affected by distracting external stimuli, LSD would appear to reduce sensory input or make the spiders less

Web A (the control web) was built by an adult female cross spider (*Araneus diad-ematus*) on the morning of the first day of the experiment. Partial destruction of the northwest quadrant was caused when the spider ran out of the web toward the upper left. That evening the spider was given phenobarbital (Luminal), a sedative drug. The following morning the spider built web B, which shows characteristic effects of drug influence.

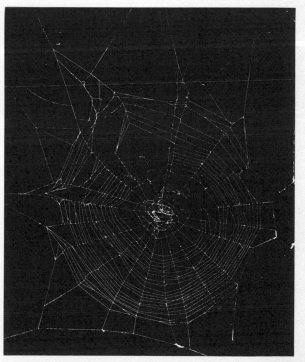

A   B

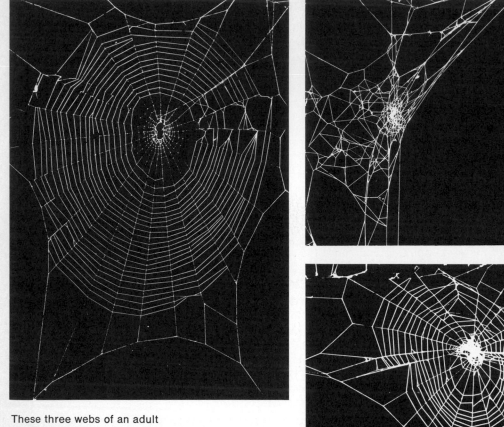

These three webs of an adult female cross spider were built on different days. Web C is the control web, built on the first day of the experiment in about 20 minutes in the early morning hours. At 4:00 p.m. the spider drank 0.1 ml of sugar water containing 1 mg of dextro-amphetamine (also known as speed). Web D was built about 12 hours later by a severely disturbed animal; it shows some remnants of a hub, a few irregular and frequently interrupted radii, and some erratic strands of sticky spiral. Web E was built 24 hours after web D and shows signs of re-covery, but it took several more days for the spider to build a web approaching the geometric precision of web C.

sensitive to external stimuli. In contrast, mescaline, while reducing the regularity of the angles, also reduced the regularity of the sticky spiral thread —a net effect different from that of LSD. Other investigators found the effects of psilocybin and mescaline on the web-spinning activity of *Araneus diad-ematus* to be similar to the effects of mescaline as reported by Witt. It is of particular interest that the effects of mescaline could be reproduced by simply attaching small pieces of lead to the spiders, thereby effectively increasing their body weight.

IN LOWER VERTEBRATES: When specimens of *Betta splendens* (Siamese fighting fish) are exposed to solutions of various concentrations of LSD for six hours and then returned to fresh water, the behavior of the fish is most bizarre —backward swimming, a head up–tail down vertical positioning often com-bined with a Cartesian diver effect, a barrel-roll behavior (rolling on the long axis), motionless attitudes for several minutes, slow and deliberate movements sharply contrasting with the sudden movements of untreated controls. Similar results are seen with several LSD analogs, but mescaline is totally inactive. These actions of LSD on *Betta splendens* appear to be virtually peculiar to this species, another quandary for the psychobiologist.

IN HIGHER VERTEBRATES: Administration of LSD to birds causes aberrations in various behavioral patterns: courting, nesting behavior, pecking behavior, and others. Many studies have been performed on rodents of various types. In general, the effects are the same. LSD and other hallucinogens elicit abnormal behavioral performances: head shaking, enhanced responsivity to external stimuli, peculiar huddling behavior, apparent catatonic or daydreaming states, and other unexpected actions. Cats and dogs show similar aberrant behavior, including hyperirritability, peculiar stances, back-arching, defensive hostility, and a tendency to appear unsure of their normal environment. Interestingly enough, in an attempt to duplicate the so-called "musth" madness (berserk behavior), L. J. West and C. M. Pierce administered a dose of LSD to an adult elephant; very few behavioral symptoms were observed as the animal died in about one hour, even though the dose was a relatively low one.

IN PRIMATES: Behavioral effects on experimental animals include apparent disorders of sensory phenomena, reaching for invisible objects, unusual varieties of escape behavior, an uncertain gait, and, as with virtually all species of animals tested, a tendency to withdraw to a catatonic type of non-responsive state.

EFFECTS ON OPERANT BEHAVIOR

Hundreds of studies of a variety of animals have attempted to show significant and unique effects of LSD and other hallucinogens on conditioned behavior. Whether bar pressing, rope climbing, jumping, or performing other physical tasks for reward or to escape punishment, the results are basically non-unique to the psychotomimetic drugs. Similar perturbations may be seen with other drugs or drug combinations that are not considered to be hallucinogenic in man.

In humans, the effects of these drugs on behavioral tasks is quite clear. Immediate memory is deteriorated, simple problem solving is impaired, critical judgment is lacking, recognition and recall are distorted, color-naming and color-reading are severely impaired, there is a significant increase in reaction time and in error scores in intelligence tests, and perception of sizes, directions, and distances are severely altered.

The human as a test subject

It is in the thought functioning of the human mind that one sees the greatest effects of these drugs. Vivid and pronounced changes in thought and mood occur. The visual world is filled with imagery almost defying description. Three dimensional space is altered, blurring and intermingling of images are common, rigid patterns move and ripple, after-images are common, persistent, and often continuously changing. Rich colors and varied patterns are "seen" even with the eyes closed. Indeed, auditory or tactile stimuli even evoke visual imagery. Of particular interest is that subjects blind from birth do not report visual sensations when given LSD but experience acute increases in auditory and tactile sensations. By contrast, subjects with normal vision blindfolded during the test report a "rush" of visual imagery.

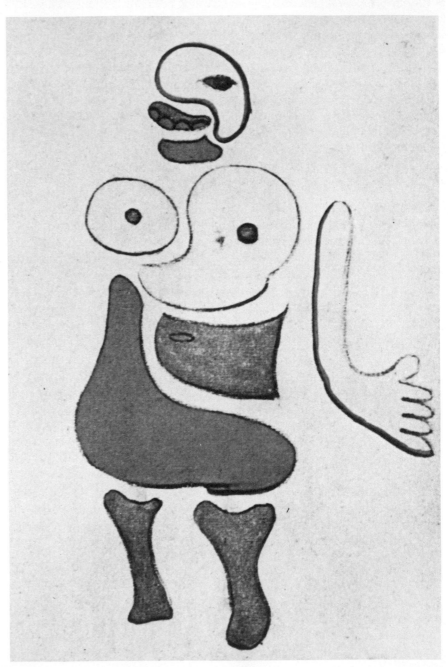

Both paintings on these pages were made by patients under the influence of LSD 25 in the course of treatment for emotional disturbance. The one on this page reflects a sensation of disintegration, limbs and other body parts dissociating themselves. The painting on the opposite page was made by a woman with a phobia of spiders.

Rorschach responses under LSD have been considered similar to those of true schizophrenics. Basic personality characteristics appear to come into play; one subject who had a fear of spiders described the image shown above as one "seen" during an LSD-evoked session. Another subject subvisualized a fear of death or physical harm when describing the distorted person seen at left. Unfortunately, the human psychotic state is so poorly defined that it is difficult to identify any one or several behavioral patterns as characteristic of psychoses.

WHAT DOES THE FUTURE HOLD?

Despite the centuries-old existence of mind-altering drugs, where do we stand today? Certainly, we are not much better off in our understanding of the aberrant functions of the human mind than we were when LSD was first synthesized and tested. Ergot, psilocybe, and fly agaric are known in ancient writings. Their use in rituals is historical fact; their mechanism of action on the human mind remains hypothesis and speculation. In this age of technological advancement, we have successfully transported man to the Moon and our instruments have reached into outer space, yet we remain basically inept at delving into the inner mind. The discovery of a satisfactory animal model for psychosis, when and if such a discovery is achieved, will be a crucial step toward better understanding of the human mind.

1　Conditioning is a form of learning. Try to think of at least two examples of conditioned learning in your own experience that have proven to have lasting beneficial value. Are there others that may have been beneficial at one time, but tend to be of questionable value now?

2　What is meant by the expression "species-probable science of behavior," and why is it favored over what has been termed the "species-possible science of behavior"?

3　When an experimental psychologist designs intelligence tests for various species of animals, what are some of the things he must consider about the particular species he wants to examine?

4　Assume that some sort of biochemical change takes place in an animal's brain when it learns. How would you go about identifying the type of change taking place? How would you test whether this biochemical change could be transferred from the "trained" animal to an "untrained" animal?

5　What are some of the difficulties faced by psychologists in trying to develop a test of intelligence which is absolutely culture-free? Can you think of any type of IQ test which would bypass the culture element?

6　Compare the approach to the study of trained behavior taken by laboratory psychologists to that taken by field ethologists.

SELECTED READINGS

Hansel, C. E. *ESP: A Scientific Evaluation.* New York: Charles Scribner's Sons, 1966. A panorama of research into extrasensory perception, reporting and evaluating results obtained in ESP experimentation since the latter part of the 19th century. An excellent introduction to the subject with numerous entertaining moments.

Kimble, Gregory A. *Hilgard and Marquis' Conditioning and Learning.* New York: Appleton-Century-Crofts, 1961. The classic textbook on classical and instrumental conditioning procedures. Treats the subject in a descriptive and non-theoretical manner.

Mednick, Sarnoff A. *Learning.* Englewood Cliffs, N.J.: Prentice-Hall, Inc., 1964 (Foundations of Psychology Series). A short book on the introductory level including chapters on methods of investigating learning, classical and operant conditioning, serial learning, motivation and learning, transfer of learning, and memory.

Thorpe, William H. *Learning and Instinct in Animals.* Cambridge, Mass.: Harvard University Press, 1963. A comprehensive general study of learning in a variety of species. One of the major values of this book is the emphasis placed on the interdependence of psychologists and learning theorists on the one hand and zoologists and physiologists on the other.

Part 6

UNDERSTANDING MAN

We have noted in this book that behavior tends to be adaptive and has evolved along with the morphology and physiology of organisms. Much of the behavior of many animals appears to be genetically determined and to express itself in the form of rather stereotyped motor patterns dependent on internal motivating and releasing mechanisms or on innate learning dispositions. We are now ready to examine to what extent similar adaptations pre-program human behavior, to what degree they are still adaptive today, and to what extent culture and learning affect these adaptations.

Figure 24–1 Much of our human behavior is culturally determined, a fact that distinguishes man from all other species. To what extent inborn human behavior is universal among cultures is a concern of both anthropologists and ethologists.

24
ETHOLOGY AND HUMAN BEHAVIOR

BIOLOGY AND CULTURE

Most of us have dreamt at some time or other of what life might have been like had we grown up alone on a desert island—a waif cast adrift from a sinking ship. Could we have survived? Would we have invented tools? Language? Could we have abided the loneliness? Writers have echoed these thoughts and created romantic figures like Robinson Crusoe and the Swiss Family Robinson. Others have painted more devastating pictures of what happens to individuals or groups cut off from society. The behavior of the marooned boys in William Golding's *Lord of the Flies*, for example, becomes increasingly cruel and violent.

This nostalgia for origins, for what man must be like in essence, stripped of all that is current or contingent, constrained or controlled by society, is an ever-recurring theme in human thought and philosophy. We muse about getting down to the "natural man" as if by this means we could discover what human beings were truly like.

That attempt is doomed. Man is a creature of culture. By this we mean that he is born into association and communication with his fellows. In this way he acquires a vast set of symbols: the tools and techniques of living that have developed in specific groups over the generations, as well as the abstract rules, codes, customs, and conventions that govern behavior. Foremost of these abstract acquisitions, serving as the chief tool by which man is educated into his culture, is language itself.

Biologically man is an animal, subject to the physiological needs common to all living organisms. But of all animals man is the most helpless at birth, the most in need of the care of others. It is through these very acts of caretaking, however, that adults immerse a child in culture. Through interactions with him, by word and deed, adults civilize the child according to their fashion. He learns *their* "native" tongue; he learns to dress, eat, play, work, laugh, love, and even die in ways that conform to a cultural tradition. Even if he departs from the rules, he always does so with a knowledge of what those rules are and of the consequences of breaking them.

Man's capacity for culture is as much a part of his evolutionary heritage as his ability to walk upright, to see in depth and color, or to have the fine fingertip control to turn the pages of this book. And it is precisely this capacity for culture which distinguishes man from all other species (Fig. 24–1). The anthropologists Theodosius Dobzhansky and Ashley Montagu wrote, "Man is a unique product of evolution in that he, more than any other creature, has escaped from the bondage of the physical and the biological into the multi-form social environment."

No one gene or other simple combination of hereditary factors accounts for man's inventiveness or his capacity for culture. Our pre-human ancestors were not transformed overnight into modern man, *Homo sapiens*, by a few random mutations. Most authorities agree that our capacity for culture grew out of two broad and interrelated trends observed in the evolution of higher organisms. One is a trend away from a wholesale dependence on the environment in favor of an increasing number of self-regulating mechanisms. The other is a trend away from automatic or stereotyped patterns of behavior in response to environmental challenges toward an extension and enrichment of the quality of response. Man is not a snake whose daily round of activities is governed by how sunny a day it is. Nor is he a spider forced always to spin the same pattern of web. In man the trend toward self-regulation—toward internal controls of temperature (a trait we share with birds and mammals but not snakes), and of sexual fertilization and early development (a mammalian trait)—continues and extends to other aspects of behavior. Psychologist Jerome Bruner, for example, speaks of man's internal control of attention as a prime factor in learning. We can impose restrictions on the vast amount of stimuli bombarding us every second in order to focus on aspects or problems that interest us.

This ability makes us supremely educable and is of course related to the other major development in the evolution of man—the growing complexity of the nervous system. This complexity underlies the richness of man's adaptive responses and his success as a species. He has the ability to plan and to execute plans; to remember and to reason; to use imagery and symbols in private thoughts as well as public discourse.

By the time individuals existed who possessed these characteristics they were already a cultural group, equivalent in mental potential to the most urbane *Homo sapiens* among us today. A century ago, in the infancy of psychology, sociology, and anthropology, such a statement would not have gone uncontested. So diverse were the human cultures observed by early field workers that it seemed natural to some to assume that societies were like living organisms in stages of evolution. Those with the most primitive tools, no written language, and little in the way of art or technology must be associated with more primitive and inferior minds, it seemed, and so on up to the superior refinements of European and American society.

Nowadays no scientist takes this argument seriously. Indeed George Murdock of the University of Pittsburgh has compiled a partial list (in alphabetical order) of the traits common to all cultures everywhere, past or present. This list makes it abundantly clear that the most "primitive" tribe shares equally with contemporary western society in the talent for constructing the complex fabric of culture:

> . . . age-grading, athletic sports, bodily adornment, calendar, cleanliness training, community organization, cooking, cooperative labor, cosmology, courtship,

dancing, decorative art, divination, division of labor, dream interpretation, education, eschatology, ethics, ethnobotany, etiquette, faith healing, family, feasting, firemaking, folklore, food taboos, funeral rites, games, gestures, gift giving, government, greetings, hair styles, hospitality, housing, hygiene, incest taboos, inheritance rules, joking, kin-groups, kinship nomenclature, language, law, luck superstitions, magic, marriage, mealtimes, medicine, modesty concerning natural functions, mourning, music, mythology, numerals, obstetrics, penal sanctions, personal names, population policy, post-natal care, pregnancy usages, property rights, propitiation of supernatural beings, puberty customs, religious ritual, residence rules, sexual restrictions, soul concepts, status differentiation, surgery, toolmaking, trade, visiting, weaning, and weather control.

Comparisons of behavior among different cultures in any of these categories are interesting in their own right, and they have given rise to a number of theories in biology, psychology, anthropology, sociology, and linguistics. Of special relevance, however, is the significance of culture itself. It introduces a non-biological or, as it has sometimes been called, an "extrasomatic" (outside-the-body) means of inheritance. For implicit in the idea of culture is a concept of time and continuum: The concrete objects and symbols of culture are accumulated over many lifetimes. But man is able to incorporate them in one. In so doing he bridges a temporal gap, inheriting the experience of many earlier generations. This ability to learn from the past, incorporate the present, and pass on to the future an accumulation of lore and learning has been an extraordinarily powerful tool in human evolution. Not only has it greatly enhanced man's ability to cope with environmental challenges, but it has greatly speeded up the process of adaptation. Instead of having to wait for the relatively slow mechanism of random genetic change to produce individuals more fit to survive, man makes use of strategies and tactics transmitted to him through external means, by learning.

One of these strategies includes the ability to alter the environment itself, and herein lies the essential check on the extrasomatic process. Man's alterations of the environment may have serious biological consequences for man himself. A contemporary example is the irrigation of desert lands made possible by the construction of the Aswan Dam in Egypt. An unforeseen consequence of this advance in technology has been the proliferation of fresh water snails and major infestations of the snail-borne debilitating disease schistosomiasis in areas where the disease never before existed.

Human culture and the natural environment are intimately tied to each other by a feedback process. A change in one perturbs the other, which, in turn, stirs up more ripples, a process which can be seen as a kind of spiral through time that continues at present. Today we are more aware of this interplay than ever as an increasing number of social commentators and scientists remind us of the consequences of population and pollution crises. Man's fate as a species may well be determined by how he behaves toward others and toward the life-sustaining resources of the planet. More than ever we need to know about man's behavior; about his drives and motivations; about the biological laws he must obey and the non-biological ones he constructs for himself. This is the theme we will explore in the pages that follow.

Figure 24–2 Certain facial expressions seem to be universally understood among people of different cultures and transcend language as a means of communication. Shown here are two smiling people (an American boy and a Schom-Pen man from Great Nicobar Island), a Kabuki actor in an expression of rage, and an injured Vietnamese girl who has just lost her parents in the war.

COMPARATIVE STUDIES OF HUMAN BEHAVIOR

Universal expressions

The question of if and how much in complex human behavior is inborn may be answered by the comparison of behavior in individuals of different cultures. If one can demonstrate communalities in expressions and gestures, then we may conclude that they derived from a common inherited root, especially the more specific the behavior patterns concerned and the more widespread their occurrence in people of different ecology and cultural and racial background. This line of thought was expressed by Darwin, and many present-day psychologists are aware of the basic agreement in mimic expression among different peoples.

> The findings of the ethnologists agree that there are basic expressions which occur without exception in all human societies. Cries of pain and of grief are universally distributed: When frightened one becomes pale and trembles; laughing and smiling are quite generally an expression of joy and happiness. It is probable that the agreements are even more encompassing and that reactions such as surprise, boredom, and astonishment are included. We may therefore speak of certain invariables in our emotional expressions, even though they have not been described in sufficient detail (S. Asch, 1952).

Others state that no expressive movement has any universal meaning, that they are all the product of culture and are not inborn. Such far-reaching generalizations are certainly unjustified. Even the comparison of the facial ex-

 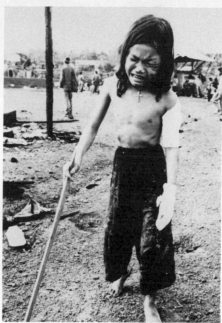

pressions of still photographs shows a widespread agreement, although a photograph captures only a short moment out of the entire behavior sequence. The pictures here show friendly smiles, rage, and sadness and pain in various peoples (Fig. 24–2). The best proof, however, is motion picture film, but no relevant material is available. No one seems to have thought about documenting human behavior objectively, that is, through films taken without the subject's awareness. As unbelievable as it may seem, the ethogram of man has not yet been documented and registered in a way that would permit one scientist to examine data of another which are not already colored by the interpretation of the observer.

If one wants to know whether a Papuan, Bantu, Japanese, or Italian stomps his foot when he is angry, one will search in vain in the film archives for unstaged films of people in rage. The same is true if one searches for comparative pictures of flirting, laughing, crying, gestures of disdain, and other expressive movements. This surprising discrepancy in the documentation of cultural activities, on the one hand, and of expressive behavior, on the other, is partially rooted in the historical development of psychology and ethnography. There are also certain methodological difficulties. Making of pots, weaving of mats, and cultural activities are readily performed for observers. The documents, then, do not actually reflect reality, but in general it is possible to capture the process. Facial expressions and gestures, on the other hand, must be recorded without the subject's awareness. Even a learned activity changes markedly when it is performed; this is even more true for emotional behavior. People are shy by nature and they do not like to be photographed. It is amazing over what great distances people perceive when a camera is pointing at them. And their behavior changes instantly. The facial expression

Figure 24–3 At left is a motion picture camera lens with a built-in prism that permits filming to the side. A mock lens presents a false "front." At right the camera is in use.

becomes rigid, most people look restlessly toward the camera, smile in embarrassment, or exaggerate or overdo the behavior if they decide to continue it. Even in learned skills the smoothness of the performance is often lost (Fig. 24–3).

Although the work is still in progress, we have filmed enough to say that some of the more complex human expressions can be traced back to the superposition of a few fixed action patterns which do not seem to be culturally determined. To give just one example, we found agreement in the smallest detail in the flirting behavior of girls from Samoa, Papua, France, Japan, Africa (Turcana and other Nilotohamite tribes) and South American Indians (Waika, Orinoko).

FLIRTING AND GREETING: The flirting girl at first smiles at the person to whom it is directed and lifts her eyebrows with a quick, jerky movement upward so that the eye slit is briefly enlarged. This most probably inborn greeting with the eyes is quite typical (Figs. 24–4 and 24–5). After this initial, obvious turning toward the person, in the flirt there follows a turning away. The head is turned to the side, sometimes bent toward the ground, the gaze is lowered, and the eyelids are dropped. Frequently, but not always, the girl may cover her face with a hand and she may laugh or smile in embarrassment. She continues to look at the partner out of the corners of her eyes and sometimes vacillates between looking at and an embarrassed looking away. We were able to elicit this behavior when girls observed us during our filming. While one of us operated the camera the other would nod toward the girl and smile.

Here we already find that the superposition of a few invariable components (intention movements of turning toward someone, responsiveness, and turning away) yields a relatively complex and variable expression. The assertion

Figure 24–4 Greeting with the eyes by a French woman, reading from top down: neutral face, then two stages of eyebrow raising followed by a smile. The entire sequence of raising the eyebrows and then lowering them includes only 18 frames (at the rate of 48 frames per second). (H. HASS)

Figure 24–5 Greeting with the eyes by a Samoan girl, reading from top down: neutral face, then a smile followed by raised eyebrows, and a lingering smile. The eyebrows are clearly raised for only one-sixth of a second (48 frames per second). (H. HASS)

Figure 24–6 Eyebrow flash during greeting by a Balinese male of the island Nusa Penida. The entire sequence lasted only 19 frames (48 frames per second).

of some that there are no culturally independent expressions and that everything is learned is disproved by these results.

The comparative investigation of greeting behavior in people from different cultures showed additional agreement, even in the smallest details. During a friendly greeting over a distance the greeting person smiles, and if he is in an especially good mood will lift the eyebrows in the manner previously described and then nod the head. This behavior has been filmed in stone age Papuans only recently in contact with government patrols (Figs. 24–6 and 24–7).

Wide agreement is also found in many other expressions. Thus arrogance and disdain are expressed by an upright posture, raising of the head, moving back, looking down, closed lips, exhaling through the nose—in other words through ritualized movements of turning away and rejection. When enraged, people bare their teeth at the corners of the mouth.

CROSSCULTURAL GESTURES: With respect to gestures one also finds many agreements among peoples of different cultures. Bowing everywhere seems to be a gesture of submission, for example, during greeting or if one approaches a high-ranking person or in praying. Differences apply only to the extent; we may nod, while a Japanese bows very low. In triumph and when we are enthusiastic we throw up the arms. Members of the most varied cultures greet by raising the open hand. If one man wants to impress another—to display— it is again done quite similarly in different peoples by an erect posture, mean facial expression, and frequently with an artificial enhancement of the body size and width of the shoulders. The only difference is in the means to achieve this expression in the various cultures. Some men place feathered crowns on their heads, others fur caps made of bear hide, another displays with weapons

Figure 24–7 Eyebrow flash during greeting by a Papuan native of New Guinea. The sequence lasted for 45 frames (48 frames per second).

and colorful dress—the principle remains the same. When we are angry we become indignant, that is, we jump up into an intention movement for attack, make fists, and may even bang the table, which is a redirected attack behavior. When angry we may stomp with a foot, an intention of attack which among Europeans is especially found in small, uncontrolled children; adults usually suppress it. I saw the same gesture in an angry Bantu boy. It remains to be investigated to what degree the gestures of approval or disapproval have an innate basis. Many races indicate a general "no" by shaking the head, closing the mouth, some by showing the tongue (Fig. 24–8), and they say "yes" by nodding their heads. Darwin points out that the first act of saying "no" (disapproving) in children is the rejection of food, by turning the head to the side from the breast or a spoon. One could think of a shaking-off movement.

SAYING "NO": It is possible that several primary forms of saying "no" exist, such as rejection or disapproval, and that people in different cultures accept one or the other by convention. One movement of rejection can be traced from the intention of turning away. In saying "no" a Greek, for example, lifts his head with a jerk backward, at the same time lowering his eyelids and often raising one or both hands with the open palms showing to the opponent. This behavior can be observed in northern Europe as a gesture of emphatic refusal ("for heaven's sake"). It is also very similar to the posture of arrogance. Sometimes instead of lifting the head backward we can observe a turning-to-the-side movement. Another widespread gesture of refusal or no is head shaking, and sometimes one can observe a rejecting form of shaking the hand, which may be a ritualized shaking off.

NODDING: Nodding was derived, according to Darwin, from an intention movement to eat. Another possible interpretation is that nodding could be taken as an intention movement to bow, as a ritualized gesture of submission, so to speak. When expressing agreement one does submit to the will of another. Much is to be said for this interpretation. Nodding is a widespread gesture of approval. Papuans nod and so do Waika Indians or Bantu. Like others, many Indians and Ceylonese also nod when stating, "Yes, this is so." However, when expressing their agreement to do something they were asked to do, they sway their head in a peculiar sideways movement. If one asks a Ceylonese, "Do you drink coffee?" he will nod upon confirmation. If we address him, however, saying, "Let us drink coffee," he sways his head in agreement.

Figure 24–8 Showing the tongue is a widespread gesture of contempt and rejection particularly in children, but also in adults, as observed by Captain Cook among New Guinea warriors in 1784.

KISSING: If the accounts are correct, the kiss is not found everywhere. In spite of this, however, one might think of it as a kind of ritualized feeding derived from the care-of-young behavior system which has been taken over as one of the expressions of tenderness. Among the inhabitants of the Hinterzillertal, a mountain valley in Austria, it is the custom to chew pine resin, which gradually changes into a viscous mass that is no longer sticky and is changed from one cheek into the other and sometimes is visible from the corners of the mouth. According to L. V. Hörmann, "When chewing pitch the same custom, that of mutual exchanging of the wad prevails, as is also done with chewing tobacco. Among lovers this exchange plays an important role."

The boy exposes a piece of pitch from between his teeth and invites the girl to pull it out with her teeth, an attempt that the boys try to prolong as a kind of love play. When the dancing partner responds to this invitation of the boy, it is a sign of her interest and affection and even more.

It has frequently been stated that in cultures in which tenderness is expressed by rubbing noses, no kissing exists, for example, the Papuans, Polynesians, Indonesians, and Eskimos. This statement is based, however, on incomplete observation. In the first three cultural regions I observed that mothers hugged and kissed their children, even among stone age Papuans of a remote Kukukuku village who had only 7 months prior to my visit had their first brief contact with a government patrol. It is very unlikely that these mothers learned this behavior from the patrol members. In the same Papuans I also saw a father kiss his son on the cheek when he greeted him.

FOOD SHARING: Passing of food as a gesture of contact readiness can also be observed in small children. I recently observed this in a 3-year-old girl who was a guest in our house for the first time. The child observed her parents, who were engaged in friendly conversation with us, but she was at first shy. After lunch while we were drinking coffee the girl suddenly came up, took a cookie from a plate, and gave it to me smiling somewhat embarrassedly. She repeated this with an obvious flirtatious behavior and was happy when I accepted and ate the cookie. From then on she felt completely at ease.

This gesture appeases even those who are enemies, as an acquaintance of mine experienced during the war. He had been ordered to capture a prisoner from an enemy trench to obtain information from him, an act that he had carried out successfully on previous occasions. When he jumped into the trench with a drawn pistol and pointed it at the enemy soldier, the soldier, scared as he was, held out his hand with a piece of bread in it. This gesture so changed the mood of my acquaintance that he was unable to carry out his task and withdrew. After that he was unable to carry out similar missions.

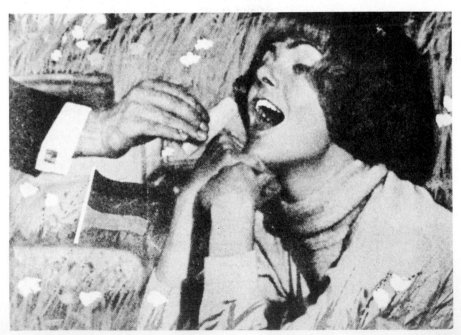

Figure 24–9 Appeal to the group-uniting function of feeding is a common advertising theme.

528

text continued on page 529

SOCIAL BEHAVIOR IN PRIMATES

Fighting and partner grooming are two conspicuous examples of social behavior in primates. What do these activities have in common? Because both involve physical contact, they are easily recognized patterns of social behavior. However, communication among primates includes many more subtle patterns. For example, specific vocalizations, postural changes, or facial expressions may convey particular moods, and the patterns may be exchanged between individuals spaced relatively far apart. In Chapters 9 and 10, we made broad comparisons of social systems among vertebrate orders; here we will look for the trends in morphological and ecological constraints influencing the social organization within a single order of mammals.

Grooming, here being carried out by Ceylonese toque macaques, is a social behavior that helps strengthen social bonds between members of the group. (WOLFGANG DITTUS)

The Colombian *Douroucouli* is a ceboid. One of its un-monkey-like characteristics is that it is nocturnal; the contrasting black and white striped pattern on the face allows the animal to be seen by other *Douroucoulis*.
(ROY PINNEY)

COMMUNICATION AMONG PRIMATES

Within the primate order, we can distinguish three major adaptive radiations which were independent due to geographical isolation. The South American monkeys, or ceboids, include both the diminutive marmosets and large species with prehensile tails. The Old World monkeys, or cercopithecoids, range from leaf-eating monkeys to baboons. Independent of these lines, lemurs diversified on the island of Madagascar. Within the Old World, the primate diversity is greatest since representatives of both suborders, Prosimii and Anthropoidea, may occur within the same habitat. Prosimians include tree shrews, lorises, galagos, and tarsiers as well as lemurs. Anthropoids include the other monkeys, the great apes, and man.

The primates' ancestors were small, insectivorous mammals with many of the characteristics of tree shrews. Four trends in primate evolution are apparent from a comparison of known species: 1. an increase in the use of visual and auditory communication at the expense of chemical communication; 2. a reduction in the number of young—from a litter that is left in a den to a single infant transported by the mother from birth; 3. an increase in body size and longevity paralleled by a long period of maturation available for social learning; and 4. the formation of permanent social groupings that include males.

Some prosimians and New World monkeys have specialized glandular areas and stereotyped movements for depositing secretions. Lemurs have a conspicuous wrist gland and certain ceboids have both sternal glands and perineal glands. Secretions may be deposited on branches that are used frequently, around resting or denning sites, or on one another—thereby producing a communal odor. In a comparison of the nocturnally active prosimians and the diurnally active cercopithecoid monkeys, there is a decrease in the proportion of the sensory areas of the brain devoted to smell and an elaboration of those areas concerned with vision and hearing. As the importance of scent glands diminishes, marking patterns associated with scent glands disappear.

Although the function of detecting secretions deposited by other animals in the environment may be reduced, several olfactory functions are retained. The males' ability to discriminate the receptive condition of females and the ability to discriminate ripe or palatable foods are widespread.

An elaboration of the vocal apparatus parallels that of vision and may result in special structures. The vocal sac of the siamang acts as a resonating chamber for its loud calls. Calling exchanges between breeding pairs frequently occur around dawn and apparently allow neighboring bands to locate each other and to space themselves. With an increased reliance on vision, signals involving body postures are embellished by discrete gestures. The reassuring extended hand of a chimpanzee illustrates this trend. Bright pigments on the muzzles of mandrills and the red, white, and blue of the anogenital region of vervet monkeys designate mature males in these species. Color vision or, more specifically, cone cells in the eyes must be present in these species before such signals can be fully interpreted.

Adult males may be conspicuous behaviorally as well as by their larger size

An increased reliance on vision in certain species has led to social signals that involve body posture, as demonstrated here by an infant gorilla reaching out to be picked up by its foster mother. Among older apes an extended hand is a signal of reassurance. (LUCY HUDSON)

An adult male gray langur with tail raised as his troop moves through the tall grass. Though all troop members travel with raised tails, the large size and confident gate of the focal male render his tail conspicuous. This behavioral adaptation enables other troop members to keep track of the focal male. (MCKAY)

or coloration. The figure above illustrates an adult male gray langur during a troop progression. Although there are no marked physical differences between the sexes in langurs, the unhurried or confident gait often accompanied by soft vocalizations draws attention to an adult male. The elevated tail may be the only part of the monkey that can be seen bobbing above tall grass. The erect posture and contrasting color of the tail aid troop members in maintaining contact with the focal male during shifts within the home range. The tail position also changes during encounters between males.

While the illustrated tail posture is characterstic of langurs in Ceylon, the gray langurs of India hold their tails looped over their backs or directed toward their heads. Does the signal value of the raised tail remain the same among different populations even though the exact position varies? Or does the signal value itself change and reflect differences in habitats? Many new questions in behavior and ecology have been raised by such observations of geographical variation in different primate groups. As a rule visual, auditory, and olfactory signals have been studied one at a time. This approach has largely ignored the obvious fact that combining signals from different senses greatly increases the flexibility of communication. Furthermore communication cannot be understood only in terms of which sense organs are involved. The age and sex class of the animals responding and the distance over which the signal is transmitted must also be considered.

SOCIAL ORGANIZATION IN PRIMATES

These members of a troop of toque macaques, exposed to possible predation, are rapidly stuffing their cheek pouches, after which they will quickly retreat to the shelter of trees and eat at leisure. (MCKAY)

In several early studies of primate behavior, the focus was on identifying the drives (sex, aggression, fear) that appeared to explain the motivation of animals. Later, investigators found that breeding in several species was highly seasonal. This ruled out the idea that sexual drives were the primary factor underlying social organization. With an understanding of social roles of different age and sex classes, such questions could be reframed.

What are the possible advantages of year-long association with other animals? Two selective pressures are immediately apparent. Social coordination may increase the chances of finding food and avoiding predators. Certain species have specific food calls and alarm or mobbing calls that alert other monkeys nearby. These calls may reduce the energy wasted in the search for food and in avoiding predators, because the position of the object noted by one animal is communicated to the rest. Macaque troops frequently forage on the ground. Many individuals may move into an exposed area where food is concentrated, stuff their cheek pouches, and then retreat quickly to the shelter of trees to eat at leisure.

The energy costs of rearing young may be particularly severe for small primates and may have led to the development of a pair bond in species like marmosets. After a pregnancy, there are still energy demands on a female marmoset to produce milk for twins. However, the energy load on the female is limited since the male takes the role of carrying the young.

In general, primates occupying similar habitats show comparable social organizations. Primates living in the upper levels of the forest canopy tend to have a small troop size and a single adult male in a reproductive troop. They also have small home ranges that overlap little with those of neighboring groups; leaf-eating monkeys share these characteristics. Similar-sized primates that forage on higher energy foods, such as insects and fruits, must travel relatively farther than leaf eaters. For example, macaques have larger home ranges that frequently overlap extensively with those of neighboring troops. Their troops are generally larger and as a result include more maturing males. Savanna baboons move in herds that may number more than 200 individuals and travel several miles each day. Several fully adult males move with these groups and provide protection against predators.

A similar theme appears in ungulates. Forest browsers live spaced or in small groups while open grassland species may congregate into vast herds that move much larger distances. This correlation between type of food eaten, group size, and home range size in terrestrial as well as in arboreal herbivores emphasizes both the opportunities and limitations that ecology places on social organization and indicates that the social trends observed in primates are not unique or specific to the lineage most closely related to the ancestors of man.

EXCEPTIONS TO THE RULE

Every generalization has its exceptions, and the diversity of primate societies illustrates room for variation around a central mode. Ringtailed lemurs from Madagascar provide the only described example of social groups in which females are dominant over adult males. In chimpanzees and a few other species, groupings are loosely organized and individuals associate for short periods of time before separating again.

Dominant individuals have been identified frequently as those males that can keep others away from a particular female and as those individuals that can monopolize a favored resting spot or food supply. If a dominant individual walks toward another individual, an unchallenging or submissive individual may avoid eye contact by turning away, by vacating its position or by standing and "presenting." Care must be taken in comparing species because similar postures may have different functions and be used in different contexts. Genital presenting is not restricted to sexually receptive females. It is performed by dominant adult male marmosets, and may also be performed as a greeting by chimpanzees.

In the majority of primate societies, adult males are dominant over females. They protect their troops from encroachment by neighboring troops and from predators. However, females are not simply passive members of the societies. Females may mob a predator, retrieve a fallen infant, and influence the direction and rate of troop progressions. By forming subgroups of females with similar-aged young, the females provide a social setting for play groups.

Mouth open wide and lips withdrawn to expose the canines constitute a graded visual threat signal of an adult male gelada baboon. The threat is mild when the male does not expose his canines completely and keeps his arms crossed over his chest. (NAN A. MUCKENHIRN)

A curious female ape wanting to inspect the newborn infant of another troop member often presents her genitals as an appeasement gesture. If all is well, the protective female may simply turn her face away, as this gelada baboon has just done. (NAN A. MUCKENHIRN)

Potato washing among stump-tailed macaques of Koshima, Japan is a learned behavior. At left an infant observes as its mother washes a potato in a stream. When adult, right, the individual continues the behavior and, in turn, the next generation of young learn by observing. (JAPANESE MONKEY CENTER, AICHI)

Through constant association with infants, adult females facilitate learned traditions. Young individuals learn what food to eat, where to feed, drink, and sleep in the home range, and what other animals to avoid.

Populations of the same species have rarely been studied in different habitats. At least one species shows as much social variation within the species as occurs between some species. The social organization of gray langurs (*Presbytis entellus*) varies from troops containing several "age-graded" males in dry zone forests of Ceylon to troops containing only one adult male in some areas of India. In Ceylon, there are no "bachelor" groups of males excluded from reproductive troops as there are in India.

Other species are more predictable. The closely related purple-faced langur (*Presbytis senex*) of Ceylon lives in habitats as different as montane cloud forest and lowland dry zone forest yet everywhere maintains a troop structure containing a single male.

Some of the most complex feeding behavior described in primates involves the tool use by chimpanzees. By removing the outside leaves from a grass stalk, the chimpanzees fashion tools that can be used to remove termites from their mounds. By partially chewing leaves, chimpanzees can make a sponge for removing drinking water from holes in trees. A study of a different chimpanzee population lacking these behaviors has suggested that these behaviors are local traditions. Current generalizations are based primarily on comparisons *between* species. Some of these generalizations may have to be modified as we increase our understanding of the flexibility or stability of different social organizations *within* species.

The food industry uses the function of forming bonds by means of food and drink in its advertising (Fig. 24–9).

In the cases described last, the agreement lies in the principle, not in the formal pattern of movements. The motor patterns are not innate but certain inclinations are. It remains to be ascertained whether these are caused by innate releasing mechanisms or by specific drives.

GREETING BEHAVIOR: Not only the comparison of people from different cultures, but also comparison with other animals can be very revealing. Chimpanzees have a smile that is in certain ways similar to the human smile. Many similarities can be found in greeting behavior: We mentioned the eyebrow flash, nodding, and kissing. The form of greeting that is found among many peoples, the rubbing of noses, is probably not derived from the kiss but has another origin. When Bali lovers greet each other in this way and they breathe in deeply, it is a kind of friendly sniffing. The sense of smell does play a larger role in the social relations between people than is generally realized. In the German language one speaks of not being able to stand another's odor when one cannot stand another person. According to K. Nevermann, among the Kanum-irebe tribe of southern New Guinea it is an expression of close friendship when one takes something of the odor of the person who leaves. The person who remains reaches under the armpits of the one who is leaving, smells the hand, and rubs the odor over himself.

Of old inheritance is our threat posture, which is expressed by rolling our arms inward in the shoulders, and during which the hair erectors on the shoulders and back contract, although we no longer have any fur. We experience this contraction only as a shudder. In chimpanzees, which assume the same posture, the hair becomes erect and their outline is enlarged.

In response to strong acoustic stimuli people raise their shoulders, bend their head slightly forward, and close their eyes. Reactions homologous to this "neck–shoulder reaction" are known from other mammals.

SEXUAL DISPLAYS AND DOMINANCE: A very curious display behavior of many primates, including man, has been pointed out by D. W. Ploog and others. Squirrel monkeys display against conspecifics by presenting the erect penis when they meet. Even young animals show this. In the common marmoset (Callithrix jacchus) males display in defense of their families by raising their tail and exposing the rear to the opponent. The testes are pressed into the scrotum, an erection takes place, and the males urinate. After this display, they retreat to a marking place and mark it with urine. During the threat display they look back to the opponent. The posture of showing the rear to the viewer is probably explained by the flight motivation of the animal. Females display in a similar posture, and not knowing the behavior of the males one could be misled to assume that the posture derived from a female sexual presentation. This is not the case, however. The females imitate the male posturing.

Vervet monkeys, baboons, and many other monkeys have been observed where several males sit at the periphery of their group "on guard." It was believed that they were watching out for predators. But this precisely they do not

Figure 24–10 Genital displays of male primates. From left to right: squirrel monkey, vervet monkey, proboscis monkey, and baboon. (FROM W. WICKLER)

do. Instead they slink away as inconspicuously as possible in such cases. W. Wickler has discovered that this behavior is directed against neighboring troops. The "guards" always sit with their backs to their own group and display their male genitals prominently (Fig. 24–10), which in these animals are very conspicuously colored. When a strange conspecific approaches, the penis becomes erect and in some species it is moved rhythmically. This behavior is a display that serves to mark the territory. Interestingly enough, the same behavior could be demonstrated in man. Some Papuan tribes emphasize their masculinity by artificial means (Fig. 24–11).

On the Nicobar Islands and on Bali, I saw fetishes with an erect penis which are used to ward off ghosts. Wickler called attention to stone columns in ancient Greece with a man's head and a penis that were used as property markers Phallic "guardians" carved in wood or stone can be discovered in Romanesque churches (in Lorch, West Germany, and St. Remy, France). In modern Japan phallic amulets are still used, for example, to protect against car accidents. In the Museum of Linz (Austria) one finds amulets that depict male sexual organs. It is possible that pathological exhibitionism can be traced back to a drive to display.

Figure 24–11 Genital displays in man. From left to right: two Papuans from Kogume on the Konca River, Herme of Siphnos (490 B.C.), and a house guardian of the natives of the island of Nias. In the Greek statue the beard is also emphasized as a male symbol. In beardless peoples, male head ornaments are emphasized. (FROM W. WICKLER)

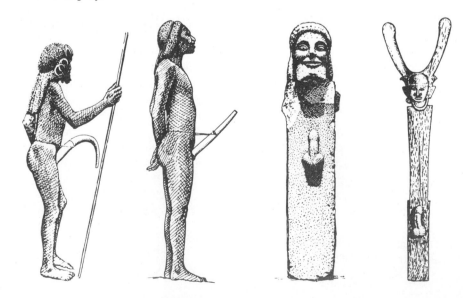

Wickler derives the genital displays of primates from urine ceremonies which contain elements of copulation behavior. In many mammals males mount conspecifics of the same sex during an aggressive assertion of rank. In rhesus monkeys "rage copulations" were also observed during the course of aggressive conflicts, where the aggressively aroused individuals often mount a third one who is not involved. It should be examined to what degree this occurs in humans. In a recent Polish novel, *The Painted Bird*, I found the reference that young herdsmen rape strangers who enter their territory. In some prisons in the United States new prisoners are occasionally beaten up by the other inmates. If the person does not fight back "like a man," he is treated like a girl and is raped. In short, mounting, in many primates, possibly including man, is a demonstration of rank of an aggressive nature. It appears warranted to me to interpret the "sitting on guard" of many primates as a further ritualization of this behavior (the threat to mount).

RELEASING STIMULI IN MAN

The experiments carried out on a large scale by industry and the arts using various models show, just as certain miscarriages of our esthetic and ethical value judgments, that we react almost automatically to certain releasing stimulus situations in a predictable manner. This is likely to be on an innate basis, although a definite proof cannot be obtained because persons who have grown up without experience are not known. We know, however, from infants that they react innately by smiling to certain stimulus configurations. Children prefer a schematic representation of a human face over an array of other stimuli during their first week of life.

Responding to shapes

Lorenz stated that the behavior patterns of caring for young and the affective responses which a person experiences when confronted with a human child are probably released on an innate basis by a number of cues that characterize infants. Specifically the following characteristics are involved:

1 Head large in proportion to the body.
2 Protruding forehead large in proportion to the size of the rest of the face.
3 Large eyes below the midline of the total head.
4 Short, thick extremities.
5 Rounded body shape.
6 Soft-elastic body surfaces.
7 Round, protruding cheeks, which are probably genuine differentiations with a signal function. Sometimes it is said that in the corpus adiposum buccae we have a mechanical reinforcement of the sides of the mouth to aid in sucking, but this is not proved. Such an additional function is feasible, of course, but we notice that monkeys and other mammals can get along without this formation. This argues for a specifically human organ that evolved in the service of signaling.

These physical attributes are further enhanced by behavioral ones such as clumsiness. When an object possesses some of these characteristics it releases in children some typical affects and behavior patterns. We find these objects "cute" and may want to pick them up—to cuddle them. B. Hückstedt demonstrated experimentally that the rounded forehead and the relatively large brain case are important characteristics of "cuteness" (Fig. 24–12) which can be exaggerated in an experiment. The doll and film industry utilizes this possibility and constructs "supernormal" models to elicit behavior of caring for young. Animals are also considered cute if they have some of the child characteristics. To be considered cute it is enough that the parakeet has a round head and that a young dog is clumsy and has feet much too big for his body. In Pekinese

Figure 24–12 Head proportions of young and adults are compared. (FROM K. LORENZ)

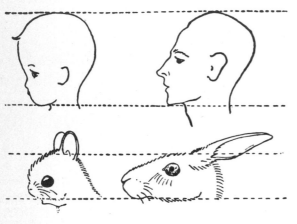

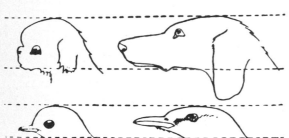

Figures 24–13 It is all too easy to read human moods into the expressions of non-human animals. For example, we tend to mistake the bony ridge above the eagle's eye as a wrinkling of the forehead. Together with the pulled-back corners of the mouth, the expression can be erroneously interpreted as one of "pride" and "defiance." The camel's presumed "aloofness" can be accounted for by man's innate releasing mechanism that responds to the level of the camel's eyes relative to its nose. Only in man does this mean an "arrogant turning away." (FROM K. LORENZ)

dogs breeders seem to have produced a perfect substitute object for the unfulfilled mothering reaction of older ladies. By offering cats to experimental persons of different ages P. Spindler released the typical patterns of caring for. The reactions (affection, euphory, patting, bending down the head, talking pet names in a high-pitched voice) mature at an age of 3.

It is also possible that the understanding of expressions is given a priori by innate releasing mechanisms, because we are easily deceived by simple models. A crying or laughing face can be depicted with a few strokes. When we see such expressions in animals we consider them "friendly" (Mandarin ducks), "arrogant" (camel), or "daring" (eagle), although this has nothing to do with the actual mood of the particular animal (Fig. 24–13). Finally, the automatic reactions to the expressions of another person argue for innate releasing mechanisms that determine a response to an expression.

Response to human expressions

P. Ekman and others found that observers in both literate and preliterate cultures (New Guinea, Borneo, United States, Brazil, and Japan) chose the predicted emotion for photographs of the face. The association between facial muscular movements and discrete primary emotions is evidently the same crossculturally.

BEAUTY: We judge our fellowmen on the basis of information which is most likely also inborn. The wide agreement of certain male and female ideals of beauty among people of different cultures points in this direction, as well as the fact that exaggeration of individual characteristics on models is so effective. In men broad shoulders are desirable, and rarely will we find a hero in art or literature who has narrow shoulders. The width of the shoulders in relation to the narrow hips is very effective, although it may be tremendously overdone, as is the case with Greek vases and statues. The shoulders are also frequently emphasized by men through clothing (Fig. 24–14). Furthermore,

Figure 24–14 Exaggeration of shoulder width in costumes and by conventional shoulder padding in men's clothing provides a greater contrast between shoulder and hip width, a common culturally derived characteristic of "attractiveness" in males.

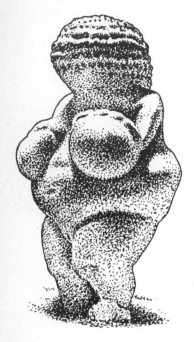

we value long limbs as well as slenderness as noble and against all reason consider gazelles and other animals with such characteristics as noble, whereas the plump hippopotamus is considered the opposite, although gazelle and hippopotamus each are perfect adaptations to a particular ecological niche. The female ideal of beauty seems to consist of characteristics that may be illustrated, according to Lorenz, by the shape of the classical Venus and the prehistoric Venus of Willendorf (Fig. 24–15). To this day people exist whose ideal of beauty corresponds to that of the prehistoric Venus in the main outlines, which is characterized, among other things, by a conspicuous fat deposit, a character displayed to this day by Hottentot women.

SEX: The secondary sexual characteristics of the woman are immediate indicators of the hormonal sexual functions. Some of the important components that are indicators of normal sexual function in a woman are a slender waistline, red cheeks and lips, as well as perhaps the shape of the pubic hair region. This is not a complete list nor does it apply to members of all races necessarily. We know of some of these characteristics that they are exaggerated in art and are emphasized by fashion. Fashion designers improve the releasing effect of the female breast by the use of padding, and in the previous century the buttock region was especially enlarged.

D. Morris interprets the breasts and lips of women as sexual signals that are projected to the front. Our apelike ancestors, so argues Morris, mated by mounting from behind and reacted to releasers visible from behind (fleshy buttocks, red labia). Walking erect led to a redirection of the copulatory position and it became necessary to develop sexual releasers on the front of the body. According to Morris, this came about by the evolution of copies of the labia as lips and buttocks as bosom on the front. The pulled-up breast of a movie star may evoke such associations, but a normal breast is just as dissimilar to buttocks as lips are to the labia. Morris also overlooks the fact that men also have red lips. His thesis is hard to support, especially because more likely interpretations exist for the development of these releasers. In higher vertebrates behavior patterns of care for young have a calming effect, for example, cuddling, feeding, clasping, and social grooming. Frightened young mammals run toward their mother to nurse, and children can be calmed with a pacifier. In many higher mammals behavior patterns of caring for young have been taken over as precopulatory behavior, in man among other things sucking behavior (not to be confused with kissing, which is a form of ritualized feeding). In connection with this the offering of the breast as a female contact gesture could have been taken over into the sexual domain and in this way the breasts acquired their specific releasing function. The lips in turn acquired their signal function as a result of their role in kissing. Kissing is a mutual activity, so both sexes evolved lips with signal functions.

The advertising industry uses our readiness to respond to sexual releasers to attract our attention and to direct it to the actual message (Fig. 24–16).

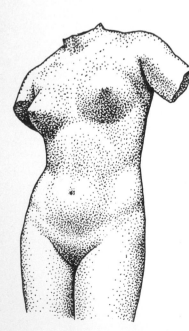

Figure 24–15 Two Venus figures, each culturally derived expressions of ''beauty'' in form. Above, Venus of Willendorf; below, Aphrodite of Cyrene.

Releasing mechanisms in man

There is much evidence that even our esthetic judgments about the external environment beyond members of our own species are influenced by innate releasing mechanisms. The paintings of chimpanzees indicate that certain basic esthetic perceptions are already present in animals. This has been demonstrated for other apes or monkeys and for some birds (carrion crows and jackdaws), which preferred regular geometric patterns over irregular ones.

SENSORY RELEASERS: We know only very little about releasing stimuli of other senses. With respect to odors, girls and women can smell musk substances when they are sexually mature, which men cannot perceive unless they have received estrogen injections. There is a report of a young man who sexually aroused peasant girls by wiping their perspiring brows after a dance with a handkerchief that he had carried in his armpit. In Mediterranean countries, forms of dancing exist where men dance around their female partners while waving a kerchief. It is said that in some areas it has also been carried previously in their armpits. It seems likely that certain pleasant as well as disgusting odors are reacted to on a primary basis; the same seems true for certain taste perceptions, although occasionally the key stimuli can be falsified, witness our reaction to saccharin. We seem to prefer sweet-tasting food. Normally such substances are rich in carbohydrates and hence in calories.

Certain perceptions of tactile stimuli release specific defensive reactions, "creeping things" on the back of the hand release a shaking movement of the hand, which Lorenz interprets as a defense against insects. A protection against damage of the teeth is prevented by a reaction to acoustical stimuli. Sharp, screeching noises release this reaction whether we bite on a hard object or scrape with a knife on a plate, which in some persons is felt as pain and projected into the teeth. The reaction consists of pulling the cheeks between the teeth and performing cleaning movements with the tongue.

Acoustical releasing stimuli have been little investigated. The crying of babies, the sobbing of another person, the desperate cry for help of a child or a woman move and alarm us so strongly that one may suspect an innate basis.

A basis of inborn releasing mechanisms may account for the effectiveness and appeal of the highest artistic expressions. In music, rhythm undoubtedly plays a large role. For instance, various physiological rhythms can be brought into phase with a metronome in humans and other animals. All of our close primate relatives display by hitting resounding objects. Drums are among the oldest musical instruments of man, and as war drums they still serve the functions of threat display. This is true also of some other typical noise-producing instruments (horns) which are used to intimidate in place of shouting. There are strong indications favoring the hypothesis that we innately recognize particular melodies as touching, charming, soothing, and so on. We describe melodies by likening them to typically inborn vocalizations such as sobbing or joyous shouting. Tender or rumbling sounds stand for the linguistic expression of tender or angry words. Tender words resemble higher notes and we know that even little girls raise their voices when they talk to a little baby. The shrill vocalizations of an angry person are universally understood and we find them uncomfortable. J. Kneutgen studied the lullaby songs of various peoples and

WE'VE GOT A GIRL WHO'S ALL WRAPPED UP IN TEXOPRINT

WANT US TO SEND HER TO YOU

Figure 24–16 The attention-getting quality of sexual releasers is used in an overwhelming majority of advertisements.

came to the conclusion that this is the most uniform musical expression throughout the world. A Chinese lullaby is just as soothing to a child as a German song or any other. When listening to lullabies, breathing becomes shallow and regular like that of a sleeping person. The characteristics of this form of breathing are also in the structure of the lullaby. The regularity of breathing is reflected in the regular components of the song. When a lullaby is played on tape, the breathing rhythm of the listener adjusts to the melody; that is, the breaths become as long as a phrase of the song. The inhaling phase of subjects generally coincides with the gradual rise of the melody; the exhaling accompanies the gradually falling melody at the end of the phrase. The breathing seems to accompany the music. The shallowness of breathing is matched by the simplicity of the melody. There are no large intervals, which gives the impression of a gentle gliding. The listeners feel relaxed, the frequency of heart beats decreases, and the psychogalvanic skin response shows little change. In another experiment, when jazz was presented under identical conditions, the subjects became excited. Breathing became irregular and the psychogalvanic skin response showed irregular changes. After the subject did kneebends, heart and breathing became normal within 3 minutes when they listened to a lullaby, and within 6 minutes without it. When jazz was played it took 8 to 9 minutes until breathing and pulse returned to the base line.

When we examine our music we discover that composers use these key stimuli intuitively to evoke various emotions in the listener—think for a moment of the rumbling drums of Beethoven's Fifth Symphony. The releasing stimuli are artfully encoded and lose much of their flashy obtrusiveness, which is a characteristic of popular music that is largely produced for commercial purposes. Because of this coding of key stimuli, it also takes awhile before one is able to "listen one's self into the music," so to speak. By the artistic manipulation of the releasing stimuli, the composer can create and dissolve tensions in the listener. The highs and lows of emotional experiences are touched in an ever-changing pattern that cannot be experienced in everyday life. This heightening of experiences is perhaps one of the most important effects of music. It is most certainly not the only component of artistic, musical creation, but it seems to be a substantial one. Added is also the pleasure in the playful experimentation and in the construction of new and different structures and sequences.

SPACE RELEASERS: Inborn releasing mechanisms also seem to determine our need for cover and unobstructed vision into the distance. Persons who have had no fateful experiences with others or with predatory animals occupy corner and wall tables first in a restaurant, the tables in the center last. Children feel comfortable in niches and like to build such cover when they play.

That the biological processing of data relating to the perception of space is inborn has been shown by experiments with cats and human babies at the visual cliff. Form constancy with various retinal representations of objects is not the result of long experience, as is widely believed. Babies less than two months old are capable of recognizing form constancies under various transformations. By turning their heads the babies were able to operate switches in their cushion. The head-turning was rewarded by the appearance of a person smiling at the baby. The babies were conditioned to operate the switch when a 30-cm cube was shown at a distance of one meter. Once the children had learned this, they recognized the cube also when it was shown at a distance of three meters. They distinguished it from a 90-cm cube shown at a three-meter distance, although the latter projects at the retina an image identical in size to the image that the 90-cm cube projects at a one-meter distance. Innate mechanisms are probably not only underlying our perceptions but also our forms of thought.

Quite remarkable finally is Lorenz's view that a number of releasing stimulus situations which affect our ethical value judgments are outlined by innate releasing mechanisms. In the art and literature of all peoples there are recurring themes, situational clichés: loyalty of friends, manly courage, love of homeland, love of wife or husband, love of children and parents—all are the noble basic motives of human actions that we follow from an inner disposition. They are the basic themes (leitmotifs) of literature and the theater from the ancient world to this day. We are gripped by the account of the friend who sacrifices himself for his fellow, and we identify with the hero of the legend or the western movie who liberates and protects the innocent girl or helpless child. If there were no innate predispositions for ethical behavior in man, if there were no binding norms for what is basically good or bad based on phylogenetically acquired adaptations, we would be in a dangerous position indeed. A cultural relativism is the logical consequence, and any cultural norm agreed upon by a society could exist rightfully.

TERRITORIALITY AND AGGRESSION

Are striving for rank and the readiness to submit characteristic of our species, as Freud, among others, assumes, or are they the products of education? To what degree are we by nature social and in the final analysis political beings? Or are we, as Hobbes asserted, forced together against our will by authority? In this section we want to examine and trace the biological bases of our social behavior and ask ourselves to what extent it may be determined by phylogenetic adaptations and what has been since acquired.

The sexual bond

It is easiest to disprove Hobbes' statement when we take the family as our point of departure. Mother and child are in a natural, well-adjusted relationship to one another on a partnership basis. The bond between them is at first brought about by a number of inborn reactions such as sucking, clasping, crying, smiling, following, and by the appropriate responses of the mother who loves her baby, in whom she responds to certain releasing stimuli.

The permanent bond of the parents to each other also seems to depend in man on something more than just tradition. Tradition does determine whether a man may have one or many wives. A permanent, long-lasting association of the partners, however, is generally the rule, and is necessitated by the slow development of the human child. Among the many mechanisms that tie people together, we also find a form of sexual bonding that we do not know of in other mammals; the latter usually mate only during the short estrous periods of the females. Only in the chimpanzee have occasional copulations outside of this time been observed. Chimpanzee females sometimes present themselves successfully outside the estrous period and gain certain advantages from a particular male such as being first at the feeding place. In humans the limitation of the sexual drive and desire to specific cycles or seasons has largely been eliminated. A woman is physiologically ready to respond most of the time to the sexual desires of the man, although she is ready to conceive only during a fraction of that time. This enables her also to maintain a tie with the man on the basis of a sexual reward, and this is probably the function of this unique physiological adaptation. Also in the service of maintaining a bond between partners is the ability of the woman to experience an orgasm comparable to that of the man. This increases her readiness to submit and, in addition, strengthens her emotional bond to the partner.

We humans do not only live in family units but find ourselves in village communities, circles of friends, and so on, and in addition to all those whom we know individually, we associate with many people in an anonymous group. We are also predestined to this type of group formation. This was emphasized by Darwin: "Since man is a social animal it is quite certain that he has inherited a tendency to be loyal towards his fellows and obedient to the leader of his tribe; since these characteristics are common to almost all social animals" (*The Descent of Man*).

Territoriality

Man is characterized as a gregarious being by a number of behavior patterns which serve in forming groups. The groupings or associations of men are exclusive to varied extents. His gregarious tendencies are opposed by nongregarious ones (Fig. 24–17). Like most vertebrates, man exhibits territorial behavior. Individuals maintain distinct distances between themselves and others. Specifically how close we are permitted to approach another person is determined by the various cultural patterns, but some generally valid basic outlines can readily be discerned. One can experimentally overstep the individual distance by casually sitting close to a person in the library. The "victims" at first try to move away from the intruder, and failing that, they erect artificial barriers against him with books, rulers, and so on. If all these efforts to withdraw fail, they leave the table. The various forms of bodily contact such as shaking hands, putting arms around another during greeting, or sitting in close contact are restricted to certain situations and social circles.

We must expect also that human beings have certain needs for space which are based on an innate disposition and whose fulfillment is necessary for our well-being. It is true that man largely creates his own environment, but its structure is surely in line with his biological constitution. Even within a family each person has his own individual domain. The areas owned by each family are more clearly marked. Apartments and gardens are areas in which we assert territorial rights, and this "natural right" is almost everywhere recognized by the makers of laws. No one may enter another's dwelling without

Figure 24-17 Although gregarious, man is also a territorial animal, his territoriality expressing itself through geographical and geopolitical boundaries ranging from national borders to the back yard fence.

special permission; this is considered illegal entrance, breaking and entering. Fences and signs designate our rightful ownership.

In everyday life we can observe examples of territorial behavior on many occasions. If one wants to sit down at an already occupied table in a restaurant, it is proper to ask politely if one may sit down. If one fails to observe this rule one releases anger in the other person. The same is true when one enters a partially occupied compartment in a train. If one does not greet in a friendly way one may experience an air of rejection.

In addition to family possessions, humans also defend group territories. Basically, human territorial behavior has the same function as in other territorial animals. Anthropological investigations support this view. In the New Guinea edition of the *American Anthropologist* (1965) it is reported that before the intervention of the Australian government some highland tribes lived in areas in which survival was just barely possible. After the tribal wars had been outlawed the people moved into already settled and more suitable regions. Overpopulation and starvation were the result. Among these people who cultivate tuberiferous plants, food production soon reached an upper limit and tribal wars served here as the spacing-out mechanism that prevented a too close spacing of the various groups.

Occasionally it is asserted that the statements of biologists are apologetic, as if the assertion that a behavioral characteristic is inborn would imply that nothing, therefore, could be done about it. This is a false attribution. Certainly many of our behavior patterns and motivations evolved as adaptations in the service of specific functions. It is as true, however, that changes in the environment can convert the adaptive value of an adaptation into the contrary. This is certainly the case with territorial aggression in our overpopulated world bristling with arms. Effective control of our aggressive impulses is needed for our survival and is certainly possible by environmental control or other measures, provided we explore the causes of this phenomenon without any bias. Those that simply deny man's inclination to act aggressively take the easy road.

Aggression as a dynamic instinct

Because aggressive behavior in human society plays a large role, there have been several attempts to understand the determinants of this behavior through the study of aggressive behavior in animals. Scott demonstrated that aggressive behavior can be decisively influenced by experience. He was able to produce very aggressive male mice by enabling them to win fights repeatedly, and he could produce peaceful males by raising them with females and by picking them up daily by their tails and stroking them gently. Aggressive puppies that were lifted off the ground so that they lost their footing also became docile. Scott came to the conclusion that aggressive behavior is learned. The habit of attack is said to emerge gradually during the course of development, when the animals experienced pain in the competition for food and during play fighting.

Others developed the hypothesis that aggressive behavior is always the result of frustration; frustration they considered to be any impediment, or external influence, which interrupts striving toward a goal. In this view aggression is primarily of a reactive nature and not the expression of a spontaneous drive. Thus Scott suggests that children be raised in an environment which is devoid of all stimuli that could release aggressive behavior through frustration. W. Craig holds that there is no appetitive behavior for fighting; an animal merely defends its interests. In short, aggression is reactive behavior in his view.

This concept of aggression is opposed by the conception of aggression as a dynamic instinct. According to Lorenz's reasoning, aggression is a true instinct with its own endogenous excitatory potential and the appropriate appetitive behavior. This concept of aggression is opposed to the earlier discussed hypotheses but has been supported by experimental results with non-human animals. There are strong indications that the dynamic instinct concept of aggression holds true for man too, but we have to admit that a clear proof for an inborn aggressive drive in man has not yet been presented.

A number of investigations have shown that rats and mice that were raised in isolation attacked conspecifics introduced into their cages, and that they exhibited all the species-typical behavior patterns of threat and fighting. Other investigators report that mice deprived of the opportunity to play with their litter mates from weaning on were more ready to fight than were mice that grew up together. The investigators presume that the mice learn during play to live peacefully together. Their fighting-play does not lead to injuries because their jaws and teeth are not fully developed.

Genetic control of aggressive behavior was demonstrated when investigators exchanged litters of mothers from aggressive and nonaggressive mouse populations. The young from the aggressive line that were raised by the docile mothers were clearly more aggressive than the animals that came from the docile strain and were raised by aggressive mothers.

Rhesus monkeys that grew up in the exclusive company of their mothers are later more withdrawn as well as aggressive when placed with playmates of the same age. In general, they adjust readily, however. The monkeys that were raised in this way are quite normal with respect to all other behavior. Scott points out the importance of early social experiences for the development of friendly social relations in mammals. Nevertheless, the fact that aggressive behavior can be so greatly influenced does not permit the conclusion that it is completely learned.

For aggressive behavior to be shown an animal must generally be in its familiar territory, or it will flee rather than attack. An animal trainer who enters the cage first and only then allows the lions to enter utilizes this knowledge. In this way he is the territory owner and the lions are inhibited in their aggression from the start.

We have already discussed those key stimuli that release fighting behavior. These are often of a simple nature. Fence lizard males (*Sceloporus undulatus*) attack females whose abdominal sides have been painted blue, and they ignore males whose abdomens were painted grey. Similarly inexperienced male stickle-backs attack simple decoys with red undersides. It is evident that fixed action patterns, releasing mechanisms, and releasing signals have evolved in the "service" of intraspecific aggression. In vertebrates, the male sexual hormone plays a decisive role in inducing the specific readiness for aggression in the adult animal, as well as in the organization of the neural structures during early ontogeny. The fact is that appetitive behavior for fighting develops in isolates, so there are strong indications that inborn drive mechanisms underlie aggression.

By means of electrical brain stimulation it is possible to release a true appetitive behavior for fighting in chickens. Investigators have also released aggression by electric punishing stimuli in squirrel monkeys. The animals learned a task following a shock, when they were rewarded by being allowed to attack a ball for a short time. Here we are not dealing with spontaneous aggression. The experiments demonstrate that by provocation a physiological state is achieved that results in an appetite for attacking which is probably similar to the physiological state responsible for the spontaneous urge to fight. That this internal aggressive urge built up by provocation can be discharged, leading to a reduction of tension, was demonstrated in experiments with humans. Experiments have induced anger in student subjects and as a result the subjects' blood pressure rose. One group of angry subjects was then given a chance to administer electric shock to the experimenter, whenever he made an error in his task. Another group could inform him of his errors by flashing a light. In those who believed they were shocking the experimenter, the blood pressure dropped rapidly, while it remained much higher in the other group. The possibility of administering verbal insults also resulted in a discharge.

The release of tension is only of short duration, however, as is the case also with other instinctive behavior patterns. In the long run, the possibility of discharging aggressive impulses constitutes a kind of training for aggression. The animal becomes more aggressive. In the same way, an aggressive drive can atrophy when an animal does not have an opportunity to discharge it for some time. We want to emphasize this point because sometimes the view is expressed that a child should have the opportunity to discharge its aggressive impulses so that it will be all the more peaceful as an adult. This possibility needs to be investigated in humans directly. There is no evidence available of such a long-lasting cathartic effect.

There are many facts that argue for the dynamic instinct concept of aggression. D. E. Davis, who investigated the behavior of gangs, pointed out that rank and territory are the objects of aggression and he concludes from his observations on humans:

> A wide variety of observations suggest that fighting for rank and territory has innate features. . . . Thus contrary to the conclusion of some authors, it seems that aggression is heavily dependent on genetics. Probably only the means of fighting and the objects of attack are learned.

In *The Territorial Imperative,* Ardrey presents evidence that supports the instinct concept of aggression quite clearly. Resistance to this concept is primarily based on philosophical convictions. Thus L. Berkowitz writes:

> But aside from its theoretical significance Freud's hypothesis has some important implications for human conduct. An innate aggressive drive cannot be abolished by social reforms or the alleviation of frustration. Neither complete parental permissiveness nor the fulfillment of every desire will eliminate interpersonal conflict entirely, according to this view. Its lessons for social policy are obvious: Civilization and moral order ultimately must be based upon force, not love and charity.

Is this conclusion actually compelling? We are in a position to deny it. The observation of aggressive animal species shows that the gregarious forms are definitely able to neutralize their aggression, which in fact is a prerequisite for the formation of groups. Individual acquaintance generally inhibits aggression. The lions, which show no social inhibitions about killing other lions as such, have an absolute inhibition against biting their own pride members. This is true for many other animals and on the whole also for man. When the Patasiwa tribe in western Seran still engaged in headhunting activities, it was their custom to attack their victims from behind in order to kill them. To attack a man from the front to take his head was considered murder. Only as long as the headhunter cannot look his victim in the eye can it be considered prey with whom there exists no personal bond. This bond is at once established, however, when one man looks the other in the eye. To kill in that circumstance was considered a crime.

The inhibitions to kill are graded. They are stronger toward members of the individualized group than toward strangers. Women and children, especially small children, are more protected than men. In Central Australia, according to one report, a woman who was suddenly surprised gripped her breasts to spray the intruders with milk. Later asked why, she explained that she did it to show that she was a mother, hoping they would then leave her unharmed. The existence of an innate killing inhibition may be presumed, especially as we find, all over the world, as subjective correlation, the emotion of pity. In this sense, innate and thus binding norms of ethical behavior seem to be programmed into man.

Controlling aggression

As an additional safeguard against the possible release of aggression in a member of the group, animals, including humans, possess a repertoire of behavior patterns which buffer aggression, including greeting ceremonies and other appeasement gestures. When animals form larger groups whose members can no longer recognize each other individually, they develop signals which unite them, for example, group odors. The familiar odor of the group inhibits aggression against a member. Man is also equipped with this additional capacity to identify with someone with whom one is not personally acquainted, and as this often involves abstract ideas and uniting symbols, it would be in the realm of the possible to create symbols that unite all mankind.

To control aggression one must promote those behavior mechanisms in man that appease aggression and facilitate the formation of bonds between members of a group—an idea advanced long ago by Freud. Freud also considered it hopeless to attempt to abolish aggression. Sometimes objections are raised which claim that man needs an enemy to discharge his aggressive drive, but experiments show that aggression can be discharged without the performance of aggressive acts. It is not even necessary that verbal insults and similar behavior be engaged in. Athletic competition is just as helpful as the passive viewing of a motion picture. When angry and non-angry college students were presented with either a 10-minute boxing film or a neutral film, the angry students were less angry after viewing the boxing film than after viewing the neutral film. There was no significant difference between the groups among the non-angry students. The film experiment suggests that the viewers can benefit in the sense of a release of tension by seeing films with aggressive content. This needs to be studied more, and further research will undoubtedly reveal additional channels for releasing aggression. In primitive people customs that serve as a kind of safety valve have been described. It has been reported that some Australian tribes come together at certain times to insult one another and to fight according to specific rules. Eskimos settle many of their disputes by song duels.

Another possible way to control aggression would be by radical counterconditioning, but to what degree this kind of training would result in a loss of general initiative is not known. It is most certainly dangerous to conduct educational experiments before the characteristics that are correlated with aggression are known. We speak of "attacking" a problem, "conquering" space, "fighting" cancer, "stamping out" this or that disease, and so on. There are many other indications that a general tendency to *explore* is positively correlated with aggression. This needs to be studied before one thinks of curing man of his aggression. The same applies to eugenic attempts to eradicate aggression.

Aggression has many positive aspects, bloodless competition being an important driving force toward cultural development. However, we must be aware that aggression can be trained to be excessive and destructive, so that the natural counterforces of love fail to curb it. Dogs deliberately conditioned to be vicious for police work are examples. Rarely can such dogs ever be reverted to a docile nature. We should not take the one-sided view of accepting our aggressive disposition as an excuse for reckless competition. To a great extent the struggle for life consists of cooperation. Our aggressive impulses are counteracted by our bonding impulses and they indeed are so strong that, for example, in trench warfare soldiers have to be shifted from time to time in order to prevent bonding over the lines by exchanging cigarettes. Indeed, any war propaganda has artificially to build up barriers against communication and bonding. And all efforts aim at making the members of their own group believe that the others are not real human beings. Perhaps this capacity of man to dehumanize fellow men made man more murderous than the invention of armament. Control of aggression requires the diligent pursuit of friendly, altruistic behavior. Only then is peaceful competition possible. If uncontrolled, aggression will lead to further murderous strife between peoples, which will endanger our very existence. The understanding of the causal relationships involved should help us in the control of our aggressive impulses.

Obedience and authority

Within the group the aggressive behavior of individuals merely leads to the establishment of rank orders, which provide society with a certain kind of stability. The high-ranking persons usually assume some kind of leadership function. The development of such a ranking presupposes not only that some members of the group succeed in establishing their authority, either by fighting or special achievements, but also that the subordinates accept this rank order.

This readiness to accept subordination, the opposite of the quest for rank, is very striking and poses particular problems for us. Obedience to the father or some other "recognized personage of public life" is generally considered of some ethical value. In all forms of government there is a tendency to the cult of personality. If necessary people will create models to be honored, and they seem to have a need to follow them. Human beings fight against the rule of brute force to be sure, but they also seem to have a distinct disposition to follow those whose authority they voluntarily accept. When one has voluntarily submitted one's self to authority, one is also at its mercy up to a certain point, as experiments by S. Milgram have shown. Milgram invited his subjects (men between 20 and 50 years of age) from various backgrounds (40 percent laborers, 40 percent white-collar workers, 20 percent professional men) to participate in a supposed learning experiment for a small honorarium. They were given the task to administer increasingly stronger electrical shocks for each error another person made. This person was supposed to be learning something but in actuality was an accomplice of the experimenter. For example, in one sequence of trials the "learner" was strapped to a chair in a separate room from the teacher (subject) and electrodes were fastened to his body. Then the experimenter explained to the "teacher"–subject that he was to administer a shock for each erroneous answer, and that he should begin with a low voltage which should be increased as more errors were made. In this way, the experimenter claimed, one would be able to study the effect of punishing stimuli on the learning process.

Frequently the "teacher"–subject would be unsure and ask the experimenter if they were to continue in view of the expressions of pain of the learner. He received the stereotyped answer, "You have no choice; you must continue." In these instances a divergence between what the subjects said and what they did appeared. Although they protested that they could not do such things to the poor fellow, they nevertheless continued to administer the shocks in obedience to the authority of the experimenter. The results of these experiments prove that a large number of persons had difficulty in opposing the authority of the person in charge of the experiment.

The postscript that Milgram attached to his paper leaves one pondering:

The results—as they were observed and felt in the laboratory—cause great concern to this author. They allow for the possibility that human nature or—more specifically—the kind of person produced by American society would not afford much protection to its citizens against brutal and inhuman treatment at the behest of an evil authority. These people did to a large percentage what they were told, irrespective of the nature of their activity and without conscientious objections, as long as they saw that the order came from a legitimate authority. When, as in this study, an anonymous experimenter could successfully order adults to force a 50-year-old man into submission and administer [supposedly] painful electric shocks to him despite his protests, then one can only be apprehensive about what a government—with much more authority—could order its subjects to do (Fig. 24–18).

The anonymous group

Usually, we tenaciously cling to the religious and political ideals of our youth. The same holds for the identification with an ethnic group. Once a young man has committed himself to a particular group, his attitude is decidedly determined for the rest of his life. Despite a similar genetic basis people can be something very different because of this imprinting-like process: Germans or Russians, Frenchmen or Americans. We owe to this tenacious clinging of a once-acquired attitude the colorful multiplicity of human cultures. However, because groups always close themselves off *against* others, we find here also the root of all ethnocentrism, whose consequences are often a destructive intolerance which remains to be overcome.

Figure 24–18 The massacre at My-lai. The complex of factors that led to this wanton slaughter of defenseless people is difficult to understand. But to shrug and dismiss the episode with the attitude that the soldiers were "only following orders" is to deny that the individuals involved were responsible for their own behavior.

In these religious, political, and ethnic groupings we are dealing with anonymous groups. The members of one religious body or of one nation do not know each other individually. However, they are united by common ideas, common representatives (head of nation, head of church), and frequently by very simple common symbols. These symbols may be badges or flags or forms of dress. How important such symbol identification is for the cohesion of a group can be seen from the fact that new nations and political groups see it as one of their first tasks to build tremendous and expensive memorials and to exhibit their insignia of state and the pictures of their presidents everywhere. An important group-binding function is also found in national holidays.

Within the anonymous group, aggression is largely well buffered, although not as well as in an individualized group. We are on the whole less altruistic toward an unknown person when he is a member of our anonymous group than toward our personal friends. The necessity of a morality based on reason seems to be a necessary consequence of this fact. We will serve a friend without question because we are fond of him, but there are also situations in which people serve anonymous members of their group with a high emotional investment, especially when they direct their attention against members of another anonymous group whose members are adherents of other ideals. This aggressive characteristic of groups could possibly be overcome by symbol identification if it were possible to create ideals and symbols that could unite the whole of mankind. In all anonymous groups there exists a strong tendency toward conformism, an assimilation to the other members in appearance and behavior. Outsiders who resist this assimilation release aggression. This conformity in behavior becomes especially obvious in activities such as sports and parades.

It has sometimes been stated that basically man is fitted for life only in an individualized group such as the family and a circle of friends. What we have said so far should have shown that man also possesses all the prerequisites for the formation of anonymous groupings that contain millions of members. He is adapted to both, though the step toward the anonymous group seems to be of a more recent date, and the processes of adaptation are still in progress.

In our feelings toward our fellow men we are in the process of developing new attitudes of social responsibility. Emotionally we are still better adapted to a life in individualized communities, the emotional ties with members of the anonymous group being less strong than those with our family and friends. The need is urgent, however, to develop a new social responsibility also toward members of the anonymous group, and ways to achieve this goal are offered by different ideologies. Christianity, as well as Marxism, propagate the identification of the individual with the anonymous group, fighting at the same time egoism and individualism. Because the source of individualism is the family, attempts have been made repeatedly in theory and practice to dissolve this core group as well as to fight the establishment of individual bonds. Thus, it was hoped, man would become one with the collective. These attempts have failed so far, owing to man's inborn inclination to form families and seek personal relationships. One will thus be compelled to look for methods that achieve social responsibility of individuals toward the anonymous community but also allow the formation of individualistic bonds. The one does not necessarily exclude the other.

EVOLUTION OF HUMAN BEHAVIOR

Man's biological adaptedness

It is commonly said that man is more helpless than any other animal and probably would not survive without the aid of technology. This view of man as a "deficient" being continues to be held in the anthropological literature and has more recently found its way into the popular literature. This view is, however, very one-sided. It overlooks the fact that there is no such thing as a perfect organism. Each specialization in one area means a loss in another. A mammal such as a seal, which has been adapted to life in the sea, can move only with difficulty on land. In addition, each presently living organism is the result of countless restructuring processes. The fact that all land vertebrates have descended from fishes is evident as an historical burden in the blood circulatory system of these vertebrates. The still incompletely separated circulatory system of amphibians and many reptiles can be considered a deficiency from the point of view of an engineer. The step-by-step transformation of the fish-blood circulatory system to include the circulation through the lungs as an adaptation to life on land at first leads to an incomplete separation of venous and arterial blood. Frogs, salamanders, and even the lively lizards, as "vertebrates with mixed blood," do not have as much endurance to reach the peak performance during an escape, as fish, birds, or mammals can easily reach. Whenever a way of life changes, the morphological and physiological adaptations limp along behind. The tendency of man to develop fallen arches and varicose veins in the legs shows that these systems still lack some of the necessary adaptations to upright walking. These things are not, however, specific "deficiencies" in man, but they are the expression of evolution in progress.

Many characteristics of man considered "faults" prove upon close observation true adaptive characteristics. This is true for hairlessness, which, along with the numerous sweat glands, makes it possible to chase prey animals with perseverance in warm climates. Bushmen pursue antelopes until the antelopes collapse from fatigue. Mammals that have fur often suffer from overheating.

Furthermore, it can hardly be considered a deficiency that man is not specialized in a particular way. He is, in Lorenz' words "a specialist in not being specialized." To this fact man owes his worldwide distribution. His sense organs are excellent and his physical capacities were illustrated by Lorenz by comparing them with those of other mammals:

> If one were to set the three tasks: to march 35 km in one day, to climb up a 5-meter-long rope, and to swim a distance of 15 meters in 4 meters depth and pick up a number of objects in a certain order from the bottom, all activities which a highly nonathletic person who sits much of his time behind a desk—like myself—can do without difficulty, then there is no single other mammal which can duplicate this feat.

This universality in the physical realm is matched by a surprising individual adaptability. Man is, as Lorenz said, a "curiosity being open toward the world." Whereas most mammals are curious only in their youth, this youthful characteristic is retained by man for the rest of his life. He is forever ready to actively explore new things and to experiment with things in his environment. From his tree-dwelling ape-like ancestors man inherited a few adaptations which were originally developed for climbing, the hand for grasping, binocular vision, and spatial intelligence—the ability to comprehend spatial relationships "centrally." He who climbs about in trees by the use of hands must be able to judge distances well and to integrate the observed relationships centrally. All these adaptations to life in the trees became useful in a new way when our ancestors were forced, with an increasing change from forest to grassland, to move on the ground. At first they probably moved from one group of trees to another, but even this requires erection of the body to look out for enemies above the grass. The hands could become free for carrying objects. Chimpanzees carry fruit in their hands while walking erect.

Use of tools and imagination

With the continued progression of the grasslands, the necessity to hunt prey probably arose, and this produced a strong selection pressure toward the use of tools, which eventually led to the making of them. The Australopithecines of South Africa and the Olduvai Gorge made tools with which they killed their prey.

Simple chipped-stone tools (Fig. 24–19) for a long time determined the state of human culture, and the explosive development of tool-producing cultures came about only in relatively recent times. Why the development stagnated for over the hundreds of thousands of years after the invention of the first stone implements, and then changed to the sudden evolution of a tool-producing culture, we do not know. Perhaps this was directly linked to the development of language. Language makes it possible to pass on the experiences of individuals to a greater extent.

Higher mammals have the capacity to solve problems without actually trying out all possibilities. A chimpanzee, confronted with the task of getting a banana fastened at the roof of a cage out of reach, may sit down quietly and, by looking around, spot a box and finally, without moving, discover the solu-

Figure 24–19 Tools, such as these chipped stone tools of the Late Stone Age in Africa (near the Vaal River), reveal precious details about the way of life of the people who made them.

tion of placing the box beneath the banana. In man the capacity to experiment in imagination is advanced so far that we may rightly call him the "fantasy being." We combine our thoughts in ever-new ways, and not only when a concrete task demands a solution. We play with these contents of our mind, build castles in the air, devise plans for our actions, and thus dissolve old habits. This capacity enables us to stay open to adaptive modifications. Sometimes, however, we create images in our fantasy which determine as imaginary forces our future behavior. This is apt to happen when our fantasy constructs originate under the influence of strong motivations (aggression, sex). To a degree man lives a second life in fantasy, and this may have cathartic effects sometimes, when real life denies the role a man would like to play.

Communication

The necessity of communal hunting enforced the evolution of a highly differentiated communication system. Typical for humans is language with words. While non-human animals merely reflect their internal state with their primarily innate repertoire of vocalizations, man gives names to objects in his environment and hence he can make statements about it.

To communicate emotions we do not necessarily require language because our innate expressive behavior repertoire is quite sufficient. It is possible that the function of language originally was only to communicate certain environmental contingencies, such as collaboration for the hunt. Children also use their first sentences for communicating about the environment and only much later express their emotions by the use of language. R. J. Andrew calls the emancipation of vocalizations from emotions an important prerequisite for human language. This fits in with the observation that the most sensitive parts of our auditory range, around 3,000 Hertz, are not utilized in speech. In this range lies the frequency of the distress calls of a child or a woman, to which we probably react innately; in other words, this range is emotionally occupied. For speech we use the available frequencies around 1,000 Hertz. Here we are also aware of the freedom from instincts, and only because of this can language become the basis for objective communication. This objectivity is a distinctly human characteristic, but the independence from instincts has its limits. It is true that, in man, learned behavior patterns predominate over innate ones. In absolute terms, however, we most likely do not have fewer fixed action patterns than other primates; more likely we have more. In addition, we have inborn motivations such as play, hunting, and gathering drives, striving for rank and status, which have no definite correlated motor patterns and which are in part recent acquisitions in our phylogeny; we may think here of our drive to speak. Such primary motivations are probably the cause of the principal analogies in various cultures, because they have a determining influence as learning dispositions. In the course of this learning, man learns by innate mechanisms when his behavior is drive-reducing or when a terminal, drive-rewarding situation has been met. This liberation of the drives from the bonds of strictly programmed courses of motor behavior allows for the wide range of adaptive modifiability of our behavior and is one more of man's distinct behavioral characteristics.

A LOOK INTO THE FUTURE

The claim of ethology to be able to contribute to a better understanding of human behavior has often been rejected by scholars of a more philosophical orientation. The methods of ethology, it is sometimes said, are not adequate for human psychology precisely because we are not "animals." Animal behavior is said to run its course like a programmed computer, and this model is not applicable to human behavior.

First we must reply that an ethologist does not uncritically extrapolate from insights gained in the study of one animal species to another. Instead he develops working hypotheses whose applicability must be verified in each individual case. However, the hypotheses that were devoloped during the study of one species are of great help in studying a new species. When we speak of man, we do so in the sense of one particular species, but not by excluding it from the animal kingdom. We are united with all animals by a natural relationship.

In human behavior we were able to demonstrate the existence of phylogenetic adaptations in the form of fixed action patterns, innate releasing mechanisms, releasers, internal motivating mechanisms, and inborn learning dispositions. Our knowledge is still filled with gaps, but we are encouraged to continue our research in line with biological viewpoints, especially as it has been shown that, especially with respect to our social behavior, our actions are to an important extent preprogrammed by phylogenetic adaptations. Our social behavior, particularly, is clearly disrupted today by certain changes in our environment, and only insight into the causal relationships can lead to successful therapy. Only exact knowledge of the determinants of our behavior will lead to its eventual mastery. If we know, for example, which releasing stimulus situations arouse certain impulses to act, then we can either seek them out or avoid them. Insight into the workings of our innate motivating mechanisms will make their control easier, as is true for all insights into relationships which allow us to extricate ourselves from a rigid stimulus–response chain by virtue of our mental capacities. We have already discussed the capacity to detach ourselves from a problem and view it from a distance, an ability that is highly developed in man. This ability to gain perspective allows us to contemplate the consequences of our actions and to choose among several alternative courses of action. Up to a certain point man can, with the help of this capacity, act against his drives. It is in a way the basis of our specifically human freedom. The prerequisite for a responsible decision is the causal understanding of those behavior mechanisms which underlie our behavior. The less we know about them, the more blindly will we follow their dictates.

1   Is there such a thing as "culture-free" behavior in humans? What cultural elements do all human societies have in common?

2   What is meant by "self-regulating mechanisms" in man? What are some of these mechanisms?

3   Name four characteristics of man which differentiate him from all other animals.

4   Many human behaviors, kissing for instance, are thought to be derived from other behaviors that served different purposes. What are some of these behaviors? From what you know about the evolution and adaptiveness of behavior, discuss how these behaviors may have been selected for.

5   List several ways in which advertising may play on biologically and culturally determined responses to certain stimuli in order to catch the viewer's eye.

6   Are there such things as "inborn releasing mechanisms" in man? What might some of these be?

7   Cite several examples of territorial behavior in man. What is the relationship between territorial behavior and aggression?

8   Discuss the assumption that man is an inferior biological specimen who survives only because of his brain.

9   What role did tool-making and language play in the evolution of human society?

SELECTED READINGS   Alland, Alexander, Jr. *Evolution and Human Behavior*. New York: Natural History Press, 1967.

————. *The Human Imperative*. New York: Columbia University Press, 1972. These are two thoughtful, lucid, and intelligent books on human behavior, its nature and evolution.

Darwin, Charles. *The Expression of the Emotions in Man and Animals*. Chicago: University of Chicago Press, 1965. It is interesting to note that Darwin, although most widely known for his *Origin of Species*, was specifically interested in the evolution of behavior. This book, published first in 1872, shows the role that behavior played in Darwin's thinking. Darwin developed the idea of the ethogram—a taxonomy of behaviors intrinsic to each individual species.

Otten, Charlotte, ed. *Aggression and Evolution*. Lexington, Mass.: Xerox College Publishing, 1973. Twenty-three essays on the subject of aggression covering the biology of aggression, man's "carnivore psychology," aggression in primates, the role of crowding and stress, and the divergent views shared on the subject by psychologists, psychiatrists, and anthropologists.

TAXONOMY AND THE DIVERSITY OF LIFE

The branch of biology concerned with describing the diversity of organisms in nature and arranging them in a meaningful way is called **taxonomy**.

There are many ways to categorize structure in the biosphere. For example, it is possible to classify organisms on the basis of their ecological roles. Thus, there is a trophic structure composed of producers, consumers, and decomposers. However, this classification is based on only one criterion—the methods for energy procurement used by organisms. Therefore, it is called a **special purpose classification** and conveys a limited amount of information. Another example of a special purpose classification might be a list of all the economically important plants occurring in a given area. Such a list would give some information about the economic worth of a certain group of plants, but it would be impossible to predict much more about any one member of the group.

A classification based on a large number of attributes or characteristics, however, would contain a large amount of information about the objects being classified, and it would be possible to predict many of the properties of one group by knowing about the properties of a similar one. This is called a **general purpose classification**, and it is widely agreed that such a system is the most desirable one for classifying the world's biota. Thus, taxonomists are primarily concerned with the theory and practice of classifying organisms based on overall similarities and the number of attributes they have in common, and with the ordering of biological diversity into useful categories.

Species are named by a combination of two Latin (or sometimes Greek) names. Similar species are grouped within the same **genus** (plural, **genera**), and the name of the genus is the first part of the species' name. Most swallow-tail butterflies in North America are considered to be sufficiently similar to be placed in one genus, *Papilio,* although a few others are placed in other genera, such as *Battus* or *Graphium*. The genus *Papilio*, however, contains 20 or so groups of butterflies considered to be sufficiently distinct from one another to rate species status, and each of these groups has been designated by another word, its specific name, such as *glaucus, rutulus,* or *multicaudata.*

In order to name any one of these species properly both its generic and specific names must be used: *Papilio glaucus*, *Papilio rutulus*. Generic names are always capitalized, while specific names (as a rule) are not, and both names always appear in italic type. When no danger of confusion will result, it is acceptable to abbreviate the generic name with its first letter, *P. glaucus.*

While species with a number of attributes in common are grouped together

	jellyfish	sparrow	fish	lion	fox	DOG	coyote	bear	deer	frog	lizard	lancet
KINGDOM Animalia	jellyfish	sparrow	fish	lion	fox	**DOG**	coyote	bear	deer	frog	lizard	lancet
PHYLUM Chordata		sparrow	fish	lion	fox	**DOG**	coyote	bear	deer	frog	lizard	lancet
SUBPHYLUM Vertebrata		sparrow	fish	lion	fox	**DOG**	coyote	bear	deer	frog	lizard	
CLASS Mammalia				lion	fox	**DOG**	coyote	bear	deer			
ORDER Carnivora				lion	fox	**DOG**	coyote	bear				
FAMILY Canidae				lion	fox	**DOG**	coyote					
GENUS Canis						**DOG**	coyote					
SPECIES C. familiaris						**DOG**						

in the same genus, genera that share important attributes are grouped together in the same **family**. As we study a number of families, we find that many of them, too, form clusters on the basis of certain shared characteristics. Clusters of families are referred to as **orders**, and, similarly, orders may be grouped together into **classes**. In turn, clusters of classes form **phyla**, and clusters of phyla are called **kingdoms**. A single example here will serve our immediate purpose to show the principle of exclusiveness (reading down) and of inclusiveness (reading up) in the hierarchy of taxonomic groups. The animal we will classify is the common domestic dog, *Canis familiaris*. Notice how diversity diminishes progressively from the kingdom level to the species level.

CLASSIFYING LIVING ORGANISMS

At the present state of our knowledge, biologists recognize five kingdoms based on differences in cellular organization—unicellular or multicellular—and the three principal means of nutrition—photosynthesis, absorption, and ingestion. These kingdoms are the Monera, the Protista, the Plantae, the Fungi, and the Animalia. Their characteristics, along with a list of the more important phyla in each, are listed here.

The classification used here is only one of many possibilities, but it is the one we feel most accurately depicts the relationships between higher categories of organisms. As our knowledge about various groups increases, we can expect classification schemes to change in order to reflect this increased knowledge. The more important phyla with living representatives are listed, and for some phyla (the vascular plants and the chordates) classes also are given.

Kingdom MONERA

Unicellular or colonial procaryotic organisms. Nutrition by absorption, photo-synthesis, or chemosynthesis. Motile or non-motile.

Phylum CYANOPHYTA	blue-green algae
Phylum EUBACTERIA	true bacteria
Phylum ACTINOMYCOTA	mycelial bacteria
Phylum SPIROCHAETAE	spirochetes

Kingdom PROTISTA

Unicellular or colonial eucaryotic organisms. Nutrition by photosynthesis, absorption, or ingestion. Motile or non-motile.

Phylum EUGLENOPHYTA	euglenoids
Phylum CHRYSOPHYTA	golden algae and diatoms
Phylum PYRROPHYTA	dinoflagellates
Phylum MASTIGOPHORA	flagellated protozoans
Phylum SACRODINA	ameboid protozoans
Phylum SPOROZOA	sporozoans
Phylum CILIOPHORA	ciliates and suctorians

Kingdom PLANTAE

Multicellular organisms with walled eucaryotic cells. Nutrition primarily by photosynthesis; primarily non-motile.

Phylum CHLOROPHYTA	green algae
Phylum PHAEOPHYTA	brown algae
Phylum RHODOPHYTA	red algae
Phylum BRYOPHYTA	liverworts, hornworts, mosses
Phylum TRACHEOPHYTA	vascular plants
Subphylum LYCOPSIDA	club mosses
Subphylum SPHENOPSIDA	horsetails
Subphylum PTEROPSIDA	ferns
Subphylum SPERMOPSIDA	seed plants
Class GYMNOSPERMAE	conifers, cycads, ginkgos
Class ANGIOSPERMAE	flowering plants
Subclass DICOTYLEDONEAE	dicots
Subclass MONOCOTYLEDONEAE	monocots

Kingdom FUNGI

Multinucleate syncytial organisms with dispersed eucaryotic nuclei. Nutrition absorptive. Primarily non-motile.

Phylum MYXOMYCOPHYTA	slime molds
Phylum PHYCOMYCOTA	algal-like fungi
Phylum ASCOMYCOTA	sac fungi
Phylum BASIDIOMYCOTA	club fungi (including mushrooms and toadstools)

Kingdom ANIMALIA

Multicellular organisms with wall-less eucaryotic cells. Nutrition primarily ingestive, primarily motile.

Phylum PORIFERA	sponges
Phylum COELENTERATA	hydras, sea anemones, jellyfish, corals
Phylum CTENOPHORA	comb jellies
Phylum PLATYHELMINTHES	flatworms (including planarians)
Phylum ASCHELMINTHES	rotifers and roundworms
Phylum BRYOZOA	moss animals
Phylum MOLLUSCA	clams, oysters, snails, squid, octopi, and other mollusks
Phylum ANNELIDA	segmented worms (including earthworms)
Phylum ARTHROPODA	insects, spiders, mites, crustaceans (including lobsters), millipedes, centipedes
Phylum ECHINODERMATA	starfish, sea urchins, sea cucumbers
Phylum HEMICHORDATA	acorn worms
Phylum CHORDATA	chordates
Subphylum UROCHORDATA	tunicates
Subphylum CEPHALOCHORDATA	lancets
Subphylum VERTEBRATA	vertebrates
Class AGNATHA	lampreys
Class CHONDRICHTHYES	sharks and rays
Class OSTEICHTHYES	bony fish (most fresh and salt-water fish)
Class AMPHIBIA	frogs, toads, salamanders
Class REPTILIA	snakes, turtles, lizards
Class AVES	birds
Class MAMMALIA	mammals

THE METRIC SYSTEM

Units of length in the metric system

10 micrometers (μm)	=	1 millimeter (mm)
10 millimeters	=	1 centimeter (cm)
10 centimeters	=	1 decimeter (dm)
10 decimeters	=	1 *meter* (m)
10 meters	=	1 dekameter (dkm)
10 dekameters	=	1 hectometer (hm)
10 hectometers	=	1 kilometer (km)

Conversion factors for units of length

1 centimeter	=	0.39 inch	1 inch	=	2.54 centimeters
1 meter	=	39.37 inches	1 foot	=	0.31 meter
1 kilometer	=	0.62 mile	1 yard	=	0.91 meter
			1 mile (statute)	=	1.61 kilometers

Units of mass in the metric system

10 milligrams (mg)	=	1 centigram (cg)
10 centigrams	=	1 decigram (dg)
10 decigrams	=	1 *gram* (g)
10 grams	=	1 dekagram (dkg)
10 dekagrams	=	1 hectogram (hg)
10 hectograms	=	1 kilogram (dg)
1,000 kilograms	=	1 metric ton

Conversion factors for units of mass

1 gram	=	0.04 ounce (avoirdupois)		1 ounce	=	31.10 grams
1 kilogram	=	2.21 pounds		1 pound	=	453.59 grams

Units of volume in the metric system

10 milliliters (ml)*	=	1 centiliter (cl)
10 centiliters	=	1 deciliter (dl)
10 deciliters	=	1 *liter* (l)
10 liters	=	1 dekaliter (dkl)
10 dekaliters	=	1 hectoliter (hl)
10 hectoliters	=	1 kiloliter (kl)

* 1 milliliter = 1 cubic centimeter (cc or cm^3)

Conversion factors for units of volume

				1 cubic inch	=	16.39 milliliters
1 milliliter	=	0.06 cubic inch		1 pint	=	0.47 liter
1 liter	=	1.06 quarts (U.S.)		1 quart (U.S.)	=	0.95 liter
				1 gallon (U.S.)	=	3.79 liters

Other units and conversions

1 Ångstrom (Å)	=	0.1 nanometer(nm)
	=	0.000 1 micrometer
	=	0.000 000 1 millimeter
	=	0.000 000 004 inch

1 astronomical unit (a.u.) = 1.496×10^{13} cm = 1.496×10^8 km
$= 9.2957 \times 10^7$ mi

1 light-year (l.y.) = 9.461×10^{17} cm = 5.88×10^{12} mi

GLOSSARY

Abiotic   nonliving (as the "abiotic" components of an ecosystem).

Absolute refractory period   that interval following the stimulus of a nerve cell when the cell is completely inexcitable.

Accommodation   tendency of excitable tissue to become less excitable when a stimulus is steadily sustained.

Ach   acetylcholine, the chemical released at the motor endplate and many other synaptic junctions. In some cases its action on the postsynaptic cell is excitatory; in others inhibitory.

AchE   acetylcholinesterase, an enzyme that destroys the chemical transmitter acetylcholine.

Acid phosphatase   an enzyme located within the Golgi which is able to break down phosphate.

ACTH   adrenocorticotropic hormone.

Actin   a protein of long chain molecules contained in myofibrils and associated with myosin in voluntary muscle contraction.

Action potential   self-propagating electrical change that spreads without decrement over the length of an axon.

Active site   a relatively small area on an enzyme molecule at which reaction with a substrate takes place.

Active transport   the net movement of a substance across a membrane, sometimes against a concentration gradient, and requiring expenditure of energy.

Actomyosin   a compound formed by combining actin and myosin and thought to be the ultimate contractile material of a muscle.

Adaptation   one of many attributes of an organism—morphological, physiological, or behavioral—that makes the species better able to survive and reproduce.

Adenine   one of four nucleic acid bases contained in RNA and DNA.

Adrenal cortex   the outer layers of the adrenal gland, and a source of several steroid hormones.

Adrenocorticotropic hormone (ACTH)   a hormone secreted by the anterior pituitary; it regulates hormone secretion by the adrenal cortex.

Aestivation   a physiological adaptation in response to heat and drought enabling an animal to avoid harsh seasonal conditions and involving a general reduction in metabolic rates during which the animal is quiescent.

Afferent neuron   (See **Sensory neuron.**)

Agonistic behavior   includes aggressive actions during territorial disputes and other hostile encounters between animals.

Albedo   the total amount of solar radiation reflected by a planet; the ratio between the amount of solar radiation reflected and received.

Aldosterone   a steroid hormone secreted by the adrenal cortex; it regulates salt balance.

Alimentary tract   that part of the digestive system including mouth, esophagus, stomach, and intestine along with associated glands. (Also called the **gastro-intestinal tract,** or **GI tract.**)

Alimentation   collectively, the processes by which an animal obtains its food supply.

Allele   one of two or more genes occupying the same locus on two homologous chromosomes.

Alternation of generations   a pattern of reproduction in plants in which one generation reproduces by asexual and another by sexual means.

Alveoli   terminal structures of the bronchioles richly supplied with capillaries and which conduct gas exchange between the lungs and blood.

Ambivalence   the alternation or mixing of two discrete motor patterns.

Amino acid   the building block of proteins, consisting of an amino ($—NH_2$) group, a carboxyl ($—COOH$) group, and an R group, which is variable. Since there are about 20 different R groups, there are about 20 different kinds of amino acids.

Ampulla   a small enlargement containing hair cells on each of the semicircular canals.

Anabolism   metabolism involving the synthesis of materials; for example, the synthesis of glycogen from sugar.

Anaerobic   without oxygen.

Androgens   male sex hormones; the predominant secretions of the Leydig cells of the testes.

Anion   an ion with a negative charge and therefore attracted to the anode or positive pole of a battery.

Antagonists   a pair of muscles, for example the flexor and extensor, whose activities alternate or work in opposite directions in such a way as to permit the lower arm, for example, to be raised or lowered.

Antennary gland   in crayfish, crabs, and their relatives, an organ that is roughly analogous in function to the kidney.

Antibodies   proteins within the blood that attack and destroy or neutralize antigens.

Antigen   a protein in the blood that can induce the formation of and combine with antibodies.

Aposematic displays   warning displays that discourage predation, including the distinctive markings of skunks, the bright colors laid out in very simple, contrasting patterns in certain poisonous reptiles, and so on.

Appeasement gesture   any stereotyped signal that inhibits further attack in the stronger of two animals (for example, the belly-up posture of a dog).

Appetitive behavior   behavior that is usually variable, sometimes in temporal patterning, and that rarely ends a bout.

Aqueous humor   fluid filling the space between cornea and lens in the vertebrate eye.

Arterioles   finely branching extensions of the arteries.

Ascending limb of Henle's loop   part of the kidney tubule or nephron.

Asexual reproduction   duplication of living things from one parent only and with only a single set of genes; for example, fission or budding.

Association   a stable plant community characterized by a few species that occur throughout its range; for example a coniferous forest "association," a heath "association."

ATP   adenosine triphosphate, the ultimate and almost universal chemical source of energy for cells.

Atria   (See **Auricle.**)

Auditory canal   external channel whereby sound reaches the eardrum.

Auricle   a chamber in the heart which receives blood from the veins and pumps it to a ventricle.

Autochthonous activities   discrete motor patterns produced in normal contexts and in a normal manner, in contrast to displacement activities, which occur in irrelevant contexts.

Autonomic nervous system   that part of the nervous system that controls the involuntary activities of the organism.

Autonomic pattern   pattern of activity, such as blushing, sweating, or hair erection, that is usually involuntary.

Autosome   any chromosome except a sex chromosome.

Autotroph   a self-nourishing organism; for example, the plant producers.

Auxins   a class of plant growth hormones that affect plant growth and development.

Axon   an extension of the nerve cell, up to a meter or more in length, that is the conducting part of the cell. (Also called the **nerve fiber.**)

Basilar membrane   the sheet of tissue bearing the organ of Corti.

Binary fission   the division of an organism or cell into two more or less equal parts by asexual reproduction.

Biogeochemical cycles   the paths followed by nutrients as they circulate through the environment, through both the living and nonliving components of a community and back again; for example, the carbon "cycle" and the nitrogen "cycle."

Biological clocks   (See **Circadian rhythm.**)

Bioluminescence   the emission of light by living organisms, involving chemical reactions that produce very little heat.

Biomass   the total quantity of material making up living organisms in a given area.

Biome   highest category of community classification, differentiated on the basis of predominant vegetation, integrated with animal constituents; for example, grassland "biome," deciduous forest "biome."

Biosphere   that region embracing the collective total of all living organisms on Earth.

Biotic   living (as the "biotic" components of an ecosystem)

Blastomere   one of many small cells produced by division during the cleavage stage of development of the egg.

Blastula   that stage of the animal embryo after cleavage.

Bout   a sequence of stereotyped behaviors following a more or less consistent pattern.

Bowman's capsule   part of the kidney that strains blood passing into the kidney tubule.

Bronchi   branches of the trachea leading to each lung.

Bronchioles   fine branches of the bronchi.

Brownian movement   a random vibratory motion of small particles due to impacts from molecules driven by thermal agitation, operating in fluid suspensions.

Budding   a means of asexual reproduction whereby a new individual develops from an outgrowth (bud) occurring on the parent organism.

Calcitonin   a hormonal product of certain cells in the thyroid gland; it regulates plasma calcium.

Calorie   the amount of energy required to raise the temperature of one gram of water 1°C. We distinguish between a *calorie* and a *Calorie,* the one with the capital "C" being defined as the amount of energy required to raise one kilogram of water 1°C, and hence called a "kilocalorie."

Capillaries   that part of the vascular system intermediate between the arterioles and venules.

Carbohydrases   enzymes that attack sugars and starches.

Care-giving behavior   all those parental behaviors that result in care of the young during their period of dependency.

Care-soliciting behavior   all those behaviors of offspring alerting the parents that the young are in need of attention.

Carnivore   an organism that eats other consumers; those that eat herbivores are termed *primary* carnivores while those that eat primary carnivores are termed *secondary* carnivores, and so on.

Casein   an important milk protein.

Catabolism   metabolism involving the breakdown of materials; for example, the breakdown of sugar in fermentation and glycolysis.

Catalyst   a chemical agent, such as an enzyme, that hastens a chemical reaction without itself being permanently altered during the reaction.

Cation   an ion with a positive charge.

Cell   the basic biological unit of all living things except viruses, containing a nuclear control center and a variety of organelles including a selectively permeable membrane that selectively segregates the cell from the external environment.

Cell membrane   the selectively permeable membrane forming the outer layer of animal cells and lying just inside the cell wall of plant cells. Also called the plasma membrane.

Cell respiration   a series of oxidative reactions in which cells break down glucose molecules and so obtain an energy source.

Cell wall   a rigid case that gives structural support to plant cells, but that is not present in animal cells.

Centralization   the collection of nerve cells of the diffuse nerve net gathering into a compact and closely-knit bundle, or central nervous system.

Centriole   a cell organelle occurring in pairs outside the nucleus of most animal cells. During mitosis the two centrioles migrate to opposite ends of the dividing cell and form the spindle apparatus.

Cephalization   the concentration of important nerve centers into a brain at the anterior end of the animal.

Cerebellum   developed from the posterior half of the brain rudiment, especially well developed in active vertebrates and concerned with muscular coordination.

Cerebral hemispheres   the paired enlargements of the anterior forebrain of vertebrates.

Character displacement   the divergence in the patterns of vocalizations of overlapping populations of two species that make the song of individuals of one species distinguishable from the song of individuals of a related species.

Chemotaxis   a movement in response to a chemical stimulus.

Chlorophyll   the green pigment in plant cells required for photosynthetic activity.

Chloroplast   green structure (plastid) occurring in plant cells and containing chlorophyll; the site of photosynthesis in plants.

Choking   a stereotype movement of the head during courtship displays used by certain birds, kittiwakes for example.

Choroid   pigmented layer of cells lying outside the retina.

Chromatin   the granular portion of a cell nucleus which contains the genes and is readily stainable by certain dyes.

Chromosome   a structure composed of chromatin and located in the nucleus; the carrier of genes.

Circadian rhythm   regularly occurring rhythms of activity that more or less keep pace with the solar day.

Clasp knife reflex   The automatic reflex relaxation of a muscle when a level of tension is reached that might damage its tendon.

Cleavage   a period of cell divisions of the fertilized egg that result in numerous small cells having a total volume approximately equal to the volume of the zygote.

Climax community the community at the endpoint of succession.

Clumped a dispersion pattern of organisms in a population that occurs when the individuals are closer together than would be expected in a random pattern.

Coacervates molecular aggregates that may have been important stages in the prebiochemical evolution of life.

Collecting duct part of the kidney tubule.

Command fibers belonging to those interneurons of the central nervous system that synapse with and control other interneurons and motoneurons in such a manner that coordinated patterns of movement are produced.

Commensalism an interspecific association in which one member of the partnership benefits without benefiting or harming the other member.

Community all the populations occurring in a particular area.

Competition occurs when there is an active demand by organisms of the same or different species for some resource which is in short supply.

Competitive exclusion principle If two non-interbreeding populations occur together and occupy the same niche, eventually one will eliminate the other.

Complete linkage process in cell division in which all the linked genes on a given chromosome segregate as an entire group.

Concentration gradient the gradual change in concentration of a substance from the region of higher concentration to the region of lower concentration.

Conditioned reflex a reflex that has been modified by experience in such a way that the original sensory component (food for example) is replaced by a different sensory component (a bell for example), but the motor component (drooling for example) remaining unchanged.

Cones cells of the vertebrate retina that are sensitive to color and are mainly responsible for form vision.

Conflict behavior the simultaneous occurrence of two opposing tendencies (for example, the conflicting urges to flee and to attack).

Conjugation a form of sexual reproduction occurring in certain bacteria and algae in which DNA is exchanged across a bridge from one cell to another, after which the two cells divide.

Consumatory behavior behavior, usually stereotyped in form and temporal patterning, that usually terminates bouts.

Consumer any organism that depends on other organisms as a source of energy and building materials.

Contest competition a form of intra-specific competition in which successful individuals in a population obtain an adequate supply of some limiting resource and prevent less successful individuals from obtaining any of the resource.

Cornea transparent outer tissue of the eye lying over the lens.

Cortisol a steroid hormone, the major secretion of the human adrenal cortex; it functions in adjustments to stress and carbohydrate metabolism.

Cretinism the syndrome associated with permanent impairment of intelligence and other neural functions as a result of thyroid hormone deficiency before or immediately after birth.

Crop in birds, that part of the esophagus that functions as a storage area. In some invertebrates the mechanical breakdown of food occurs in the crop.

Crossed extension reflex the reflex extension of one leg so as to bear the added weight of the body when the other leg is caused to flex due to a noxious stimulus of the foot.

Crossing-over the mutual exchange of genetic material occurring when chromosomes forming homologous pairs separate; a source of variation in organisms.

Cryptic behavior remaining hidden while motionless, possible because an animal's form and/or color causes it to blend with the immediate surroundings.

Cupula patch of jelly-like material resting on the hair cells of the organ sensing the direction of gravity in the inner ear.

Cycle a class of change in population size brought on by some regularity of fluctuation; for example, voles often reach peak abundances followed by sharp declines every three or four years.

Cytochromes oxygen-activating compounds involved in cellular respiration.

Cytoplasm that living material of a cell occupying the region between the cell membrane and the nuclear membrane, excluding cell organelles and particles.

Cytoplasmic streaming a special motion of the cytoplasm that supplements motion resulting from diffusion.

Cytosine one of four nucleic acid bases contained in RNA and DNA.

Dark reactions those reactions during photosynthesis that do not require light energy and can take place in the dark.

Daughter cells the two cells resulting from the mitotic division of a single cell.

Decomposers those organisms occupying the end position in the trophic hierarchy and functioning as agents of decay; mostly bacteria and fungi, which feed on the remains of all members at all levels in the trophic hierarchy.

Dendrite twig-like extension branching out from the nerve cell body.

Density-depressing factors those limiting environmental factors that prevent a population from ever reaching the full carrying capacity of the environment (among them predation, dramatic weather change, genetic, physiological, and behavioral changes brought on by changes in population density).

Deoxyribonucleic acid (See **DNA**.)

Deoxyribose the sugar contained in DNA, possessing one less oxygen atom than the sugar ribose.

Diastole resting stage of the heart beat.

Differentiation a gradual process in the development of animal and plant cells whereby they acquire the capabilities to perform specialized functions.

Diffusion the net movement of a material down its concentration gradient.

Dihybrid cross a cross involving two pairs of traits, such as seeds that are yellow *vs.* green and round *vs.* wrinkled.

Diploid (2n) having two sets of chromosomes.

Dispersal the transport, either active or passive, of individuals from one place to another.

Dispersion the spatial distribution of organisms within a local population.

Displacement behavior the production of a motor pattern in an abnormal (or irrelevant) context.

DNA (deoxyribonucleic acid) the constituent of genes, hence the carrier of genetic information in cells, and a kind of overseer of protein synthesis.

Dominance hierarchy   the stable and predictable order of dominance of one individual over another ("pecking order") from the most dominant to the least dominant individuals comprising a social unit.

Dominant   said of one trait that masks the effect of another; a gene for tallness, for example, may mask its allele for dwarfness.

Dormancy   a physiological adaptation involving a response to adverse environmental conditions and involving a temporary reduction in metabolic activity, in plants and animals alike. (See also **Hibernation.**)

Echolocation   emitting sound pulses and then locating an object by interpreting the echo of the sound rebounding from the object; a means of navigation and food location used by bats and porpoises.

Ecology   the science of relationships between living organisms and their environment.

Ecosphere   the biosphere plus the nonliving components with which it interacts; the ecosystem on a global scale.

Ecosystem   a community of organisms plus all aspects of the physical environment.

Ecotone   that area where two recognizable communities merge, often exhibiting some characteristics of both overlapping areas.

Ectoderm   the outermost layer of tissue in the gastrula stage of embryonic development.

Efferent neuron   (See **Motor neuron.**)

Electrical potential   the force due to the separation of electrical charges across a membrane.

Electrochemical equilibrium   the state at which the electrostatic force of the membrane potential balances the physical force due to the concentration gradient of a specific ion.

Electron   a unit of negative charge moving about the nucleus of atoms and having a mass only 1/1,845 that of a proton.

Electrotonic potential   the passive change in membrane potential as a result of partial depolarization of the membrane.

Eliminative behavior   defecation and urination, including the different ways in which various species keep their areas clear of feces and urine.

Endocrine system   the system of glands that release into the general circulation hormones which regulate the functions of specific target tissues.

Endoderm   the innermost layer of tissue in the gastrula stage of embryonic development.

Endolymph   fluid filling the cochlear duct, semicircular canals, and sacculus of the inner ear.

Endoplasmic reticulum (ER)   a cell organelle in the form of a series of tubules and vesicles enclosed by membranes superficially resembling the plasma membrane.

Endosperm   tissue stored as food in seeds and generated by the joining of a sperm nucleus with a fusion nucleus.

Endplate potential (e.p.p.)   the local potential developed as a result of local depolarization of the plasma membrane of the muscle fiber. (Also called **junction potential.**)

Entropy   in a living or mechanical system, that portion of energy produced that is not available for the performance of work.

Environment   the total of physical and biological factors that may influence an organism.

Enzyme   a special class of proteins essential to the chemical reactions occurring in cells.

Epithelial cells   cells that form one or more regular layers of lining tissue, such as those forming the mucosal layer of the intestine.

Equilibrium potential   the potential developed by an unequal distribution of anions and cations that just balances their tendencies to diffuse.

Esophagus   the passageway from the pharynx to the stomach.

Estrogen   female sex hormones that are the predominant secretions of the ovarian follicle during the preovulatory phase of the menstrual cycle.

Estrus   that time in the reproductive cycle of certain female animals during which they are receptive to sexual advances by the male, generally coincident with ovulation.

Ethogram   a catalog of the various behavior patterns of a species.

Ethologist   a scientist who studies the behavior of animals in their natural environment.

Eustachian tube   connecting the middle ear to the oral cavity so as to equalize pressure changes.

Excitatory postsynaptic potential (e.p.s.p.)   Local transient depolarizations of a muscle fiber or nerve cell that render it more liable to contract or discharge an impulse.

Exocrine glands   glands that secrete their products into a system of ducts that serve to transport secretions out of the body; for example, mammary glands, salivary glands.

Extrafusal fibers   the main body of muscle fibers in a voluntary muscle that produce the actual shortening.

Extrinsic isolating mechanisms   environmental barriers (rivers, mountains, oceans) that prevent gene exchange between two closely related species.

Facilitation   an interaction of successive impulses arriving at a muscle membrane site, resulting in greater sensitivity to the subsequent arrival of additional impulses.

Feces   undigested waste products that are eliminated into the external environment.

Feedback   in a communication system information that may either inhibit (regulate) or promote (reinforce) further operation of the system; in the former case we speak of *negative* feedback, in the latter case, *positive* feedback.

Fermentation   the catabolism of organic compounds by an organism in the absence of oxygen, usually producing alcohol or lactic acid.

Ferredoxin   a protein that acts as a reducing agent during the light reactions of photosynthesis.

Fetus   the post-embryonic period prior to birth in the development of a mammal.

Filter-feeding   a common form of ingestion during which the organism brings into play a filter of some type through which the ambient medium is strained and food collected.

Firing threshold   that critical value of the local potential at which there begins an inward and self-sustaining "avalanche" of Na^+ across the nerve membrane.

Fixed action patterns   certain patterns of action that are stereotyped and characterize a species.

Flexion reflex   the automatic flexion of the leg when the foot encounters a noxious or injurious stimulus.

Fluctuation   a class of change in population size due to any type of numerical variation without respect to a trend or consistency; most natural populations show this sort of variation.

Follicle a sac of cells in the ovary associated with nourishment of the developing ovum and the secretion of female sex hormones.

Follicle-stimulating hormone (FSH) a hormone that is secreted by the anterior pituitary and regulates the development of sperm in the testes and the ovum in the ovary.

Food chain a straight-line movement of energy from one trophic level to another in a one-way direction only—from the producers to the decomposers.

Food generalist an organism that uses many kinds of food and has varied feeding habits.

Food inclusions cellular structures that consist mainly of glycogen, lipids, and other organic materials.

Food specialist an organism concentrating on a narrow range of food and having relatively limited feeding habits.

Food web a complex of food chains.

Fovea concentration of cones at one point on the vertebrate retina providing color sense and the greatest detail of form vision.

FSH follicle-stimulating hormone.

Gamete a mature egg cell or sperm cell; also called a sex or germ cell.

Ganglia (sing. ganglion) collections of nerve cells that function as a local control or relay center.

Ganglion cells neurons.

Gastric mill in crayfish and other animals, a gizzard-like storage area containing teeth, in which food is ground up.

Gastro-intestinal tract (GI tract) (See **Alimentary tract.**)

Gastrula that stage of development when the single-layered blastula develops into an embryo consisting of two or three tissue layers, each of which will eventually specialize into various structures.

Gene a unit of inheritance; a section of a chromosome that determines one or more specific hereditary traits.

Genotype the assortment of genes possessed by an organism that determine its hereditary make-up.

Geotaxis a movement in response to gravity.

Geotropism a growth response to gravity.

Germ cell sex cell; gamete.

Gills structures in most aquatic organisms enabling the animal to carry on gas exchange with the external medium.

Gizzard in birds, a food storage area containing small pebbles and sand that serve as artificial "teeth" by grinding up food.

Glomerulus a cluster of capillaries in the kidney that helps strain blood passing into the kidney tubule.

Glycocalyx the outermost portion of cells, made up largely of complex sugar molecules.

Glycogen a polysaccharide made up of many units of glucose.

Glycolysis the oxidation of glucose or other carbohydrates to form pyruvic acid, in the process generating two molecules of ATP.

Golgi bodies (apparatus, material) cell structures associated with cellular secretions and the synthesis of large carbohydrate molecules.

Golgi tendon organs sense organs in the tendon of a muscle that detect a degree of stretch that might cause the tendon to break.

Gonadotropins a class of pituitary hormones that regulate the activity of the ovaries and testes (FSH, LH, prokectin).

Graded signal any signal delivered over a range of intensity, such as a dog's growl or the degree to which a blue jay's crest is raised, thus denoting the degree of aggression.

Grana stacks of membranes observed within chloroplasts.

Greenhouse effect the heat-trapping action of the atmosphere due to the blocking of long-wave radiation reflected from Earth's surface. While short-wave radiation from the Sun penetrates the atmosphere, the CO_2 layer blocks the return passage of the longer, reflected wavelengths.

Grey matter collectively those regions of the brain and spinal cord that consist largely of nerve cell bodies and fibers lacking a myelin sheath.

Guanine one of four nucleic acid bases contained in RNA and DNA.

H zone that region of the sarcomere in relaxed vertebrate voluntary muscle between the inner ends of the actin filaments.

Habitat the place where an organism lives; for example, a stream "habitat" or a field "habitat."

Habituation that learning process leading to an organism's eventually ceasing to respond to a stimulus on repeated exposure to it.

Hair cells The receptor cells of the sense of hearing.

Haploid (1n) having a single set of chromosomes per cell or individual.

Helicotrema small opening at the apex of the cochlea equalizing the static pressure between the various chambers of the inner ear.

Hemoglobin an iron-containing blood pigment that combines with and carries oxygen from the alveoli to other parts of the body.

Henle's loop the U-tube part of the kidney tubule or nephron.

Herbivore a consumer that eats plants or plant products directly.

Heredity the transmission of traits from parents to progeny.

Heterotroph an organism that relies on other organisms as a source of nutrients that it cannot manufacture for itself.

Heterozygous having non-identical alleles (Tt) at the same locus on homologous chromosomes.

Hexose a sugar compound, such as glucose, that contains six carbons.

Hibernation a physiological adaptation involving a response to adverse environmental conditions and involving a marked reduction in metabolic activity during which heart beat, rate of respiration, and temperature fall to extremely low levels. Hibernation is common among certain small mammals and in at least one bird species.

Homeostasis the maintenance of a more or less steady-state in the internal physiological environment.

Homeotherm a warm-blooded animal maintaining a steady-state temperature.

Home range the entire range over which an individual organism conducts its activities.

Homozygous having identical alleles (TT or tt) at the same locus on homologous chromosomes.

Hormones chemical messengers of the endocrine system released directly into the general circulation by various glands and regulating cell function in other parts of the body.

Hydrocarbon any compound containing a chain formation of carbon atoms the free electrons of which are linked with hydrogen atoms.

Hydrolysis   the splitting of a molecule involving the chemical uptake of water.

Hydrolases   enzymes that break molecules apart by adding water to them.

Hyperplasia   an increase in the number of cells, usually by mitosis, during the process of making up deficient tissue.

Hyperpolarization   occurs when the outside of a nerve membrane becomes more positive electrically with respect to the inside.

Hypertrophy   a process of growth involving the enlargement of a cell or organ.

Hypothalamus   a small area of the ventral surface of the brain immediately overlaying the pituitary and having a number of functions including regulation of the reproductive cycle, sex behavior, eating and drinking behavior.

Hypoxia   oxygen deprivation.

I band   in vertebrate voluntary muscle, the area of thin filaments and the Z line that is shared with the neighboring sarcomere.

Ileum   that part of the small intestine preceding the large intestine.

Imprinting   the tendency of certain animals at birth, or very soon thereafter, to follow the first moving object they see.

Impulse   A disturbance propagated over the length of a nerve fiber and whose presence is indicated by a spike or action potential.

Incus   one of the ear bones that transmits sound energy across the middle ear.

Induction   the phenomenon whereby a group of cells conditions the course of differentiation of another group of cells.

Inhibitory postsynaptic potential (i.p.s.p.)   a local increase in the membrane potential of a postsynaptic neuron that prevents or makes less likely the discharge of an impulse.

Inner ear   the sensory portion of the ear also containing the semicircular canals detecting inertial displacement and the sacculus detecting the direction of gravity.

Insulin   the hormone secreted by the endocrine pancreas; it regulates carbohydrate metabolism.

Interneuron   a neuron connecting sensory neurons and motoneurons and forming the bulk of the central nervous system.

Inter-specific competition   competitive interactions between members of two or more different species.

Interspersed   term used to describe the distribution of local populations within a total population.

Interstitial fluid   the fluid comprising the external environment of cells. (Also called the **extracellular fluid**.)

Intrafusal fibers   small muscle fibers contained within the muscle spindle that serve only to regulate the length of the whole muscle.

Intra-specific competition   competitive interactions between members of the same species.

Intrinsic isolating mechanisms   adaptations or biological differences that prevent individuals of different species from interbreeding.

Investigative behavior   the exploratory behavior exhibited by an animal when it finds itself in a new environment.

Involuntary muscles   muscles, such as the heart and those of the intestines, over which we have no voluntary control and which are controlled by the autonomic nervous system.

Iodopsin   pigment in cones of the retina that absorbs light energy and changes its chemical composition.

Ion   an atom with an electric charge. If an atom loses an electron it is said to be ionized and has a charge of $+1$. If an atom gains an electron it is left with a charge of -1.

Iris   adjustable circular curtain of tissue that limits the intensity of light falling on the retina.

Island model   a description of population structure from an evolutionary and genetic viewpoint when two or more populations are spatially separated.

Isolating mechanisms   environmental or biological barriers preventing closely related species from exchanging genes.

Isomers   compounds that may be identical in composition but differ in structure.

Isometric   used to describe the contraction of a muscle if the tendons on both ends of it are clamped to a fixed support so that it cannot shorten and only develops tension.

Isotonic   used to describe the contraction of a muscle that shortens against a light and constant load.

Jejunum   that part of the small intestine between the duodenum and the ileum.

Juvenile hormone   a hormone that is present in all but the last larval stage of metamorphosing insects; its absence in the last stage is associated with development of the adult.

K   designates the carrying capacity of the environment.

Labeled lines   conducting pathways whose transmitted information is determined not by the nature of the signals but by their source.

Larva   an immature, independent stage in the life-cycle of some animals; caterpillars and tadpoles are both larval stages.

Law of segregation   Mendel's conclusion that genes can be shown to appear in succeeding generations in predictable ratios.

Lek   a display ground, generally in a very limited area, where many males gather and set up tiny territories within which they perform elaborate courtship displays, thus attracting females to the communal mating site.

Lens   The element in the eye mainly responsible for focusing an image on the retina.

LH   a luteinizing hormone secreted by the anterior pituitary; it induces ovulation and ovarian hormone secretion in the female and testicular hormone secretion in the male.

Light reactions   those reactions during photosynthesis that require light energy.

Linkage   any two or more genes on a given chromosome segregating together without changing their positions relative to each other.

Lipases   enzymes that break down lipids (fats).

Local population   a transient sub-unit of a population that may be thought of as having many of the properties of a total population.

Local potential   a brief and non-propagated change in the membrane potential of nerve and muscle cells.

Lumen   the hollow region of an organ.

Lymph   a clear field, derived from body tissue, which functions to help maintain the body's osmotic balance, control disease, and circulate lipids.

Lymph nodes   small organs in the lymphatic system which produce lymphocytes and act to purify the lymph.

Lysosome   a cell organelle, frequently associated with the Golgi, that performs digestive functions.

Macrophages   animals that consume large parcels of food.

Malleus   the ear bone in contact with the ear drum that transmits sound energy to the stapes and incus.

Maltose   a sugar.

Meiosis   the process of cell division that reduces the diploid ($2n$) number of chromosomes in the parent cell to a haploid ($1n$) number in the daughter cells; a reduction–division process.

Mesoderm   the middle layer of tissue in the gastrula stage of embryonic development.

Metabolism   the sum total chemical and physical activities involved in the production and destruction of matter in an organism and the conversion of matter into energy.

Metamorphosis   the change from larval to adult form involving distinctive morphological change; for example, from caterpillar to butterfly, from tadpole to frog.

Metastasis   the process whereby cancer cells spread to various organs throughout the body.

Microphages   animals that consume relatively small parcels of food.

Microtubules   Submicroscopic structures found inside many cells.

Middle ear   The cavity between the ear drum and the inner ear that contains the three ear bones transmitting acoustic energy to the organ of Corti.

Migration   an adaptation involving the movement of an animal from one area to another during times of hardship (seasonal food shortage or occurrence of adverse climate). The migratory cycle often includes the animal's return to its original area when conditions there are again favorable.

Mitochondria   structures within a cell associated with energy production.

Mitosis   the process by which a cell nucleus divides and gives rise to two daughter cells with the same number of chromosomes as the original nucleus.

Molecule   the smallest possible piece of a compound, consisting of two or more atoms in association; for example, a molecule of water consists of one atom of oxygen associated with two atoms of hydrogen: H_2O.

Monogamy   the formation of single breeding pairs that may last only through the mating season or that may be of lifelong duration.

Monohybrid cross   a cross involving only one pair of traits, such as tall *vs.* dwarf, or red flower *vs.* white.

Monosaccharide   a sugar sub-unit that constitutes a complete molecular structure.

Motile   capable of actively moving about.

Motoneuron   (See **Motor neuron.**)

Motor neurons   nerve cells that lie within the central nervous system and extend their axons to muscles or glands. (Also called **efferent neurons** and **motoneurons.**)

Motor unit   the motor neuron and the muscle fibers under its control.

Muscle spindle organs   distributed among the muscle fibers and connected to the origin and insertion of most voluntary muscles, they are part of a feedback system that enables the muscle to maintain constant length under changing loads.

Mutation   a change in the nucleotide sequence of a gene often resulting in offspring that differ in one or more characteristics from the parent; a source of variation in a population.

Mutualism   an interspecific association in which each member of a partnership benefits as a result of the association.

Mutual-mimicking behavior   behavior that results when each individual tends to do what most other individuals are doing at the moment; includes the schooling of fish, V-formation flights of gueese, herding of grazing animals.

Myofibrils   parallel filaments packed with the main body of vertebrate voluntary muscle fibers.

Myofilaments   parallel longitudinal structures contained in myofibrils.

Myosin   a protein of long chain molecules contained in myofibrils and associated with muscle contraction.

Neighborhood model   a description of population structure of a large population distributed more or less uniformly over a wide area, but in which mating individuals are restricted to a neighborhood of limited distance, with the result that widely separated individuals have no chance to mate.

Neophilia   the expression of a preference for new as opposed to familiar foods.

Neophobia   the avoidance of any new food.

Nephron   the functional unit of the kidney, consisting of the glomerulus, proximal and distal tubules, Henle's loop, and collecting ducts.

Nerve fiber   (See **Axon.**)

Nerve net   in most coelenterates, elongated cells connected to one another and capable of conducting excitation over their membranes. The forerunner of a central nervous system.

Nerve ring   in jellyfish, for example, that part of the nerve net shaped as a ring that encircles the mouth opening.

Neural tube   a structure in the vertebrate embryo the anterior part of which develops into the brain and the posterior part of which develops into the spinal cord.

Neuromuscular junction   the synapse formed by a motor axon and a muscle membrane. (Also called a **motor endplate.**)

Neuron   a nerve cell.

Neutron   a sub-atomic particle contained in the nucleus of an atom with a mass about equal to that of a proton but without electrical charge.

Niche   the action or "occupation" of an organism in its habitat; for example, the "niche" of a sucker is grazing algae from rocks on a stream bottom. Also, the total of environmental parameters that establish the conditions in which a population can exist and reproduce.

Nuclear bag   central region of the muscle spindle containing proprioceptive endings that detect changes in its length.

Nuclear membrane   the selectively permeable membrane enclosing the nucleus.

Nucleic acid   an organic acid make up of nucleotides, the principal types being DNA and RNA (deoxyribonucleic acid and ribonucleic acid). Nucleic acids have three components—bases, sugars, and phosphate groups.

Nucleolus   a body within the nucleus associated with the synthesis of ribosomal RNA.

Nucleoprotein   a substance occurring in the nucleus of cells and containing nucleic acids and proteins.

Nucleotide   a basic building block of nucleic acids consisting of a pentose sugar, a phosphate group, and either a purine or a pyrimidine base.

Nucleus   a dense body occurring in most cells and containing the genetic apparatus of the cell; also the core of an atom composing nearly the entire mass of the atom.

Nutrients   mineral elements (for plants), and for animals mineral elements plus carbohydrates, which animals, fungi, and most bacteria cannot manufacture for themselves.

Olfactory bulb   the anterior part of the vertebrate brain that receives nerve fibers sensitive to olfactory stimuli in the nose.

Olfactory epithelium   the surface lining part of the vertebrate nose and covered with chemoreceptors mediating the sense of smell.

Oligophagous   used to describe food specialists, such as certain caterpillars, that will eat only a few species of food plants.

Ommatidium   a single self-contained (lens, receptor cells) light-sensitive element of an invertebrate compound eye.

Oocyte   a stage in the maturation of the egg.

Opsin   a colorless protein that combines with retinaldehyde to form the photopigment rhodopsin.

Organ   an assemblage of a variety of tissue all working cooperatively and bringing about a group function; for example, the heart, lungs, plant roots, and so on.

Organ of Corti   the sensory organ of hearing bearing regular rows of hair cells.

Organelle   one of several structures in the cell having a definite function; for example mitochondria, Golgi bodies, and nucleoli.

Organic   referring to molecules that contain those carbon atoms essential to life.

Organism   any living creature, including unicellular and multicellular beings.

Oscillation   a class of changes in population size that tend to return to a mean value.

Osmosis   the passage (net movement) of water through a semipermeable membrane to the side of higher concentration of solute and, therefore, lower concentration of water. Net movement of water molecules continues until there is an equal number of water molecules striking both surfaces of the membrane.

Otolith   mineral deposit in a sac of the inner ear that by its weight displaces the processes of certain sense cells and indicates to an animal the direction of gravity.

Outer ear   the pinna and auditory canal.

Oval window   the opening covered by a membrane through which sound energy is transmitted from the ear bones in the middle ear to the fluid of the inner ear.

Oviduct   the duct through which the egg travels from the ovary.

Ovulation   release of the oocyte from the ovary.

Ovum   the mature egg cell carrying the haploid number of chromosomes.

Oxidative phosphorylation   the process by which ATP is formed.

Oxytocin   hormone synthesized by the hypothalamus and stored in the posterior pituitary; it stimulates uterine contractions during parturition and "milk-let-down" during lactation.

Pair bond   a social system in which the mated pair may defend a territory during the breeding season only, or for the duration (sometimes for life) of their time together.

Parasitism   an interspecific association in which one member of the partnership benefits (the parasite) at the expense of the other member (the host).

Pentose   a sugar that contains five carbons.

Pepsin   an enzyme that attacks proteins and is secreted by the stomach.

Peptide bond   a chemical bond linking amino acids into protein molecules and achieved by the removal of one hydrogen atom from the $-NH_2$ and by the removal of one hydrogen atom and one oxygen atom from the $-COOH$ group.

Peripheral filtering   the specialization of peripheral receptors to respond only to specific components in complex stimuli.

Pharynx   the passageway, in vertebrates, linking the mouth and the esophagus.

Phasic contraction   occurs when maximum but brief contraction takes place in a muscle and the individual fibers twitch and shorten more or less in step.

Phenotype   the physical appearance of an individual organism, expressed in height, eye color, blood type, and so on, and reflecting both genetic and environmental influences.

Pheromones   chemical signals that alter the behavior or physiology of another member of the same species.

Phonotaxis   a movement in response to a sound source.

Photolysis   the breakdown of water by light.

Photoperiod   a rhythmic response to alternating light and darkness.

Photoperiodism   a physiological adaption to seasonality involving a response to changes in day length, resulting in an animal's being put in a condition to mate or to migrate, or a plant's development of flowers, for example.

Photosynthesis   the process involved in the manufacture of carbohydrate in plants in which carbon dioxide is combined with water in the presence of chlorophyll and light; the products of the reaction, in addition to carbohydrate, are water and oxygen.

Phototaxis   a movement in response to light.

Phototransduction   the process whereby light energy generates a membrane potential change in photoreceptor cells.

Phototropism   a growth response to light.

Pinna   external flap of the ear.

Pinocytosis   occurs when a particle in contact with the outer surface of a cell membrane is pinched off and "swallowed" into the cell.

Pituitary   the "master gland" of the endocrine system located at the base of the brain and connected to it by a single nerve tract and a specialized blood portal system; it is the source of a number of hormones that regulate the function of several other endocrine glands.

Placenta   that structure through which an exchange of metabolites takes place between an embryo and its mother, present in most species of mammals.

Planetesimals   small bodies, composed of a mixture of silicates, metallic iron, water, and ammonia, that according to theory compacted in the process of the formation of planets.

Plasma   the fluid portion of the blood containing the materials necessary for coagulation to take place.

Plasma membrane   (See **Cell membrane.**)

Pleura   the lining surrounding the lungs.

Poikilotherms   cold-blooded animals, whose temperature tends to vary with the temperature of the external environment.

Polyandry   the type of polygamy in which one female mates with several males (rare in vertebrates).

Polygamy   the formation of a pair bond with more than one mate, either simultaneously or sequentially.

Polygenic inheritance   several genes interacting and giving rise to a single trait.

Polygyny   the type of polygamy in which one male mates with several females.

Population   a group of similarly adapted, interbreeding organisms of the same species.

Population density   the number of individuals occupying a given area at a given time.

Population dynamics   the study of the rates of growth or decline in population size.

Postsynaptic cell   the cell that receives excitation.

Postsynaptic inhibition   the change in a postsynaptic neuron produced by presynaptic impulses that makes the discharge of an impulse less likely.

Presynaptic cell   the cell along which neural signals arrive at the synapse.

Primary sense cells   receptor cells that both detect and transduce stimuli as well as transmitting them along axons.

Primary social unit   the smallest group in which individuals of a given population normally can interact, survive, and reproduce.

Primate Order   that order of mammals including prosimians, monkeys, apes and man.

Producers   those organisms, such as green plants, capable of carrying on photosynthesis and thus producing food and energy by using only solar radiant energy and inorganic constituents of the environment.

Progesterone   a female sex hormone, the hormone of gestation (pregnancy).

Promiscuous   mating behavior characterized by the lack of formation of pair bonds, although mating does not take place at random.

Proprioceptors   sense organs that detect changes in the length or position of organs within the body.

Proteases   enzymes that break down proteins.

Protein   a class of large-molecule organic compounds made up of amino acids held together by peptide bonds.

Proton   a unit of positive charge contained in the nucleus of an atom and having a mass 1,845 times that of an electron.

Protoplasm   all living substance within a cell, including cytoplasm and nuclear material alike.

Proximal tubule   that part of the kidney tubule lying close to the glomerulus.

Ptyalin   a starch-splitting enzyme contained in saliva.

Pulmonary artery   artery through which blood flows from the right ventricle to the lungs.

Pupa   an immature stage in the metamorphosis of an insect. Caterpillars of moths and butterflies pupate and emerge as adults.

Radula   in mollusks a saw-like structure used in the process of grinding down food.

Random dispersion   occurs when the location of one organism in a population does not significantly influence the location of another organism of the population.

Range   that area regularly occupied by a species on a wide geographic scale.

Receptive field   the external area from which a stimulus can be detected.

Recessive   said of one trait that is masked by the effect of another; a gene for dwarfness, for example, may be masked by its allele for tallness; recessive traits are therefore expressed only in homozygous individuals.

Redirected behavior   an act involving a response (aggression, for instance) to a stimulus, the response being directed, however, toward a weaker second stimulus; punishing Person B for something that Person A did.

Reflex   the simplest kind of behavior involving rapid and consistently specific response to a given stimulus.

Reflex arc   the nerve pathway along which the impulses causing an involuntary response travel to and from the central nervous system.

Reflex ovulator   an animal in which the release of ovulating hormone (LH) is induced by a nervous reflex initiated by copulation (rabbits, cats, ferrets).

Regeneration   an adaptation of some organisms to replace body parts that have become damaged or lost.

Reisner's membrane   membrane separating the cochlear duct of the inner ear from the vestibular duct.

Relative refractory period   that period following the absolute refractory period when a second action potential can be generated, but only if the second stimulus in a rapid sequence is larger than the first.

Releaser   a complex stimulus that is strong enough to elicit a particular behavioral pattern.

Rennin   a substance contained in the stomach of infant mammals that converts casein into curds and whey.

Respiration   the process of breaking down nutrient molecules with the subsequent release of energy; also the intake of oxygen and expulsion of carbon dioxide.

Responsive requisites   those environmental factors that are affected by the presence or abundance of a given population; for example, food supply, nest sites, and the like.

Resting membrane potential   the electrical potential between the inside and outside of a nerve fiber when the fiber is inactive.

Retina   sheet of light-sensitive cells at the back of the eye upon which falls the image focused by the lens.

Retinaldehyde   one of the products of the breakdown of rhodopsin by light.

Retinula cells   cells that detect light in invertebrate compound eyes.

Rhabdome   the light-sensitive portions of the retinula cells in an invertebrate ommatidium.

Rhabdomere   the light-sensitive portion of one of the retinula cells composing a rhabdome in an invertebrate ommatidium.

Rhodopsin   the best known photopigment in the retinal cells of vertebrates.

Ribonucleic acid   (See **RNA**.)

Ribose   the sugar contained in RNA and containing one more oxygen atom than DNA.

Ribosome   a small cytoplasmic particle, the site of protein synthesis in the cell.

Ritualization   the evolution of a behavioral pattern into a signal, usually involving a loss of some elements, elaboration of others, and changes in temporal patterning.

RNA (ribonucleic acid)   a nucleic acid associated with protein synthesis.

Rods   cells of the vertebrate retina that are sensitive to low light intensities (night vision) but cannot detect color differences.

Rough endoplasmic reticulum   the intracellular membrane system probably involved in circulation of materials through the cell.

Round window   connects the scala tympani to the middle ear.

Rumen   a special stomach in ruminant animals, where bacteria break down cellulose.

Salivary glands   glands in the mouth that pour digestive juices into the oral cavity.

Sarcomere   the repeating unit between any two Z lines along the fibril in vertebrate voluntary muscle tissue.

Scala media   the central compartment of the cochlea containing the organ of Corti, also called the cochlear duct.

Scala tympani   one of the three chambers of the cochlea and connected to the round window.

Scala vestibuli   one of the three chambers of the cochlea and connected to the oval window.

Sclera   tough outer layer of cells surrounding the eyeball.

Scramble competition   a form of intra-specific competition in which all members of a population have equal access to a limiting resource.

Secondary sense cells   receptors cells specialized for reception only and lacking axons.

Selectively permeable   characteristic of cell membranes through which substances pass with varying velocities, due to their charge, size, or chemical properties.

Semicircular canals   fine membranous canals arranged in each of the three dimensions. Inertial movement of fluid in each canal is sensed by hair cells in each ampulla and indicates accelerations or decelerations of the body in each plane.

Sensory neurons   nerve cells whose dendrite ends respond to physical or chemical changes either outside or inside the body and transmit impulses to the central nervous system.

Seres   any of the recognizable stages of succession.

Serum   the fluid portion of the blood when it lacks the materials necessary for coagulation to take place.

Sex cell   germ cell; gamete; for example, sperm or egg.

Sex-linked   said of a trait, such as colorblindness, which is associated with and transmitted by the X chromosome.

Sexual reproduction   the union of two gametes, which combine as a zygote, each gamete contributing a set of genes to the new individual.

Shelter-seeking behavior   includes the roosting of birds for optimal protection, construction of lodges by beavers, selection of dens by bears and other animals.

Sigmoid growth curve   the curve that sometimes results when population size is plotted against time. Growth is slow at first (lag phase) but later increases at a geometric rate (log phase), then slows as "environmental resistance" increases. After reaching this level, the population may remain in steady state, decline gradually, or crash.

Signal   any stimulus, behavioral or chemical, that is immediately recognizable by a conspecific and produces a predictable response; for example, a smile, a growl, the release of a pheromone.

Sign stimuli   very simple cues (such as a fragment of a bird's song, a pheromone, or decorative plumage) necessary to elicit and synchronize behavior.

Skeletal muscle   (See **Voluntary muscle**.)

Smooth endoplasmic reticulum   an intracellular membrane system that often acts as a storage depot for various kinds of materials.

Smooth muscle   involuntary muscle tissue consisting of short spindle-shaped fibers and surrounding, for example, hollow internal organs in vertebrates—digestive tract, blood vessels, and various ducts.

Social behavior   interaction of two or more animals of the same or different species.

Social facilitation   the performance of an act caused by the performance of the same act in other animals.

Solute   any substance dissolved in a liquid and forming a solution.

Soma   the cell body of a nerve cell.

Somatotropic hormone (STH)   growth hormone secreted by the anterior pituitary.

Species distinctiveness   that attribute of mating and courtship signals that makes the signals meaningful only between conspecifics, thus reducing the probability of mis-mating.

Specific hunger   in rats, the learned preference for the taste of food associated with the animal's recovery from nutritional deficiencies.

Sperm (spermatozoan)   male haploid sex cell.

Spermatid   the four haploid cells resulting from the meiotic division of a spermatocyte.

Spiral ganglion   collection of ganglion cells in the organ of Corti that relay nerve signals from the acoustic hair cells to auditory centers in the brain.

Spiracles   air passageways for breathing that lead from the body of insects to the external environment.

Stapes   the last in the train of ear bones that transmits sound energy to the oval window.

Startle display   the display of some mock feature—false eyes being common among insects—that startles, if only momentarily, a would-be predator, thus increasing the likelihood of the prey species' escape.

Stereotyped behavior   often repeated and easily recognized individual behavior fairly consistent from one bout of behavior to the next.

STH   somatotropic hormone.

Stomata   openings regulated by paired cells present in leaves and fleshy stems and that function as a passageway for gas exchange between the plant and the atmosphere.

Striated muscle   muscle tissue, the fibers of which are much longer than involuntary muscle fibers and contain a series of highly ordered sarcomeres that give the appearance of striations across the muscle.

Sub-song   soft, tentative utterances of young male birds.

Substrate   biochemical term describing any substance which is chemically altered by the action of an enzyme, generally combining with the enzyme in the process.

Succession   the patterns of change that occur as an ecosystem ages; often such patterns are predictable.

Summate, summation   the collective effect of separate nerve impulses arriving at a nerve cell.

Super-normal stimuli   any stimulus that is more likely to evoke a given response than is the normal sign stimulus. Exaggerated sign stimuli frequently operate as super-normal stimuli.

Survivorship curve   the percentage of survivors in each age class of a population plotted against time. The resulting curve shows the probability of survival for an individual at any age.

Sympatric speciation   animal species that may have evolved from a single ancestral species without the influence of physical or spatial isolation achieved by environmental barriers.

Sympatric species   species that either co-exist geographically or have co-extensive breeding distributions.

Synapse   the point(s) at which the axon of one nerve cell makes close contact with the dendrites or soma of another nerve cell.

Synaptic cleft   the submicroscopic gap separating the plasma membrane of an axon from the membrane of a muscle fiber or another nerve cell.

Synaptic knobs   terminal enlargements of nerve fibers that make close functional contact with other neurons.

Synaptic transmission   the process whereby signals are communicated across the junction of one nerve cell with another.

Synaptic vesicles   submicroscopic sacs contained just inside the branch endings of nerve axons and possible storage areas for a chemical called the *transmitter substance.*

Synergist muscles   in contrast to antagonists, muscles that all pull in the same direction; for example, those that together flex the forearm.

Systole   the contractile phase of the heart beat.

Taste buds   groups of taste receptors on the surface of the tongue.

Taxis (pl. taxes)   movement toward or away from a stimulus by an animal; for example, *photo*taxis is a response to light. The equivalent growth response is referred to as a *tropism.*

Tectorial membrane   a structure in the cochlear duct that lies in contact with the acoustic hair cells and plays a part in their selective stimulation by sound.

Territory   a smaller area within the home range, an area that the organism defends against other individuals of the same species.

Tetanus   the maximal contraction that results when many striated muscle fibers are re-excited simultaneously before they have time to relax from the previous stimulus.

Thermophilic   heat-loving; for example, "thermophilic" bacteria that thrive at temperatures only a few degrees below the boiling point.

Thorax   in insects, the segments posterior to the head and anterior to the abdomen; in air-breathing vertebrates, the chest region.

Thymine   one of four nucleic acid bases contained in DNA.

Tissue   a group of similar cells all of which cooperate in the performance of one or more particular function.

Trachea   tube leading from the pharynx to the lungs in air-breathing vertebrates, and from the body surface to body tissues in insects.

Tracheoles   small branches of a trachea, most frequently used in connection with insect respiratory systems.

Transmitter substance   the chemical whose release into the synaptic cleft by the nerve axon ending is triggered by the arrival of a nerve action potential.

Triose   a sugar that contains three carbons.

Trituration   the grinding down of ingested food.

Trophallaxis   an exchange of material regurgitated by bees and ants, a behavior that seems to function as a social bond between nest mates.

Trophic structure   the structure of an ecosystem based on the method of energy acquisition of its organisms; for example, the plant producers occupy the anchor position in the trophic hierarchy.

Tropism   a growth toward or away from a stimulus; for example, *photo*tropism is a response to light. The equivalent movement is referred to as a *taxis.*

Tympanic membrane   ear drum.

Unresponsive requisites   those environmental factors that are not affected by the presence or abundance of a given population; for example, climate.

Uracil   one of four nucleic acid bases contained in RNA.

Uterus   the lower ends of the oviducts in most mammals in which the developing embryo and fetus are nourished.

Vacuole   a space within a cell, delimited by a membrane and containing granular or fluid material.

Vacuum activities   the performance of normal behavior patterns in the absence of the stimuli usually needed to elicit them.

Vegetative reproduction   a form of asexual reproduction in plants whereby an entire new plant is generated from a leaf, root, or stem cutting from the parent plant.

Vegetation zone   all the land surface where the same association regularly occurs.

Ventricle   a chamber in the heart that serves to pump blood out of the heart to the lungs or body.

Villi   finger-like projections of the mucosal surface of the gut, containing both blood and lymphatic vessels.

Vitamins   low molecular weight compounds required in many cellular chemical reactions and which an organism cannot synthesize for itself.

Vitreous humor   transparent jelly-like tissue filling the space between the vertebrate lens and the retina.

Voluntary muscle   the muscle tissue responsible for most of an organism's behavior and over which the organism has voluntary control. (Also called **skeletal muscle.**)

White matter   collectively those regions of the brain and spinal cord that consist largely of nerve fibers enclosed in myelin sheaths.

Z lines   transverse lines that mark the junction of one sarcomere with the next in striated muscle.

Zona glomerulosa   the outermost layer of the adrenal cortex, source of a steroid hormone that regulates ion and water homeostosis.

Zygote   a fertilized ovum, a cell resulting from the fusion of the male with the female gamete.